Natural Disasters

Canadian Edition

Patrick L. Abbott

San Diego State University

Claire Samson

Carleton University

McGraw-Hill
Ryerson

Toronto Montréal Boston Burr Ridge, IL Dubuque, IA Madison, WI New York
San Francisco St. Louis Bangkok Bogotá Caracas Kuala Lumpur Lisbon London
Madrid Mexico City Milan New Delhi Santiago Seoul Singapore Sydney Taipei

Natural Disasters
Canadian Edition

ISBN-13: 978-0-07-098037-2
ISBN-10: 0-07-098037-3

1 2 3 4 5 6 7 8 9 10 QPD 0 9

Printed and bound in

Vice President, Editor-in-Chief: *Joanna Cotton*
Executive Sponsoring Editor: *Leanna MacLean*
Marketing Manager: Mary Costello
Developmental Editor: *Kelly Dickson*
Editorial Associate: *Stephanie Hess*
Permissions Editor: *Alison Derry*
Supervising Editor: *Graeme Powell*
Copy Editor: *Karen Rolfe*
Senior Production Coordinator: *Paula Brown*
Cover Design: *Kyle Gell*
Cover Image: Drought Image: Superstock, Ice Image: Jupiter Images/Dennis MacDonald,
Storm Clouds: Ethan Meleg/Getty images, Forest fire: Andoni Canela/A.G.E. Foto Stock,
Wave image: Jeremy Koreski/© AllCanadaPhotos.com
Interior Design: *Kyle Gell*
Page Layout: *Laserwords Private Limited*
Printer: *Quebecor*

Library and Archives Canada Cataloguing in Publication

Abbott, Patrick L
    Natural disasters / Patrick L. Abbott, Claire Samson. — 1st Canadian ed.
Includes index.
ISBN 978-0-07-098037-2
    1. Natural disasters. I. Samson, Claire, 1960- II. Title.
GB5014.A33 2008   904'.5   C2008-903080-X

About the Authors

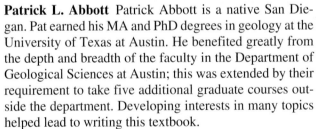

Patrick L. Abbott Patrick Abbott is a native San Diegan. Pat earned his MA and PhD degrees in geology at the University of Texas at Austin. He benefited greatly from the depth and breadth of the faculty in the Department of Geological Sciences at Austin; this was extended by their requirement to take five additional graduate courses outside the department. Developing interests in many topics helped lead to writing this textbook.

Pat's research has concentrated on the Mesozoic and Cenozoic sedimentary rocks of the southwestern United States and northwestern Mexico. Studies have focused on reading the history stored within the rocks—depositional environments, provenance, paleoclimate, palinspastic reconstructions, and high-energy processes.

Pat has long been involved in presenting earth knowledge to the public, primarily through local TV news. He has produced videos for TV broadcast in a series called *Written in Stone*. The first video, *The Rise and Fall of San Diego*, won 2002 awards in the Videographers (Award of Distinction) and AXIEM (Silver Axiem) competitions. The second video, *Earthquake Country—Los Angeles*, was completed in 2004, is now playing on some California TV stations, and is being used in school curricula in several states. During part of each year, Pat lectures on Holland America and Abercrombie & Kent cruises around the Mediterranean, South America, Antarctica, and elsewhere.

Originally from Quebec City, **Claire Samson** is a professional engineer with an undergraduate degree in engineering physics from Laval University, a Masters of Science in geological sciences from McGill University, and a Ph.D. in physics from the University of Toronto.

Claire has a wide range of experience, both in industry and academia, in Canada, as well as in Europe. From 1991 to 1992, she was a research associate at Cambridge University in England, and from 1993 to 1999, she worked for the Shell Oil group at three locations in the Netherlands, including the Shell International Research Laboratory. Upon relocating to Canada in 2000, she joined Neptec Design Group, an Ottawa high-tech company specializing in vision systems for space applications. In 2003, she was appointed to the Department of Earth Sciences at Carleton University, where she now teaches a popular course on Natural Disasters, an introduction to the earth sciences for engineering students, and exploration geophysics.

Claire's research activities proceed on several fronts, including laser imaging of earth materials, electromagnetic prospecting, and planetary geology. In both her research and field work, Claire is keen to address practical problems, from pipeline corrosion to rock stability in underground mines, and to involve industry partners.

Claire is an enthusiastic world traveller. She has visited over 30 countries and speaks four languages.

Contents

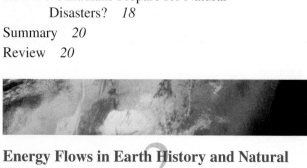

Earthquake Geology, Seismology, and Engineering 79 4

When the Earth Shakes in Canada 117 5

Tsunami   *143*

**Volcanic Eruptions: Plate Tectonics
and Magma   *170***

Volcano Case Histories: Killer Events   *201*

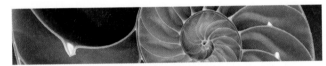

The Great Dyings   *435* 15

Hazards From Space   *458* 16

Preface

New to the Canadian Edition

Based on the solid foundation of this popular textbook—now in its sixth edition!—this adaptation brings a Canadian focus on natural disasters while keeping an international perspective. The aim is to move beyond the headlines and develop a better understanding of the processes leading to natural disasters, and society's response to the challenge. Concepts are illustrated by case histories from past natural disasters that are part of Canada's folklore and history, like the deadly avalanches slowing the advance of the railway through the Rockies. Case histories also feature recent events that challenge today's society and question the impact of climate change on the severity of natural disasters; for example, the 2003 forest fires in British Columbia and Hurricane Juan in the Atlantic provinces. The book has been extensively reorganized with the addition of a new chapter on earthquakes in Canada, and the inclusion of geomagnetic hazards. It also provides practical information on what to do before, during, and after several types of natural disasters. The visual impact of the material is captured in over 150 new photographs and maps, and enhanced by the use of full colour. Chapter-by-chapter content changes are as follows:

Chapter 1: A Global and Canadian Outlook on Natural Disasters

- Provides statistical trends on the frequency and impact of natural disasters in Canada and the world
- Defines disaster, hazard, vulnerability, and risk
- Gives a detailed account of the 1998 St. Lawrence River Valley ice storm
- Introduces the Canadian approach to disasters management.

Chapter 2: Energy Flows in Earth History and Natural Disasters

- Features two Canadian meteorites and the world's oldest rock, the Acasta gneiss from the Northwest Territories
- Describes the effects of the post-glacial rebound in Canada.

Chapter 3: Plate Tectonics and Earthquakes

- Highlights the contribution of Professor John Tuzo Wilson, the father of plate tectonics
- Expands on the evidence for continental drift and plate tectonics throughout Earth's history
- Summarizes the tectonic history of Canada with an emphasis on events from the Pacific coast.

Chapter 4: Earthquake Geology, Seismology, and Engineering

- Introduces the phenomenon of resonance between seismic waves, soils, and buildings
- Illustrates the procedure for locating the source of an earthquake with an example from Charlevoix, Quebec
- Devotes more attention to the various factors affecting the intensity of earthquakes.

Chapter 5: When the Earth Shakes in Canada. . .

- Establishes the relation between the geology and seismicity of Canada
- Describes six significant Canadian earthquakes
- Gives concrete examples of mitigation against earthquakes, including the seismic provisions of the National Building Code of Canada.

Chapter 6: Tsunami

- Presents the personal account of a witness of the 1929 Grand Banks tsunami
- Gives an overview of tsunami hazard in coastal British Columbia
- Explains recent technological advances in tsunami warning systems.

Chapter 7: Volcanic Eruptions: Plate Tectonics and Magmas

- Discusses the relation between volcanic ash and soil fertility

- Features representations of volcanoes in art
- Is accompanied by new original photographs from around the world

Chapter 8: Volcano Case Histories: Killer Events

- Explores three Canadian volcanoes
- Explains the relation between diamonds and volcanism
- Expands on the hazards posed by volcanic activity to aviation.

Chapter 9: Mass Movements and Snow Avalanches

- Discusses rock instability in the Rockies and the engineering efforts undertaken to reduce risk
- Covers extensively the Quebec City rock falls
- Considers the problem of mass movements in sensitive clays
- Emphasizes the risk posed by snow avalanches in the past and present
- Is abundantly illustrated by more than 40 new photographs and diagrams.

Chapter 10: Atmosphere, Oceans, and Climate

- Includes an interesting comparison between the greenhouse effect on Venus, Earth, and Mars
- Shows photos of the Canadian landscape reflecting changing climatic conditions.

Chapter 11: Severe Weather

- Provides economical data on the rising costs of weather-related disasters in Canada and the world
- Features several extreme weather events in Canadian history from record-breaking blizzards to tornadoes
- Reflects on the effects of El Niño in Canada.

Chapter 12: Hurricanes

- Offers a more thorough description of the life cycle of a hurricane
- Profiles several destructive Canadian hurricanes that affected the Atlantic and Pacific coasts, and central Canada
- Gives a more detailed explanation of post-tropical transition
- Discusses mitigation against hurricanes with an example from Bermuda.

Chapter 13: Floods

- Provides an extensive coverage of the Red River floods

- Proposes a more rigorous classification of flood styles
- Presents two examples of large-scale engineering infrastructure protecting against floods, the Red River Floodway and the London Flood Barrier.

Chapter 14: Fire

- Introduces the Canadian Forest-Fire Danger Rating System
- Describes fire in the Canadian boreal forest, highlighting the 2003 fires in British Columbia
- Reflects on the impact of climate change on forest fires.

Chapter 15: The Great Dyings

- Elaborates further on the causes of the Cretaceous-Tertiary extinction
- Expands on the debate on the role of humans in the extinction of large mammals in the Quaternary.

Chapter 16: Hazards from Space

- Includes geomagnetic hazards, hazards of our technological era
- Tours seven Canadian impact craters
- Devotes more attention to close asteriod encounters.

Features

- Each chapter opens with an outline that alerts students to the main themes of the chapter.

- Canadian and world maps help to identify key areas of topical coverage and discussion.

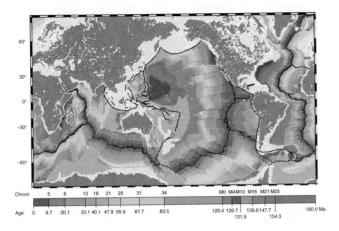

- In Greater Depth boxes zoom in on a particular topic in more detail without interrupting the main flow of the text. Several boxes present information of what to do in the case of natural disasters.

In Greater Depth

What to Do Before, During, and After an Earthquake

Before
We have seen that earthquakes don't kill us: it is our own buildings and belongings that fall during the shaking and harm us. What should you do? *First*, walk into each room of your house, assume strong shaking has begun, and carefully visualize what might fall (for example, ceiling fan, chandelier, mirror, china cabinet, gas water heater). Now reduce the risk. Nail them. Brace them. Tie them. Velcro™ them. Lower them. Remove them.

Second, walk outside, assume strong shaking, and visualize what might fall (for example, trees, power lines, brick chimney). Now reduce the risk. Trim them. Chop them. Replace them.

Third, repeat the visits inside and outside your home. This time, locate safe spots where protection exists, for example, under a heavy table, beneath a strong desk,

under a bed. Remember these safe spots so you can use them quickly when shaking begins. Drop, cover, and hold on.

During
After examining your home, prepare yourself to stay composed during the shaking. Remember that the severe shaking probably will last only 5 to 60 seconds. So, be calm and protect yourself for one minute. In most places, if you are inside, you should stay inside; if you are outside, stay outside.

After
Expect aftershocks. If you feel aftershocks, stay where you are until they stop.

Do a safety check around your property. Check for fire hazards such as gas leaks and damaged electrical wiring. Check for structural damage to your home. Approach chimneys with caution. Turn on a battery-powered radio for information and damage reports.

- Eye-witness accounts describe natural disasters in the words of the people who experienced them.

- Art reproductions, historical photographs, and panoramas show the wonders of the natural world and the drama of disasters through the eyes of artists and photographers.

- Study aids are found at the end of each chapter and include:
  - Summaries reiterate the main points of the chapter in crisp bullet-point format.
  - "Terms to Remember" lists all the boldfaced terms that are defined in the glossary at the end of the book.
  - The "Questions for Review" section contains questions that help students test their knowledge.
  - "Questions for Further Thought" aim to examine issues in a broader perspective and stimulating debate.

Why the Book Was Written

We are all engaged, amazed, shaken and moved by the news of great natural disasters broadcast on the media. Could similar events take place in Canada? Have they occurred in the past in our country? Several universities and colleges throughout Canada offer courses on natural disasters, reaching large classes of undergraduate students. Students want to understand why natural disasters happen not only abroad but also closer to home. This book has been tailored to meet this dual perspective.

Students are equally interested in society's response to natural disasters. In our class at Carleton University in Ottawa, several people have experienced a great natural disaster, the 1998 St. Lawrence River Valley ice storm. Discussing the event brings back vivid memories. It raises questions on the decision-making processes of authorities faced with emergency situations, a topic addressed throughout the book.

Finally, our large class is a microcosm of society in which all fields of activity are represented, from architecture to zoology. This book therefore endeavours to broaden the topic of natural disasters beyond the natural sciences and economics, to include elements of visual arts, archeology, and anthropology.

About the Book

Natural Disasters, Canadian Edition focuses on natural disasters: how the normal processes of the Earth concentrate their energies and deal heavy blows to humans and their structures. It largely ignores the numerous case histories describing human actions and resultant environmental responses; these topics are left to the excellent textbooks on environmental geology. Nor does this book address resource extraction, utilization, and disposal; these subjects are covered by fine textbooks on earth resources, minerals, energy, soils, and water. This book is concerned with how the natural world operates and, in so doing, kills and maims humans and destroys their works.

Throughout the book, certain themes are maintained:

- Energy sources underlying disasters
- Plate tectonics and climate change
- Earth processes operating in rock, water, and atmosphere
- Significance of geological time
- Complexities of multiple variables operating simultaneously
- Detailed and readable case histories from Canada and the world.

The Canadian edition aims to explain important principles about the Earth and then develop further understanding through numerous case histories.

The primary organization of the book is based on an energy theme. Chapter 1 leads off with data describing natural disasters and the human population. Chapter 2 examines the energy sources underlying disasters: (1) Earth's internal energy from its formative impacts and continuing decay of radioactive elements; (2) gravity; (3) external energy from the Sun; and (4) impacts with asteroids and comets.

Disasters fuelled by Earth's internal energy are addressed in chapters 3 through 8 and are organized on a plate-tectonics theme. Chapter 3 provides the basic description of plate tectonics and its relationship to earthquakes. Chapter 4 covers the basic principles of earthquake geology, seismology and engineering. Chapter 5 focuses on Canadian earthquakes: Why do they occur where they do? What significant seisms shook Canada in the past? Chapter 6 discusses tsunami. Chapters 7 and 8 discuss volcanoes; their characteristic magmas are organized around the three Vs—viscosity, volatiles, and volume. Eruptive behaviours are related to plate-tectonic setting. As throughout, case histories are employed to enliven the text.

Disasters powered primarily by gravity are covered in chapter 9 on mass movements and snow avalanches. Many types are discussed and illustrated, from falls to flows and slides to subsidence, from earth materials to snow.

Disasters fuelled by the external energy of the Sun are examined in chapters 10 through 14. Chapter 10 begins with principles of atmosphere and ocean underlying weather and climate, and then moves on to long-term climate change over timescales of millions, thousands, and hundreds of years. The time focus shrinks through the chapter, leading into chapter 11 on severe weather phenomena, such as heat waves, thunderstorms, and tornadoes. Chapter 12 examines hurricanes. The emphasis on water continues in chapter 13 on floods and how human activities increase flood damage. Chapter 14 on fire examines the liberation of ancient sunlight captured by photosynthesis and stored in organic material.

Before moving to the fourth energy source (impacts), chapter 15 examines the great dyings encased in the fossil record. The intent is to document the greatest of all natural disasters and to use multiple variables in analyzing their causes. Specific mass extinctions are examined using causative factors, such as continental unification and separation, climate change, flood-basalt volcanism, sea-level rise and fall, impacts, biological processes, and the role of humans in the latest mass dying. Chapter 16 examines impact mechanisms in greater detail and includes plans to protect Earth from future impacts. It also expands on the hazards related to our planet's proximity to the Sun by incorporating material on geomagnetic hazards.

There is a lot of material in this book, probably too much to cover in one semester. But the broad range of natural disasters topics allows each instructor to select those chapters that cover his or her interests and local hazards. The goal is to involve the students for a lifetime in understanding the Earth, atmosphere, oceans, and skies—to observe, think, explain, and discuss.

Supplements

For the Student

Online Learning Centre at www.mcgrawhill.ca/olc/abbott

This site gives you the opportunity to further explore topics presented in the book using the Internet. The site contains interactive quizzing with immediate feedback, animations, web links, a career centre, and more.

For the Instructor (All of the Instructor supplements can be found on the text's Online Learning Centre)

Online Learning Centre at www.mcgrawhill.ca/olc/abbott

Take advantage of the Instructor's Manual and Microsoft® PowerPoint® lecture outlines.

Computerized Test Bank

Available for Macintosh or Windows users, the computerized test bank using EZ Test—a flexible and easy-to-use electronic testing program—allows instructors to create tests from book-specific items. EZ Test accommodates a wide range of question types and allows instructors to add their own questions. Test items are also available in Word format (Rich text format). For secure online testing, exams created in EZ Test can be exported to WebCT, Blackboard, and EZ Test Online. EZ Test comes with a Quick Start Guide, and once the program is installed, users have access to a User's Manual and Flash tutorials. Additional help is available online at www.mhhe.com/eztest.

Image Gallery

The complete set of visuals from the text can be downloaded from the Image Gallery on the Online Learning Centre and easily imbedded into Instructors' PowerPoint slides.

Acknowledgments

I am indebted to an extensive network of scientists and engineers from the Canadian earth science community, research collaborators, students, and friends who helped me make this textbook adaptation a reality. They all deserve my deepest gratitude. In particular, I want to acknowledge the involvement of the following people who contributed entire chapters: Dr. Tim Patterson, of Carleton University (Chapter 10); Dr. David Phillips, of Environment Canada (Chapter 11); Dr. David Martell, of the University of Toronto (Chapter 14); and Dr. Stuart Sutherland, of the University of British Columbia, and Dr. Fiona MacEachern (Chapter 15). I would also like to thank the following people for their outstanding contributions:

- Coleen Lapointe-Lavictoire, Lianne Bellisario, and Adam Hatfield from Public Safety Canada for their help with statistical data and government policy;
- Don Dodds for showing me the damage of the 1998 St. Lawrence River Valley ice storm on his sugar bush;
- Dr. Marc St-Onge from Natural Resources Canada and Dr. Richard Ernst from Ernst Geoscience for their insight into the tectonic history of Canada;
- Susie Wilson, who provided a photograph of her father, Prof. Tuzo Wilson, from the Wilson family archives;
- Maurice Lamontagne from Natural Resources Canada for his help with the content and structure of the chapter on Canadian earthquakes, and for providing the example of how to locate the source of an earthquake;
- Philip Munro from Natural Resources Canada for a visit of the Ottawa seismograph station;
- Robert Mitchell, Dr. Ian Hammond and Dr. Margaret Hill, who made it possible to interview Joseph Mitchell about the 1929 Grand Banks tsunami;
- Alan Ruffman and Dr. Tad Murty for contributing their expertise on tsunami;
- Dr. Jacquest Locat of Laval University for sharing his passion about the Quebec City rock falls;
- Dr. Andrée Blais-Stevens, Dr. Jan Aylsworth, and Dr. Réjean Couture from Natural Resources Canada for sharing their knowledge on Canadian mass movements;
- Ronuk Modha from the Manitoba Flood Authority for an unforgettable visit to the Red River Floodway;
- Dr. Greg Brooks from Natural Resources Canada for kindly answering my questions about floods;
- Dr. David Boteler and Dr. Larry Newitt from the Ottawa Geomagnetic Laboratory for their help with geomagnetic hazards;
- Dr. Henry Halls for a thrilling account of the discovery of the Slate Islands impact site;
- Claudette Pelikan, who always pointed me to the right person and the best source of information within the vast Natural Resources Canada organization.

The quality of the book was significantly improved by the insights provided by comments from the following reviewers:

Ihsan Al-Aasm, *University of Windsor*
Michael Badyk, *Humber College*
Aaron Berg, *University of Guelph*
William Buhay, *University of Winnipeg*
Stan Dosso, *University of Victoria*
Michael Gipp, *University of Toronto at Scarborough*
Jeremy Hall, *Memorial University*
William Last, *University of Manitoba*
Judith Patterson, *Concordia University*
Alexander Paul, *University of Regina*
David Rowbotham, *Nipissing University*
Steven Sadura, *University of Guelph*
Gerard Szejwach, *University of Alberta*
Lucy Wilson, *University of New Brunswick*

In closing, I would like to sincerely thank the team at McGraw-Hill Ryerson for their mentoring and encouragement. Many thanks to my husband and four children for their patience during this adventure!

Claire Samson
mlcsamson@gmail.com

CHAPTER

1

A Global and Canadian Outlook on Natural Disasters

"Mankind was destined to live on the edge of perpetual disaster. We are mankind because we survive."

—*James A. Michener, 1978,* Chesapeake

Outline

- Great Natural Disasters
- Natural Disasters and Natural Hazards
- Worldwide Trends
- The Canadian Perspective
- Vulnerability and Risk
- How Do Canadians Prepare for Natural Disasters?
- Summary

View of Nelson Street in Kingston, Ontario on 9 January 1998 during the St. Lawrence River Valley ice storm

Used with permission of the Library and Archives Canada nic010689-v3.

Great Natural Disasters

Great natural disasters—tsunami, earthquakes, hurricanes, floods, and heat waves—cause death and destruction around the world. They commonly kill thousands of people, leave hundreds of thousands homeless, and devastate regional economies. These extremely traumatic events so overwhelm regions that international assistance is needed to rescue and care for people, clean up the destruction, and begin the process of reconstruction.

Figure 1.1 shows the number of natural disaster fatalities in recent decades. The sawtooth shape of the curve is created by the great natural disasters, which kill so many people in one event. Year 2004 was particularly devastating, with 245,000 people losing their lives in the Indian Ocean tsunami. In 2005, there were six great natural disasters, and they all occurred in August through October: the Pakistan earthquake, Hurricanes Katrina and Rita in the United States, Hurricane Stan in Central America, Hurricane Wilma in Mexico, and floods in India.

This book will explore the several natural hazards posing a threat to humans from an earth science perspective, while focusing on the Canadian people and the Canadian landscape. Reaching beyond the emotions and sensationalism of the headlines, an understanding of the science behind the dynamic processes shaping planet Earth will guide our actions toward building a society more resilient to natural disasters.

KASHMIR, PAKISTAN EARTHQUAKE, 8 OCTOBER 2005

It was 8:52 a.m. on Saturday, a school day, and 17-year-old Uzair Mohammed Qureshi was reading his chemistry book in school when the ground began to shake. He ran toward the door to save his life, but suddenly, the roof collapsed. After regaining consciousness, he rushed home but found it had fallen into a pile of rubble that had killed his father, mother, and grandmother. A day after the disaster, Qureshi sat amid the rubble of his collapsed school, in his school uniform, because all else was gone. He asked: "Is there anybody who can help me?"

The Pakistan earthquake was the deadliest disaster of 2005. The Earth tore apart and shook violently for 50 seconds about 10 kilometres north of Muzaffarabad, Pakistan, killing about 88,000 people when their houses collapsed on them. Many families in this region along the steep southern edge of the Himalaya build their own houses using low-quality mortar to bind rocks. So many of these stone-wall houses collapsed that 3.3 million people were left homeless.

Most of the public buildings were built as reinforced concrete-frame structures that should have handled the shaking, but, in many cases, the building materials and construction were of low quality. During the earthquake, concrete columns buckled and heavy concrete ceilings gave way. Many of these buildings were schools, and now a generation of young people in the region is almost gone.

The earthquake shook loose hundreds of landslides, ruining roads in the mountainous region and making relief efforts difficult. Transportation was mainly by helicopter or foot. As October progressed, freezing temperatures and falling snow further stressed injured survivors, leading to a second wave of deaths from the cold, infected injuries, and unsanitary water.

The Himalayan region experiences many earthquakes. The quality of construction materials and workmanship must improve there because major earthquakes will continue to occur.

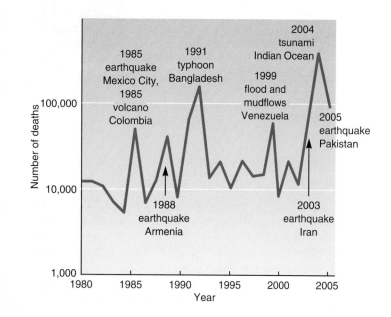

Figure 1.1

Deaths Due to Natural Disasters, 1980–2005.

Source: © Swiss Reinsurance Company.

HURRICANE KATRINA, 29 AUGUST 2005

In September 2004, New Orleans lay in the path of Hurricane Ivan with its wind speeds of 240 km/h. The mayor of New Orleans ordered an evacuation of the city. Upward of 1 million people fled, mostly in bumper-to-bumper traffic on highways turned into one-way evacuation routes for 2.5 days. But luck favoured New Orleans in 2004 as Ivan veered to the right and came ashore 160 kilometres to the east. Luck also favoured the 600,000 people who did not evacuate.

But the lessons from the active hurricane season of 2004 were not learned. One year later, another hurricane headed toward New Orleans, and this time it did not miss. The costliest natural disaster of 2005 was also the costliest disaster in U.S. history—Hurricane Katrina. The storm made a direct hit on Mississippi, but its huge size engulfed 150 kilometres of the Mississippi, Louisiana, and Alabama coastline. Wind speeds were over 180 km/h, but the worst damages were caused by water pushed over 1 km inland. The pressure of this huge volume of water caused levees to fail along canals, the Mississippi River, and Lake Pontchartrain, allowing water to flood much of New Orleans, with some neighbourhoods being submerged 6 m. It took until early October to pump all this water out of the city and expose the houses, many of which were total losses. Damages are estimated at US$135 billion, but money alone will not repair all the damages. It will take time—many years—to restore the city. Much of the new New Orleans may be built differently, and some may be rebuilt at different, higher elevation sites.

Natural Disasters and Natural Hazards

Natural disasters are extreme natural events in which a large amount of **energy** is released in a short time with catastrophic consequences for life and infrastructure in the vicinity. The word "disaster" originates from Ancient Greek and combines the prefix "dis," meaning "without," and the word "astro," meaning "celestial body." Greek astrologers believed in a connection between calamities and unfavourable positions of the planets in the sky.

There is no universal definition of "**natural disaster**." A natural disaster generally involves significant casualties and disruption to society, large economic losses, and calls for exterior help. It gets attention from the media and government officials. The key aspect is its impact on society. This aspect plays such an important role that the expression "natural disaster" is somewhat of a misnomer, giving the impression that these disasters are primarily the fault of nature. In fact, natural disasters are often triggered when society ignores hazardous conditions in the natural environment.

Natural hazards become natural disasters when they intersect with vulnerable communities. Unstable snow and rock, and high water levels are natural hazards having the potential to cause harm. Snow avalanches large enough to bury a person occur several times a day during the winter months in the Rockies. The great majority of them, however, happen in remote uninhabited areas and are not considered natural disasters. Snow avalanches are declared natural disasters only when they kill people or engulf infrastructure at the foot of the slopes. This is what happened to the small Inuit community of Kangiqsualujjuaq in Northern Quebec on 31 December 1999 as several people had gathered in the school gym to celebrate the arrival of the new millennium. In a few seconds, tonnes of snow slid from a 150-m-high steep hill nearby and smashed into the building, burying people inside. This snow avalanche, a tragic natural disaster, left 9 people dead and 25 people critically injured. Evacuation of the injured was especially challenging due to the remoteness of the community, located 1,500 km north of Montreal.

Sites with natural hazards need to be studied and understood. Their risk must be evaluated. Then we can try to prevent natural hazards from causing natural disasters. Remember: *Natural hazards are inevitable, but natural disasters are not.*

FREQUENCY, RETURN PERIOD, AND MAGNITUDE

Several metrics are used to describe hazard levels, including frequency, return period, and magnitude.

The **frequency** of an event is the number of occurrences in a given length of time. For example, Earth experiences on average one great earthquake per year. Recall the following earthquakes that made the international news: Bam, Iran (2003); offshore Northern Sumatra, Indonesia (2004); Kashmir, Pakistan (2005); and Sichuan, China (2008). Another way of expressing how often events occur is the **return period**, which is the length of time between similar events. The frequency and return period are the inverse of one another:

$$Frequency = \frac{1}{Period}$$

and

$$Period = \frac{1}{Frequency}$$

Let us illustrate this relation by an example. On average, four former tropical cyclones affect Atlantic Canada annually. The frequency of these storms is four times per year; the corresponding return period is therefore three months (12 months ÷ 4 cyclones).

The longer the return period, the smaller the chance of an event occurring in any given year. For example, since the Conquest of the French in North America in 1763, historical documents reveal that major rockfalls, causing fatalities and/or severely damaging buildings, recur approximately every 25 years along the Cap-aux-Diamants cliff in Old Quebec City. This translates into a 4% chance of rockfall in any one year (1/25 = 4%). A common misinterpretation is to use the return period to predict exactly when a similar event will happen in the future. A return period of 25 years does not mean that, if a rockfall has just occurred—the most recent was in 2004—the next one won't happen another 25 years, bringing us to 2029. Such misconception can create a false sense of security.

The **magnitude** is related to the amount of energy fuelling a natural event. An expression of magnitude, for example, is the force of hurricane winds. The energy released during an earthquake, based on the amplitude of ground motion, is also frequently quoted in terms of magnitude.

Larger-magnitude disasters happen less often. For example, clouds and rain are common, hurricanes are uncommon; streams overflow frequently, large floods are infrequent.

Knowing the frequency, return period, and magnitude for a given event in a given area provides us with useful information, but it does not answer all our questions. There are still the cost–benefit ratios of economics to consider. For example, given an area with a natural hazard that puts forth a dangerous pulse of energy with a return period of 600 years, how much money should be spent constructing a building that will be used about 50 years before being torn down and replaced? Is it wise to spend the added money necessary to guarantee that the building will withstand the rare destructive event? Or do economic considerations suggest that the building be constructed to the same standards as similar buildings in nearby non-hazardous areas?

Worldwide Trends

THE NUMBER OF GREAT NATURAL DISASTERS IS INCREASING WITH TIME

The annual occurrence of great natural disasters ranges from zero (in 1952) to 15 (in 1993), with an average of nearly five (Figure 1.2). The yearly trend is upward; the increase is partly due to the human population more than doubling in size since 1960.

Table 1.2 divides natural disasters in two subgroups according to their underlying causes. A first subgroup, the "**geological disasters**" includes phenomena like **earthquakes, volcanoes**, and **mass movements**. A second subgroup, the "**weather-related disasters**," lumps together heatwaves, **droughts**, **wildfires**, **floods**, and **storms**. Whereas the trend line of the geological disasters is almost stable between 1950 and 2005, in Figure 1.2 that of the weather-related disasters increases with time. These data

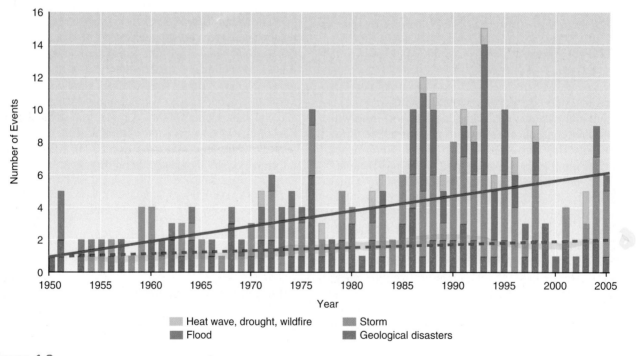

Figure 1.2
Great natural disasters, 1950–2005. Straight lines have been fitted to the data. The dotted subhorizontal line shows the stable trend of the geological disasters; the solid oblique line, the increasing trend of the weather-related disasters.
Source: © Munich Reinsurance Company.

indicate that changing weather patterns, including those related to global warming, may increase the frequency of certain natural disasters in the future.

THE NUMBER OF NATURAL-DISASTER FATALITIES IS INCREASING WITH TIME

The number of natural-disaster fatalities worldwide between 1980 and 2005 varies markedly from year to year, yet shows an increasing trend (Figure 1.1).

The data presented in Table 1.1, going back from 1947 to 1980, gives insight into the what, where, and who of natural-disaster types versus geographical area and fatalities. The numbers presented understate the number of deaths (because, in many cases, the statistics report only fatalities, not missing people), yet the patterns in the data are quite instructive. During this 34-year period, the biggest killers worldwide were earthquakes and hurricanes, and the water-related phenomena of severe weather and floods killed more people than volcanoes and landslides. The 40 deadliest disasters in the 36-year period from 1970 to 2005 are shown in Table 1.2. Notice that 38 of the 40 disasters were due to natural causes. The data presented in Table 1.2 confirm the conclusions derived from Table 1.1: the most frequent mega-killers were earthquakes (24 of 40) and storms (7 of 40).

What is the correlation between human population density and the number of natural-disaster deaths? The data of Tables 1.1 and 1.2 paint a clear picture: densely populated Asia dominates the list with 86% of the fatalities.

Notice that 26 of the 38 worst natural disasters occurred in a belt running from China and Bangladesh through India and Iran to Turkey. Nine happened in Latin America. Only two mega-killer disasters happened in Western Europe, and none in Canada and the United States. Where humans are concentrated, disasters kill many more people during each high-energy event.

ECONOMIC LOSSES FROM NATURAL DISASTERS ARE INCREASING WITH TIME

The deaths and injuries caused by natural disasters grab our attention and squeeze our emotions, but, in addition, there are the economic losses. The destruction and disabling of buildings, bridges, roads, and power-generation plants; as well as transmission systems for electricity, natural gas, and water—and all the other built works of our societies—add up to a huge cost. But the economic losses are greater than just damaged structures: industries and businesses are knocked out of operation, causing losses in productivity and wages for employees left without places to work.

In 2005, about 650 events associated with substantial economic losses occurred globally, not an unusual number. The year 2005, however, was the costliest ever for the insurance industry. Economic losses were about US$212 billion, with insured losses representing 44% of the total. The increasing trend in economic losses is evident when the dollar figures are averaged over longer time intervals such as decades (Figure 1.3). Does this mean Earth is experiencing more earthquakes and hurricanes?

Table 1.1

Fatalities from Natural Disasters, 1947–80

Number of Killing Events	Earthquake 180	Tsunami 7	Volcanic Eruption 18	Flood 333	Hurricane 210	Tornado 119	Other Severe Weather 147	Landslide/ Avalanche 45	Fatalities by Geographical Area
North America	77	60	96	1,633	1,997	4,568	5,003	323	13,757
Caribbean and Central America	30,613	—	151	2,575	16,541	26	510	260	50,676
South America	38,837	—	440	4,396	—	—	340	5,262	49,275
Europe	7,750	—	2,000	11,199	250	39	6,816	640	28,694
Asia	354,521	4,459	2,805	170,664	478,574	4,308	34,403	4,356	1,054,090
Africa	18,232	—	—	3,891	864	548	5	—	23,540
Oceania	18	—	4,000	77	290	—	117	—	4,502
Fatalities by Natural-Disaster Type	450,048	4,519	9,492	194,435	498,516	9,489	47,194	10,841	Total Number of Fatalities 1,224,534

Source: © Shah.

Table 1.2

The 40 Deadliest Disasters, 1970–2005. Events not due to natural causes are in italics.

Fatalities	Date/Start	Event	Country
400,000	14 Nov 1970	Hurricane	Bangladesh
255,000	28 Jul 1976	Earthquake (Tangshan)	China
245,000	26 Dec 2004	Earthquake and tsunami	Indonesia, Sri Lanka, India, Thailand
140,000	30 Apr 1991	Hurricane Gorky	Bangladesh
88,000	8 Oct 2005	Earthquake	Pakistan
66,000	31 May 1970	Earthquake and landslide (Nevados Huascaran)	Peru
50,000	15 Dec 1999	Floods and mudslides	Venezuela
50,000	21 Jun 1990	Earthquake (Gilan)	Iran
41,000	26 Dec 2003	Earthquake (Bam)	Iran
35,000	Aug 2003	Heat wave	Europe
25,000	7 Dec 1988	Earthquake	Armenia
25,000	16 Sep 1978	Earthquake (Tabas)	Iran
23,000	13 Nov 1985	Volcanic eruption and mudflows (Nevado del Ruiz)	Colombia
22,000	4 Feb 1976	Earthquake	Guatemala
20,103	26 Jan 2001	Earthquake (Gujarat)	India
19,118	17 Aug 1999	Earthquake (Izmit)	Turkey
15,000	19 Sep 1985	Earthquake (Mexico City)	Mexico
15,000	*11 Aug 1979*	*Dam failure (Morvi)*	*India*
15,000	1 Sep 1978	Flood (Monsoon rains in north)	India
15,000	29 Oct 1999	Hurricane (Orissa)	India
11,000	22 Oct 1998	Hurricane Mitch	Honduras
10,800	31 Oct 1971	Flood	India
10,000	25 May 1985	Hurricane	Bangladesh
10,000	20 Nov 1977	Hurricane (Andhra Pradesh)	India
9,500	30 Sep 1993	Earthquake (Marashtra state)	India
8,000	16 Aug 1976	Earthquake (Mindanao)	Philippines
6,425	17 Jan 1995	Earthquake (Kobe)	Japan
6,304	5 Nov 1991	Typhoons Thelma and Uring	Philippines
5,300	28 Dec 1974	Earthquake	Pakistan
5,112	15 Nov 2001	Floods and landslides	Brazil
5,000	10 Apr 1972	Earthquake (Fars)	Iran
5,000	23 Dec 1972	Earthquake (Managua)	Nicaragua
5,000	30 Jun 1976	Earthquake (West Irian)	Indonesia
5,000	5 Mar 1987	Earthquake	Ecuador
4,800	23 Nov 1980	Earthquake (Campagna)	Italy
4,500	10 Oct 1980	Earthquake (El Asnam)	Algeria
4,375	*21 Dec 1987*	*Boat collision*	*Philippines*
4,000	15 Feb 1972	Storm; blizzard	Iran
4,000	24 Nov 1976	Earthquake (Van)	Turkey
4,000	30 May 1998	Earthquake (Takhar)	Afghanistan
1,692,337	Total deaths		

Source: © Swiss Reinsurance Company.

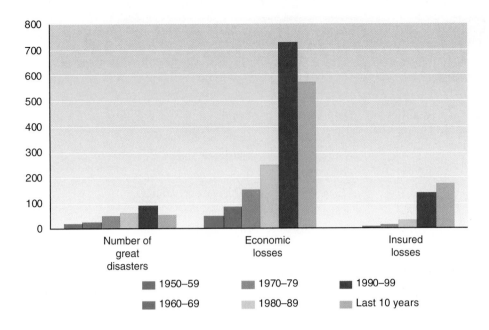

Figure 1.3
Dollar losses from great natural disasters 1950–2005 (billions of 2005 US$).
Source: © Munich Reinsurance Company.

Or are these increasing economic losses related to the global population of humans doubling from 3 billion in 1959 to 6 billion in 1999, with increasing percentages of the population living in cities?

Insured Portion of Economic Losses

The 40 costliest natural disasters between 1970 and 2005 from the insurance industry perspective are listed in Table 1.3. Notice that 37 of the 40 most expensive disasters were due to natural processes. The list is dominated by storms (28 of 40), whereas earthquakes contributed only four events.

Compare Tables 1.2 and 1.3. The locations of the costliest disasters for the insurance industry are different from the worst locations for fatalities. The most expensive natural disaster in history, Hurricane Katrina, does not even appear on the list of the deadliest disasters. Conversely, the deadliest disaster in recent decades, the 1970 cyclone in Bangladesh, is not included in Table 1.3. The highest insurance losses occurred in the United States (24 of 40), Europe (9), and Japan (4). Developed countries experience larger economic losses and fewer deaths. Their people are better insured, live in safer buildings, and have better warning and evacuation plans. In the developing world, the general population cannot afford a safety net, and states are stretched for resources. In the event of a great natural disaster, the poor countries have no other alternative than to turn to the international community. The International Red Cross and Red Crescent Movement plays a pivotal role in this respect, channelling practical and financial help to those affected. Individual donors, however, tend to have a short attention span, and often funds dry out before the situation has even stabilized. Official state-to-state aid tends to suffer from administrative delays. In 2006, to alleviate these problems, the United Nations launched a $500 million fund—the Central Emergency Relief Fund—to jump-start relief operations in future natural and human-made disasters.

The Canadian Perspective

We inhabit a vast landmass bounded by three oceans. Our Canadian territory features an amazing variety of environments from the ruggedness of the Rockies to the vast expanse of the prairies, from the boreal forest of the Canadian Shield to the sensitive tundra of the Arctic. This rich diversity, however, means that the Canadian population is exposed to many types of natural hazards. Storms can strike anywhere. Tsunami can hit Canada's coastlines. Flooding rivers can cover large areas of the central plains. The rough topography of the Rockies can cause deadly snow avalanches and landslides. The same forces that created these magnificent mountains are responsible for the volcanoes and earthquakes observed in Western Canada.

Table 1.3

The 40 Most Costly Insurance Disasters, 1970–2005. Events not due to natural causes are in italics.

Losses in Millions of 2005 US$	Fatalities	Date/Start	Event	Country
45,000	1,326	29 Aug 2005	Hurricane Katrina	USA
22,274	43	24 Aug 1992	Hurricane Andrew	USA
20,716	*2,982*	*11 Sep 2001*	*Terrorist attack*	*USA*
18,450	57	17 Jan 1994	Earthquake (Northridge)	USA
11,684	124	2 Sep 2004	Hurricane Ivan	USA
10,000	34	20 Sep 2005	Hurricane Rita	USA
10,000	35	16 Oct 2005	Hurricane Wilma	USA
8,272	24	11 Aug 2004	Hurricane Charley	USA
8,097	51	27 Sep 1991	Typhoon Mireille	Japan
6,864	95	25 Jan 1990	Winter Storm Daria	Europe
6,802	110	25 Dec 1999	Winter Storm Lothar	Europe
6,610	71	15 Sep 1989	Hurricane Hugo	USA
5,170	38	26 Aug 2004	Hurricane Frances	USA
5,155	63	17 Oct 1989	Earthquake (Loma Prieta)	USA
5,150	22	15 Oct 1987	Storm	Europe
4,770	64	26 Feb 1990	Winter Storm Vivian	Europe
4,737	26	22 Sep 1999	Typhoon Bart	Japan
4,230	600	20 Sep 1998	Hurricane Georges	USA, Caribbean
4,136	3,034	13 Sep 2004	Hurricane Jeanne	USA, Haiti
3,707	45	6 Sep 2004	Typhoon Songda	Japan
3,475	41	5 Jun 2001	Tropical Storm Allison	USA
3,403	45	2 May 2003	Tornadoes	USA
3,304	*167*	*6 Jul 1988*	*Explosion on Piper Alpha offshore oil rig*	*UK*
3,169	6,425	17 Jan 1995	Earthquake (Kobe)	Japan
2,814	45	27 Dec 1999	Winter Storm Martin	France
2,768	70	10 Sep 1999	Hurricane Floyd	USA, Bahamas
2,695	38	6 Aug 2002	Floods	Europe
2,692	59	4 Oct 1995	Hurricane Opal	USA
2,438	26	20 Oct 1991	Fire—into urban area, drought	USA
2,427	—	6 Apr 2001	Storms (tornado/hail)	USA
2,366	246	10 Mar 1993	Storm (East Coast)	USA
2,233	20	3 Dec 1999	Winter Storm Anatol	Europe
2,227	4	11 Sep 1992	Hurricane Iniki (Hawaii)	USA
2,088	*23*	*23 Oct 1989*	*Explosion at Phillips Petroleum*	*USA*
2,068	240,000	26 Dec 2004	Earthquake/Tsunami	Indonesia
2,024	—	12 Sep 1979	Hurricane Frederic	USA
1,993	39	5 Sep 1996	Hurricane Fran	USA
1,981	2,000	18 Sep 1974	Hurricane Fifi	Honduras
1,947	100	4 Jul 1997	Floods	Europe
1,923	116	3 Sep 1995	Hurricane Luis	Caribbean
$261,859 Billion	**265,308 Total deaths**			

Source: © Swiss Reinsurance Company.

THE 1998 ST. LAWRENCE RIVER VALLEY ICE STORM

The 1998 ice storm in the St. Lawrence River Valley left a profound impression on people who experienced it. This great natural disaster, the second most expensive in Canadian history, highlights the vulnerability of Canadian society to extreme weather conditions, and its dependency on electricity. As straightforwardly stated by Mark Abley, "storm survivor" and author of two books on the topic: "…the evacuees didn't pray for a return of fine weather. They prayed for a return of power."

People in Eastern Canada are used to freezing rain, a form of precipitation in which rain droplets freeze immediately on contact with cold objects, enveloping them in a smooth veneer of ice. Freezing rain occurs when the near-surface air temperature is hovering around 0°C, which typically happens 12–17 days per year, resulting in an average of 45–65 hours of freezing rain precipitation annually (Table 11.7). The ice storm of 1998 was anomalous because of the stability of the weather conditions. As a mass of cold Arctic air and a warm and moist low-pressure system from the Gulf of Mexico remained static over the St. Lawrence River Valley, freezing rain fell for 80 hours over 5 days, from 5 to 9 January. In Montreal, the thickness of ice accumulated on trees and infrastructure reached 20 mm on day 1, 55 mm on day 3 and in excess of 100 mm on day 5. An ice thickness in excess of 25 mm causes major damage to trees.

As freezing rain kept falling, heavy branches broke off and fell to the ground, cutting power lines and blocking streets in countless locations. The electrical pylon is often described as "the official tree of Quebec" since the province has an extensive electrical network and many Quebeckers rely on this energy source to heat their homes. The pylons, designed to withstand an ice thickness of 15 mm, started to collapse, interrupting the regional transport of electricity (Figures 1.4 and 1.5). Sporadic blackouts became widespread and, by 9 January, four of the five main power lines feeding Montreal were out of commission. A staggering 3.5 million people were without electricity in mid-winter temperatures. The treacherous driving conditions made it impossible for people to leave their homes. They felt trapped in the cold and the dark.

Figure 1.4
Major power transmission line collapsed under the weight of ice.
Photo: Hydro-Quebec.

Figure 1.5
Pylons lie crumpled following 80 hours of freezing rain, St. Bruno, Quebec, 10 January 1998.
Photo: © Peter W. Weigand.

Figure 1.6

Almost ten years after the 1998 ice storm, tree damage is still visible in this maple bush in Middleville, Lanark County, Ontario. Not only several millions of maples were lost during the storm, but sap flow is reduced in remaining trees because their branches were damaged. It will take decades for the forest to heal and production to recover, as it takes at least 40 years until a small maple is large enough to be tapped.

© Claire Samson.

In the countryside, the situation was equally dramatic. Farmers were struggling to protect animals and keep dairy operations running using generators. Maple producers were hit hard: 22% of all sugar maple taps in Canada were subjected to the weight of over 40 mm of ice. Ten years after the storm, overarched trees are still visible in the forest. It will take decades for production to recover, as a small maple must grow for 40 years before it is large enough to be tapped.

On 7 January, the provinces of New Brunswick, Ontario, and Quebec requested aid from the federal government and "Operation Recuperation," led by the Canadian Armed Forces, began the following day. It was the largest domestic deployment of Canadian troops in response to a natural disaster in history, involving more than 15,000 army, navy, and air force personnel. Canadian Forces members sheltered and fed about 100,000 people evacuated from their homes, and maintained law and order.

Military engineers and technicians worked with hydro and telephone crews to repair and replace downed pylons and utility poles. At the peak of the outage, nearly 10,000 people were working to restore power.

Finally, on 9 January, the weather pattern changed, signaling a gradual return to normal conditions. On that day, however, both water filtration plants providing drinking water to the Montreal metropolitan area shut down simultaneously after pumping stations lost power, an example of cascading effects of systems failure. The situation was resolved quickly but could have had disastrous consequences on public health if it had persisted. In total, the ice storm crisis claimed 28 lives in Canada and 17 lives in the neighbouring U.S. states. People died from hypothermia, ice falls, and carbon monoxide poisoning and fire while using unsafe alternate heating sources.

In the words of a senior executive from Hydro-Québec, the public electricity company in Quebec: "The crisis was a great teacher for us, a real-life classroom where we painfully learned more about building a robust network." Since the 1998 ice storm, Hydro-Québec has taken several concrete actions to reinforce its network. Efforts have focused on diversifying the sources of supply so that major urban centres are now serviced from many different power lines. Anti-cascading towers, aimed at preventing the collapse of adjacent pylons, are used systemically along new lines: one tower is built every ten pylons. New pylons are built of stronger and thicker steel elements. Finally, on critical corridors, a new de-icing technology uses direct current flowing along power lines to prevent ice buildups. Nature has already tested these new developments. In April 2005, a severe ice storm hit the North Shore of the St. Lawrence River with ice accumulation in excess of 50 mm. Fourteen pylons collapsed and three main power transmission lines went out of service. Nevertheless, using the experience acquired during the 1998 ice storm, this crisis was managed efficiently and resulted in no interruption of service.

THE NUMBER OF NATURAL DISASTERS IN CANADA IS INCREASING

In line with global trends, statistics show that the number of natural disasters per year in Canada has been increasing from 1900 to 2005 (Figure 1.7). As the number of geological disasters remained stable, the overall increase reflects mainly a rise in the number of weather-related disasters. As for the global trend, the increase is closely related to population growth. From 1900 to 2001, the

population of Canada has increased sixfold, from 5 to 30 million (Figure 1.8). Events such as floods, which are part of the natural rhythm of rivers, commonly inundate farmers' fields. However, the same floods might start to be reported as "natural disasters" after subdivisions are built on the river's flood plain. The increase in the number of weather-related disasters might also indicate that weather events have become more extreme in the last 50 years and that Canadian society has not adapted adequately.

The impact of the media should not be neglected in the analysis of the data presented in Figure 1.7. Canada's first television station, CBFT-TV, began broadcasting in Montreal in 1952. The steep increase in the overall number of natural disasters started at the same time. Is it a coincidence? Television was instrumental in broadening the awareness of Canadians to major events both at home and in the "global village," a term coined by University of Toronto Professor Marshall McLuhan. This societal trend continues today with the rapid deployment of journalists and audio/video links anywhere in the world and the miniaturization of personal communication devices like cellular and smart phones.

THE NUMBER OF NATURAL-DISASTER FATALITIES IN CANADA IS DECREASING

Table 1.4 lists the deadliest Canadian disasters from 1900 to 2005. Contrary to the global trend, a majority of disasters (26 of 40) are not due to natural causes. Several entries in the table reflect the dangers associated with travelling

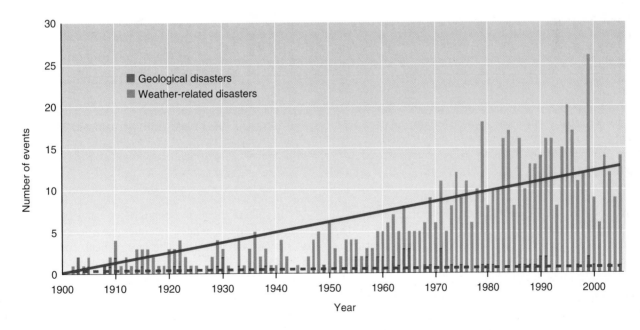

Figure 1.7

Canadian natural disasters 1900–2005. Straight lines have been fitted to the data. The dotted subhorizontal line shows the stable trend of the geological disasters; the solid oblique line, the increasing trend of the weather-related disasters.

Source: Canadian Natural Disasters 1900–2005, Canadian Disaster Database, http://ww5.ps-spgc.ca/res/en/cdd/search-en.asp. Reproduced with the permission of the Minister of Public Works and Government Services 2008.

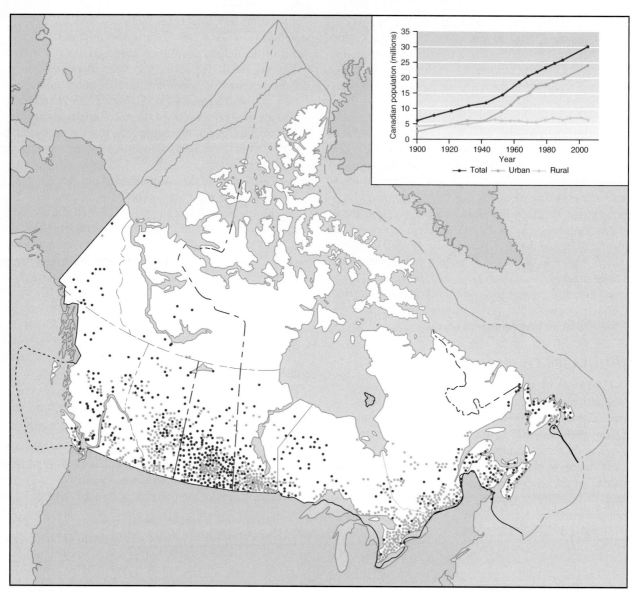

Figure 1.8

Population distribution map of Canada (2001). The blue and peach symbols indicate population centres of less and more than 1,000 people, respectively. The insert shows the Canadian population between 1900 and 2001. Since 1930, a majority of Canadians live in cities.

Source: Population distribution map of Canada (2001).Atlas of Canada 2001 http://atlas.nrcan.gc.ca/site/english/maps/peopleandsociety/population/population2001/ distribution2001 The data plotted in the insert is from URL: http://www40.statcan.ca/l01/cst01/demo62a.htm. Reproduced with the permission of the Minister of Public Works and Government Services, 2008.

across the vast expanses of Canada several decades ago. Two major disasters are of biological origin: the 1918 influenza and the 1953 polio epidemics. The threat of a pandemic is still present today. In an expert review commissioned by the City of Ottawa in 2004, for example, a flu pandemic was identified as the most serious threat to the National Capital, ahead of an earthquake and a nuclear accident. Although Ottawa is the centre of Canada's political life, the risk of a terrorist attack ranked only seventh in the list.

In spite of the increase in the frequency of natural disasters in Canada, related fatalities have been decreasing, as shown in Figure 1.9. The largest peak corresponds to the July 5–17, 1936 pan-Canadian heat wave during which temperatures from the Ottawa River Valley to Southern Saskatchewan were in excess of 32°C for one and half weeks, causing the deaths of 1,180 people. The 1916 peak is the great forest fire that destroyed 800,000 sq. km of boreal forest in the region of Cochrane in Northern Ontario and officially claimed the lives of 73 people (the actual death

Table 1.4

The 40 deadliest Canadian disasters 1900–2005. Events not due to natural causes are in italics.

Fatalities	Date	Event	Location
50,000	1918–1925	*Influenza epidemic*	Across Canada
1,963	1917	*Halifax explosion*	Halifax, NS
1,180	1936	Heat wave	Across Canada
1,024	1914	*Sinking of the "Empress of Ireland"*	St. Lawrence River, QC
481	1953	*Polio epidemic*	Across Canada
343	1918	*Sinking of the "Princess Sophia"*	West Coast, BC
270	1913	Storm	Lakes Huron, Erie and Ontario
256	1985	*Aircraft accident due to terrorist bomb*	Gander, NF
233	1916	Forest Fire	Cochrane area, ON
229	1998	*Aircraft accident*	Peggy's Cove, NS
203	1942	Storm	Newfoundland
189	1914	*Mine explosion*	Hillcrest, AB
173	1914	Storm	Newfoundland
126	1906	*Sinking of the "Valencia"*	Vancouver Island, BC
125	1902	*Mine explosion*	Fernie, BC
118	1949	*City fire*	Toronto, ON
118	1963	*Aircraft accident*	Sainte-Thérèse-de-Blainville, QC
117	1982	Blizzard	Newfoundland
115	1928	*Sinking of the "Acorn"*	Halifax, NS
109	1970	*Aircraft accident*	Pearson Airport, ON
101	1963	*Aircraft accident*	West Coast, BC
100	1908	*City fire*	Fernie, BC
99	1942	*City fire*	St. John's NF
88	1918	*Mine explosion*	Pictou County, NS
81	1954	Hurricane Hazel	Southern Ontario
79	1957	*Aircraft accident*	Quebec City QC
77	1914	Blizzard	Labrador, NF
76	1927	*City fire*	Montréal, QC
76	1941	Blizzard	Prairie provinces
75	1907	*Bridge collapse*	Quebec City, QC
75	1957	*Radioactive release*	St. Lawrence, NF
75	1958	*Mine collapse*	Springhill, NS
73	1911	Forest fire	Cochrane, ON
70	1903	Mass movement	Frank, AB
69	1940	Storm	Great Lakes, Lake Ontario
65	1917	*Mine explosion*	New Waterford, NS
64	1901	*Mine explosion*	Grand Forks, BC
63	1910	*Derailment*	Spanish River, ON
62	1910	Snow avalanche	Rogers Pass, BC
62	1956	*Aircraft accident*	Mount Slesse, BC

Source: 40 Deadliest Canadian Disasters 1900–2005, Canadian Disaster Database http://ww5.ps-sp.gc.ca/res/em/cdd/search-en.asp. Reproduced with the permission of the Minister of Public Works and Government Services, 2008.

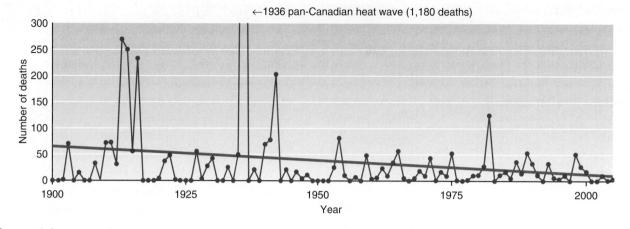

Figure 1.9
Deaths due to natural disasters in Canada (1900–2005). The trend is decreasing.

Source: 1936 Pan-Canadian Heat Wave, Canadian Disaster Database http://ww5.ps-sp.gc.ca/res/em/cdd/search-en.asp. Reproduced with the permission of the Minister of Public Works and Government Services, 2008.

toll probably reached hundreds). Most of the other large peaks coincide with severe storms causing ships, in 1913, 1914, and 1942, and more recently in 1982, an ocean-drilling rig, the *Ocean Ranger*, to sink.

What factors have helped Canadian society become more resilient to natural disasters? Undoubtedly, this success has been achieved by a multi-faceted approach, which includes improved engineering, long-term prevention, extensive disaster education, better warning systems, and rapid intervention.

IN CANADA, ECONOMIC LOSSES ARE MOSTLY DUE TO WEATHER-RELATED DISASTERS

Weather-related disasters dominate the lists of the most costly Canadian disasters both in terms of total costs (Table 1.5) and insured losses (Table 11.4). Between 1900 and 2005, prairie droughts recur the most often. The increasing frequency at which weather-related disasters occur is of serious concern as climate-change scenarios predict that meteorological activity will intensify in the future.

In Canada, written historical records exist only since the arrival of the Europeans in the 16th century, and the statistics presented in this section cover only the last 105 years (1900–2005). In terms of geological processes, a century represents only a quick snapshot. A word of caution: the impact of geological disasters like earthquakes and volcanoes is under represented in statistics not because the risk does not exist, but because danger has not materialized in historical times. Canada's costliest natural disasters (Table 11.4: insured costs only) do not make the international list (Table 1.3: insured costs only) because Canada has not experienced a great natural disaster in its history.

Vulnerability and Risk

In the context of natural disasters, **vulnerability** is the likelihood that a community will suffer, both in terms of fatalities and physical damage, when exposed to hazards in the environment. **Risk** can be defined as the product of vulnerability and hazard:

$$Risk = Vulnerability \times Hazard$$

From the equation above, we can see that the same hazard poses a more significant threat to vulnerable communities. A large earthquake (severe hazard) could cause significant damage to the highly populated downtown core of Vancouver (high vulnerability) and therefore risk is high. A similar earthquake (severe hazard) occurring in the Arctic is likely to disturb only a few polar bears (low vulnerability) and therefore risk is low.

What factors increase vulnerability and, combined with the proximity of hazards, can lead to a high risk of natural disasters?

POPULATION GROWTH

On a global scale, population growth is closely linked to the increase of life and economic loss related to natural disasters. Figure 1.10 shows the growth of the world population of humans. In 1999, the world population reached 6 billion and is heading toward 7 billion in 2013. Notice the continuing decline in the number of years it has taken for a net gain of another 1 billion people on Earth. The world population has been growing exponentially at about 1.2% per year for a doubling time of approximately 58 years. Even after subtracting all the human lives lost each year to accidents, diseases, wars, and epidemics such as AIDS, the human population has recently grown by about 80 million per year. This is equivalent to a net addition of 2.5 people per second.

Table 1.5

The 40 most costly Canadian disasters 1900–2005 (insured and uninsured costs combined). Events not due to natural causes are in italics.

Total estimated cost (in million 1999 CDN$)	Fatalities	Date	Event	Location
5,795	0	1980	Drought	Prairie provinces
5,410	28	1998	St. Lawrence River Valley Ice Storm	Ontario to New Brunswick
4,080	0	1988	Drought	Prairie provinces to Ontario
3,362	0	1979	Drought	Prairie provinces
1,944	0	1984	Drought	Prairie provinces
1,722	10	1996	Flood	Saguenay, QC
1,093	1	1950	Flood	Winnipeg, MB
1,032	81	1954	Hurricane Hazel	Southern Ontario
1,000	0	1931	Drought	Prairie provinces
990	0	1989	Drought	Prairie provinces
885	0	1991	Hailstorm	Calgary, AB
863	0	1961	Drought	Prairie provinces
817	0	1997	Flood	Southern Manitoba
707	0	1985	Drought	Western Canada
665	27	1987	Tornado	Edmonton, AB
596	0	1977	Drought	Prairie provinces
582	0	1990	Drought	Prairie provinces
575	0	1992	Drought	Prairie provinces
427	10	1948	Flood	Fraser River, BC
404	0	1993	Flood	Winnipeg, MB
400	Unknown	2003	Forest fires	Alberta and British Columbia
386	1963	1917	*Explosion*	Halifax, NS
377	0	1993	Drought	Prairie provinces
324	0	1983	Drought	Prairie provinces
306	0	1996	Hailstorm	Calgary, AB
303	0	1986	Drought	Prairie provinces
301	12	1985	Tornado	Hopeville to Barrie, ON
289	0	1981	Drought	Prairie provinces
288	2	1981	Hailstorm	Calgary AB
225	229	1998	*Aircraft accident*	Peggy's Cove, NS
216	0	1996	Blizzard	Southwestern BC
194	0	1974	Drought	Prairie provinces
157	0	1995	Flood	Southern AB
155	0	1996	Hailstorm	Winnipeg, MB
150	0	1984	Blizzard	Alberta
148	0	1985	Forest fires	Northeast of Vancouver, BC
147	0	1991	Drought	Prairie provinces
141	0	1986	*City fire*	Montréal, QC
140	18	1958	*Bridge collapse*	Vancouver, BC
128	14	1988	Heat wave	Prairie provinces to Ontario

Source: 40 Most Costly Canadian Disasters, 1900–2005, Canadian Disaster Database http://ww5.ps-sp.gc.ca/res/em/cdd/search-en.asp. Reproduced with the permission of the Minister of Public Works and Government Services, 2008.

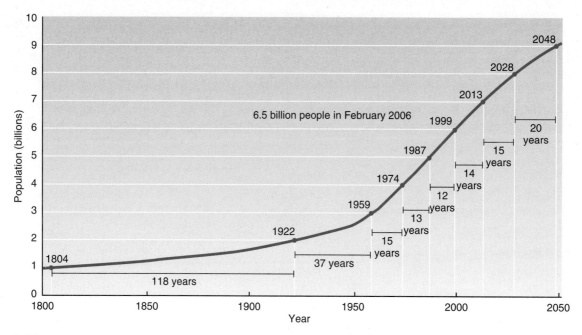

Figure 1.10
Growth of the world population of humans. Notice how the time to add another billion people has decreased to date but is projected to start increasing in the future.
Source: © US Census Bureau.

More recently, the growth has changed to a linear increase of population with time. This is expected as the **carrying capacity** of Earth is approached. As illustrated in Figure 1.10, some experts anticipate population to level off at 9 or 10 billion. Population growth places increasing numbers of people in hazardous settings. They live and farm on the slopes of active volcanoes, build homes and industries in the lowlands of river flood plains, and move to hurricane-prone coastlines.

As mentioned above, Asia is particularly vulnerable to great natural disasters because of its high population density (Figure 1.11). In addition, there is a geographical coincidence between populated centres and significant natural hazards. Large segments of the Asian population live in close proximity to the active volcanoes of the Pacific Ring of Fire, and to earthquake-prone areas. Asia is particularly at risk from great natural disasters because of its high population density (high vulnerability) and the high frequency of catastrophic geological events on this continent (severe hazards).

The distribution of the Canadian population leads to contrasting circumstances (Figure 1.8). Since World War II, the Canadian population is largely concentrated in cities. The large metropolitan areas of Toronto, Montreal, and Vancouver, where almost a third of Canadians live, are vulnerable because of their high population density. On the other hand, centres of fewer than 1,000 people—from Abbey, Saskatchewan to Zeballos, British Columbia—are vulnerable because they are scattered on

an immense territory and, in the event of an emergency, help might take a long time to reach them.

OVERRELIANCE ON TECHNOLOGY

Although scientific advances have resulted in a better understanding of natural hazards, contributing to enhancing safety, the overreliance of our modern societies on technology has created new vulnerabilities. Modern city life depends on complex and interrelated technological networks, including power transmission lines, telephone and Internet cables, water mains, and pipelines. Other networks, less tangible but equally important, include advanced systems for communications and data transmission that ensure the smooth flow of goods and services. In contradiction to these multiple links, however, urban life has also proven to be very lonely for some of the most fragile members of society.

In the event of a natural disaster, the failure of a network can cascade in a dangerous domino effect. Imagine the immediate aftermath of a medium-size earthquake in a crowded city centre. Buildings are structurally intact but power lines are damaged and some gas lines have ruptured. In the ensuing power blackout, out-of-commission traffic lights cause congestion impeding the movement of emergency response vehicles dispatched to stop gas leaks. During heat waves, prolonged power blackouts often occur because there is not enough electricity to supply the demand for air conditioning. Think of the

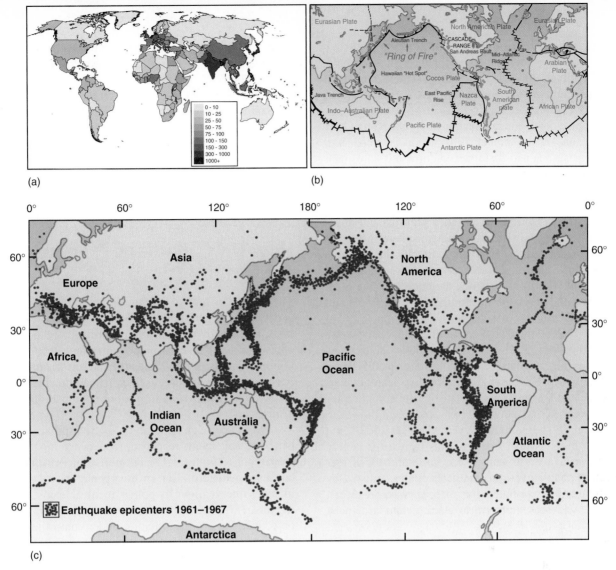

Figure 1.11

World population density per square kilometre. (a) World population density per square kilometre. (b, c) Red and blue dots mark earthquake epicentres and active volcanoes, respectively.

Source: a) David Vignoni, 6 December 2005 http://commons.wikimedia.org/wiki/Image:World_population_density_map. PNG. b) United States Geological Survey http://vulcan .wr.usgs.gov/Imgs/Gif/PlateTectonics/Maps/map_plate_tectonics_world.gif c) United States Geological Survey http://vulcan.wr.usgs.gov/Imgs/Gif/PlateTectonics/Maps/map_ plate_tectonics_world.gif

hopelessness of a senior citizen who, without functioning elevators, becomes literally trapped in his overheated flat in a high-rise apartment building. These are simple examples. In many cases, systems are so complex that it is difficult even to predict the cascading effects of the failure of a single system. Any factor disrupting the vast flows of energy and matter necessary to our modern lifestyles could potentially lead to a collapse of society. The bad news is that we are far more dependent on these flows than we were, say, a century ago.

POVERTY AND AFFLUENCE

Poor countries are already struggling to meet the basic needs of their citizens. They do not have enough resources to invest in long-term solutions that would decrease their vulnerability, like safer buildings and early-warning systems. In the short term, they do not have the response infrastructure, such as ambulances, pumps, and fire trucks, to deal with critical situations.

A magnitude 6.6 earthquake struck San Simeon, California on 22 December 2003. Four days later, an earthquake of exactly the same magnitude shook Bam, Iran, located in a similar geological environment. The San Simeon earthquake disturbed the lunchtime rush hour and caused two fatalities. The Bam earthquake was a tragedy of international proportion with 41,000 fatalities. Why were the consequences of the two events so different? Californians have invested massively to ensure their infrastructure is earthquake resistant, using the most recent advances in engineering seismology. In contrast, in remote areas of Iran, people live in traditional houses made of sun-dried, mud-brick walls topped by heavy roofs, according to designs unchanged in millennia. These buildings, including the Bam Citadel, the largest adobe structure in the world, completely disintegrated during the earthquake.

Compare death and destruction along the path of hurricane Jeanne in September 2004. Jeanne formed over the Caribbean Sea and first reached hurricane status near the eastern tip of the Dominican Republic. It slightly declined in intensity and travelled offshore north of Haiti. It regained strength over the Bahamas, veered east and made landfall in Florida as a category 3 hurricane. Haiti is the poorest country in the western hemisphere. Although Jeanne did not strike the country directly, heavy rains caused floods and mudslides, leaving more than 3,000 people dead. The disaster struck the poorest of the poor. In contrast, the death toll in Florida was five people and the insurance bill was in excess of US$4 billion.

Nevertheless, there are vulnerabilities associated with affluent lifestyles. The number of fatalities due to snow avalanches in Canada, for example, has steadily been rising. Between 1970 and 2003, there has been an average of 11 fatalities per year. If statistics are compiled for the five-year period between 1998 and 2003, however, the average is 16 fatalities per year, the year 2002 being especially tragic with 29 deaths. This increase is largely attributable to a significant rise in the numbers of recreationists heading off into the backcountry, assisted by improvements in equipment that make it easier for skiers, boarders, and snowmobilers to venture into avalanche terrain.

SOCIAL BEHAVIOUR

Authorities around the world, from local groups to central governments, are working to reduce the vulnerability of their communities by raising the awareness of the general public. They issue practical advice on what to do in case of danger in the form of leaflets, evacuation drills, and short courses. Short and crisp messages are often the most effective such as the international **tsunami** warning sign (Figure 6.28) posted in coastal states around the Pacific and Indian oceans.

Unfortunately, public education efforts are met in certain cases by fatalism or apathy. The return periods of several natural disasters like volcanic eruptions often span several generations. People forget the tragedies of the past and repeat the same mistakes. Mount Vesuvius erupted violently in 79 **CE**, causing the destruction of the Roman cities of Pompeii and Herculaneum. Volcanism was intermittent until 1631 when a more sustained phase of activity started, lasting until 1944. During this 300-year period, historical records report 24 eruptions. Dating of ash and other eruptive products reveals that Mount Vesuvius experiences an eruption similar to that of 79 CE every 2,000 years. Today, even with this well-documented eruptive history, the large city of Naples, home to one million people, lies at the foot of the majestic volcano.

Another counterproductive attitude is the overreliance on "society" to fix problems in the event of a natural disaster. This mindset leads individuals to neglect simple but important precautions like designing a home evacuation plan and keeping a home emergency kit (see In Greater Depth box: Home Emergency Kit and Plan).

How Do Canadians Prepare for Natural Disasters?

The Canadian federal institution responsible for emergency management is Public Safety Canada (PSC). PSC is an "all-hazards" organization coordinating the handling of events as diverse as natural disasters, technological failures, threats to public health, and terrorism. In practice, the organization focuses on managing emergencies, and decides *a posteriori* to label or not a particular event a "disaster."

PSC's approach is based on the four pillars of emergency management: response, recovery, mitigation, and preparedness (Figure 1.12). **Response** refers to the actions taken immediately after an emergency has occurred. It includes interventions by police, medical teams, and firefighters. Effective response is swift and coordinated. Its objective is to get the situation under control as quickly as possible. **Recovery** takes much longer and aims at getting the situation "back to normal"; that is, to its pre-disaster state. Depending on the extent of physical and psychological trauma, it might take several decades for a community to rebuild.

Mitigation and preparedness are long-term actions based on the lessons learned during past disasters and aimed at reducing the impact of future events. **Mitigation** involves activities to reduce risk. For example, the downtown core of the City of Calgary is built on the flood plain of the Bow River. This historical legacy makes Calgary's older neighbourhoods vulnerable to floods. To mitigate further flood risk, the expanding city has a strict land-use plan that prevents development in its newest districts on land prone to flooding by the Bow River. These areas are dedicated to recreational use rather than urban development. **Preparedness** comprises proactive steps taken to plan for disasters and to put in place the resources needed to cope with them. Stockpiling goods and conducting regular building evacuation drills are examples of preparedness. In Southern British Columbia, where seismic risk is highest in Canada, children practise earthquake drills in school. Earthquake noise is played in the public address system and children are taught to quickly duck under

In Greater Depth

Home Emergency Kit and Plan

In the case of a major disaster, regardless of its nature, Public Safety Canada (PSC) recommends that you and your family be autonomous for 72 hours, while emergency responders attend to those in urgent need. Be ready by preparing a home emergency kit and a plan. Pay special attention on how to stay warm in winter.

Basic items you will need to survive for 72 hours:

☐ **Water**—at least two litres of water per person per day (include small bottles that can be carried easily in case of an evacuation order)

☐ **Food** that won't spoil, such as canned food, energy bars, and dried foods (remember to replace the food and water once a year)

☐ **Manual can opener**

☐ **Flashlight and batteries**

☐ **Candles and matches or lighter** (remember to place candles in sturdy containers and to put them out before going to sleep)

☐ **Battery-powered or wind-up radio** (and extra batteries)

☐ **First aid kit**

☐ Special items such as **prescription medications, infant formula,** and **equipment for people with disabilities**

☐ **Extra keys** for your car and house

☐ Some **cash** in smaller bills, such as $10 bills (travelers cheques are also useful) and change for payphones

☐ A copy of your emergency plan including **contact information**

To create your emergency plan, you will need to think about:

- where the exits are from your home and neighbourhood
- a meeting place to reunite with family or roommates
- a designated person to pick up your children should you be unavailable
- close-by and out-of-town contact persons
- health information
- a place for your pet to stay
- the risks in your region
- the location of your fire extinguisher, water valve, electrical box, gas valve, and floor drain.

PSC has created an on-line tool to help you make an emergency plan. Visit www.getprepared.gc.ca.

Source: Basic Emergency Kit http://getprepared.ca/kit/basic_e.asp and Make and Emergency Plan http://getprepared.ca/plan/plan_e.asp. Reproduced with the permission of the Minister of Public Works and Government Services 2008.

their desk and to hold firmly on its legs. When the "earthquake" is over, they congregate in the schoolyard where teachers ensure that everyone is accounted for. In May 2007, during Emergency Preparedness Week in Canada, over 57,000 children and 3,200 staff at all public schools in Vancouver took part in such an earthquake drill.

Emergency management in Canada follows a "bottom-up" strategy in a hierarchical jurisdictional environment. The responsibility for health and safety rests mainly in the individual. Moving up one level, municipal responders handle 95% of emergencies, mainly following up from calls to the 9-1-1 phone line. The underlying assumption is that municipalities are aware of the hazards facing their communities and closer to the citizens. When a natural disaster strikes, however, municipal resources can become overwhelmed. Provincial authorities are then called upon for assistance. As a final resort, following a provincial request, the federal government assumes leadership. PSC coordinates the response, most often solely at a strategic level. It liaises with organizations like the Canadian Armed Forces, the Canadian Red Cross, the Meteorological Service of Canada, and Natural Resources Canada for the delivery of concrete assistance on the ground.

Although the administrative structure is in place and its mandate is clear, there are many challenges to effective management of natural disasters in Canada. Canadians face many risks but society has limited resources. How should risks be prioritized? The recovery period after a natural disaster is a good period to reflect and plan for the

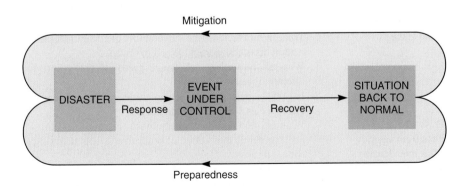

Figure 1.12
The four pillars of emergency management. The length of the arrows indicate duration: response covers a short period of time, whereas recovery takes much longer. Mitigation and preparedness are feedback loops representing long-term actions aimed at reducing the risk and impact of future events.

future. The temptation, however, is too often to prepare for the last disaster, not the next one. Should mitigation efforts privilege low-frequency/high-magnitude events like volcanic eruptions or high-frequency/low-magnitude events like local floods? Mitigation, with its long-term benefits, is in general tougher to "sell" to the public than response activities, but, as the old adage says, "an ounce of prevention is worth a pound of cure." A shining example of successful mitigation is the Winnipeg floodway. Since its completion in 1968, the floodway has saved Winnipeg from flooding no fewer than 18 times by safely channelling excess water away from the downtown area.

Summary

- Several hazardous conditions in the natural environment—unstable slopes or severe weather, for example—can cause harm to society. Several aspects contribute to increase the vulnerability of communities, including a high population density and a number of socio-economic factors.
- Natural disasters occur when natural processes suddenly release a large amount of energy, causing disruption to society. At any one site, the greater the magnitude of a disaster, the less frequently it occurs.
- Worldwide, the number of geological disasters has remained stable in the last century whereas the number of weather-related disasters keeps increasing.
- Great natural disasters are associated with a large number of fatalities and widespread destruction. Their frequency is increasing, a phenomenon partly linked to population growth. The two deadliest events are hurricanes and earthquakes.

- In the last century in Canada, major transport accidents, large-scale technological failures and biological disasters have outnumbered natural disasters. An integrated approach to emergency management, including response, recovery, mitigation and preparedness, has contributed to reduce the number of natural-disaster fatalities.
- The long-term trend is for economic losses associated with natural disasters to increase. Worldwide, between 1970 and 2005, seven of the ten most costly natural disasters have been tropical storms. Between 1900 and 2005, six of the ten most costly Canadian natural disasters have been Prairie droughts.
- Canadian citizens are encouraged to be proactive regarding natural disasters by preparing a home emergency kit and plan.

Terms to Remember

carrying capacity 16	magnitude 4	risk 14
CE 18	mass movement 4	storm 4
drought 4	mitigation 18	tsunami 18
earthquake 4	natural disaster 3	volcano 4
energy 3	natural hazard 3	vulnerability 14
flood 4	preparedness 18	weather-related disaster 4
frequency 3	recovery 18	wildfire 4
geological disaster 4	response 18	
great natural disaster 2	return period 3	

Questions for Review

1. What is the difference between a natural disaster and a natural hazard?
2. What is the relationship between the magnitude of a given disaster and its frequency of occurrence?
3. In the 20th century, has the frequency of geological and that of weather-related disasters changed over time?
4. What natural disasters killed the most people worldwide in the 20th century? Where in the world are deaths from natural disasters the highest? Where in the world are insurance losses from natural disasters the highest?
5. What natural disasters killed the most Canadians in the 20th century? What natural disasters were the most costly to the Canadian economy? To insurers?

6. What factors increase the vulnerability of communities to natural disasters, worldwide and in Canada?
7. What are the particular challenges faced by poor countries affected by natural disasters?
8. In Canada, what guiding principles are applied to managing emergencies due to natural disasters?
9. What are the four pillars of emergency management? In which order do they occur in the chain of events following a natural disaster?

Questions for Further Thought

1. Would we call a large earthquake or major volcanic eruption a natural disaster if no humans were killed or buildings destroyed?
2. Could global building designs be made disaster-proof, thus reducing the large number of fatalities?
3. How are mass media influencing the perception that the number of natural disasters is increasing with time?
4. What are the strengths and weaknesses of the "bottom-up" (from the individual to the central government) and "top-down" (from the central government to the individual) models of emergency management?
5. In natural disaster management, how much resources should be allocated to response and recovery versus mitigation and preparedness?
6. What could Canadians do to reduce the vulnerability of their communities to natural disasters?
7. Will the new United Nations Central Emergency Relief Fund be an effective mechanism to help poor countries affected by natural disasters?

Energy Flows in Earth History and Natural Disasters

2

"Civilization exists by geologic consent, subject to change without notice."

—Will Durant (1885–1981)

Outline

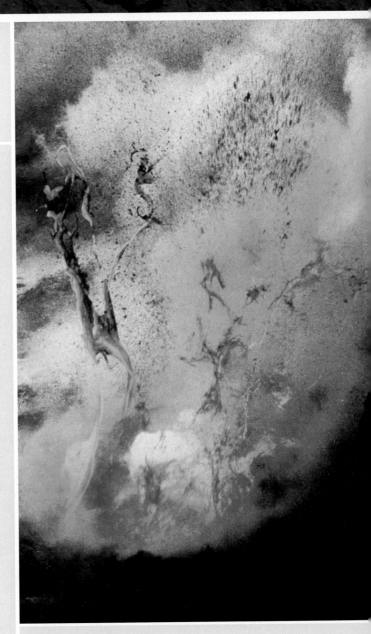

Lava meets the sea on Hawaii.

Photo by StockTrek/Getty Images.

Energy Sources of Disasters

Disasters occur where and when Earth's natural processes concentrate energy and then release it, killing life and causing destruction (Figures 2.1–2.7). As the world's population increases, more and more people find themselves living close to Earth's most dangerous places. As novelist Booth Tarkington remarked: "The history of catastrophe is the history of juxtaposition."

The natural disasters that kill and maim unwary humans can be classified on the basis of the energy sources that fuels Earth processes (Table 2.1). Four primary energy sources make Earth an active body: (1) Earth's energy; (2) gravity, (3) solar energy, and (4) the impact of extraterrestrial bodies.

The interior of Earth holds a tremendous store of heat released primarily from the ongoing decay of **radioactive elements**. Earth's internal energy flows unceasingly toward the surface. Over short time spans, it is released as eruptions from volcanoes and by earthquakes. Over longer intervals of geological time, the flow of internal energy has produced our continents, oceans, and atmosphere. On a planetary scale, this outward flow of internal energy causes continents to drift and collide, constructing mountain ranges and elevated plateaus.

Gravity is an attractional force between bodies. At equal distances, the greater the mass of a body, the greater its gravitational force. The relatively great mass of Earth has powerful effects on smaller masses such as ice and rock, causing snow avalanches and landslides.

About a quarter of the Sun's energy that reaches Earth evaporates and lifts water into the atmosphere to begin the hydrologic cycle. At the same time, the constant pull of gravity helps bring atmospheric moisture down as snow and rain. On short timescales, unequal heating of the oceans and atmosphere at Earth's poles versus the equator creates density differences in water and air acted on by gravity to create weather, including storms, strong winds, and ocean waves. On a long timescale, the Sun and gravity power the agents of **erosion**—glaciers, streams, underground waters, winds, ocean waves, and currents—that wear away the continents and dump their broken pieces and dissolved remains in the seas. Solar energy is also stored in plant tissue to be released later as fire.

Figure 2.1
Earth's internal heat provides energy for earthquakes. A typical earthquake not only destroys buildings, but also unleashes fires. A city block in Kobe, Japan, burns on 17 January 1995 following the magnitude 6.9 earthquake that killed 6,425 people.
Photo: © Kelvin West/Liaison/Getty Images.

Figure 2.2
Earth's internal energy fuels volcanism. Soufriere Hills Volcano glows as hot, sticky magma wells up and flows down the mountain on the island of Montserrat in the Caribbean Sea, 8 January 1997.

Photo: © Pat Abbott.

Figure 2.3
The pull of gravity brings down hillsides. This earthquake-triggered debris flow destroyed 300 homes and killed 680 people in Santa Tecla, El Salvador, on 13 January 2001.

Photo: © Larry Mayer.

Figure 2.4
External energy from the Sun fuels tornadoes. This aesthetically sculpted tornado touched down in New Mexico, United States.

Figure 2.5
External energy from the Sun powers hurricanes and their rains and floods. Hurricane Mitch stalled off the coasts of Honduras and Nicaragua from 27 to 29 October 1998, creating record rainfalls and floods that killed about 11,000 people. Here, residents watch the Choluteca River in flood in Tegucigalpa, Honduras, on 31 October 1998.

Figure 2.6
External energy from the Sun is stored inside plants and can be released by fire as in this example from Yukon.

Figure 2.7
Asteroids and comets can hit Earth and kill life worldwide. Comet Hale-Bopp misses Earth as it streaks above the telescope domes on 4,205 m high Mauna Kea, Hawaii, in early 1997.

Table 2.1

Energy and Natural Disasters

Source of energy	Natural disaster
Earth's internal energy	Earthquake
	Tsunami
	Volcano
Gravity	Mass movements
	Snow avalanche
Solar energy	Meteorological storm
	Flood
	Drought
	Wildfire
	Magnetic storm
Impact energy	Impact with space objects

Geological disasters
Weather-related disasters

An energy source for disasters arrives when visitors from outer space—**asteroids** and **comets**—impact Earth. Impacts were abundant and important early in Earth's history. In recent times, collisions with large bodies have become infrequent, although when they hit, their effects on life can be global.

Origin of the Sun and Planets

Impacts are not rare and insignificant events in the history of our Solar System; they probably were responsible for its formation. The most widely accepted model of the origin of the Solar System was formulated by German philosopher Immanuel Kant in 1755. He proposed that the Solar System formed by growth of the Sun and planets through collisions of matter within a rotating cloud of gas and dust.

The early stage of growth of the Solar System began within a rotating spherical cloud of gas, ice, dust, and other solid debris, the solar nebula (Figure 2.9a). Gravity acting upon matter within the cloud attracted particles, bringing them closer together. Small particles stuck together and grew in size, resulting in greater gravitational attraction to nearby particles and thus more collisions. As matter drew inward and the size of the cloud decreased, the speed of rotation increased and the mass began flattening into a disk (Figure 2.9b). The greatest accumulation of matter occurred in the centre of the disk, building toward today's Sun (Figure 2.9c). The two main constituents of

the Sun are the lightweight elements hydrogen (H) and helium (He). As the central mass grew larger, its internal temperature increased to about 1,000,000°C and the process of **nuclear fusion** began. In nuclear fusion, the smaller hydrogen atoms combine (fuse) to form helium with some mass converted to energy. We Earthlings feel this energy as **solar radiation** (sunshine).

The remaining rings of matter in the revolving Solar System formed into large bodies as particles continued colliding and coalescing together to create the planets (Figure 2.9d). Late-stage impacts between ever-larger objects would have been powerful enough to melt large volumes of rock, with some volatile elements escaping into space.

The inner planets (Mercury, Venus, Earth, Mars) formed so close to the Sun that solar radiation drove away most of their volatile gases and easily evaporated liquids, leaving behind rocky planets. The next four planets outward (Jupiter, Saturn, Uranus, Neptune) are giant icy bodies of hydrogen, helium, and other frozen material.

Jupiter, with its enormous mass, created in its vicinity a zone of gravitational perturbations too unstable for the formation of large bodies. Chunks of rocks remained as discrete entities instead of amalgamating. They still gravitate around the Sun in the asteroid belt located between Mars and Jupiter, and are the main source of **meteorites** found on Earth. There are two main classes of meteorites: stony and iron-rich meteorites (Figure 2.10). Most stony meteorites include small rounded grains, called **chondrules**. Chondrules are condensed droplets from the solar nebula and represent the most primitive material in the Solar System. Iron meteorites are more evolved, having experienced processes that segregated metals from other elements.

AGE OF EARTH

The oldest Solar System materials are about 4.57 billion years old. The 4.57-billion-year age has been measured using radioactive **isotopes** and their decay products collected from Moon rocks and meteorites (see In Greater Depth box: Radioactive Isotopes). The oldest Earth rocks found to date are 4.055 billion years old and originate from the Northwest Territories (Figure 2.11). These rocks are of crustal composition, implying that they were recycled and formed from even older rocks. The oldest ages obtained from Earth materials are 4.37 billion years, measured on zircon sand grains collected from a 3.1-billion-year-old sandstone in western Australia.

Earth must be younger than the 4.57-billion-year old materials that collided and clumped together to form the planet. The time it took to build Earth is possibly as short as 30 million years. The collision of Earth with the Mars-size body that formed our Moon seems to have occurred between 4.537 and 4.533 billion years ago, suggesting

Energy, Force, Work, Power, and Heat

The effectiveness of agents and events is measured using the related terms of energy, force, work, power, and heat. Energy is the ability to do **work**; it may be potential or kinetic. **Potential energy** (PE) is poised and ready to go to work. For example, a house-size boulder resting precariously high on a steep slope has the potential to roll and bounce downhill and do a lot of damage (Figure 2.8a). The potential energy of the huge boulder is equal to its mass (m) times gravitational acceleration (g) times its height (h) above a certain level, which in this case is the elevation of the valley floor below it.

$$PE = mgh$$

If the boulder starts to roll, its potential energy now becomes kinetic—the energy of motion (Figure 2.8b). **Kinetic energy** (KE) is determined by half the product of mass (m) times the velocity (v) squared:

$$KE = 1/2 \, mv^2$$

Downslope collisions might cause other boulders to move and the resultant moving mass brings soil, trees, and other debris downhill with it. The work done on the sliding mass is determined as **force** (F) times distance (d), where force equals mass times acceleration:

$$work = Fd$$

The landslide triggered by the bouncing mega-boulder may move rapidly (faster than a human can run) or slowly. Whether fast or slow, the amount of work is the same. However, the power is different. **Power** is defined as the rate at which work occurs:

$$power = work/time$$

After the boulder initiated the downslope movement of earth material, what happened to slow and stop it? Friction—friction with the underlying ground and friction among the boulders, sand grains, trees, and other debris inside the moving mass. As you know from sliding into second base or across a dance floor, friction generates heat. Thus, **heat** is a form of energy.

Force is measured in newtons (N) where 1 newton is the force required to accelerate a mass of 1 kg 1 ms squared:

$$newton \, (N) = 1 \, kg \; m/s^2$$

(a)

(b)

Figure 2.8 (a) When the boulder is poised and ready to move, it has potential energy. (b) When the boulder is rolling, its energy is kinetic.

Drawings © Jacobe Washburn.

Energy, work, and heat are expressed in joules (J):

$$joule \, (J) = newton \times metre = 1 \, kg \; m^2/s^2$$

Power is measured in watts:

$$watt \, (W) = joule/second$$

To put things in perspective, geologists have estimated that the potential energy of the 1903 Frank slide, Alberta (see Chapter 9) was on the order of 3×10^{14} joules, which is equivalent to 5 Hiroshima atomic bombs, or to about 21 seconds of current worldwide power consumption.

---

that Earth was already a large, coherent mass at that time. Approaching this question another way, Earth must be older than the 4.37-billion-year-old zircon grains collected from sandstone in Australia. In sum, our planet has existed for about 4.5 billion years.

The work to exactly determine the age and early history of Earth continues today. It is challenging to try to find the oldest minerals and rocks because Earth is such an energetic planet that surface rocks are continually being formed and destroyed. Because of these active processes, truly old materials are rarely preserved; there have been too many events over too many years.

Earth History

To understand the origin and structure of Earth, we must know the flows of energy throughout the history of our planet. Earth appears to have begun as an aggregating mass of particles and gases from a rotating cloud.

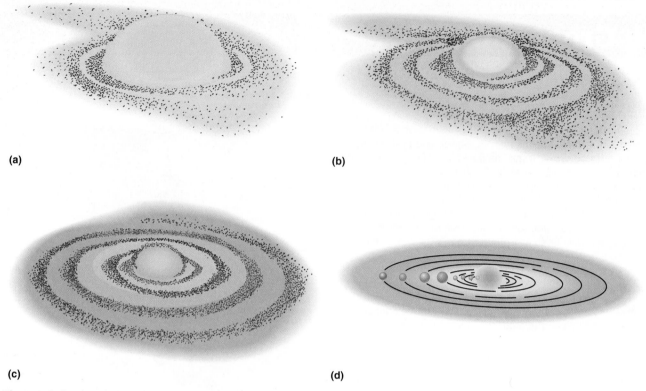

Figure 2.9

Model of the origin of the Solar System. (a) Initially, a huge, rotating spherical cloud of ice, gas, and other debris forms.
(b) Spinning mass contracts into a flattened disk with most mass in the centre. (c) Planets grow as masses collide and stick together.
(d) Ignited Sun is surrounded by planets. Earth is the third planet from the Sun.

During a 30- to 100-million-year period, bits and pieces of metal-rich particles (similar to iron-rich meteorites), rocks (similar to stony meteorites), and ices (of water, carbon dioxide, and other compounds) formed some 4.57 billion years ago, accumulated to form Earth. As the ball of coalescing particles enlarged, the gravitational force may have pulled more of the metallic pieces toward the centre, while some of the less-dense materials may have concentrated near the exterior. Nevertheless, Earth in its infancy probably grew from random collisions of debris that formed a more or less homogeneous mixture of materials.

But Earth did not remain homogeneous. The very processes of planet formation created tremendous quantities of heat, which fundamentally changed the young planet. The heat that transformed the early Earth came from impact energy, gravitational energy, differentiation into layers, and decay of radioactive elements.

As the internal temperature of Earth rose beyond 1,000°C, it passed the melting points of iron at various depths below its surface. Iron forms about one-third of Earth's mass, and although it is much denser than ordinary rock, it melts at a much lower temperature. The buildup of heat caused a large quantity of iron to melt. The high-density liquid iron was pulled by gravity toward Earth's centre. As these gigantic volumes of liquid iron

moved inward to form Earth's core, they released a tremendous amount of gravitational energy that converted to heat and probably raised Earth's internal temperature by another 2,000°C. The release of this massive amount of heat would have produced widespread melting likely to have caused low-density materials to rise and form (1) a primitive crust of low-density rock at the surface of Earth; (2) large oceans; and (3) a denser atmosphere. The formation of the iron-rich core was a unique event in the history of Earth. The planet was changed from a somewhat homogeneous ball into a density-stratified mass with the denser material in the centre and progressively less-dense materials outward to the atmosphere. It seems that oceans and small continents existed by 4.4 billion years ago, life probably was present as photosynthetic bacteria 3.5 billion years ago, and large continents were present at least 2.5 billion years ago when the process of plate tectonics was initiated.

The Layered Earth

Earth today is differentiated into layers. Earth's layering can be described either as (1) separations based on density due to varying chemical and mineral compositions or (2) layers with different strengths (Figure 2.12).

(a)

(b)

Figure 2.10
Canadian meteorites. (a) Tagish Lake is a stony meteorite found in 2000 in northern British Columbia. It features abundant chondrules, seen as rounded grains within its rust-coloured matrix. (b) Annaheim is an iron-rich meteorite found in 1916 some 100 km east of Saskatoon by a farmer who was mowing hay. Note the well-developed "thumbprints" generated as the meteorite passed through Earth's atmosphere.

Source: (a) ROM2006_7156_3 Royal Ontario Museum © ROM. (b) Reproduced with the permission of Natural Resources Canada 2008, courtesy of the Geological Survey of Canada (Photo 2008-186 by Richard Herd).

DENSITY LAYERS

At Earth's centre is a dense, iron-rich **core** measuring about 7,000 km in diameter. The inner core is a solid mass 2,450 km in diameter with temperatures up to 4,300°C. The outer core is mostly liquid, and convection currents within it are responsible for generating Earth's magnetic field. The core is roughly analogous in composition to a melted mass of iron-rich meteorites.

Surrounding the core is a rocky **mantle** nearly 2,900 km thick, comprising 83% of Earth's volume and 67% of its mass. The rock of the mantle can be approximated

Figure 2.11
The world's oldest rocks, the Acasta gneiss, are found 350 km northeast of Yellowknife in the Northwest Territories. They have been dated at 4.055 billion years by scientists of the Geological Survey of Canada.

Photo by Marc St-Onge, Geological Survey of Canada.

by melting a chondritic meteorite in the laboratory and removing most iron-loving elements and some volatiles. The uppermost 700 km thickness of mantle is depleted in light elements and thus differs from the lower zone, which is 2,200 km thick.

Continued melting of a chondritic meteorite produces a separation in which an upper froth rich in low-density elements rises above a residue of denser elements. The low-density material is similar to continental **crust** that, through melting and separation, has risen above the uppermost mantle. All the years of heat flow toward Earth's surface have "sweated out" many low-density elements to form a continental crust. Today, the continents comprise only 0.1% of Earth's volume.

As we can see, Earth can be described as a series of floating layers where less-dense materials successively rest upon layers of more-dense materials. The core, with densities up to 16,000 kg/m^3, supports the mantle, with densities ranging from 5,700 to 3,300 kg/m^3. Atop the denser mantle float the **continents**, with densities around 2,700 kg/m^3, which in turn support the salty oceans, with a density about 1,030 kg/m^3, and then the least-dense layer of all—the **atmosphere**. The concept of floating layers holds true on smaller scales as well. For example, the oceans comprise layered masses of water of differing densities. Very cold, dense Antarctic waters flow along the ocean bottoms and are overlain by cold Arctic water, which is overlain by extra-salty waters, which in turn are overlain by warmer, less-dense seawater.

STRENGTH LAYERS

Adopting a different perspective, Earth can also be described as a stratified body made of layers of different strength. Before examining the physical behaviour

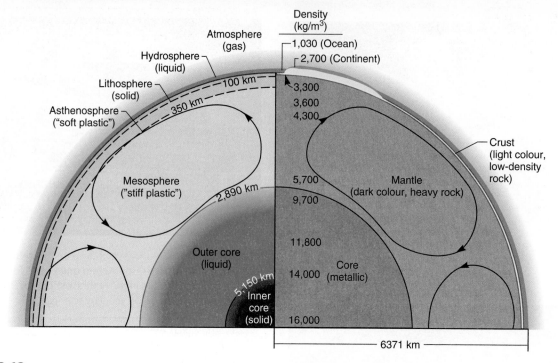

Figure 2.12

Density stratification within Earth, that is, lower-density materials float atop higher-density materials. Pressure and temperature both increase from surface to the centre of Earth. Layers illustrated on the left show the differences in physical properties and strengths. Layers on the right emphasize different mineral and chemical compositions. Arrows indicate large convection cells.

of Earth material at a planetary scale, however, let us describe the response of material subjected to different pressure and temperature conditions.

When materials are subjected to sufficient external forces or **stress**, they will deform or undergo **strain**. Stress can be applied perpendicular to the surface of a body, causing it to stretch under **tension** or to contract under **compression**. On the other hand, **shear stress**, which is applied parallel to the surface, tends to deform a body along internal planes slipping pass one another (Figure 2.13).

Materials respond to stress in different ways (Figure 2.14). Stress may produce **elastic** or recoverable deformation, such as when you pull on a spring. The spring deforms while you pull it, but when you let go, it recovers and returns to its original shape. If greater stress is applied, then **ductile** deformation may occur and the change is permanent. You can visualize this with a wad of chewing gum or Silly Putty®. If you squeeze them in your hands, they deform. Set them down and they stay in the deformed shape.

However, these definitions do not state the effect of time. What is the behaviour of materials over different time scales? If stress is applied rapidly to a material, it might abruptly fracture or break into pieces in **brittle** deformation. If stress is applied for a longer time or at higher temperatures, some solids yield to pressure by deforming and flowing, that is, by behaving like fluids. This type of behaviour is called "**plastic**" in the sense used by William James in his 1890 *Principles of Psychology*. He defined "plastic" as "possession of a structure

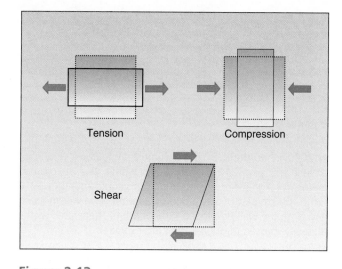

Figure 2.13

A square of material deforms into an elongated rectangle under tension or compression. It becomes a parallelogram when shear stress is applied.

weak enough to yield to an influence, but strong enough not to yield all at once."

A familiar example of a material exhibiting a variety of behaviours is **glacier** ice. The style of ice behaviour depends on the amount of pressure confining it. Near the surface, there is little pressure on the rigid ice and it abruptly fractures when stressed. When a glacier is hit with a rock hammer, solid chunks of brittle ice are broken off. On the other hand, deep within the glacier, where the weight of overlying ice creates a lot of pressure, the ice

(a) Elastic—recovers

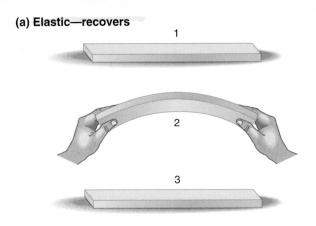

(b) Ductile—deforms

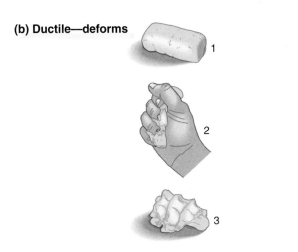

(c) Brittle—breaks

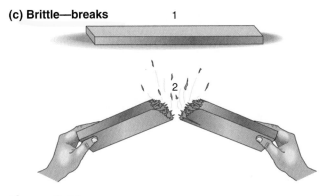

Figure 2.14
Behaviour of materials. (a) Elastic: bend thin board; let it go and board recovers its original shape. (b) Ductile: squeeze a wad of bubblegum or Silly Putty®; let it go but mass stays in the deformed shape. (c) Brittle: bend thin board sharply and it breaks.

deforms and flows. Atoms are changing positions within the ice and dominantly moving to downhill positions of lower stress. At no instant in time does the glacier fit our everyday concept of a liquid, yet over time, the glacier is flowing downhill as a highly **viscous** fluid (Figure 2.15).

The response of earth material to pressure and temperature is a complex balance between different effects. When a material such as rock is subjected to the same large amounts of stress on all sides, it compresses. When

Figure 2.15
The Elephant Foot glacier from East Greenland flowing toward the sea.
Photo by Dr. Fiona Darbyshire GEOTOP-UQAM McGill, Université du Québec à Montréal.

Figure 2.16
The Little Beehive near Lake Louise, Alberta exhibits two styles of deformation. Plastic deformation has given rise to large-scale undulations whereas brittle deformation has produced a pervasive network of small-scale horizontal and vertical fractures.
Photo © Claire Samson.

stresses coming from different directions vary, then strain can occur. When the differences in stress are low, then strain is elastic and reversible. As stress differences increase, permanent strain eventually occurs. Increasing temperature causes rock to expand in volume and become less dense and more capable of flowing. Increasing pressure causes rock to decrease in volume and become more dense and more rigid. Most rocks are brittle at the low temperatures and low pressures at Earth's surface. They fracture and create faults. Most rocks become ductile at the high temperatures and high pressures found at greater depths. They deform plastically, producing undulations called folds (Figure 2.16).

Changes in physical behaviour mark the different layers of Earth and are partly responsible for earthquakes and volcanoes. Both temperature and pressure decrease continuously from Earth's core to its surface, yet their effects on materials are different. At the centre of Earth is the inner core where intense pressure has tightly packed iron atoms into solid crystals. The inner core is enveloped by the outer core where iron exists in liquid form. The **mesosphere**, which extends from the core-mantle boundary to a depth of 360 km below Earth's surface, is a "stiff plastic" solid. Surrounding the mesosphere is the "soft plastic" **asthenosphere** (from the Greek word *asthenes,* meaning "weak"). The material in these two plastic layers flows in large convection cells where certain areas rise and other sink due to spatial variations in Earth's internal heat. At a flow rate of a few centimetres per year, it takes rock approximately 200 million years to complete a convection cycle. Finally, the outer layer of Earth is the rigid **lithosphere** (from the Greek word *lithos,* meaning "rock") whose thickness ranges from a few kilometres under the oceans to 100 kilometres under the continents (Figure 2.17). From a perspective of geological disasters, the most important boundary between the different strength layers is that between the lithosphere and asthenosphere as we will explore in more detail in Chapter 3.

Isostasy

The concept of **isostasy** was developed in the 19th century. It applies a buoyancy principle to the low-density continents and mountain ranges that literally float on the denser mantle below. Just as an iceberg juts up out of the ocean while most of its floating mass is beneath sea level, so does a floating continent jut upward at the same time it has a thick "root" beneath it (Figure 2.17).

Just how solid and firm is the surface of the Earth we live on? Vertical movements of the rigid lithosphere floating on the flexible asthenosphere are well documented. An example of isostasy is the post-glacial rebound affecting Canada and other northern countries. Some 18,000 years ago, Canada was buried under a gigantic continental glacier (Figure 10.33) with ice thickness reaching 5 km around Hudson Bay. The weight of the ice sheet caused the land to sink more than a kilometre as rock in the asthenosphere oozed away under the load as a ultra–high viscosity fluid. By 10,000 years ago, the ice sheet had melted and retreated. Responding elastically, the

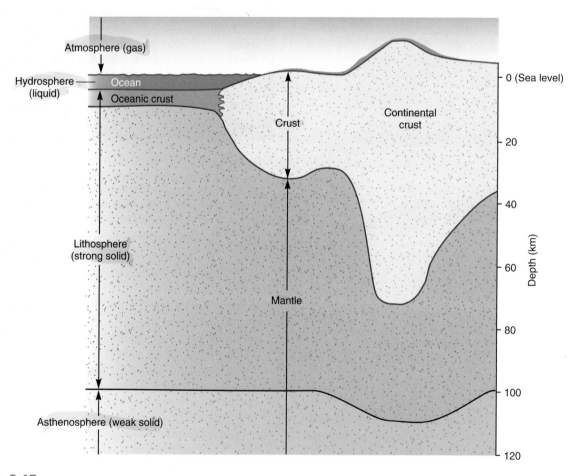

Figure 2.17
Upper layers of Earth may be recognized (1) compositionally, as lower-density crust separated from the underlying higher-density mantle, or (2) on the basis of strength, as strong, solid lithosphere riding atop weak, solid asthenosphere. Notice that the lithosphere includes both the crust and the uppermost mantle.

Figure 2.18
The velocity of the post-glacial rebound can be measured using the global positioning system (GPS). The Hudson Bay area where the ice load was heaviest during the last glaciation is rising fastest.

Source: Sella et al., 2004.

Figure 2.19
The post-glacial rebound has elevated beaches in the Boothia peninsula, Northwest Territories, above present-day sea level.

Source: Reproduced with the permission of Natural Resources Canada 2008, courtesy of the Geological Survey of Canada (Photo A8).

long-depressed landmass, now freed from its heavy load, is currently rebounding upward at a velocity of a few millimetres per year (Figures 2.18 and 2.19).

The surface of Earth is in a delicate vertical balance. Major adjustments and movements also occur horizontally.

These horizontal movements between the lithosphere and asthenosphere bring us into the realm of plate tectonics, addressed in Chapter 3.

Internal Sources of Energy

Energy in Earth's interior comes mainly from the ongoing decay of radioactive elements, with smaller contributions from impacts and gravitational compaction, acquired earlier in Earth's history.

Radioactive atoms are unstable and must eject subatomic particles to attain stability. This decay mechanism, nuclear fission, is accompanied by a release of energy. Heat generated by nuclear fission within Earth flows to the surface constantly via **conduction** and, more importantly, **convection** through the mesosphere and asthenosphere, magma in volcanoes, and water in hot springs.

The radioactive-decay process is measured by the **half-life**, which is the length of time needed for half the present number of atoms of a radioactive isotope (parent) to disintegrate to a decay (daughter) product. As the curve in Figure 2.20 shows, during the first half-life, one-half of the atoms of the original radioactive isotope decay. During the second half-life, one-half of the remaining atoms decay (equivalent to 25% of the original parent atoms). The third half-life witnesses the third halving of radioactive atoms present (12.5% of the original parent atom population), and so forth.

In the beginning of Earth, there were abundant, short-lived radioactive isotopes, such as aluminium-26, that are now effectively extinct, as well as long-lived radioactive isotopes, many of which have now expended much of their energy (Table 2.2). Young Earth had a much larger

Table 2.2

Some Radioactive Isotopes in Nature

Parent	Decay Product	Half-Life (Billion Years)
Carbon-14	Nitrogen-14	0.00000573 (5,730 years)
Aluminum-26	Magnesium-26	0.00072 (720,000 years)
Uranium-235	Lead-207	0.71
Potassium-40	Argon-40	1.3
Uranium-238	Lead-206	4.5
Thorium-232	Lead-208	14
Rubidium-87	Strontium-87	47
Samarium-147	Neodymium-147	106

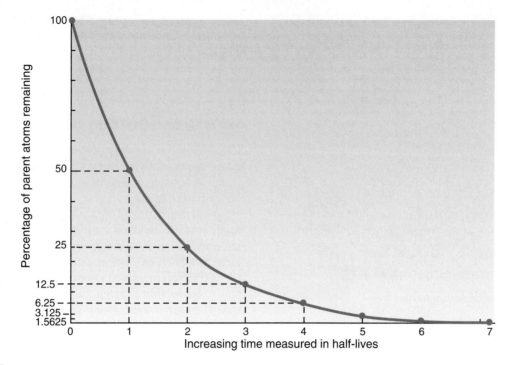

Figure 2.20
A negative exponential curve showing decay of radioactive parent atoms to stable daughter atoms over time. Each half-life witnesses the disintegration of half the remaining radioactive parent atoms.

complement of radioactive isotopes and a much greater heat production from them than it does now (Figure 2.21). The immense amount of heat generated, however, did not readily escape because heat conducts very slowly through rock. Some of this early heat still is flowing to the surface today and provides enough energy for tectonic plates to move, volcanoes to erupt, and earthquakes to shake.

External Sources of Energy

Energy flowing from Earth's interior to the surface accomplishes impressive geological work, yet the total amount of energy is miniscule compared to the radiated energy received from the Sun. Only a minute percentage of the radiant energy of the Sun reaches Earth, yet it is about 4,000 times greater than the heat flow from Earth's interior (Table 2.3).

Energy is also supplied externally via gravitational attractions between Earth, Moon, and Sun that add tidal energy to Earth. In addition, incoming meteorites, asteroids, and comets still impact our planet.

THE SUN

Earth's climate is powered primarily by heat energy emitted from the Sun. The energy radiated from the Sun covers a broad spectrum of wavelengths ranging from radio waves with wavelengths of tens of kilometres to gamma rays with wavelengths smaller than one-billionth of a centimetre; this is the electromagnetic spectrum (Figure 2.24). Most of the solar radiation is concentrated in the part of the spectrum visible (light) or nearly visible (infrared and ultraviolet) to humans. Visible light is about 43% of the solar radiation received on Earth; it ranges in wavelength from 0.7 (red) to 0.4 (violet) micrometres.

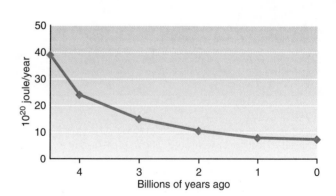

Figure 2.21
The rate of heat production from decay of radioactive atoms has declined throughout the history of Earth. The flow of energy from Earth's interior is on a slow decline curve heading toward zero.

In Greater Depth

Radioactive Isotopes

Each chemical element has a unique number of positively charged protons that define it. However, the number of neutrons varies, giving rise to different forms of the same element, known as isotopes. Some isotopes are radioactive and release energy during their decay processes. In **nuclear fission,** unstable, radioactive parent atoms shed excess subatomic particles, reducing their weight and becoming smaller daughter atoms (Figure 2.22). The overly heavy radioactive isotopes slim down to a stable weight by splitting apart by emitting alpha particles consisting of two protons and two neutrons (effectively, the nucleus of a helium atom). Beta particles are electrons freed upon a neutron's splitting. Gamma radiation, which is similar to X-rays but with shorter wavelength, is emitted, lowering the energy level of a nucleus. As the rapidly expelled particles are slowed and absorbed by surrounding matter, their energy of motion is transformed into heat.

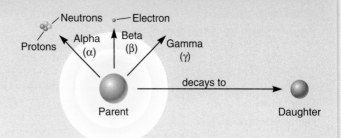

Figure 2.22 A radioactive parent atom decays to a smaller daughter atom by emitting alpha particles (such as the nucleus of a helium atom, i.e., two protons and two neutrons), beta particles (electrons), and gamma radiation.

Dating the Events of Earth History

The same decaying radioactive isotopes producing heat inside Earth also may be read as clocks that date events in Earth history. For example, uranium-238 decays to lead-206 through numerous steps involving different isotopes and new elements (Figure 2.23). By emitting alpha and beta particles, 32 of the 238 subatomic particles in the U-238 nucleus are lost, leaving the 206 particles of the Pb-206 nucleus. Laboratory measurements of the rate of the decay process have given us the U-238-to-Pb-206 half-life of 4.5 billion years. These facts may be applied to quantifying Earth history by reading the radiometric clocks preserved in some minerals. For example, some **igneous rocks** (crystallized from **magma**) can be crushed, and the very hard mineral zircon (from which zirconium, the diamond substitute in jewellery, is synthesized) separated from it. Zircon crystals contain uranium-238, which was locked into their atomic structure when they crystallized from magma, but they originally contained virtually no lead-206. Thus, the lead-206 present in the crystal must have come from decay of uranium-238.

The collected zircon crystals are crushed into a powder and dissolved with acid under ultra-clean conditions. The sample is placed in a mass spectrometer to measure the amounts of parent uranium-238 and daughter lead-206 present. Then, with three known values—(1) the amount of U-238, (2) the amount of Pb-206, and (3) the half-life of 4.5 billion years for the decay process—it is easy to calculate how long the U-238 has been decaying into Pb-206 within the zircon crystal. In other words, the calculation tells us how long ago the zircon crystal formed and consequently the time of formation of the igneous rock.

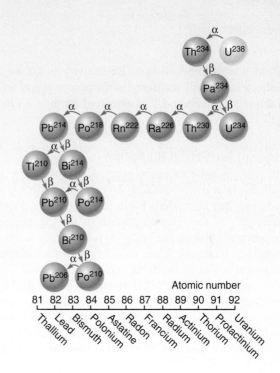

Figure 2.23 Radioactive uranium-238 (U^{238}) decays to stable lead-206 (Pb^{206}) by steps through many intermediate radioactive atoms. The atomic number is the number of protons (positively charged particles) in the nucleus.

All objects radiate energy. The hotter the object, the more energy it radiates and increasingly more of the energy is at shorter wavelengths. The Sun radiates hundreds of thousands times more energy than does Earth and mostly at shorter wavelengths. Solar radiation commonly is referred to as short wavelength, and radiation from Earth is called long wavelength.

Incoming Solar Radiation

Earth receives different amounts of solar energy at different latitudes. If we consider the planet as a whole, then about 70% of the Sun's energy reaching Earth enters Earth's climate system; it is involved in accomplishing work (creating activity in and among Earth's systems; Figure 2.25). About 30% is directly reflected back to space

Table 2.3

Power Flow to and from Earth

	Power flow ($\times 10^{12}$ J/s)		Energy flow (%)
	To Earth	From Earth	
Solar radiation	173,410		99.97
Direct reflection		52,000	
Direct conversion to heat		81,000	
Evaporation		40,000	
Water transport in oceans and atmosphere		370	
Photosynthesis		40	
Heat flow from interior	44.2		0.025
General heat flow by conduction		43.9	
Volcanoes and hot springs		0.3	
Tidal energy	3		0.0017

© Data from Hubbert (1971).

as short-wavelength radiation. Reflectivity is known as **albedo** and is usually measured as the percentage of solar radiation that is reflected. The albedo of Earth as a whole is 30%.

Outgoing Terrestrial Radiation

Earth receives solar radiation every day, year after year, but all this heat is not retained. An equivalent amount of heat is radiated back from Earth to space in the longer wavelengths of the infrared portion of the electromagnetic spectrum. But all this energy is not returned to space as simply as it arrived. When the average surface temperature of Earth is calculated, the value is about 15°C. This temperature seems reasonable from our day-to-day life experience. However, temperature measurements from satellites tell us that Earth is sending heat to space as if its average temperature is −16°C. Why this discrepancy? Because of the **greenhouse effect**. Gases in the lower

atmosphere such as carbon dioxide, methane, and water vapor trap much of the outbound long-wavelength energy and then reradiate it downward to Earth's surface, keeping it warm.

The Hydrologic Cycle

About 24% of the solar radiation received by Earth is used to evaporate water and begin the **hydrologic cycle**. Evaporated water rises convectively, due to its lower density, up into the atmosphere, performing the critical initial work of the hydrologic cycle. The hydrologic cycle was in part recognized in the third century **BCE** in Ecclesiastes 1:7, where it is stated: "Into the sea all the rivers go, and yet the sea is never filled, and still to their goal the rivers go." The Sun's radiant energy evaporates water, primarily from the oceans, which then drops on the land and flows back to the sea both above and below ground (Figure 2.26). The same water, for the most part, has run through this same cycle, time and time again.

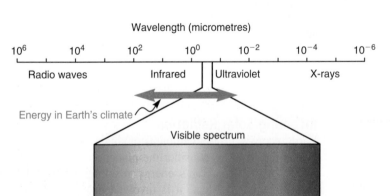

Figure 2.24
The electromagnetic spectrum. One micrometre = 0.001 millimetre = one-millionth of a metre.

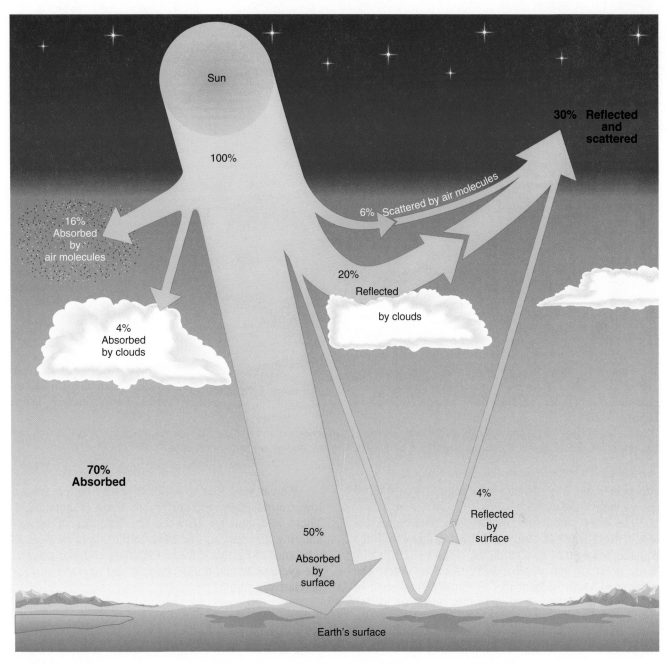

Figure 2.25
Solar radiation reaching Earth is 30% reflected and scattered, and 70% absorbed into Earth's climate system.

The hydrologic cycle is a continuously operating distilling-and-pumping system. The heat from the Sun evaporates water, while plants transpire (evaporate from living cells) water into the atmosphere. The atmospheric moisture condenses and precipitates as snow and rain. Some falls on the land and then is pulled back to the sea by gravity as glaciers, rivers, and underground water flow. The system is over 4 billion years old and will continue to operate as long as the Sun shines and water lies on the surface of Earth.

Energy Transfer in the Atmosphere

Different areas of Earth receive different amounts of incoming solar radiation. Equator and low latitudes receive more solar radiation, but energy loss via infrared radiation to space begins to exceed gains around 32° to 34° latitude and the net loss (outgoing-incoming) progressively increases to the poles (Figure 10.2). The imbalances in heat between the tropical and polar latitudes help cause ocean currents and winds that transfer heat from the tropics toward the poles. The ocean and the

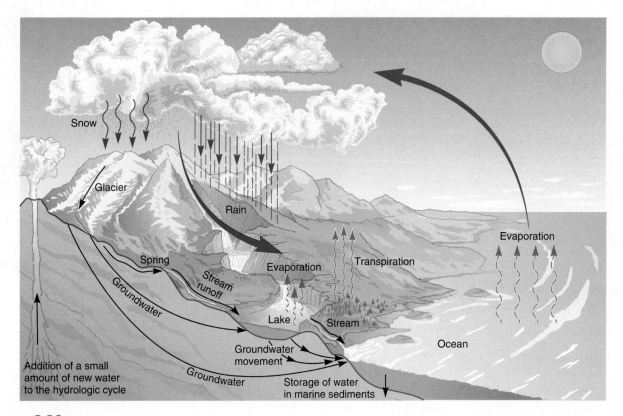

Figure 2.26
The hydrologic cycle. The Sun lifts water into the atmosphere by evaporation and transpiration. Atmospheric water condenses and falls under the pull of gravity. The water then flows as glaciers, streams, and groundwater, returning to the seas.

atmosphere act like gigantic heat engines that transfer energy around the world.

The warm air masses of the equatorial region are less dense, rising buoyantly and flowing away from the equator, where they cool and sink (Figure 10.9). Cold, dense polar air masses flow away from the poles. The rotation of Earth beneath its low-density fluid shell of atmosphere adds complexities to this simplistic model. The circulation of the atmosphere distributes heat around Earth.

For water at its normal boiling point of 100°C, evaporation requires about 2,260,000 joules per kilogram (Figure 10.5). This energy is absorbed and stored in the water vapour as **latent** (hidden) **heat**, or specifically, as the latent heat of vaporization. When water vapour condenses, or changes back to a liquid such as rain or fog, it releases its stored latent heat at the same 2,260,000 joules per kilogram. Although only a fraction of a percent of water near Earth's surface is in the atmosphere (Table 2.4), this water vapour is important because of the solar energy it holds, transports, and releases. On a broad scale, the latent heat of vaporization is an important factor in global climate and, on a local scale, it is the energy behind severe weather such as hurricanes and tornadoes.

We can now look at a global energy budget for the lower atmosphere and surface of Earth (Figure 2.27). There is a balance between the amounts of energy entering and leaving the lower atmosphere as well as a balance at Earth's surface. On this grand world scale, the average annual temperature at and near the surface is relatively stable.

Energy Transfer in the World Ocean

Where is the water on Earth held? The oceans hold the greatest share: 97.2% of Earth's water, covering 71% of Earth's surface. Three-quarters of the remaining 2.8% of all water is locked up in glaciers (Table 2.4).

Satellite photos of Earth show the abundance of water in the oceans and moving as moisture in the atmosphere (Figure 2.28). Water is uniquely qualified to absorb and release solar energy (see In Greater Depth box: Water—The Most Peculiar Substance on Earth). Water has an exceptionally high heat capacity, allowing storage of great amounts of heat in the ocean. Water gains and loses more heat per degree of temperature change than any common substance on Earth. The unceasing motion of ocean water transfers its stored solar energy throughout the world. Winds blowing across the water surface cause circulation of surface water (Figure 10.20). Deep-ocean

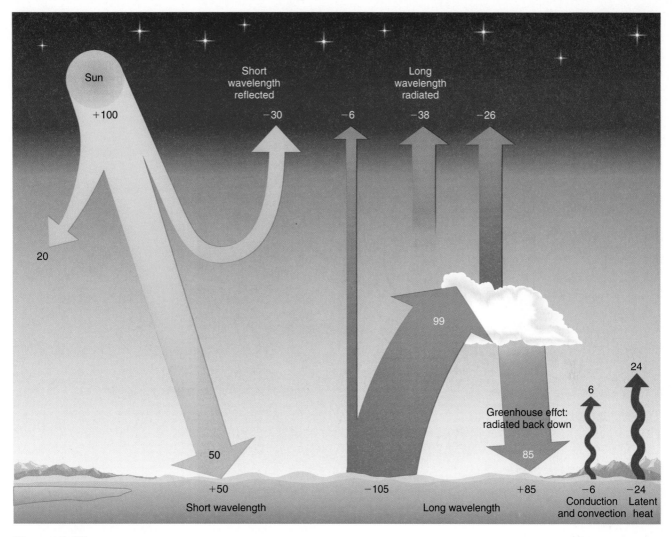

Figure 2.27

A global energy budget. The numbers balance for incoming and outgoing energy along the uppermost line in the atmosphere and along the ground surface.

Source: Peixoto and Oort (1992).

Table 2.4

Where Is the Water?

World's ocean	97.2%
Glaciers	2.15
Groundwater	0.60
Lakes (fresh and saline)	0.017
Soil moisture	0.005
Atmosphere	0.001
Rivers	0.0001

circulation is mostly driven by density differences caused by colder and/or saltier water masses sinking and flowing at depth in a global circuit (Figure 2.29). The ocean currents also are affected by Earth's rotation, which alters the direction of water movements, and by continents, which block and divert the flow of warm ocean water, sending it up to colder latitudes. The solar energy stored in the oceans acts as a thermal regulator, strongly influencing global climate. On an average day, the amount of solar energy absorbed by the global ocean and then reradiated back as long-wavelength radiation would be enough heat to raise the temperature of the whole atmosphere around 2°C. However, the atmosphere does not have as great a capacity to store heat; its total heat storage is equivalent to that held in the upper 3 m of the ocean.

Figure 2.28
Satellite view showing atmosphere and ocean; two fluid masses in continual motion transporting energy about Earth.
Photo: © NASA/JPL.

GRAVITY

The existence of gravity was first discussed scientifically by Isaac Newton (1642–1727). Newton's accomplishments were many, including being one of the inventors of calculus and determining the laws of motion and the universal law of gravitation. The importance of fundamental laws was underscored by Ralph Waldo Emerson in 1841, when he wrote: "Nature is an endless combination and repetition of a very few laws. She hums the old well-known air through innumerable variations."

Gravity is an attraction between objects. It is a force that humans are unable to modify; it cannot be increased, decreased, reversed, or reflected. The law of gravity states that two bodies attract each other with a force directly proportional to the product of their masses and inversely proportional to the square of the distance between them:

$$\text{gravity} = \frac{G \times \text{mass 1} \times \text{mass 2}}{\text{distance} \times \text{distance}}$$

where G is a universal constant.

Using Newton's equation to assess the gravitational effects of the Sun and Moon on Earth requires knowledge of masses and distances. The volume of the Moon is only about 1/49 that of Earth, and the Moon's lower average density of 3,340 kg/m^3 means its mass is only about 1/80 that of Earth. By comparison, the Sun's diameter is about 1,395,000 km and, even though its density is only about 1/4 that of Earth, its mass is still about 332,000 times greater. Gravitational attraction is directly proportional to mass but is reduced by dividing by distance times distance. The Sun is 150 million km away and the Moon is about 386,000 km away. Taking into account both the effects of mass and distance, calculations show that the Sun exerts a pull on Earth more than 170 times stronger than the Moon.

The gravitational system of Earth, Moon, and Sun, and their interactions, generates tidal energy. The tidal force is caused by the differences in gravitational forces on the Moon-facing side of Earth compared to the back side. Newton was the first to correctly calculate tidal forces as the inverse cube of the distance (that is, by including a third distance term in the denominator of the equation above). His calculations show that, because the distance between the Sun and Earth is considerably larger than the distance between the Moon and Earth, the tidal force exerted by the Sun on Earth is only 45% as strong as

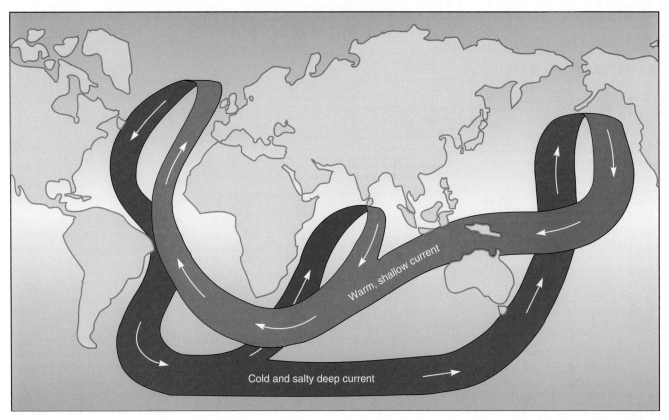

Figure 2.29
This schematic drawing of the ocean circulation system shows warm, shallow water moving into the North Atlantic, thus keeping Europe 5° to 10°C warmer. Cooling in the Arctic increases ocean-water density, causing it to sink and flow at depth south ward out of the Atlantic Ocean. This ocean flow system is the equivalent of 100 Amazon Rivers.

the pull from the Moon; that is, the Moon's role in causing tides on Earth is more than double that of the Sun.

Earth has rather unique tidal effects because (1) 71% of its surface is covered by oceans; (2) it has a long period of rotation compared to many other planets; and (3) its relatively large Moon is nearby. The gravitationally attracted bulges we call tides affect the land, water, and air but are most visible in the daily rises and falls of the ocean surface. The Sun appears overhead once every 24 hours, while the Moon takes about 24 hours and 52 minutes to return to an overhead position. Thus, the Moon appears to move in the sky relative to the Sun. So, too, will the tidal bulges attracted by the Moon move in relation to the tidal bulges caused by the Sun. The two sets of tidal bulges will coincide twice a month, at the new and full moons, when the Sun and the Moon align with Earth (Figure 2.31). These highest tides of the month are called spring tides. In the first and third quarters of the Moon, the Sun and Moon are at right angles to Earth, thus producing the lowest tides, called neap tides.

The tidal bulges moving across the face of Earth and within mobile regions in Earth's interior cause a frictional braking of Earth's rotation. Following Newton's law of

motion, as the rotations of Earth and Moon slow, they move farther apart, days become longer, and the years have fewer days. At present, Earth and Moon are separating an additional 3.8 cm per year. Substantiation of the lengthening days is evident in the fossil record. For example, careful counting of growth ridges in the skeletons of corals (broadly similar to tree rights) shows daily additions that vary in size according to the season of the year. A study of 370-million-year-old corals has shown that each day on Earth during their life was about 22 hours long and a year had 400 days.

Additional sources of energy lie in the rotational motions of Earth—the daily rotation of Earth about an axis that pierces its centre, and the monthly rotations of the Earth–Moon system about its common centre of gravity lying about 4,680 km from the centre of Earth toward the Moon.

IMPACTS WITH ASTEROIDS AND COMETS

Earth moves though space at a high speed, as do asteroids and comets. When their paths intersect, there are explosive impacts. Earth travels over 950 million km around the Sun

Water—The Most Peculiar Substance on Earth?

It is an understandable human trait to consider things that are common and abundant as being ordinary and those that are uncommon and rare as being extraordinary. The most common substance at the surface of Earth is water. It is so much a part of our daily lives that it is all too easy to regard water as being ordinary. Nevertheless, water is a truly extraordinary chemical compound. Were it not such an odd substance, everything on Earth, from weather to life, would be radically different.

1. Water is the only substance on Earth that is present in vast quantities in solid, liquid, and gaseous states.
2. Water has the highest **heat capacity** of all solids and liquids except liquid ammonia. Because water stores so much heat, the circulation of water in the ocean transfers immense quantities of heat.
3. Water has the highest heat conduction of all liquids at normal Earth surface temperatures.
4. Water has the highest **latent heat of vaporization** of all substances. At 100°C, it takes 2,260,000 joules to evaporate a kilogram of water. This latent heat is carried by water vapour into the atmosphere and is released when water vapour condenses to liquid rain. Much heat is transported about the atmosphere as air masses circulate.
5. Water has the second highest **latent heat of fusion**, exceeded only by ammonia. When ice melts at 0°C, it absorbs 334,000 joules per kilogram. When water freezes, it releases 334,000 joules per kilogram.
6. Water is a bipolar molecule. The negative oxygen and positive hydrogen atoms bond together, yielding a molecule with

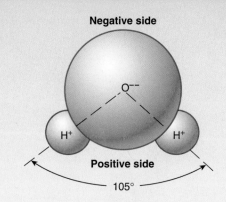

Figure 2.30 Water is a bipolar molecule exhibiting a negative and a positive side. This bipolarity greatly increases the activity of water.

a negative and a positive side (Figure 2.30). This positive and negative polarity allows water to readily bond with charged **ions**.

7. Water has the highest **dielectric constant** of all liquids. This property tends to keep ions apart and prevent their bonding, thus maintaining a solution. This is why water has been called the universal solvent.
8. Water has the highest **surface tension** of all liquids.
9. Water expands about 9% when it freezes. This is anomalous behaviour. Usually, as a substance gets colder, it shrinks in volume and becomes denser. The maximum density for water occurs at about 4°C. Imagine what lakes and oceans would be like if ice were heavier than liquid water and sank to the bottom.

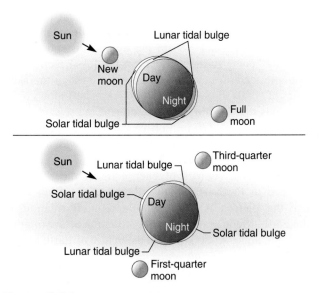

Figure 2.31
Earth tides are caused by the gravitational attractions of the Sun and the Moon. The greatest daily range of tides occurs at the new and full moons; the lowest daily range occurs at first- and third-quarter moons.

each year—an orbital speed in excess of 108,000 km/h (Figure 2.32). The kinetic energy of this orbital motion is about 2.7×10^{33} joules. When this tremendous amount of energy is involved in a head-on collision with a large asteroid moving 65,000 km/h or comet travelling 150,000 km/h, the effects on life are catastrophic and worldwide.

Processes of Construction versus Destruction

Another way to visualize the amount of energy flow on Earth involves understanding the rock cycle and the construction and destruction of land (continents). Energy flowing up from Earth's interior melts rock that rises as magma and then cools and crystallizes to form igneous rocks; they are plutonic rocks if they solidify at depth or volcanic rocks if they cool and harden at the surface. These newly formed rocks help create new land (Figure 2.33). Igneous rock formation is part of the internal energy-fed **processes of construction** that create and elevate landmasses.

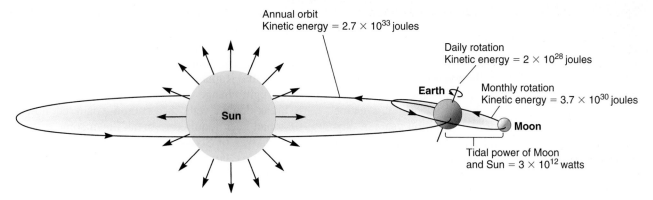

Annual orbit
Kinetic energy = 2.7×10^{33} joules

Daily rotation
Kinetic energy = 2×10^{28} joules

Earth

Monthly rotation
Kinetic energy = 3.7×10^{30} joules

Sun

Moon

Tidal power of Moon
and Sun = 3×10^{12} watts

Figure 2.32
The rotations and orbits of the Earth-Moon-Sun system result in tremendous amounts of energy.

At the same time, the much greater flow of energy from the Sun drives the hydrologic cycle, which weathers the igneous rocks exposed at or near the surface and breaks them down into **sediment**. Physical weathering disintegrates rocks into gravel and sand, while chemical weathering decomposes rock into clay. The sediment is eroded, transported mostly by water, and then deposited in topographically low areas, ultimately the ocean. These processes are part of the **processes of destruction**, which work to erode the lands and deposit the debris into the oceans.

Consider the incredible amount of work done by the prodigious flows of energy operating over the great age of Earth. A long-term conflict continues to rage between the internal-energy-powered processes of construction, which create and elevate landmasses, and the external-energy-powered processes of destruction, which erode the continents and deposit the continental debris into the ocean

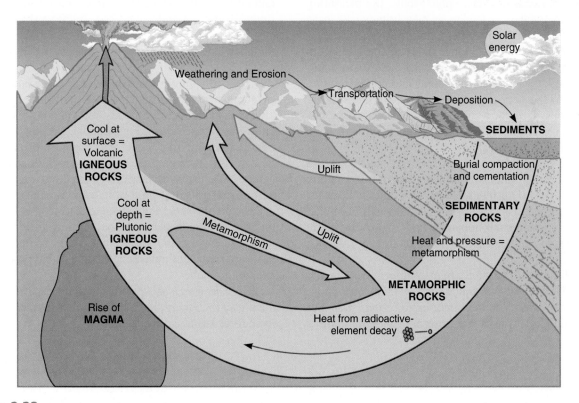

Figure 2.33
The rock cycle. Magma cools and solidifies to form igneous rocks. Rocks exposed at Earth's surface break down and decompose into sediments (e.g., gravel, sand, clay), which are transported, deposited, and hardened into sedimentary rock. With increasing burial depth, temperature and pressure increase, transforming rocks into metamorphic rocks.

basins. Visualize this: If the interior of Earth cooled and the flow of internal energy stopped, then mountain building and uplift also would stop; then the ongoing solar-powered agents of erosion would reduce the continents to below sea level in just 45 million years. There would be no more continents, only an ocean-covered planet.

Think about the time scales involved in eliminating the continents. At first reading, 45 million years of erosion may seem like an awfully long time, but remember that Earth is 4.57 billion years old. The great age of Earth indicates that erosion is powerful enough to have levelled the continents about 100 times. The internal processes of construction have tremendous power to keep elevating old continents and adding new landmasses. And woe betide humans and other life forms that get too close to these processes of construction and destruction, for this is where disasters occur.

How We Understand Earth

We human beings stand a couple of metres tall and live on Earth's surface, where mountains rise higher than 9 km above sea level and ocean waters can be deeper than 11 km. The mountains and oceans are so huge compared to us that some explanations for their presence call upon gigantic upheavals or catastrophic events. But measuring Earth using our human bodies as measuring sticks leads us astray. The appropriate measuring rod is the diameter of Earth itself. When the 9 km high mountains and 11 km deep oceans are compared against the 12,740 km diameter of Earth, we see that mountains and oceans are tiny features on the surface and do not require catastrophic explanations. If Earth were reduced to the size of a billiard ball, the surface of Earth would be smoother than the surface of the billiard ball.

In the same fashion, we human beings live 60 to 100 years on a planet that is 4.5 billion years old. If we think about Earth history using our human lifetimes of decades, then misconceptions can arise. Understanding Earth history means ignoring our human lengths of time and doing our thinking in geological time using thousands, millions, and billions of years.

Thousands of years ago, human thought had already made great advances in topics such as philosophy, government, religion, drama, and engineering. But our understanding of Earth was insignificant until Earth's great age was realized. This recognition came late in human history; it started with James Hutton in the 1780s. Hutton carefully observed his Scottish landscape and thought deeply about it. For example, he saw rock walls built by the Romans that had stood for 15 centuries with only slight change. If 1,500 years was not long enough to break down a wall, then Hutton wondered, how much time had been required to break down some of the hard rock masses of Scotland into the abundant pebbles and sand grains he saw? And how much more time had been necessary to lift the pebbly and sandy sedimentary rocks to form hills? All the active processes that Hutton observed worked slowly, so his answer to the questions was that great lengths of time were required. In 1788, Hutton described the history of Earth with: "The result, therefore, of our present enquiry is that we find no vestige of a beginning, no prospect of an end." And this was Hutton's great gift to human thought: time is long, and everyday changes on Earth add up to major results.

UNIFORMITARIANISM

Hutton's thought pattern is called **uniformitarianism**; it has revolutionized our understanding of Earth. Uniformitarianism implies that natural laws are uniform through time and space. Physical and biological laws produce certain effects today, as they have in the past, and will in the future. If we can understand how Earth works today, we can use this knowledge to read the rock and fossil record to understand Earth history. The present is the key to the past.

The term "uniformitarianism" has come under attack by some who assume it says that Earth processes have always acted at a uniform and slow rate; however, we all know that rates can vary. For example, the flow of internal heat has declined through Earth's history (Figure 2.21), but the laws governing the melting of rock do not change just because the rates vary. Some suggest using the term **actualism** instead of uniformitarianism, but the concept is basically the same. Actualism tells us to understand the processes actually operating on and in Earth today, and use these known and testable processes to interpret the past; do *not* invent unknown and untestable processes to explain problems.

How do we go about understanding Earth? We study the present to understand the past and then make probabilistic forecasts about the future.

Summary

The sources of energy fuelling Earth's natural processes originate from the interior of the planet and from external sources. The amount of energy reaching Earth from external sources is several thousand times larger than the energy coming from internal sources.

The main source of Earth's internal energy is heat generated by the ongoing decay of radioactive elements. Smaller contributions come from relic-impact energy and gravitational attraction. Because several radioactive isotopes have reached stability, the flow of internal energy is slowly decreasing with time. Nevertheless, Earth's internal energy still drives major geological processes responsible for volcanoes and earthquakes.

Earth's external energy sources are solar irradiation, tidal energy, and new impact energy. The largest contributor of energy is by far the Sun. The energy of the Sun and its interaction with the atmosphere and oceans is responsible for weather, in the short term, and for climate, in the longer term.

Nearly one-quarter of the Sun's energy that reaches Earth is used to evaporate water to begin the hydrologic cycle. Under the pull of gravity, snow and rain fall back to the land and then run downslope as glaciers, streams, and groundwater until the water is returned to the ocean to complete the cycle. While in motion, ice, water, and wind act as agents of erosion that wear down the land and deposit the debris into the ocean basins.

Radioactive isotopes act as clocks that can be used to date astronomical and geological events. The Solar System formed over a relatively short period of time; therefore, meteorites and planets all have approximately the same age. Earth is about 4.57 billion years old.

The physical laws governing energy are immovable but energy flow rates have changed throughout Earth's history. Massive amounts of internal heat within the early Earth caused widespread melting. Gravity has pulled Earth into layers of differing density, ranging from a heavy metallic core outward through layers of decreasing density through the mantle to the continents, then the ocean, and finally, the atmosphere. Earth can also be described as a stratified body with layers of differing strength. The solid inner core is surrounded by the liquid outer core. Large convection cells slowly circulate material in the plastic mesosphere and asthenosphere. Earth's outer layers are the rigid lithosphere, the hydrosphere, and the atmosphere.

Terms to Remember

actualism   46
albedo   38
asteroid   28
asthenosphere   34
atmosphere   31
BCE   38
brittle   32
chondrule   28
comet   28
compression   32
conduction   35
continent   31
convection   35
core   31
crust   31
dielectric constant   44
ductile   32
elastic   32
element   24
erosion   24

force   29
glacier   32
gravity   24
greenhouse effect   38
half-life   35
heat   29
heat capacity   44
hydrologic cycle   38
igneous rocks   37
ion   44
isostasy   34
isotope   28
kinetic energy   29
latent heat   40
latent heat of fusion   44
latent heat of vaporization   44
lithosphere   34
magma   37
mantle   31
mesosphere   34

meteorite   28
nuclear fission   37
nuclear fusion   28
plastic   32
potential energy   29
power   29
processes of construction   44
processes of destruction   45
radioactive elements   24
sediment   45
shear stress   32
solar radiation   28
strain   32
stress   32
surface tension   44
tension   32
uniformitarianism   46
viscous   33
work   29

Questions for Review

1. What energy source is mainly responsible for earthquakes? Snow avalanches? Floods? Impact with space bodies?
2. What energy sources caused the interior of the early Earth to heat up?
3. How does nuclear fusion differ from nuclear fission?
4. What can we learn from the study of stony meteorites? From the study of iron-rich meteorites?
5. What is the age of Earth? How is this determined?
6. Where are the oldest known Earth rocks found? How old are they?
7. How did Earth's continents, ocean, and atmosphere form?
8. Describe how Earth became segregated into layers of differing density.
9. What are the differences between brittle, ductile, and elastic behaviour?
10. What causes vertical movements of Earth's surface?
11. How does the amount of energy flowing from the interior of Earth compare to the energy received from the Sun?
12. Explain how the hydrologic cycle operates. What are the roles of the Sun and gravity?
13. What properties make water so peculiar?
14. Why does our relatively small Moon have a greater tidal effect on Earth than the gigantic Sun?
15. Describe the effects on Earth's surface of the "internal processes of construction" versus the "external processes of destruction."
16. Explain the concept of uniformitarianism.

Questions for Further Thought

1. Your lifetime will be what percentage of geological time? Why is it challenging to understand Earth processes from a human perspective?
2. Why is it difficult to unravel the early history of planet Earth?
3. Earth is commonly called "terra firma," literally meaning "firm ground." Does this make good geological sense?
4. If the heat flow from Earth's interior ceased, what would happen to the landmasses? After the internal heat flow had stopped for 100 million years, how would Earth appear to a future visitor from space?
5. What are the consequences of changing the chemical composition of the lower atmosphere due to pollution or the greenhouse effect?
6. How does Earth compare with other rocky planets in its energy balance?
7. How does the lack of atmosphere or oceans affect the surfaces of other rocky planets?

Plate Tectonics and Earthquakes

3

Many geologists have maintained that movements of the Earth's crust are concentrated in mobile belts, which may take the form of mountains, mid-ocean ridges or major faults . . . This article suggests that these features are not isolated, that few come to dead ends, but that they are connected into a continuous network of mobile belts about the Earth which divide the surface into several large rigid plates.

—*John Tuzo Wilson*, Nature, *1965*

Outline

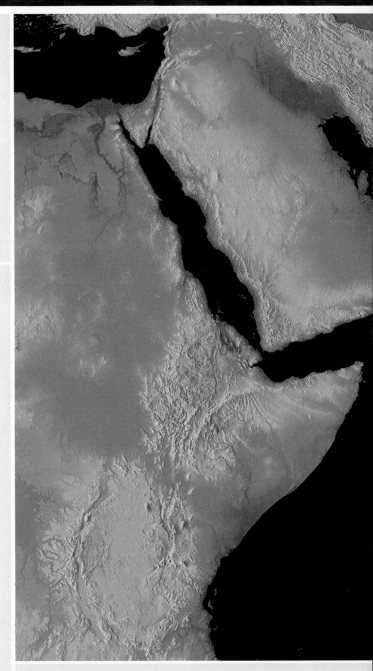

Satellite view of Arabia moving away from Africa.
Photo: © NOAA.

On Friday morning, 26 January 2001, Hidendre Barot was at home with his wife in their apartment on the top floor of a ten-storey building in Ahmedabad in the state of Gujarat in west-central India. At 8:46 a.m. the apartment building began shaking, and Barot and his wife fled onto the roof, held hands, and waited for the violent motions to stop. But the building failed, and Barot fell ten stories with the collapsing structure, ending up surrounded by debris but with no serious injuries. For days afterward, he helped search the building wreckage looking for his wife, but she was one of the 20,103 people killed by this major earthquake, the deadliest natural disaster of 2001.

Our planet is mobile and active; its uppermost rocky layers move horizontally in the process of plate tectonics. These movements are directly responsible for most of the earthquakes, volcanic eruptions, and mountains on Earth.

Plate Tectonics

The lithosphere of Earth is broken into pieces called **plates** (Figure 3.1). These gigantic pieces pull apart during seafloor spreading at **divergence zones**, slide past at **transform faults**, or collide at **convergence zones**. The study of the movements and interactions of the plates is known as **plate tectonics**. The Greek word *tekton* comes from architecture and means "to build"; it has been adapted by geologists as the term **tectonics**, which describes the deformation and movement within Earth's outer layers, and the building of **topography**. The topographic and bathymetic map of the world reveals several prominent features created by tectonic forces—on continents, the Himalaya and the Tibetan Plateau, and the cordillera of the west coast of the Americas; on the ocean floor, mid-oceanic **ridges**, deep trenches, and chains of volcanic islands and seamounts (Figure 3.2).

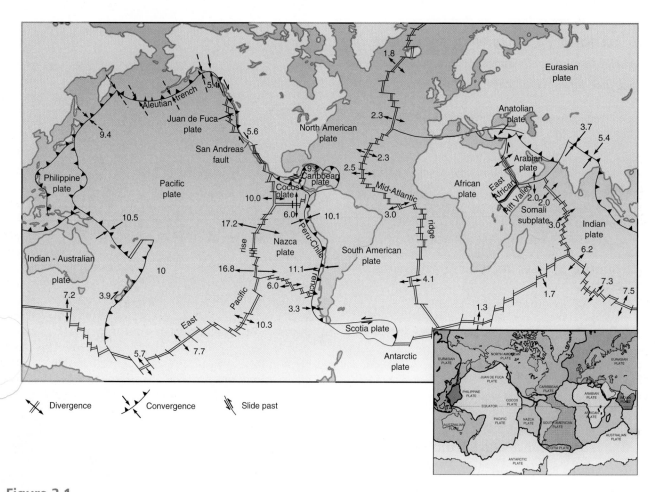

Figure 3.1

A tectonic view of the world. In the context of natural disasters, the boundaries between the different plates are more important than the familiar continental coastlines. Arrows indicate the direction of plate movement. Rates of movements are shown in centimetres per year.

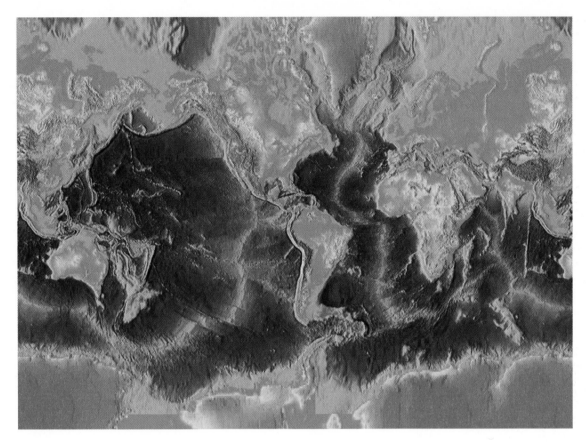

Figure 3.2
Topographic and bathymetric map of the world. Red and dark blue correspond to the most elevated and depressed regions, respectively.
Source: NOAA http://whale.wheelock.edu/whalenet-stuff/MAPSindex.

To grasp the concepts of plate tectonics, we must adopt a new perspective when looking at the world's map. We must move our focus away from the continental coastlines and concentrate on plate boundaries. Several of these boundaries are underwater, which explains why the initial development of the plate tectonics concept was closely linked to the exploration of the oceans.

We saw in the previous chapter that Earth's surface is subjected to vertical forces. Adding the horizontal components of movements on Earth allows us to understand the **tectonic cycle**, which can be simplified as follows (Figure 3.3). First, melted asthenosphere flows upward as magma and cools to form new lithosphere on the ocean floor. Second, the new lithosphere slowly moves laterally away from the zones of oceanic crust formation on top of the underlying asthenosphere (**seafloor spreading**). Third, when the leading edge of a moving slab of oceanic lithosphere collides with another slab, the denser slab turns downward and is pulled by gravity back into the asthenosphere (**subduction**), while the less-dense, more buoyant slab overrides it. Last, the slab pulled into the asthenosphere is reabsorbed. The time needed to complete this cycle is long, commonly in excess of 250 million years.

Another way that plate tectonics can be visualized is by using a hard-boiled egg as a metaphor for Earth. Consider the hard-boiled egg with its brittle shell as the lithosphere, the slippery inner lining of the shell as the asthenosphere, the egg white (albumen) as the rest of the mantle, and the yolk as the core. Before eating a hardboiled egg, we break its brittle shell into pieces that slip around as we try to pluck them off. This hand-held model of brittle pieces being moved atop a softer layer below is a small-scale analogue to the interactions between Earth's lithosphere and asthenosphere.

Development of the Plate Tectonics Concept

Human thought about Earth has long been limited by the smallness of our bodies and the restricted range of our travels in relation to Earth's gigantic size; it also has been

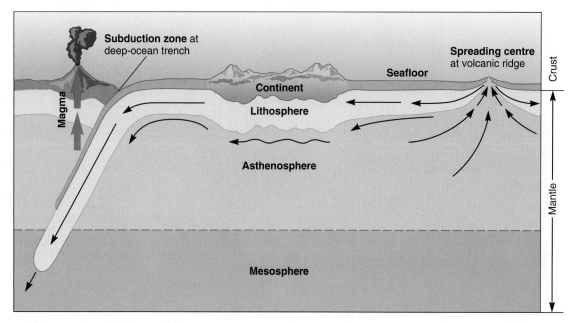

Figure 3.3

Schematic cross-section of the tectonic cycle. First, magma rises from the asthenosphere to the surface at the oceanic volcanic ridges where it solidifies and adds to the plate edges. Second, as the igneous rock cools, the plate moves laterally away. Third, the plate continues to cool, grows thicker at its base, becomes denser, collides with a less-dense plate, and subducts. Finally, it is ultimately reassimilated in the asthenosphere.

Adapted from A. Cox and R. B. Hart, *Plate Tectonics: How It Works.*

limited by the shortness of our life spans compared to the age of Earth. Our planet is so large and so old that the combined efforts of many geologists and philosophers over the last few hundred years have been required to amass enough observations to begin understanding how and why Earth changes as it does. The first glimpse of our modern understanding began after the European explorers of the late 1400s and 1500s made maps of the shapes and locations of the known continents and oceans. These early world maps raised intriguing possibilities. For example, in 1620, Francis Bacon of England noted the parallelism of the Atlantic coastlines of South America and Africa and suggested that these continents had once been joined. During the late 1800s, Austrian geologist Eduard Suess presented abundant evidence in support of Gondwanaland, an ancient southern supercontinent composed of a united South America, Africa, Antarctica, Australia, India, and New Zealand, which later split apart. The most famous and outspoken of the early proponents of **continental drift** was the German meteorologist Alfred Wegener. In his 1915 book, *The Origin of Continents and Oceans,* he collected powerful evidence, such as the continuity of geological structures and fossils, on opposite sides of the Atlantic Ocean (Figure 3.4). Wegener suggested that all the continents had once been united in a supercontinent called **Pangaea.**

Much is made of the fact that during his lifetime, Wegener's hypothesis of continental drift gathered more ridicule than acceptance. But why were his ideas not widely accepted? Wegener presented an intriguing hypothesis well supported with observations and logic, but failed to provide a plausible mechanism for the movements of the continents. When Wegener presented his evidence for continental drift, geologists and geophysicists were faced with trying to visualize how a continent could break loose from the underlying rock and plow a path over it. It seemed physically impossible then. When it became known that the rigid lithosphere decouples from the plastic asthenosphere and moves laterally, then the relatively small, low-density continents, set within the oceanic crust, were seen to be carried along as incidental passengers (Figure 3.3).

By the mid-1960s, the plate tectonics theory was developed and widely accepted. Tuzo Wilson, a professor of geophysics at the University of Toronto, was instrumental in formulating several of the key concepts of plate tectonics (see In Greater Depth box: John Tuzo Wilson (1908–1993)). It is rare in science to find widespread agreement on a broadly encompassing theory such as plate tectonics. But when data from Earth's magnetic field locked inside seafloor rock were widely understood, skeptics around the world became convinced that seafloor spreading occurs and that the concept of plate tectonics is valid.

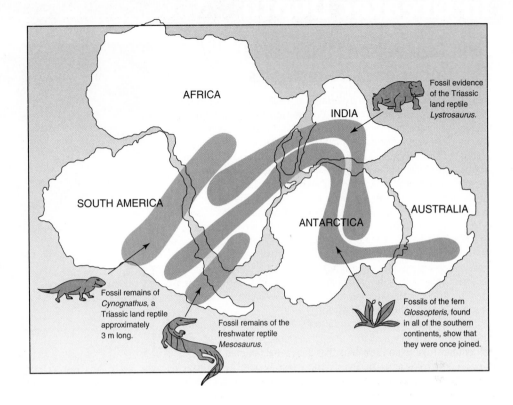

AFRICA

INDIA

Fossil evidence of the Triassic land reptile *Lystrosaurus.*

SOUTH AMERICA

ANTARCTICA

AUSTRALIA

Fossil remains of *Cynognathus,* a Triassic land reptile approximately 3 m long.

Fossil remains of the freshwater reptile *Mesosaurus.*

Fossils of the fern *Glossopteris,* found in all of the southern continents, show that they were once joined.

Evidence of Plate Tectonics from Seafloor Surveys

MAGNETIZATION PATTERNS ON THE SEAFLOORS

As the **lava** erupted from a volcano cools at the surface of Earth, minerals begin to grow as crystals. Some of the earliest formed crystals incorporate iron into their structures. After the lava cools below the **Curie point**, at about 550°C, atoms in iron-bearing minerals become magnetized in the direction of Earth's **magnetic field** (see In Greater Depth box: Earth's Magnetic Field in Chapter 16) at that time and place. The lined-up atoms in the iron-rich crystals behave like compass needles, pointing toward the **magnetic pole** of their time: the north magnetic pole (normal polarity) or the south magnetic pole (reverse polarity). Lava flows pile up as sequences of stratified rock, and the magnetic polarity of each rock layer can be measured (Figure 3.6). Many of the volcanic rocks also contain minerals with radioactive elements that allow determination of their age. When this information is plotted together in a vertical column, a timescale of magnetic polarities emerges (Figure 3.7).

Since the late 1940s, oceanographic research vessels criss-crossing the Atlantic Ocean have towed magnetometers to measure the magnetization of the seafloor. As the number of voyages grew and more data were obtained, a striking pattern began to emerge (Figure 3.8). The floor of the Atlantic Ocean is striped by parallel bands of magnetized rock that show alternating polarities. The pattern is symmetrical and parallel with the mid-ocean volcanic ridge. That is, each striped piece of seafloor has its twin on the other side of the oceanic mountain range.

A remarkable relationship exists between the time of reversals of magnetic polarity, as dated radiometrically from a sequence of solidified lava flows (Figure 3.7), and the widths of alternately polarized seafloor (Figure 3.8): they are comparable. How stunning it is that the widths of magnetized seafloor strips have the same ratios as the lengths of time between successive reversals of Earth's magnetic field. This means that distance in kilometres is proportional to time in millions of years. Magma is injected into the ocean ridges where it is imprinted by Earth's magnetic field as it cools to form new rock. Then the seafloor is physically pulled away from the oceanic ridges as if they were parts of two large conveyor belts going in opposite directions (Figure 3.9).

AGES FROM THE OCEAN BASINS

Another stunning fact discovered during the exploration of the oceans is the youthfulness of the ocean basins.

In Greater Depth

John Tuzo Wilson (1908–1993) The Father of Plate Tectonics

John Tuzo Wilson was born in Ottawa in 1908, the first child of Henrietta Tuzo and John Armistead Wilson (Figure 3.5). His mother was an accomplished mountaineer and his father an engineer. This heritage was reflected by Tuzo Wilson's choice of studies: he graduated from the University of Toronto in 1930 with a double major in physics and in geology, and earned a second undergraduate degree from the University of Cambridge in England, taking a collection of lectures in the same topics. After a brief period of employment at the Geological Survey of Canada, Tuzo Wilson went on to do a Ph.D. at Princeton where he met Harry Hesse and Maurice Ewing, leading scientists studying geological processes in ocean basins. Like many young men of his generation, Tuzo Wilson's career was interrupted by World War II, during which he served overseas as an engineer in the Canadian Army. After the war, Tuzo Wilson returned to Canada to become professor of geophysics at the University of Toronto.

Initially opposed to continental drift, Tuzo Wilson developed his vision of a dynamic Earth through several years of study of the different geological domains that have amalgamated to form the Canadian Precambrian Shield. The word "vision" is particularly fitting here since Tuzo-Wilson's problem-solving approach was largely visual and stemmed from field observations and the detailed examination of maps. He is reported to have reflected on the formation of the Hawaiian islands using the bucolic image of someone lying on his back in a stream and blowing bubbles to the surface through a straw.

Between 1963 and 1966, Tuzo Wilson presented his views on hot spots and transform faults in three papers that would cause a revolution in the earth sciences. His first paper, entitled "A Possible Origin of the Hawaiian Islands," was first rejected by the leading American geophysical journal before being published in the *Canadian Journal of Physics,* not exactly a widely read journal in earth science circles! Nevertheless, Tuzo Wilson went on to make an outstanding contribution in providing an integrated framework for understanding geology at a planetary scale.

Tuzo Wilson was not only a towering figure in the earth science community, but also a gifted communicator. After retiring from the University of Toronto, he became director-general of the Ontario Science Centre, a pioneering interactive science museum, and shared with a large public his passion for science.

Figure 3.5 Prof. Tuzo Wilson in the Andes (Chile) in 1960. A few years later, Tuzo Wilson would put forward ideas bringing a new understanding of the process of mountain building.
Photo courtesy of Susan Wilson.

Two seamounts, located 200 km west of Vancouver Island, have been named in Tuzo Wilson's honour, a very appropriate gesture to acknowledge the contribution of the scientist who provided insight into their formation. The tectonic cycle is also often referred to as the Wilson cycle.

The oldest rocks on the ocean floors are about 200 million years in age; this is less than 5% of the age of Earth. Why? Because the ocean basins are young features that are continuously being formed and destroyed. Along the oceanic ridges, volcanism is active, and new seafloor is forming (Figure 3.9). Moving away from the ridges, the seafloor volcanic rocks and islands become progressively older. The oldest seafloor rocks are found at the edges of the ocean basins (Figure 3.10).

OCEANIC HOT SPOTS

At certain locations, deep-seated **hot spots** produce more heat, causing hotter rock with lower density; these **plumes** of buoyant hot rock rise through the mesophere,

begin to melt near the top of the overlying asthenosphere, and pass up through the lithosphere as magma. Hot spots have active volcanoes above them on Earth's surface. The volcanoes rest on moving plates that carry them away from their hot-spot source. This process forms lines of extinct volcanoes on the ocean floor, from youngest to oldest, pointing in the direction of plate movement (Figure 3.11). In other words, the ages of the former volcanoes increase with their distance from the hot spot.

BATHYMETRY

Bathymetry provides additional supporting evidence for plate tectonics (Figure 3.2). The greatest mountain ranges

Figure 3.6

A stratified pile of former lava flows of the Columbia River flood basalt exposed in the east wall of Grand Coulee, Washington State. The oldest flow is on the bottom and is overlain by progressively younger flows.

Photo by John S. Shelton.

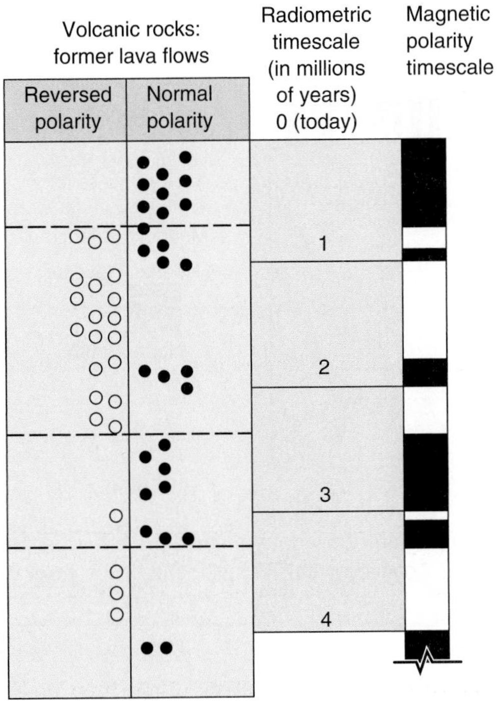

Figure 3.7

A portion of the magnetic polarity timescale. Magnetic polarity measurements in volcanic rocks combined with radiometric ages determined from the same rocks allow formation of a timescale based on magnetic polarity reversals. Notice the unique and nonrepetitive pattern of the polarity reversals.

Source: © John Wiley & Sons, Inc.

on Earth, the oceanic ridges, lie on the seafloor and extend more than 65,000 km. These long and continuous volcanic ridges are forming at **spreading centres** where plates pull apart and magma rises to fill the gaps. Above the oceanic ridges, the water depth is relatively shallow. However, moving progressively away from the ridges, the water depth increases systematically with seafloor age (Figure 3.12). This is due to the cooling and contraction of the oceanic crust with a resultant increase in density. Also, there is some down-warping due to the weight of sediments deposited on the seafloor. The older the seafloor, the more time it has had to accumulate a thick cover of silt, clay, and fossils.

The ocean floor has an average depth of 3.7 km, yet depths greater than 11 km exist in elongate, narrow **trenches**. These long and deep trenches were known since the *Challenger* oceanographic expedition in the 1870s, but they were not understood until the 1960s, when it was recognized that they are the tops of the subducting plates turning downward to re-enter the asthenosphere.

Evidence of Plate Tectonics from Earthquakes and Volcanoes

The **epicentre** of an earthquake is the projection on Earth's surface of the **hypocentre**, the location at depth of initial energy release during an earthquake (Figure 4.2). Because most earthquakes are caused by a release of stress

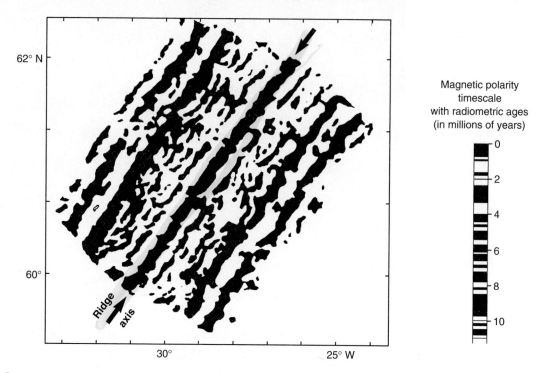

Figure 3.8
Map of the magnetically striped Atlantic Ocean floor southwest of Iceland. Black areas are magnetized pointing to a north pole and white areas to a south pole. Notice the near mirror images of the patterns on each side of the volcanic ridge (spreading centre).

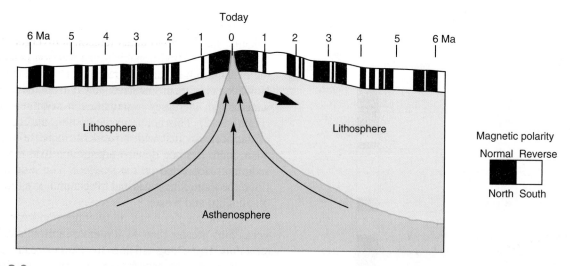

Figure 3.9
Cross-section of magnetically striped seafloor. Numbers above the seafloor are radiometrically determined ages in millions of years. The near mirror-image magnetic pattern is like a tape recorder that documents "conveyor belt" movements away from volcanic ridges.

accumulated at plate boundaries, it is no surprise that there is a close relationship between earthquake epicentre and hypocentre locations, and plate tectonics.

1. Earthquake epicentres outline tectonic plates. The map of earthquake epicentres (Figure 1.11) can be viewed as a connect-the-dots puzzle. Each epicentre represents a place where one major section of rock has moved past another section. Take your pen or pencil, connect the epicentres, and you will outline and define the edges of the tectonic plates, the separately moving pieces of lithosphere (compare Figures 1.11 and 3.1). Remember that these plates are about 100 km thick and thousands of kilometres across.

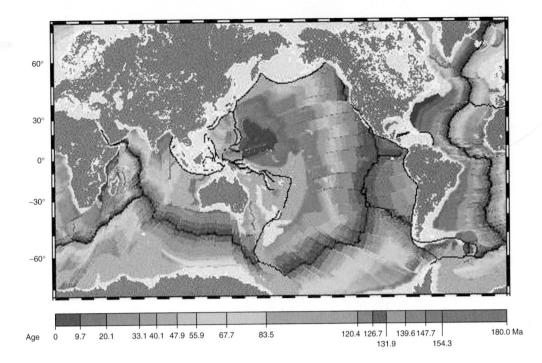

Figure 3.10

Age of the ocean basins.

Source: Mueller, R.D., Roest, W.R., Royer, J-Y., Gahagan, L.M., and Sclater, J.G., 1997. Digital isochrons of the World's ocean floor. *Journal of Geophysical Research* Volume 102, No. B2, p. 3211–3214. 10 February 1997. Plate 1(a) on page 3212. Copyright 1997 by the American Geophysical Union.

Age 0   9.7   20.1   33.1 40.1 47.9 55.9   67.7   83.5   120.4 126.7   139.6 147.7   180.0 Ma
                                                                                  131.9   154.3

A popular way of forecasting the locations of future earthquakes uses the **seismic-gap method**. If segments of one fault have moved recently, then it seems reasonable to expect that the unmoved portions will move next and thus fill the gaps. It is easy to see the gaps in earthquake locations on a map of earthquake epicentres (Figures 3.30 and 4.42). Although seismic-gap analysis is logical, however, it yields only expectations, not guarantees. One segment of a fault can move two or more times before an adjoining segment moves once.

2. Earthquake hypocentres follow subducting plates. Hypocentres are classified as shallow (depth less than 100 km), intermediate (depth ranging from 100 to 300 km) or deep (depth ranging from 300 to 700 km). Intermediate and deep hypocentres are found along inclined planes adjacent to ocean trenches (Figure 3.13). These hypocentres define the subducting plates being pulled forcefully back into the asthenosphere.

3. A majority of active volcanoes are found on the edges of tectonic plates (Figure 1.11). The creation of new lithosphere and the destruction of old lithosphere is generally accompanied by volcanic activity.

Recycling Earth's Outer Layers

The upper few hundred kilometres of Earth are constantly being recycled according to the tectonic cycle. Figure 3.14 shows how Earth's outer layers are operating today in plate-tectonic action and introduces the four tectonic environments: (1) divergent, (2) convergent, and (3) transform plate boundaries, and (4) hot spots.

1. Divergent plate boundaries

Plates are pulled apart under tension at divergent boundaries. Hot rock flowing in rising convection cells reaches the asthenosphere and begins to melt. The buildup of magma and heat causes expansion and topographic elevation of the overlying lithosphere, which then fractures and begins to be pulled apart sideways by gravity. This downward and outward movement of the lithosphere is aided by convection cells moving laterally in the asthenosphere. It occurs because the rigid lithosphere decouples from the soft plastic asthenosphere and provides a sliding surface over which plates can be dragged. Convection in the asthenosphere is the main driving mechanism of plate movement, the crucial element missing in Wegener's continental drift hypothesis. In an ocean basin, the pulling apart of oceanic lithosphere causes a reduction in pressure on the superheated asthenosphere rock, which liquefies even more and rises upward to fill the fractures and create new oceanic lithosphere via seafloor spreading. The same pull-apart movement can also split a continent, forming a rift zone, a young divergent plate boundary such as the East African Rift Valley. Earth's surface may bulge upward into a dome, causing the elevated rock to fracture into a pattern radiating out from a **triple junction**, a point where three plate edges touch (Figure 3.15). Gravity can then pull the dome apart, allowing magma to swell up and fill three major fracture zones, and the spreading process is initiated.

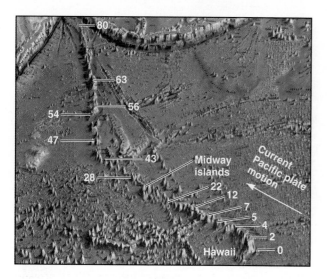

(a) Map

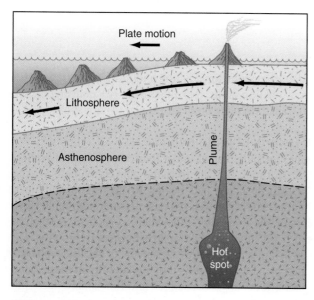

(b) Cross-section

Figure 3.11

A hot spot and its path. (a) Map shows the Hawaiian Islands-Emperor Seamount chain of hotspot-fed volcanoes with plots of their radiometric ages in millions of years. The map pattern of volcano ages testifies to movement of the Pacific plate through time. (b) Cross-section shows a hot spot at a depth where hot mantle rock rises up through the asthenosphere and passes through the lithosphere as a plume of magma supplying a volcano. Because the lithospheric plate keeps moving, new volcanoes are formed.

2. Convergent plate boundaries

Plates deform under compression at convergent boundaries. When oceanic lithosphere collides with another plate, the denser plate goes beneath the less-dense plate in the process of subduction. If an oceanic plate goes beneath another oceanic plate at a convergent plate boundary, an **island arc** of volcanoes next to a trench can form, such as Japan and the Aleutian Islands of Alaska (Figure 3.16a). If the subducting oceanic plate is pulled beneath a continent-carrying plate, the top of the downbending oceanic plate forms a trench, and a line of active volcanoes builds on the continent edge, such as the Cascade Range of British Columbia and northwestern United States (Figure 3.16b). As the leading edge of the subducting plate turns downward, gravity exerts an even stronger pull on it, which helps tear the trailing edge of the plate away from the spreading centre.

3. Transform plate boundaries

Oceanic spreading ridges are subjected to shear stress at transform plate boundaries. Figure 3.17 shows this process. Spreading plates are rigid slabs of oceanic rock, tens of kilometres thick, that are being wrapped around a near-spherical Earth. To accommodate the Earth's curvature, the plates must fracture, and these fractures are transform faults, first recognized by Tuzo Wilson in 1965. In the region between two spreading centres, the relative motions of the two plates are in opposite directions. However, passing both to the right and left of the spreading centres, the two slabs are moving in the same direction. In the first case, the plates are separated by a transform fault; in the second case, by a fracture zone.

4. Hot spots

Originating deep in the mesosphere, hot spots send up hot, buoyant rock that turns into magma near the surface, building shield volcanoes on the seafloor, such as in Hawaii, or explosive mega-volcanoes on continents, such as in Yellowstone National Park in the northwestern United States.

In summary, the combination of convection in the asthenosphere and gravity pulling on elevated spreading-centre mountains and on down-going plates at subduction zones keeps the lithospheric plates moving. Thus, an ongoing tectonic cycle operates where each moving part stimulates and maintains motions of the others in a large-scale, long-term recycling operation. Subducted plates are reassimilated into the asthenosphere as physical slabs that remain solid enough to be recognized by their effects on propagation velocities of seismic waves. Plate movements are now so well understood due to the magnetic record of seafloor rock that not only are the plates outlined, but also their rates of movement are measured using the global positioning system (GPS) (Figure 3.1).

Plate tectonics provides us with new perspectives about Earth that are quite different from those encountered in our life or historical experiences. Because Earth is so much older and so much larger than a human being, we must set aside our personal time and size scales. If we change our time perspective to millions and billions

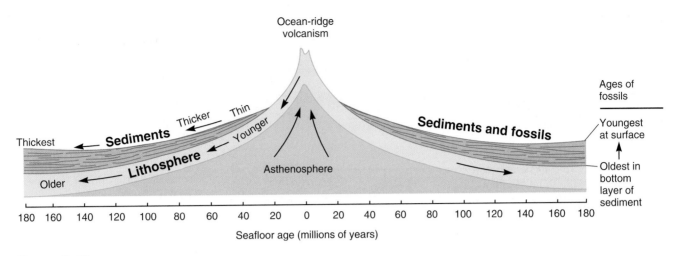

Figure 3.12
Schematic cross-section perpendicular to a volcanic ridge. Moving away from the ridge: (1) radiometric ages of seafloor increase, (2) thicknesses of accumulated sediments increase, and (3) ages of fossils in the sediments increase, and (4) water depths increase. The systematic increases in water depth are due to cooling, shrinking, and increase in density of the aging seafloor rocks.

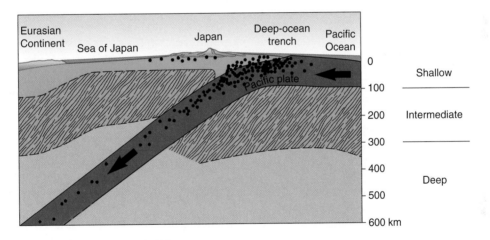

Figure 3.13
Cross-section showing earthquake hypocentre locations at depth; notice the inclined plane defined by the earthquake hypocentres. The earthquake locations define the subducting plate beneath Japan. At shallow depths, earthquakes are generated in brittle rocks in both subducting and overriding plates. At greater depths, only the interior of the subducting Pacific plate is cold enough to maintain the rigidity necessary to produce earthquakes. Striped areas are hot rocks defined by relatively lower-velocity seismic waves.

of years and our size scales to continents and plates, then, and only then, can we begin to understand Earth. The rates of plate movement are comparable to those of human fingernail growth. An active plate may move 1 cm in a year—only 75 cm in a human lifetime. But when we consider Earth over its own time span of 4.5 billion years, there is plenty of time for small events to add up to big results. The plate moving 1 cm/yr travels 10 km in just 1 million years; therefore, the 1 cm/yr process is fast enough to uplift a mountain in a small amount of geological time. Uniformitarianism is key to understanding how Earth behaves; we must think of repeated small changes occurring for great lengths of time to create large features such as mountains.

So far, plate tectonics has been recognized only on Earth. Mars is a one-plate planet where several hot spots have been identified although none are feeding active volcanoes at present. The Martian lithosphere being static, lava outpours at the same location over tens of millions of years, creating gigantic volcanoes. Venus seems to have experienced a dramatic resurfacing event 750 million years ago and its surface has not significantly evolved since then, other than bearing the scars from numerous impacts with space bodies.

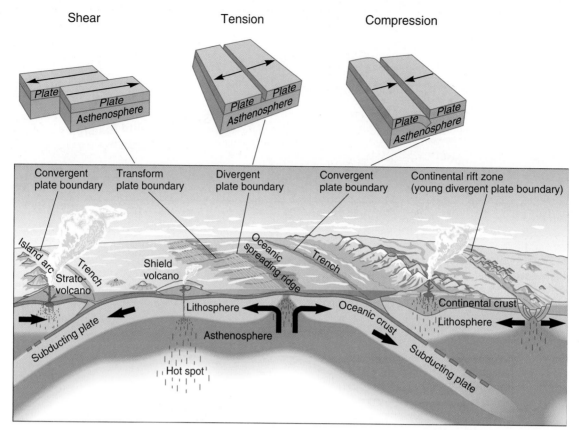

Figure 3.14

Three-dimensional view of tectonic plates with divergent, convergent, and transform boundaries plus volcanoes above subducting plates and a hot spot.

From Kious and Tilling, *US Geological Survey.*

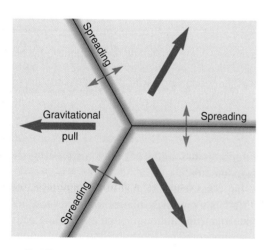

Figure 3.15

Schematic map of a triple junction formed by three young spreading centres. Heat may concentrate in the mantle and rise in a magma plume, doming the overlying lithosphere and causing fracturing into a radial set with three rifts. Gravity may then pull the dome apart, initiating spreading in each rift.

The Dance of the Continents

Undoing the seafloor spreading of the last 220 million years restores the continents of today into the supercontinent Pangaea (*pan* meaning "all" and *gaea* meaning "earth"), which covered 40% of Earth. Although the present continents had yet to form, Figure 3.18 shows their relative positions within Pangaea before its breakup. The remaining 60% of Earth's surface was a massive ocean called **Panthalassa** (meaning "all oceans").

Figure 3.19(a) shows the breakup of Pangaea at 180 million years before present. An equatorial spreading centre separated the northern supercontinent **Laurasia** from the southern supercontinent **Gondwanaland**. Much of the sediment deposited in the Tethys Sea at that time has since been uplifted to form mountain ranges from the Himalaya to the Alps. Another spreading centre began opening the Indian Ocean and separating Africa–South America from Antarctica–Australia.

At 135 million years ago, seafloor spreading had begun opening the North Atlantic Ocean, India was moving toward Asia, and the South Atlantic Ocean was a narrow sea similar to the Red Sea today (Figure 3.19b).

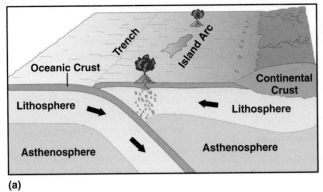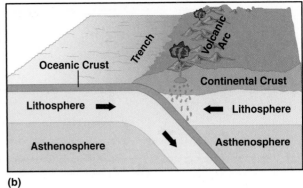

(a)

(b)

Figure 3.16

(a) Oceanic–oceanic convergence results in the formation of a deep offshore trench and volcanoes on the seafloor. Over time, the erupted lava and volcanic debris pile up until submarine volcanoes rise above sea level to form an island arc. (b) Oceanic–continental convergence creates a coastal trench and a chain of continental volcanoes.

Source: United States Geological Survey.

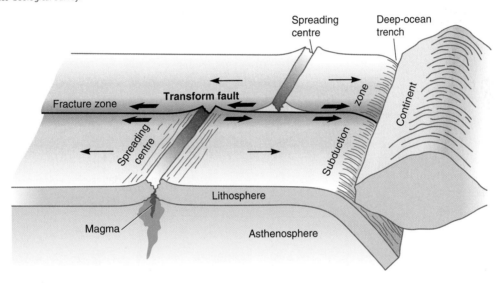

Figure 3.17

Plate-tectonics model of transform faults. Notice that the transform fault connects the two separated spreading centres; seafloor moves in opposite directions here. Beyond the spreading centres, the two plates move in the same direction and are separated by a fracture zone; there is no transform fault here.

By 65 million years ago, seafloor spreading had opened the South Atlantic Ocean and connected it with the North Atlantic, and Africa came into contact with Europe, cutting off the western end of the Tethys Sea to begin the Mediterranean Sea (Figure 3.19c). Although the modern world had become recognizable, note that North America and Eurasia were still connected and that Australia had not yet left Antarctica.

Nearly half of the present ocean floor was created during the last 65 million years (Figure 3.10). India has rammed into Asia, continued opening of the North Atlantic has split Eurasia from North America, and Australia has moved a long way from Antarctica.

Throughout Earth's history, there have been several cycles of supercontinent amalgamation and breakup. Reconstructing the dance of the continents becomes more and more difficult as scientists try to unravel the geological record further back in time. Figure 3.20 shows Rodinia, the supercontinent predating Pangaea. Pieces came together to form Rodinia about 1 billion years ago, including Greenland and large portions of the Canadian Precambrian Shield, which were located in its central core. Rodinia existed as a unified landmass until 750 million years ago.

Plate Tectonics and Earthquakes

Most earthquakes are explainable based on plate tectonics theory. The lithosphere is broken into rigid plates that move away from, past, and into other rigid plates. These

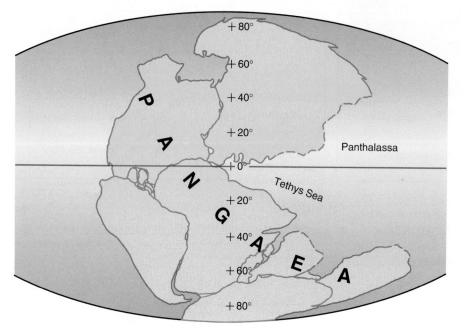

Figure 3.18
Pangaea, the supercontinent, 220 million years before present. The modern continents are drawn to be recognizable in this restoration. The superocean of the time (Panthalassa) exists today in shrunken form as the Pacific Ocean.
Source: © 1970 American Geophysical Union.

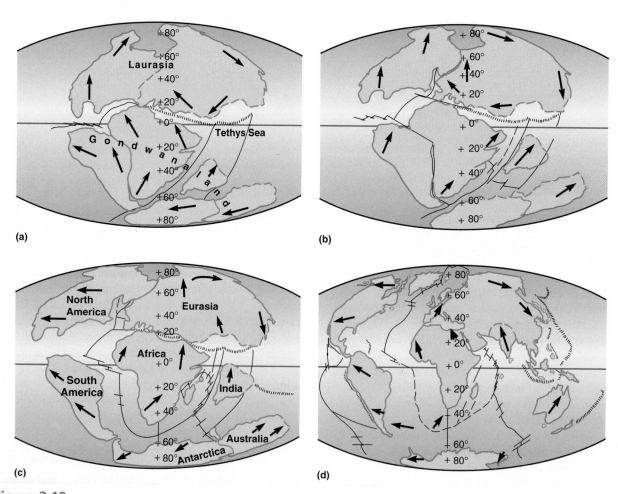

Figure 3.19
Changing positions of the continents. (a) 180 million years ago. (b) 135 million years ago. (c) 65 million years ago. (d) Today.

Figure 3.20

The supercontinent Rodinia, which existed between 1,000 and 750 million years ago. The coloured area corresponds to the Canadian Precambrian Shield and Greenland.

Source Li et al., (2008) *Precambrian Research* (Vol. 160, 179–210).

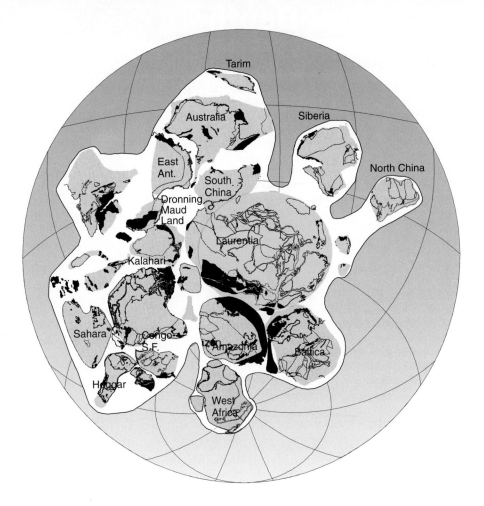

global-scale processes are seen on the ground as individual **faults** where Earth ruptures and the two sides move past each other in earthquake-generating events.

Figure 3.24 shows an idealized tectonic plate and assesses the varying earthquake hazards that are concentrated at plate edges:

1. The divergent or pull-apart motion at spreading centres causes rock to fail in tension. Rock ruptures relatively easily when subjected to tension. Also, much of the rock here is at a high temperature, causing early failures. Thus, the spreading process yields mainly smaller earthquakes that do not pose an especially great threat to humans.

2. The slide-past motion occurs as the rigid plates fracture and move around the curved Earth. The plates slide past each other in the dominantly horizontal movements of transform faults and are subjected to shear stress. This process creates large earthquakes as the plate boundaries retard movement because of irregularities along the faults. It takes a lot of stored energy to overcome the rough surfaces, non-slippery rock, and bends in faults. When these impediments are finally overcome, a large amount of seismic energy is released.

3. At subduction zones and in continent–continent collisions, rock deforms mainly under compression. The convergent motions pulling a 70 to 100 km thick oceanic plate back into the asthenosphere at a subduction zone or pushing continents together—such as India slamming into Asia to uplift the Himalaya—involve incredible amounts of energy. This results in Earth's greatest earthquakes.

Moving from an idealized plate, let's examine an actual plate—the Pacific plate. Figure 3.25 shows the same type of plate-edge processes and expected earthquakes as described in Figure 3.24. The Pacific plate is created at the spreading centres along its eastern and southern edges. The action there produces smaller earthquakes that also happen to be located away from major human populations. The slide-past motions of long transform faults occur (1) along the Queen Charlotte fault, located in northern British Columbia; (2) along the San Andreas fault in California; and (3) at the southwestern edge of the Pacific Ocean where the Alpine fault cuts across the South Island of New Zealand. The Pacific plate subducts along its northern and western edges and creates enormous earthquakes, such as the 1923 Tokyo seism and the 1964 Alaska event.

In Greater Depth

The Tectonic History of Canada

Canada grew gradually over the whole of geological time from a core of very old rock (Figure 3.21). This large area, the Canadian Precambrian Shield, includes the oldest rock so far discovered on our planet, the Acasta gneiss (Figure 2.11). The older portions of the Canadian Shield have been described as a "sea of granite" after their most abundant rock type. The geology of these older parts, which constitute the Archean **cratons**, is radically different than that of younger areas. It attests of vigorous processes, fuelled by the abundant heat of the early Earth, in which the fragile primitive crust was continuously recycled at a fast pace. The Archean cratons consist, therefore, of relatively small subunits, organized in alternating bands of primitive continental and oceanic crust.

Earth progressively cooled, and large rafts of low-density crust floating on top of turbulent oceans of magma slowly consolidated into continents. Modern plate tectonics probably started 2.5 billion years ago when the Rae, Slave, and Hearne cratons in Canada, as well as the Wyoming and North Atlantic cratons in the United States and Greenland respectively, amalgamated together through plate convergence and collision. The Superior craton was added to this landmass 1.8 billion years ago with the first recorded large-scale continent–continent collision in Earth history. Finally,

1.2 to 1.0 billion years ago, another massive continent–continent collision brought the Grenville province to complete the formation of the Canadian Precambrian Shield, which was subsequently incorporated into the supercontinent Rodinia 750 million years ago (Figure 3.20).

To the east, the next addition to the Canadian territory occurred much later when the Appalachians were created in association with closing of the Iapetus ocean (a precursor to the present Atlantic ocean) and the formation of the supercontinent Pangaea 250 million years ago. The present-day St. Lawrence River follows the contact between the Canadian Precambrian Shield and the Appalachians in Quebec and eastern Ontario. Appalachian rocks can also be found outcropping in Scotland and Norway. These rocks now lie thousands of kilometres away from each other, having been pushed away by the Atlantic seafloor that formed between them during the breakup of Pangaea.

Over the last 185 million years, Canada grew to the west. Small pieces of continental crust transported along the Pacific coast accreted to Canada as plates subducted underneath North America. This process led to the formation of the cordillera, which includes five major bands of added material roughly oriented parallel to the coastline. It is still active today with the subduction of the Explorer and Juan de Fuca plates beneath Vancouver Island and southern British Columbia.

Figure 3.21 Tectonic map of Canada.

After Lucas et al. *Geology of the Precambrian Superior and Grenville Provinces and Precambrian Fossils in North America,* 1998.

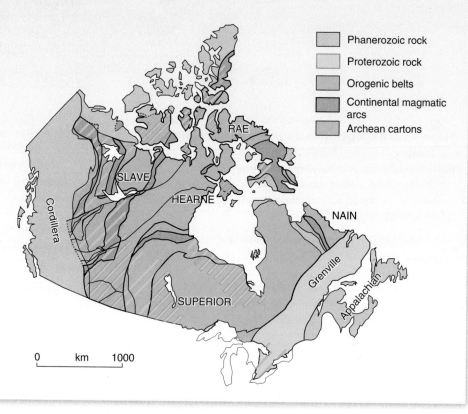

Our main emphasis here is to understand plate-edge effects as a means of forecasting where earthquakes are likely to occur and what their frequencies and sizes may be. Qualitative relationships between tectonic environments and earthquake characteristics are summarized in

Table 3.1. Worldwide, there is on average one great earthquake (magnitude 8 or higher) and 20 major earthquakes (magnitude between 7 and 8) annually (Table 4.4). Strong (magnitude between 6 and 7) earthquakes are more frequent, with about 250 occurrences per year.

In Greater Depth

Active Tectonic Zones of Western North America

The lives of the inhabitants of the west coast of North America are affected by the fate of an ancient tectonic plate, the Farallon plate. Most of the Farallon plate has now been consumed beneath North America but its effects remain today as earthquakes and volcanoes.

Until 30 million years ago, the eastern edge of the Farallon plate was destroyed by subduction underneath the North American plate, itself moving westward to accommodate the widening of the North Atlantic Ocean (Figures 3.1 and 3.19). Approximately 28 million years ago, the Pacific Ocean spreading centre collided with North America near the site of the city of Los Angeles today (Figure 3.22). The collision segmented the Farallon plate into smaller plates, the Juan de Fuca plate to the north and the precursor of the Rivera and Cocos plates to the south. The spreading

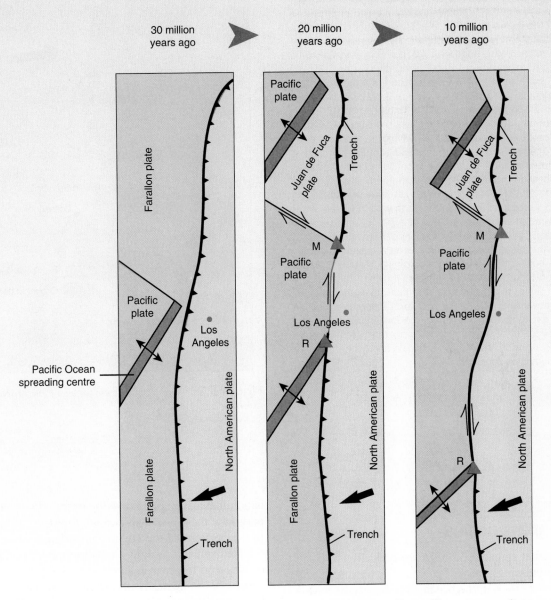

Figure 3.22 Collision of the Pacific Ocean spreading centre with the North American plate: (a) 30 million years ago—first spreading-centre segment nears Southern California, (b) 20 million years ago—growing transform fault connects remaining spreading centres, (c) 10 million years ago—the Mendocino (M) and Rivera (R) triple junctions continue to migrate north and south respectively. The long transform fault between the two triple junctions is the ancestor of the San Andreas fault. Interpretations based on work of Tanya Atwater.

Source: Kious, W. J., and Tilling, R. I., *This Dynamic Earth*. US Geological Survey, p. 77.

Continued

centres to the north and south continued to operate. What connected them? A transform fault, specifically the ancestor of the San Andreas fault. In the ensuing few millions of years, the fault grew, and the Mendocino and Rivera triple junctions migrated further north and south, respectively.

Figure 3.23 shows the present-day tectonic setting along the western edge of the North American plate. In the last 5.5 million years, continued seafloor spreading to the south of the San Andreas fault has opened the Gulf of California by approximately 300 km. This rifting action has torn Baja California and the Los Angeles areas from the North American plate and piggybacked them onto the Pacific plate. This example illustrates the fact that tectonic boundaries do not necessarily follow coastlines: the contact between the Pacific and North American plates in California is not along its famous beaches, but along the Gulf of California spreading centre and the San Andreas fault. Los Angeles, located west of the fault, is on the Pacific plate, whereas San Francisco, located east of the fault, is on the North American plate.

North of the Mendocino triple junction, the Gulf of California spreading centre is still active, but is now broken into four small segments. The northern fragment of the ancient Farallon plate is now composed of three plates. The larger Juan de Fuca plate is located in between the Explorer plate to the north and the Gorda plate to the south. These three plates are currently subducting underneath Vancouver Island and the northwestern United States along the Cascadia Subduction Zone at a rate of approximately 4 cm per year. Over the last tens of millions of years, this sustained subduction has produced outpourings of vast quantities of very fluid lavas, built the Cascade Range volcanoes (Figures 8.7, 8.8, and 8.9) and triggered major earthquakes. North of the Cascadia Subduction Zone, the Queen Charlotte fault accommodates the alongside movement of the Pacific and North American plates in a fashion similar to its southern cousin, the San Andreas fault, and has been the site of large earthquakes. Finally, the Queen Charlotte fault moves inland in the Alaska Panhandle and connects to the Aleutian Subduction Zone.

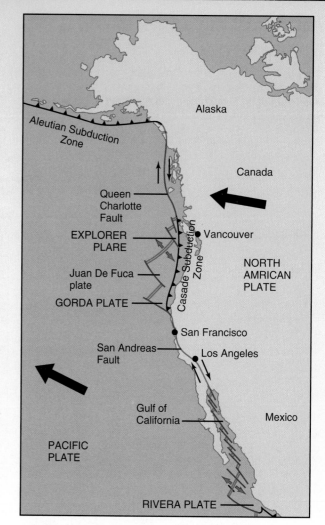

Figure 3.23 Present-day tectonic setting of Western North America.
Source: Claire Samson.

Spreading Centres and Earthquakes

Earthquakes at spreading centres are typically too small to destroy buildings and kill people. The expanded volumes of warm rock in the oceanic ridge systems have a higher heat content and a resultant decrease in rigidity. This heat-weakened rock does not build up and store the huge stresses necessary to create large earthquakes.

ICELAND

The style of spreading-centre earthquakes can be appreciated by looking at the earthquake history of Iceland, a nation that exists solely on a hot spot–fed volcanic island portion of the mid-Atlantic ridge (Figures 3.26 and 3.27). In the portions of the country underlain by north-south-oriented spreading centres, small to moderate-size earthquakes tend to occur in swarms, as is typical of volcanic areas where magma is on the move. Iceland does have large earthquakes, but they are associated with east-west-oriented transform faults between the spreading-centre segments.

RED SEA AND GULF OF ADEN

Iceland formed on a mature spreading centre that is related to the opening of the North Atlantic Ocean, which began some 135 million years ago. The specific ridge

Figure 3.24

Map view of an idealized plate and the earthquake potential along its edges.

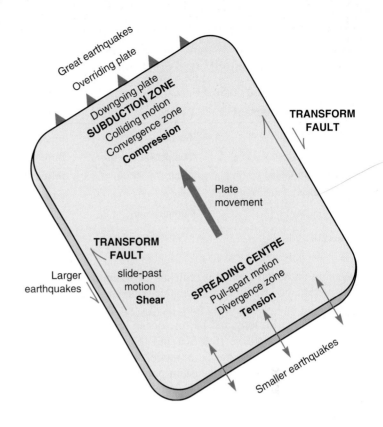

Figure 3.25

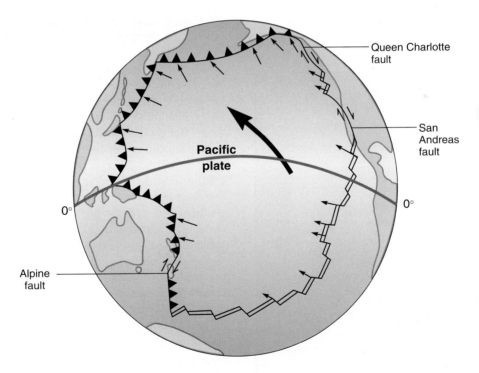

The Pacific plate is the largest in the world; it underlies part of the Pacific Ocean. Its eastern and southern edges are mostly spreading centers characterized by small- to intermediate-size earthquakes. Three long transform faults exist along its sides in Canada (Queen Charlotte), California (San Andreas), and New Zealand (Alpine); all are marked by large earthquakes. Subduction zones (shown by black triangles) lie along the northern and western edges, from Alaska to Russia to Japan to the Philippines to Indonesia to New Zealand; all are characterized by gigantic earthquakes.

Source: © 1976 John Wiley & Sons, Inc.

Table 3.1

Tectonic Environments and Earthquake Characteristics

Tectonic Environment	Deformation Force	Earthquake Characteristics		
		Frequency	Maximum Size	Maximum Hypocenter Depth
Divergent zone	Tension	Frequent	Strong	Shallow
Convergent zone	Compression	Infrequent	Great	Deep
Transform fault	Shear	Infrequent	Major	Shallow
Hot spot	Tension Compression	Frequent	Strong	Shallow

Source: Claire Samson.

segment on which Iceland is built started to open 60 million years ago. What would a much younger spreading centre and new ocean basin look like? Long and narrow. In today's world, long and narrow ocean basins exist in northeast Africa as the Red Sea and the Gulf of Aden (Figure 3.28). Following is a model explaining how spreading began: The northeastern portion of Africa sits above an extra-hot area in the upper mantle. The heat contained within this mantle hot zone is partially trapped by the blanketing effect of the overlying African plate and its embedded continent (Figure 3.29a). The hot rock expands in volume and some liquefies to magma. This volume expansion causes doming of the overlying rock, with resultant uplift of the surface to form topography (Figure 3.29b). The doming uplift sets the stage for gravity to pull the raised landmasses downward and apart, thus creating pull-apart faults with centrally located, down-dropped **rift** valleys, also described as pull-apart basins (Figure 3.29c). As the faulting progresses, magma rises up through the cracks to build volcanoes. As rifting and volcanism continue, seafloor spreading processes take over, the down-dropped linear rift valley becomes filled by the ocean, and a new sea is born (Figure 3.29d).

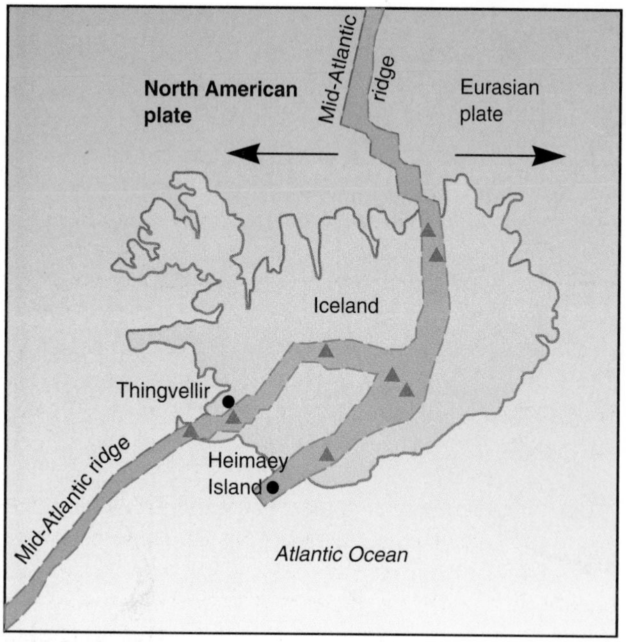

Figure 3.28 reveals another interesting geometric feature. Three linear pull-apart basins meet at the south end of the Red Sea at a triple junction. This triple junction is geologically young, having begun about 25 million years ago. To date, spreading in the Red Sea and Gulf of Aden has been enough to split off northeast Africa and create an Arabian plate and to allow seawater to flood between them. But the East African Rift Valley has not yet been pulled far enough apart for the sea to fill it. The East African Rift Valley is a truly impressive physiographic feature. It is 5,600 km long and has steep escarpments and dramatic valleys. Beginning at the Afar triangle at its northern end and moving southwest are the domed and stretched highlands of Ethiopia, beyond which the rift valley divides into two major branches. The western rift is markedly curved and has many deep lakes, including the world's second deepest lake, Lake Tanganyika. The eastern rift is straighter and holds shallow, alkaline lakes and volcanic peaks, such as Mount Kilimanjaro, Africa's highest mountain. The rift valley holds the oldest humanoid fossils found to date and is the probable homeland of the first human beings. Will the spreading continue far enough to split a Somali plate from Africa? It is simply too early to tell.

How severe are the earthquakes in the geologically youthful Red Sea and Gulf of Aden? Significant, but spreading-centre earthquakes are not as large as the earthquakes on the other types of plate edges.

Figure 3.26
Iceland sits on top of a hot spot and is being pulled apart by the spreading centre in the Atlantic Ocean. Triangles mark sites of some active volcanoes.

Figure 3.27
Looking south along the fissure at Thingvellir, Iceland. This is the rift valley being pulled apart in an east-west direction by the continuing spreading of the Atlantic Ocean.
Photo © John S. Shelton.

Convergent Zones and Earthquakes

The greatest earthquakes in the world occur where plates collide (Table 3.2). The three basic classes of collisions are (1) oceanic plate versus oceanic plate, (2) oceanic plate versus continent, and (3) continent versus continent. These collisions result in either subduction or continental upheaval. If oceanic plates are involved, subduction will occur. The younger, warmer, less-dense plate will override the older, colder, denser plate, which will then bend downward and be pulled back into the mantle. If two continents are involved, they will not subduct because their huge volume of low-density, high-buoyancy rock simply cannot sink to great depth and cannot be pulled into the denser asthenosphere rock below. The fate of oceanic plates is destruction via subduction and reassimilation within the mantle, whereas continents float about on the asthenosphere in perpetuity. Continents are ripped asunder and then reassembled into new configurations via collisions, but they are not destroyed by subduction.

SUBDUCTION ZONES

Subduction zones are the sites of great earthquakes. Imagine pulling a 100 km thick rigid plate into the weaker, deformable rock of the mantle that resist the plate's intrusion. This process creates tremendous stores of energy, which are released periodically as great earthquakes.

Although subduction zones are characterized by a dominantly compressional stress regime, earthquakes from these regions result from different types of fault movements in shallow versus deeper realms. At shallow depths (less than 100 km), the two rigid lithospheric plates are pushing against each other. Earthquakes result from compressive movements where the overriding plate moves upward and the subducting plate moves downward. Pull-apart fault movements also occur near the surface within the subducting plate as it is bent downward and snaps in tensional failure and within the overriding plate as it is lifted up from below. Notice in Figure 3.13 that the shallow earthquakes occur (1) in the upper portion of the down-going plate, (2) at the bend in the subducting plate, and (3) in the overriding plate.

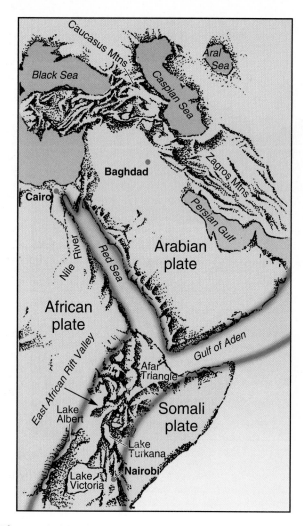

Figure 3.28
Topography in northeastern Africa and Arabia. Northeastern Africa is being torn apart by three spreading centres: Red Sea, Gulf of Aden, and East African Rift Valley. The spreading centres meet at the triple junction in the Afar Triangle.

Compare the locations of the shallow earthquakes to those of intermediate and deep earthquakes (Figure 3.13). At depths below 100 km, the upper and lower surfaces of the subducting slabs are too warm to generate large earthquakes. Thus, the earthquakes occur in the cooler interior area of rigid rock, where stress stored as gravity pulls against the asthenosphere resistance to slab penetration. Note, however, that a great earthquake that occurs deep below the surface has much of its seismic energy dissipated while travelling to the surface and is generally less destructive than a shallow earthquake.

Tokyo, Japan, 1923

Early on Saturday morning, 1 September 1923, the cities of Tokyo and Yokohama were drenched by the last squalls of a waning storm. Later that morning, the skies cleared and the Sun beamed down as the residents prepared their midday meal. Moments later, this tranquil scene was shattered by a deadly series of earthquakes. The principal shock was powerful; Earth averages less than one earthquake a year that releases this much energy. It occurred beneath Sagami Bay southwest of the big cities. The floor of Sagami Bay dropped markedly and sent a 11 m high tsunami crashing against the shore. The waves washed away hundreds of homes. Yet fishermen spending their day out on the open ocean were unaware of the monster waves. At day's end, as they sailed toward home through Sagami Bay, they were sickened to find the floating wreckage of their houses and the bodies of their families. Devastation on land was great. Houses were destroyed, bridges fell, tunnels collapsed, and landslides destroyed both forested slopes and terraced hillsides created for agriculture. The wreckage of Tokyo and Yokohama buildings begun by the shaking Earth was completed by the ensuing fires. The shaking caused the collapse of flammable house materials onto cooking fires, and the flames, once liberated, quickly raced out of control throughout both cities. Little could be done to stem their spread because the earthquake had broken the water mains. Shifting winds advanced the fires through Tokyo for two and a half days, destroying 71% of the city's houses. Infernos in Yokohama gutted the city, a 100% loss.

Possibly the most tragic event in this disaster occurred when 40,000 people, clutching their personal belongings, attempted to escape the flames by crowding into a 100-hectare garden owned by a wealthy banker on the edge of the Sumida River. People packed themselves into this open space so densely that they were barely able to move. At about 4 p.m., several hours after the earthquake, the roaring fires approached on all three landward sides of the crowd. Suddenly the fire-heated winds spawned a tornado that carried flames onto the huddled masses and their combustible belongings. After the flames had died, 38,000 people lay dead, either burned or asphyxiated. The usual instinct to seek open ground during a disaster was shockingly wrong this time.

The combined forces of earthquakes, tsunami, and fires killed 99,331 people and left another 43,476 missing and presumed dead. In Tokyo, irreplaceable records were lost, and 2,000 years of art treasures were destroyed. Yet, despite this immense catastrophe, the morale of the Japanese people remained high. They learned from the disaster. They have rebuilt their cities with wider streets, more open space, and less use of combustible construction materials.

The historical record of earthquakes in the region is thought provoking. The region 80 km southwest of Tokyo has been rocked by five very strong earthquakes in the last 400 years (Figure 3.30). The seisms have occurred roughly every 73 years, the most recent in 1923.

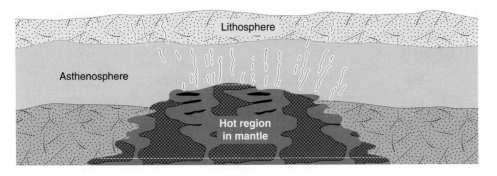

(a) Stage 1, Centring

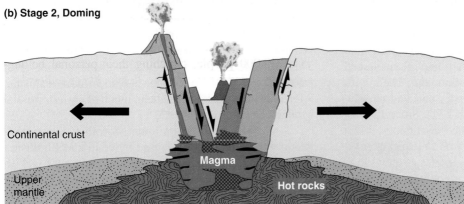

(b) Stage 2, Doming

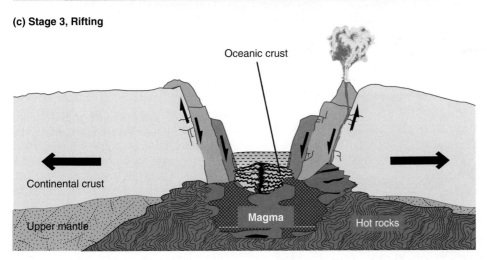

(c) Stage 3, Rifting

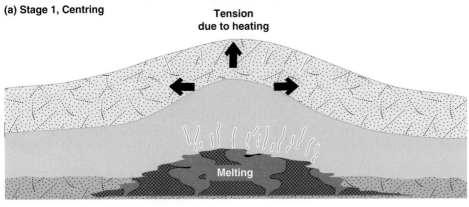

(d) Stage 4, Spreading

Figure 3.29
A model of the stages in the formation of an ocean basin. (a) Stage 1, Centring: Moving lithosphere centres over an especially hot region of the mantle. (b) Stage 2, Doming: Mantle heat causes melting and the overlying lithosphere/ continent extends. The increase in heat causes surface doming through uplifting, stretching, and fracturing. (c) Stage 3, Rifting: Volume expansion causes gravity to pull the uplifted area apart; fractures fail and form faults. Fractures/faults provide escape for magma; volcanism is common. Then, the dome's central area sags downward, forming a valley such as the present East African Rift Valley. (d) Stage 4, Spreading: Pulling apart has advanced, forming a new seafloor. Most magmatic activity is seafloor spreading, as in the Red Sea and Gulf of Aden.

Table 3.2

Earth's Largest Earthquakes, 1904–2005

Rank	Location	Year	Magnitude (M_w)	Cause
1.	Chile	1960	9.5	Subduction—Nazca plate
2.	Indonesia	2004	9.2	Subduction—Indian plate
3.	Alaska	1964	9.2	Subduction—Pacific plate
4.	Kamchatka	1952	9.0	Subduction—Pacific plate
5.	Ecuador	1906	8.8	Subduction—Nazca plate
6.	Indonesia	2005	8.7	Subduction—Indian plate
7.	Alaska	1965	8.7	Subduction—Pacific plate
8.	Assam	1950	8.6	Collision—India into Asia
9.	Alaska	1957	8.6	Subduction—Pacific plate
10.	Banda Sea	1938	8.5	Subduction—Pacific/Indian plate
11.	Chile	1922	8.5	Subduction—Nazca plate
12.	Kuril Island	1963	8.5	Subduction—Pacific plate

CONTINENT–CONTINENT COLLISIONS

The grandest continental pushing match in the modern world is the ongoing ramming of Asia by India. When Gondwanaland began its breakup, India moved northward toward Asia. The 5,000 km of seafloor (oceanic plate) that lay in front of India's northward path had all subducted beneath Asia by about 40 million years ago. Then, with no seafloor left to separate them, India punched into the exposed underbelly of Asia (Figure 3.31). Since the initial contact, the assault has remained continuous. India has moved another 2,000 km farther north, causing complex accommodations within the two plates as they shove into, under, and through each other accompanied by folding, overriding, and stacking of the two continents into the huge mass of the Himalaya and the Tibetan Plateau. The precollision crusts of India and Asia were each about 35 km thick. Now, after the collision, the combined crust has been thickened to 70 km to create the highest-standing continental area on Earth. The Tibetan Plateau dwarfs all other high landmasses. In an area the size of France, the average elevation exceeds 5,000 m. But what does all of this have to do with earthquakes? Each year, India continues to move about 5 cm into Asia along a 2,000 km front. This ongoing collision jars a gigantic area with great earthquakes. The affected area includes India, Pakistan, Afghanistan, the Tibetan Plateau, much of eastern Russia, Mongolia, and most of China.

A relatively simple experiment shows how earthquake-generating faults may be caused by continental collision (Figure 3.32). The experiment uses a horizontal jack to push into a pile of plasticine, deforming it under the force. The experimental deformation is similar to the tectonic map of the India–Asia region (Figure 3.33). The northward wedging of India seems to be forcing Indochina to escape to the southeast and is driving a large block of China to the east.

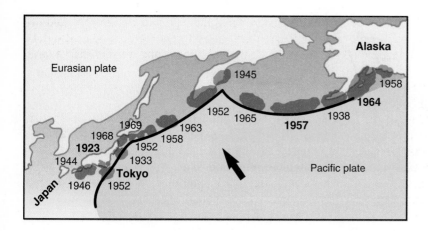

Figure 3.30
Brown patterns show severely shaken areas, with dates, from recent earthquakes caused by Pacific plate subduction. The 1957 and 1964 Alaska earthquakes are two of the largest in the 20th century. Using the seismic-gap method, where are the next earthquakes most likely to occur?

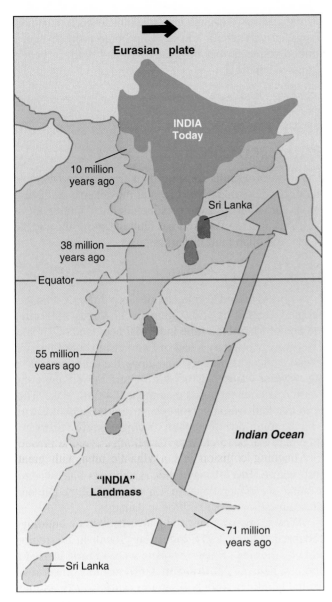

Figure 3.31
Map showing the movement of India during the last 71 million years. India continues to shove into Eurasia, creating great earthquakes all the way through China.

Figure 3.32
Simulated collision of India into Asia. A wedge is slowly jacked into layered plasticine confined on its left side but free to move to the right. From top to bottom of figure, notice the major faults that form and the masses that are compelled to move to the right. Compare this pattern to the tectonic map of India and Asia in Figure 3.33.
Source: © P. Tapponier, et al. (1982). *Geology*, 10, 611–16.

Shaanxi Province, China, 1556

The deadliest earthquake in history occurred in 1556 when about 830,000 Chinese were killed in and near Xi'an on the banks of the mighty Huang River (once known as the Yellow River). The region has numerous hills composed of deposits of windblown silt and fine sand that have very little **cohesion** (ability to stick together). Because of the ease of digging in these loose sediments, a tremendous number of the homes in the region were caves dug by the inhabitants. Most of the residents were in their cave homes at 5 a.m. on the wintry morning of 23 January, when the seismic waves rolled in from the great earthquake. The severe shaking caused much of the soft silt and sand sediments of the region to vibrate apart and literally behave like fluids. Most of the cave-home dwellers were entombed when the once-solid walls of their homes liquefied and collapsed.

Tangshan, China, 1976

The deadliest earthquake in recent times occurred directly beneath the city of Tangshan. A fault ruptured at a depth of 11 km in a local response to the regional stress created by the ongoing collision of India with Asia. The earthquake was much larger than local officials expected. Building codes were lenient—fatally so. This poor decision was instrumental in the deaths of over 240,000 people.

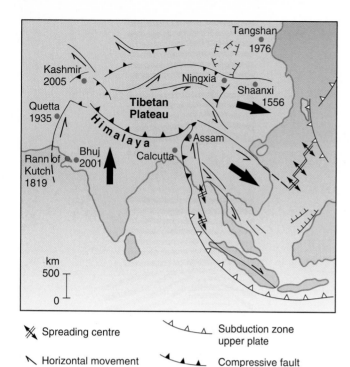

Spreading centre

Horizontal movement on fault

Subduction zone upper plate

Compressive fault overriding side

Figure 3.33
Tectonic map showing India pushing into Asia. The ongoing collision causes devastating earthquakes, each killing tens or hundreds of thousands of people. The list includes two in the Indian state of Gujarat in 1819 at Rann of Kutch and in 2001 near Bhuj, two in China in 1556 at Shaanxi and in 1976 at Tangshan, and two in Pakistan in Quetta in 1935, and in Kashmir in 2005.

In 1976, Tangshan was an industrial and mining city with two million residents. It contained the largest coal mines in China, so heavy industry found a home there also. Its coal, steel, electricity, and diesel- and locomotive-engine industries combined to create about 1% of China's gross national product. For Tangshan residents, the night of 27 July was unusually warm with rain and wind. Most unusual that night were the fireballs and lightning of all colours that rolled through the sky. At 3:42 a.m. on 28 July, the ground began the rumbling that reduced the city to almost total rubble. Most residents were at home in densely packed houses made of mud bricks held together by poor-quality mortar and covered with mud-and-lime roofs that had grown heavier through the years as new layers were added. Home was not a good place to be that day, as 93% of residential buildings collapsed. Industrial buildings fared somewhat better; still, 78% of them collapsed. Overall, older buildings performed better than newer ones. Some of the "luckier" individuals were the nightshift coal miners hard at work thousands of metres below the surface during the earthquake. Although 13 of these 15,000 miners died, as a whole, they fared far better than their dayshift comrades. Collapsing homes killed 6,500 of 85,000

off-duty miners. Through it all, the human spirit remained. Tangshan was rebuilt and is again home to more than a million residents, but now they live and work in better-designed buildings.

Transform Faults and Earthquakes

The transform faults forming the sides of some tectonic plates have dominantly horizontal movements that cause major earthquakes. Examples include the Alpine fault of New Zealand, the San Andreas fault in California, and the North Anatolian fault in Turkey.

TURKEY, 1999
A warm and humid evening made sleep difficult, so many people were still up at 3:01 a.m. on 17 August 1999 near the Sea of Marmara in the industrial heartland of Turkey. They were startled by a ball of flame rising out of the sea, a loud explosion, sinking land along the shoreline, and a big wave of water. Another big rupture moved along the North Anatolian fault as a magnitude 7.4 earthquake. This time the fault ruptured the ground surface for 120 km, with the south side of the fault moving westward up to 5 m (Figure 3.34). Several weeks later, after evening prayers for Muslims, a segment of the North Anatolian fault to the east ruptured in a 7.1 magnitude earthquake. The two devastating events combined to kill over 19,000 people and cause an estimated $20 billion in damages.

Why were so many people killed? Bad buildings collapsed (Figure 3.35). Industrial growth in the region attracted hordes of new residents who, in turn, caused a boom in housing construction. Unfortunately, many residential buildings were built on top of soft, shaky ground, and some building contractors cut costs by increasing the percentage of sand in their concrete, causing it to crumble as the ground shook.

The North Anatolian fault is a 1,400 km long fault zone made of numerous subparallel faults that split and combine, bend and straighten. It is not located on the Arabian plate, but it is caused by it (Figure 3.36). As the Arabian plate pushes farther into Eurasia, Turkey is forced to move westward and slowly rotate counterclockwise. Bounded by the North Anatolian fault in the north and the east Anatolian fault in the southeast, Turkey is squeezed westward like a watermelon seed from between your fingers.

A remarkable series of earthquakes began in 1939 near the eastern end of the North Anatolian fault with the magnitude 7.9 Erzincan earthquake, which killed 30,000 people. Since 1939, 11 earthquakes with magnitudes greater than 6.7 have occurred as the fault ruptures westward in a semiregular pattern that is unique in the world (Figure 3.34). At intervals ranging from 3 months

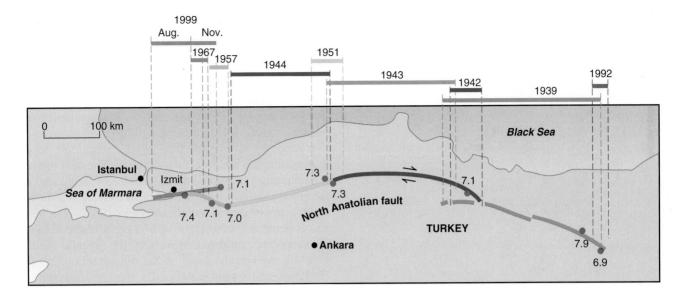

Figure 3.34
The North Anatolian fault accommodates the movement of Turkey westward into the Mediterranean basin (Figure 3.36). Note the time sequence of the fault ruptures from east to west. What does the near future hold for Istanbul?

Figure 3.35
A six-storey building pancaked in Duzce, Turkey, on 12 November 1999 when its supporting columns failed.

Photo © Roger Bilham, courtesy of NOAA.

to 32 years, over 1,000 km of the active portion of the fault has moved in big jumps.

What is likely to happen next? There is every reason to expect the fault rupture to keep moving to the west. The next big earthquake will likely occur near Istanbul, a city of 13 million people and growing rapidly. In the last 15 centuries, Istanbul has been heavily damaged by 12 earthquakes. Calculations indicate the next big earthquake affecting Istanbul has a 62(+/−15)% probability of occurring within the next 30 years.

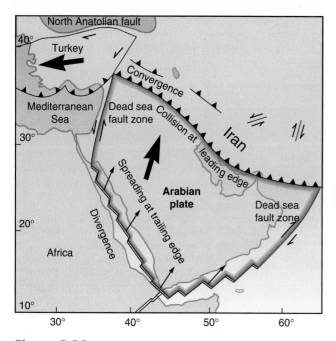

Figure 3.36
The Arabian plate pulls away from Africa, pushes into Eurasia, slices through the Middle East with a transform fault, and squeezes Turkey westward.

Hot Spots and Earthquakes

When one thinks about natural hazards in Hawaii, it is volcanism that comes to mind. But the movement of magma at hot spots can cause earthquakes, including large ones. In fact, several active volcanoes around the world, including Kilauea, are under surveillance to detect signs of increased earthquake activity leading to an eruption. When rock liquefies, its volume expands, and neighbouring brittle rock must fracture and move out of the way. The sudden breaks and **slips** of brittle rock are fault movements that produce earthquakes.

When magma is on the move at shallow depths, it commonly generates a nearly continuous swarm of relatively small earthquakes referred to as **harmonic tremors**. Figure 3.37 shows that the earthquakes below Kilauea volcano are dominantly near-surface events.

Magma movements also cause larger-scale topographic features and larger earthquakes. The land surface is commonly uplifted due to the injection of magma below the ground surface. But the land surface is also commonly down-dropped due to withdrawal of magma. Figure 3.38 shows some down-dropped valleys on Kilauea. Kilauea is "supported" on the northwest by the gigantic Mauna Loa volcano and the mass of the Big Island of Hawaii. However, on its southeastern side, there is less support; Kilauea drops off into the Pacific Ocean. The effects of subsurface magma movement, both compressive during injection and extensional during removal, combine with gravitational pull to cause large movements along faults.

On 29 November 1975, one of the seaward-inclined faults moved suddenly in a 7.2 magnitude seism. It happened at 4:48 a.m., when a large mass slipped for 14 seconds with a movement of about 6 m seaward and 3.5 m downward. The movement of this mass into the sea caused a tsunami up to 12 m high. Campers sleeping on the beach were rudely awakened by shaking ground; those who didn't immediately hustle to higher ground were subjected to crashing waves. Two people drowned. This fault movement had an effect on subsurface magma analogous to shaking a bottle of soda pop—gases escaping from magma unleashed an 18-hour eruption featuring magma fountains up to 50 m high.

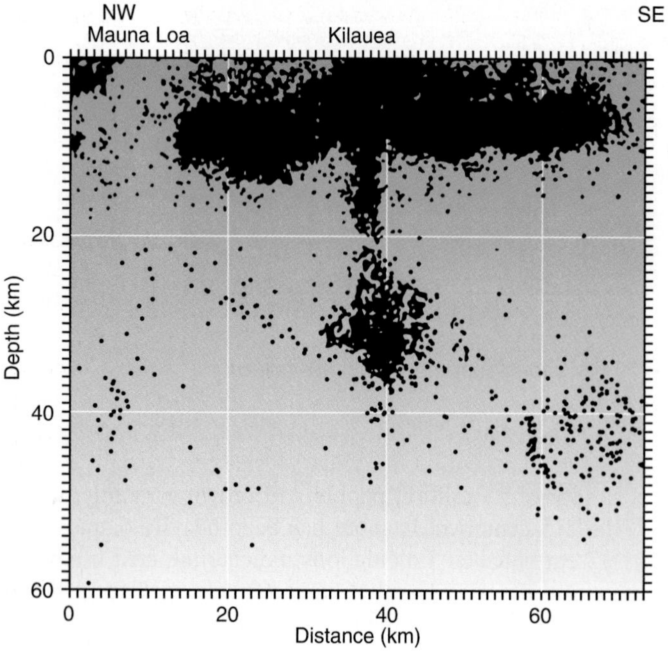

Figure 3.37
Cross-section showing hypocentres beneath Kilauea volcano on the flank of the larger Mauna Loa volcano, southeastern Hawaii, 1970–1983.
© Geological Society of America, *Decade of North American Geology*, Vol N.

Figure 3.38

Schematic block diagrams of the southeastern flank of Kilauea volcano. Intruding magma (red) forces brittle rock to break and move, generating earthquakes. Gravity-aided sliding down normal faults causes more earthquakes as rock masses slide southeastward into the ocean and cause rare mega-tsunami.
Source: © Geological Society of America, *Decade of North American Geology*, Vol N.

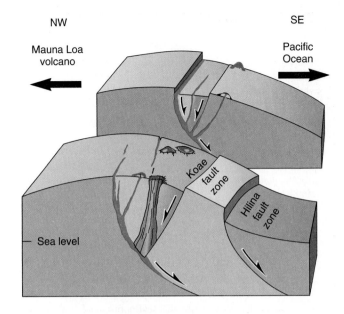

Summary

- Earth's outer layer, the lithosphere, is broken into a dozen large tectonic plates, and several smaller ones. Plates are approximately 100 km thick. The larger plates are several thousands of kilometres across.

- The boundary between the rigid lithosphere and the underlying plastic asthenosphere provides a sliding surface for plates to move. Convection in the asthenosphere and gravity are the driving mechanisms of plate movement.

- The tectonic cycle describes the recycling of Earth's outer layers over a time period of approximately 250 million years. Different processes take place in the four different tectonic environments: (1) divergent, (2) convergent, (3) and transform plate boundaries, and (4) hot spots. New lithosphere is created by seafloor spreading when plates are pulled apart at divergent zones. Old lithosphere is being reabsorbed into the asthenosphere by subduction where two plates of differing densities collide. Transform faults accommodate the along-side movements of plates without creation or destruction of lithosphere. Hot spots originate deep in Earth and are the source of isolated plumes of partially molten rock rising through the asthenosphere and lithosphere.

- Ocean studies have contributed solid evidence attesting to the movement of tectonic plates. Magnetization patterns on the seafloor delineate the newly formed lithosphere in space and time. Bathymetric surveys have mapped deep subduction trenches and relatively shallow volcanic ridges.

- Oceans and continents are fundamentally different. Ocean floors are relatively young features on the surface of Earth, being constantly recycled by seafloor spreading and subduction. Continents comprise older lower-density rock that rides on top of the denser rock of the moving plates.

- Plate tectonics has been operating on Earth for over half the planet's history. The Canadian territory has grown from a core of very old rock through successive episodes of seafloor spreading, subduction, and continental collisions.

- Most earthquakes are caused by fault movements and occur preferentially along the edges of tectonic plates. Magma movement in the shallow subsurface at spreading centres and hot spots tends to induce swarms of small earthquakes. The dominantly horizontal movements at transform faults produce large earthquakes. The compressional movements at subduction zones and continent–continent collisions generate the largest tectonic earthquakes, and they affect the widest areas.

- The west coast of Canada is tectonically active and prone to large earthquakes. The Explorer plate is currently subducting offshore Vancouver Island. To the north, the Pacific and North American plates rub uneasily against one another along the Queen Charlotte transform fault.

Terms to Remember

bathymetry 54
cohesion 73
continental drift 52
convergence zone 50
craton 64
Curie point 53
divergence zone 50
epicentre 55
fault 63
Gondwanaland 60
harmonic tremors 76
hot spot 54

hypocentre 55
island arc 58
Laurasia 60
lava 53
magnetic field 53
magnetic pole 53
Pangaea 52
Panthalassa 60
plate 50
plate tectonics 50
plume 54
ridge 50

rift 68
seafloor spreading 51
seismic-gap method 57
slip 76
spreading centre 55
subduction 51
tectonic cycle 51
tectonics 50
topography 50
transform fault 50
trench 55
triple junction 57

Questions for Review

1. Explain several lines of evidence indicating that the continents move about Earth.
2. Provide evidence indicating that seafloors spread.
3. What are the ages of the oldest (a) rocks on the continents, and (b) rocks making up the ocean floor?
4. Explain the seismic-gap method of forecasting earthquakes.
5. Why did the plate tectonics theory supersede the continental drift hypothesis and gain wide acceptance?
6. Draw and label a cross-section that explains the tectonic cycle.
7. Sketch a sequence of cross-sections that shows how a continent is separated to accommodate an ocean basin.
8. Describe a deep-ocean trench. How does one form?
9. Why do deep earthquakes tend to occur within inclined bands?
10. Why are the Himalaya the world's largest mountain range?
11. Explain why earthquakes at subduction zones are many times more powerful than spreading-centre earthquakes.
12. How do hot spots help determine the directions of plate motions?
13. Why is British Columbia vulnerable to large earthquakes?
14. What are the similarities between the Queen Charlotte fault of British Columbia and the San Andreas fault of California?

Questions for Further Thought

1. Why did the realization that Earth's surface is broken into large plates come about only a few decades ago?
2. How can the rate of motion of a plate be measured?
3. Is East Africa likely to pull away from the rest of Africa to form a Somali plate?
4. If a space body with active Earth-style plate tectonics is found, what would this discovery reveal about the internal structure of this body?

Earthquake Geology, Seismology, and Engineering

A bad earthquake at once destroys our oldest associations: the earth, the very emblem of solidity, has moved beneath our feet like a thin crust over a fluid;— one second of time has created in the mind a strange idea of insecurity, which hours of reflection would not have produced.

—Charles Darwin, 1835, notes for **The Voyage of the Beagle**

Outline

A solitary seismograph station powered with solar panels at Yamba Lake in the Northwest Territories records faint earthquake signals from around the world. It telemeters data to Ottawa via a satellite link.
Photo by Claire Samson.

The earth beneath our feet moves, releasing energy that shifts the ground and sometimes topples cities. Some earthquakes are so immense that their energy is equivalent to thousands of atomic bombs exploded simultaneously. The power of earthquakes to destroy human works, to kill vast numbers of people, and to alter the very shape of our land has left an indelible mark on many civilizations. Earthquake unpredictability instills an uneasy respect and fear in humankind that, through the millennia, have helped shape thought about life and our place in it.

Ancient accounts of earthquakes tend to be quite incomplete. Instead of providing rigorous descriptions of the Earth's behaviour, they emphasize interpretations. For over 2,000 years, based on Aristotle's ideas, many explanations of earthquakes were based on winds rushing beneath the Earth's surface. Around 1500 CE, even Leonardo da Vinci wrote in his *Notebooks* that:

> When mountains fall headlong over hollow places they shut in the air within their caverns, and this air, in order to escape, breaks through the Earth, and so produces earthquakes.

Figure 4.1
Offset of tilled farmland by 1979 movement of the Imperial fault, southernmost California. View is to the east; the west side of the fault (closest to you) has moved northward (to your left).
Photo: © Pat Abbott.

What Is an Earthquake?

The word "earthquake" is effectively a self-defining term—the Earth quakes, the Earth shakes, and we feel the vibrations. Earthquakes may be created by volcanic activity, meteorite impacts, undersea landslides, explosions of nuclear bombs, and more; but most commonly they are caused by sudden Earth movements along faults. A **fault** is a **fracture**, a crack in the Earth across which the two sides move relative to each other (Figure 4.1). Stresses build up in near-surface rock until the stress is so great that the rock fractures and shifts along a fault. The radiating shock waves sent off as the rock ruptures and moves are what we experience as an earthquake.

A fault rupture is not a one-time movement that produces "the earthquake." In fact, we never have just one earthquake. The stresses that build up in the rock in an area are released by a series of movements along the fault, or several faults, that continue for weeks to months to years. Each fault movement generates an earthquake; the biggest one is called the **mainshock**, the smaller ones before it are known as **foreshocks**, and the smaller ones after it are called **aftershocks**. There are no differences between these earthquakes other than size; they are all part of the same series of stress release on the fault. A large-scale fault movement increases the stress on adjacent sections of a fault, helping trigger additional fault movements that we feel as aftershocks.

The danger of large aftershocks is especially acute in the three days following the mainshock. Sometimes a big earthquake is followed by an even bigger earthquake, and then the first earthquake is reclassified as a foreshock.

Faults are not simple planar surfaces that glide readily when subjected to stress. Instead, faults are complex zones of breakage where rough and interlocking rock is held together over an irregular surface that extends many kilometres below the ground. Stress must build up over many years before enough potential energy is stored to allow a rupture on a fault. Fault rupture almost always follows pre-existing faults. The initial break occurs at a weak point on the fault and then propagates rapidly along the fault surface. The point where the fault first ruptures is known as the hypocentre. The point on the Earth's surface directly above the hypocentre is called the epicentre (Figure 4.2). The portion of the fault surface where rock slipped is called the rupture area. Only in some cases does the rupture area extend to the Earth's surface and the fault leave an imprint on the ground (Figures 4.1, 4.9, 4.10, and 4.13). The rupture area is limited to depths where rock is brittle. Beyond this region, rock is subjected to high temperatures and becomes ductile. It is no longer able to store the energy necessary to fail suddenly.

Types of Faults

The 19th-century recognition that fault movements cause earthquakes was a fundamental advance that triggered a whole new wave of understanding. With this

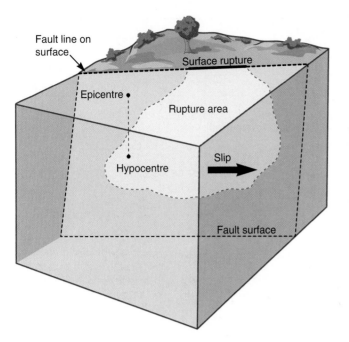

Figure 4.2

Block diagram of a fault surface. The hypocentre is the point on the fault surface where the rupture began; the epicentre is the point on the Earth's surface directly above the hypocentre. Notice that because the fault surface is inclined (it dips), the epicentre does not plot on the trace of the fault at the surface.

Source: © J. Ziony, ed., "Earthquakes in the Los Angeles Region." US Geological Survey.

(a)

(b)

Figure 4.3

(a) A 75-million-year-old sandstone layer at La Jolla Bay, California, exposed at a moderately high tide. The sea surface forms a horizontal plane against the inclined sandstone bed. (b) The strike of a rock layer is the compass bearing of the "shoreline." The dip angle is the number of degrees below horizontal that the rock layer is inclined.

Photo: © Pat Abbott.

relationship in mind, geologists go into the field to map active faults, which in turn identifies earthquake-hazard belts. Because a fault moves formerly continuous rock layers apart, the careful mapping of different rock masses can define discontinuities. These discontinuities are the surface expression of faults.

As tectonic plates split apart and collide, as mountains are elevated and basins are warped downward, the brittle rock of the lithosphere responds by fracturing. When regional forces create a large enough stress differential in rock on either side of a fracture, then movement occurs and the fracture becomes a fault. Accumulated movements of rock along faults range from millimetres to hundreds of kilometres. These movements can cause originally horizontal sedimentary rock layers to be tilted and folded into a wide variety of orientations. To describe the location in three-dimensional (3-D) space of a deformed rock layer, a fault surface, or any other planar feature, geologists make measurements known as **dip** and **strike**. Dip is seen in the two-dimensional (2-D) vertical view (**cross-section**) as the angle of inclination of the tilted rock layer measured from the horizontal (Figure 4.3). Strike is viewed in the 2-D horizontal view (**map**) as the

compass bearing of the rock layer where it intersects a horizontal plane.

DIP-SLIP FAULTS

Many ore veins were formed in ancient fault zones. The classification of faults (Table 4.1), therefore, uses some terminology of early miners working in excavated fault zones. They called the floor beneath their feet the **footwall** and the rock above their heads the **hangingwall**

Table 4.1

Classification of Faults

Fault Type		Deformation Force	Description		Tectonic Environment
Dip-slip	Normal	Tension	Vertical movement	Hangingwall moves down relative to footwall	Divergence zone
	Reverse	Compression		Hangingwall moves up relative to footwall	Convergence zone
Strike-slip		Shear	Horizontal movement		Transform fault

Source: © Claire Samson.

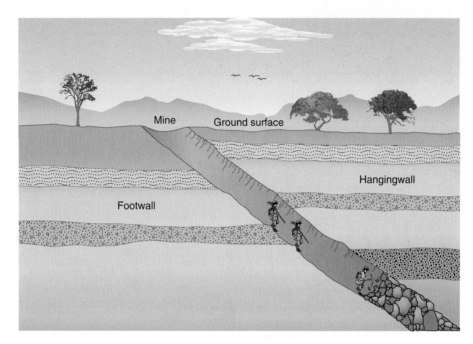

Figure 4.4
Schematic cross-section of miners excavating ore that precipitated in broken rock within an old fault zone. Notice that the rock layers in the footwall and hangingwall are no longer continuous; this gives evidence of the movements that occurred along the fault in the past.

(Figure 4.4). This terminology is used to define the two major types of faults dominated by vertical movements—the **dip-slip faults**. Dip-slip faults have the major amounts of their offset in the dip direction and are caused by either tension or compression.

Dip-slip faults where tension is dominant are recognized by the separation of the pulled-apart rock layers in a zone of omission (Figure 4.5); this type of fault is referred to as a **normal fault**. A normal fault occurs when the hangingwall moves down relative to the footwall.

Normal-style faults are typical of the faults at oceanic spreading centres and continental rift zones.

If the dominant force that creates a fault movement is compressional, then the rock layers are pushed together, or repeated, when viewed in a cross-section (Figure 4.6). With compressional forces, the hangingwall moves upward relative to the footwall; this type of fault is referred to as a **reverse fault**. The compressional motions of reverse faults are commonly found in areas of plate convergence where subduction or continental collision occurs.

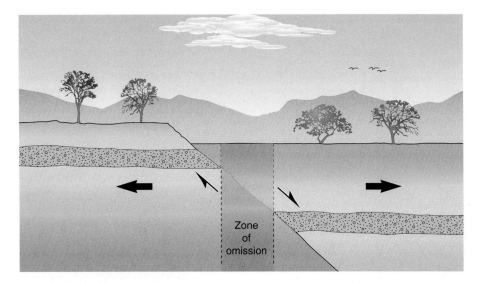

Figure 4.5
Schematic cross-section of a normal fault; that is, the hangingwall has moved downward (in a relative sense). Extensional forces are documented by the zone of omission, where the originally continuous rock layers are missing. The small arrows indicate movement; the larger arrows show force.

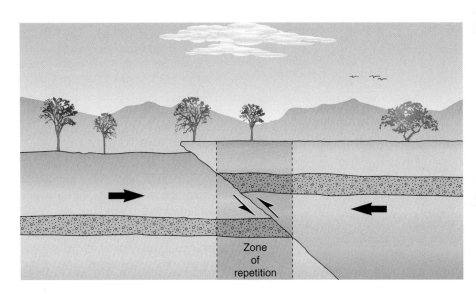

Figure 4.6
Schematic cross-section of a reverse fault; that is, the hangingwall has moved upward (in a relative sense). Compressional forces are documented by the zone of repetition, where the originally continuous rock layers have been split, shoved together, and stacked above each other. The small arrows indicate movement; the larger arrows show force.

STRIKE-SLIP FAULTS

When most of the movement along a fault is horizontal (parallel to the strike direction), the fault is referred to as a **strike-slip fault**. Strike-slip faults are further classified on the basis of the relative movement directions of the rock masses on either side of the fault (Figure 4.7). If you straddle a fault and the rock mass on your right-hand side has moved relatively toward you, then it is called a **right-lateral**, or dextral, **fault**. Similarly, if features on the left-hand side of the fault have moved closer to you, then it is a **left-lateral**, or sinistral, **fault**.

Strike-slip faults are common at transform plate boundaries. The transform faults described by Tuzo Wilson are strike-slip faults. The North Anatolian (Figure 3.34),

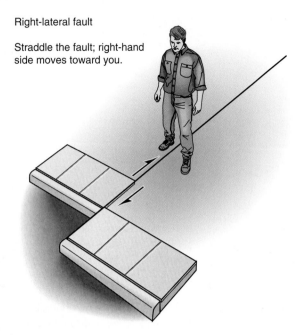

Straddle the fault; right-hand side moves toward you.

Figure 4.7
Map of a right-lateral, strike-slip fault. As the man straddles the fault, the right-hand side of the fault has moved relatively closer to him. If he turns around, will the right-hand side of the fault still have moved closer to him?

Queen Charlotte (Figure 3.23) and San Andreas (Figure 4.11) faults are right-lateral strike-slip faults. The Dead Sea fault (Figure 3.36) is a left-lateral strike-slip fault.

How Faults Work

OLD VIEW

The popular explanation of how faults move has been the elastic-rebound theory developed after the 1906 San Francisco earthquake. Based on surveyors' measurements of ground along the San Andreas fault, it appears that Earth stresses cause deformation and movement on both sides of a fault (Figure 4.8a and b). However, the rock along the fault itself does not move in response to this stress because it is rough and irregular, resulting in strong interlocking bonds with **friction** that retards movement. But as the landmasses away from the fault continue to move, energy builds up and is stored as elastic strain in the rock. When the applied stresses become overpowering, the rock at the fault ruptures, and both sides quickly move forward to catch up, and even pass, the rock away from the fault (Figure 4.8c). After a fault movement, all the elastic strain is removed from the area, and the

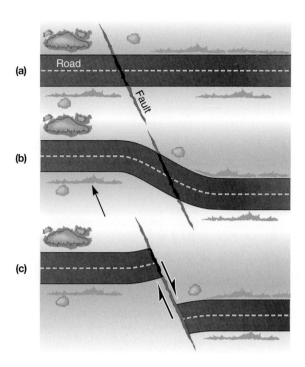

Figure 4.8
Elastic-rebound theory. (a) An active fault with a road as a reference line. (b) Deformation occurs along the fault, but friction of rock masses at the fault retards movement. (c) Finally, the deformation is so great that the fault ruptures, and the two sides race past each other and may actually catch up with and move past the earlier deformation.

buildup begins anew. This representation is a good first approximation to reality, but a better understanding has emerged in recent years.

NEWER VIEW

Movements along a fault may be better visualized as windows of opportunity. Fault movement begins at a hypocentre and then propagates outward for a certain distance and length of time. How much of the stored energy that is released during an earthquake depends on the number of seconds the fault moves. An analogous event might be opening a locked gate to a long line of people. If the gate is held open only long enough for half the people to enter and is then closed and locked, the other people will simply have to wait until the next time the gate opens. This is an important modification of elastic-rebound theory. The elastic-rebound theory has said that after a big earthquake, most of the elastic strain is removed from the rock and considerable time will be required for it to build again to a high enough level to create another big earthquake. We no longer think this is true.

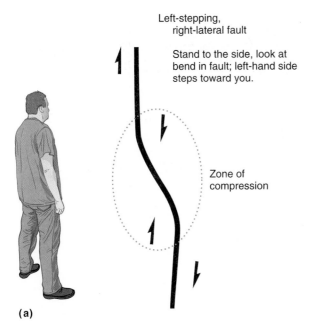

Left-stepping,
right-lateral fault

Stand to the side, look at
bend in fault; left-hand side
steps toward you.

Zone of
compression

(a)

(b)

Figure 4.9
(a) Left step in right-lateral fault. Notice that the land is pushed together at the fault bend whenever the fault moves. Movements will create a hill, which could grow to a mountain if the fault remains active for a long enough time. (b) Land offset along the Superstition Hills right-lateral fault during its 16 November 1987 earthquake. See the left step and the uplift at the bend.

Photo: © Pat Abbott.

STEPS IN FAULTS

Rupturing faults tear apart the rock along their path in numerous subparallel breaks that stop and start, bend left and bend right. The bends along a fault have profound implications for the creation of topography and the initiation, propagation, and cessation of fault rupture events as will be discussed in relation with the 1992 Landers earthquake later in this chapter.

Figure 4.9a is a sketch of a right-lateral fault with a left-stepping bend (step) in it. Notice what occurs at the bend in the fault when the two sides slide past each other—compression, pushing together, collision, constraint. The photo in Figure 4.9b shows a left step in the right-lateral Superstition Hills fault west of Brawley, California, which was created during the 16 November 1987 earthquake in the area. Notice how the compression at the bend produced a little hill.

Similarly, Figure 4.10a depicts a right step along a right-lateral fault. Visualize what happens at the bend in the fault. In this case, the two sides pull apart from each other, extend, diverge, release. The photo in Figure 4.9b is from the same earthquake, along a different length of the same fault, as in Figure 4.8b. At this right step, the two sides pulled apart and created a wide crack, a little basin, a downdropped area.

The World's Most Famous Fault: The San Andreas Fault

The famous San Andreas fault runs literally through the backyards of millions of Californians. The fault is a 1,200 km long, right-lateral strike-slip fault born some 28 million years ago from the collision between the Pacific Ocean spreading centre and the North American plate (see In Greater Depth box: Active Tectonic Zones of Western North America in Chapter 3). It is part of a complex system of subparallel faults (Figure 4.11) and has different behaviours along its length.

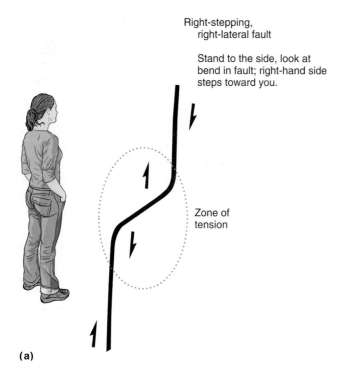

Right-stepping,
right-lateral fault

Stand to the side, look at
bend in fault; right-hand side
steps toward you.

Zone of
tension

(a)

(b)

Figure 4.10

(a) Right step in right-lateral fault. Notice that the land is pulled apart at the fault bend whenever the fault moves. Movements will create a hole, which could become a basin if the fault stays active for a geologically long time. (b) Land offset along the Superstition Hills right-lateral fault during its 1987 rupture. See the right step and the pull apart at the bend.
Photo: © Pat Abbott.

In 1906, the northernmost section of the fault broke loose just offshore of the city of San Francisco, rupturing northward and southward simultaneously over a distance of 430 km. When movement stopped, the western side of the fault (located on the Pacific plate) had shifted northward a maximum of 6 m horizontally with respect to the eastern side (located on the North American plate). In the vertical plane, the fault movement completely ruptured the 15 to 20 km thick brittle layer in the region. Today, the San Francisco section of the San Andreas fault has a deficit of earthquakes. Apparently this is a **locked zone** (Figure 4.11). Virtually all the stress from plate tectonics is stored as elastic strain for many decades until the fault finally can take no more and ruptures in a big event that releases much of its stored energy in a catastrophic movement.

The section to the south of San Francisco (Figure 4.12) has frequent small to moderate-size earthquakes. This is a **creeping zone** where numerous earthquakes accommodate the plate-tectonic forces before they build to high levels. The creeping movements of the fault are shown by the millimetres per year of ongoing offset of sidewalks, fences, buildings, and other features. Earthquakes in this fault segment do not seem to exceed magnitude 6. These are still significant seisms, but they are small compared to events on adjoining sections of the fault.

The San Andreas fault segment north of Los Angeles is another locked zone that is deficient in earthquake activity. However, on 9 January 1857, this segment of the fault broke loose at its northwestern end, and the rupture propagated southeastward in the great Fort Tejon earthquake with a magnitude of about 8.0. Due to the

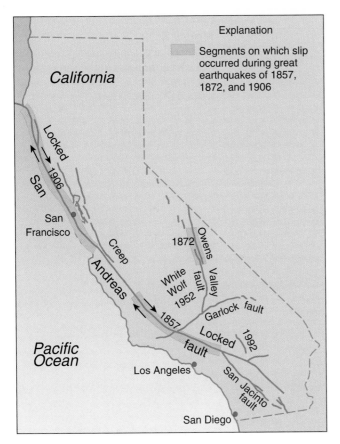

Figure 4.11

Historical behaviour of some California faults. The northern "locked" section of San Andreas fault ruptured for 430 km in 1906 (magnitude 7.9). The central "creeping" section has frequent smaller earthquakes. The south-central "locked" section ruptured for 360 km in 1857 (magnitude 8.0). The southernmost San Andreas awaits a major earthquake. The Owens Valley fault ruptured for 110 km in 1872 (magnitude 7.3). A magnitude 7.5 seism occurred on White Wolf fault in 1952, and a magnitude 7.3 seism happened in Mojave Desert in 1992.

Source: © US Geological Survey.

SAN FRANCISCO, 1906

Early in the 20th century, San Francisco was home to about 400,000 people who enjoyed a cosmopolitan city that had grown during the economic boom times of the late 19th century. During the evening of 17 April 1906, many thrilled to the special appearance of Enrico Caruso, the world's greatest tenor, singing with the Metropolitan Opera Company in Bizet's Carmen. But several hours later, at 5:12 a.m., the initial shock waves of a mammoth magnitude 8.3 earthquake arrived to begin the destruction of the city. Eyewitness accounts abound. One early riser told of seeing the earthquake approach as the street before him literally rose and fell like a series of ocean swells moving toward shore. The renowned American psychologist William James was in residence at Stanford University and reacted thusly:

> When I felt the bed begin to waggle, my first consciousness was one of gleeful recognition of the nature of the movement. "By Jove," I said to myself, "here's B's old earthquake after all." And then it went crescendo, "and a jolly good one it is, too."
>
> Sitting up involuntarily, and taking a kneeling position, I was thrown down on my face as it went fortis shaking the room exactly as a terrier shakes a rat. Then everything that was on anything else slid off to the floor, over went the bureau and chiffonier with a crash, as the fortissimo was reached; plaster cracked, an awful roaring noise seemed to fill the outer air, and in an instant all was still again. My emotion consisted wholly of glee and admiration; glee at the vividness which such an abstract idea or verbal term as "earthquake" could put on when translated into sensible reality and verified concretely; and admiration at the way in which the frail wooden house could hold itself together in spite of the shaking. I felt no trace whatever of fear; it was pure delight and welcome. "Go it," I almost cried aloud, "and go it stronger!"

During a noisy minute, the violently pitching Earth emitted dull booming sounds joined by the crash of human-made structures. When the ground finally quieted, people went outside and gazed through a great cloud of dust to view the destruction (Figure 4.33). Unreinforced masonry buildings lay collapsed in heaps, but steel-frame buildings and wooden structures fared much better. Another factor in the building failures was the nature of the ground they were built on. Destruction was immense in those parts of the city that were built on top of artificial fill that had been dumped onto former bay wetlands or into stream-carved ravines.

As repeated aftershocks startled and frightened the survivors, another great danger began to grow. Smoke arose from many sites as fires fed on the wood-filled rubble. Unfortunately, the same earthquake waves that

oneway advance of the rupture front, the fault movement lasted almost 3 minutes. The ground surface was broken for at least 360 km, and the maximum offsets in the Carrizo Plain (Figure 4.13) were a staggering 9.5 m. In 1857, the region was sparsely settled, so the death and damage totals were small. The next time a great earthquake occurs here, the effects may be disastrous.

The southernmost segment of the San Andreas fault, extending from Los Angeles almost to the American–Mexican border, has not generated a truly large earthquake in historical times. California has a well-recorded history for only about 150 years. We can extend our knowledge into the prehistoric past by dating organic-rich layers disturbed by ancient earthquakes by measuring the decay of the radioactive carbon isotope C^{14}.

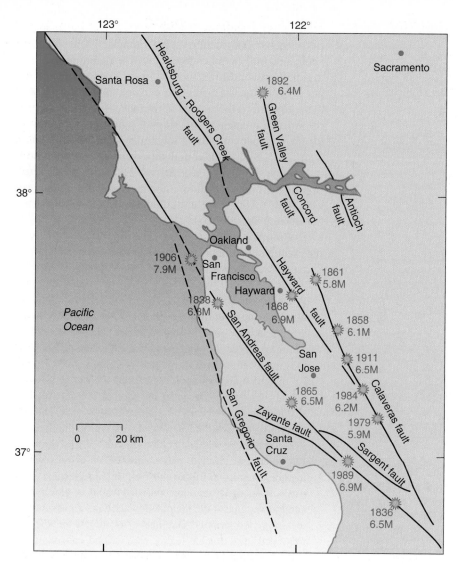

Figure 4.12
Locations and approximate sizes of significant earthquakes in the San Francisco Bay Area.
Source: © US Geological Survey.

wracked the buildings also broke most of the water lines, thus hindering attempts to stop the growing fires. From the business district and near the waterfront, fires began their relentless intrusion into the rest of the city. Desperate people tried dynamiting buildings to stop the fire's spread, but they simply provided more rubble to feed the flames and even blew flaming debris as far as a block away, where it started more fires.

The fires did about ten times as much damage as the earthquake itself; fire destroyed buildings covering 490 city blocks. More than half the population lost their homes. Death and destruction were concentrated in San Francisco, where 315 people died, but the affected area was much larger. About 700 deaths occurred in a 430 km belt of land running near the San Andreas fault. Problems continued in the months that followed as epidemics of filth-borne diseases sickened Californians; more than 150 cases of bubonic plague were reported. When all the fatalities from earthquake injuries and disease are included, the death total from the earthquake may have been as high as 5,000.

Total financial losses in the event were almost 2% of the U.S. gross national product in 1906; for comparison, Hurricane Katrina economic losses in 2005 were much less than 1%. In his book *A Crack in the Edge of the World: The Great American Earthquake of 1906,* published in 2005 in anticipation of the centennial of the event, Simon Winchester emphasizes the fact the politicians and the press were quick to label the disaster a "fire-related event." Their perception was that the American public would have a fatalistic attitude toward an earthquake, and would hesitate to rebuild the city on the same hazardous location. Fire safety, on the other hand, was perceived as an issue that could be addressed by proper planning and modern technology. Surely, with careful mitigation, such a disaster would not repeat itself. Another legacy of the 1906 earthquake is the haste with which San Franciscans rebuilt their urban infrastructure.

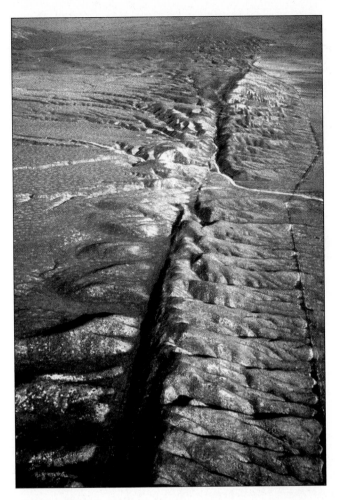

Figure 4.13
The San Andreas fault slashes across the Carrizo Plain. Notice the ridges and basins caused by local squeezing and pulling apart.
Photo by Pat Abbott.

This problem haunts the city inhabitants today because much of the early rebuilding was done badly and is likely to fail in the next big earthquake.

One of the intriguing aspects of disasters is the energizing effects they have on many survivors. Hard times shared with others bring out the best in many people. Shortly after this earthquake, resilient San Franciscans were planning the Panama–Pacific International Exposition that was to impress the world and leave behind many of the beautiful buildings that tourists flock to see today. You can't keep a good city down.

LOMA PRIETA, 1989

In 1989, the World Series was a San Francisco Bay Area affair. It pitted the American League champion Oakland Athletics against the National League champion San Francisco Giants. Game 3 was scheduled in San Francisco's Candlestick Park, where the Giants hoped the home field advantage would help them win their first game. It was Tuesday, 17 October, and both teams had finished batting practice, which was watched by 60,000 fans at the park, along with a television crowd of another 60 million fans in the United States and millions more around the world. At 5:04 p.m., 21 minutes before the game was scheduled to start, a distant rumble was heard, and a soft thunder rolled in from the southwest, shaking up the fans and stopping the game from being played. San Francisco experienced another big earthquake, and this time, it shared it with television viewers. After the earthquake, the San Franciscans at Candlestick Park broke into a cheer, while many out-of-staters were seen heading for home.

What caused this earthquake? An 83-year-long pushing match between the Pacific and North American plates resulted in a 42 km rupture within the San Andreas fault system. The southernmost section of the fault zone that moved in 1906 had broken free and moved again. There were several different aspects to the earthquake this time: (1) the fault rupture took place at depth; (2) the fault movement did not offset the ground surface; (3) there was a significant component of vertical movement; and (4) the fault rupturing lasted only 11 seconds, an unusually short time for a magnitude 6.9 event.

Movement occurred in a gently left-stepping constraining bend of the San Andreas fault zone near where the Calaveras and Hayward faults split off and run up the east side of San Francisco Bay (compare Figures 4.12 and 4.9). It is difficult for a fault to move around a left-stepping bend; thus, movements at a bend tend to be infrequent and large. This left step in the San Andreas also caused the fault plane to be inclined 70° to the southwest (Figure 4.14). The fault movement initiated at 18.5 km depth and slipped for 2.3 m. The motion can be decomposed into 1.9 m of horizontal movement and 1.3 m of vertical movement. Several fractures developed in the uplifted area and became the sites of landslides.

The Loma Prieta area had been a relatively quiet zone for earthquakes since the 1906 fault movement (Figure 4.15); before 1989, the Loma Prieta region had been a *seismic gap*. As the epicentres in Figure 4.15a show, the San Andreas fault section to the south moves frequently, generating numerous small earthquakes. But the same plate-tectonic stresses affecting the creeping zone also affect the locked zone. How does a locked zone catch up with a creeping zone? By infrequent but large fault movements. Notice in Figure 4.15 how the Loma Prieta mainshock and aftershocks filled in the seismic gap in cross-section (a). This demonstrates some merit for the seismic-gap method as a forecasting tool. Figure 4.15 also shows another seismic gap, south of San Francisco. The 1989 fault movement has increased the odds by another

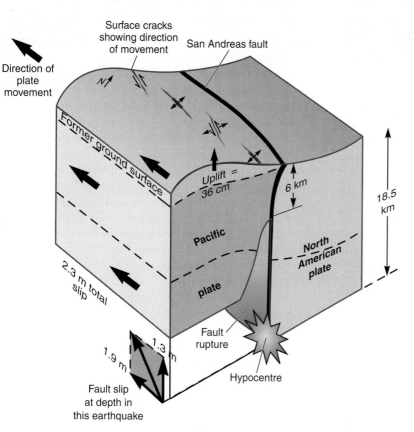

Figure 4.14
Schematic diagram of fault movement within the San Andreas zone in the World Series earthquake. The San Andreas fault dips 70° southwest because of the left-step bend. Fault movement began at 18 km depth and moved 1.9 m horizontally and 1.3 m vertically. Fault movement died out upward and did not rupture the ground, although the surface bulged upward 36 cm. Think three-dimensionally here: because of the dipping fault plane, will the epicentre plot on the ground-surface trace of the San Andreas fault? No.

Source: © US Geological Survey Circular 1045, 1989.

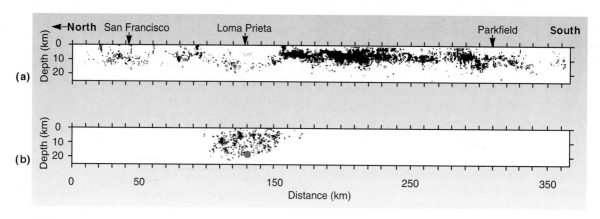

Figure 4.15
Cross-sections of seismicity along the San Andreas fault, 1969 to early 1989. (a) Notice the dense concentrations of hypocentres in the central creeping section of the fault from south of Loma Prieta to Parkfield, as well as the "seismic gap" in the Loma Prieta area. (b) Notice the deep hypocentre (in red) of the 1989 mainshock plus the numerous aftershocks. Putting the two cross-sections together fills the seismic gap. Are there other seismic gaps in cross-section (a)? Yes, south of San Francisco, just west of the densely populated midpeninsula area. When will this seismic gap be filled?

Source: © US Geological Survey Circular 1045, 1989.

10% for a large earthquake in this heavily populated area in the next 30 years.

In the Loma Prieta earthquake, the fault ruptured at greater than 2 km/s in all directions simultaneously. Table 4.3 indicates that earthquakes with magnitudes of 6 to 6.9 usually rupture for 10 to 30 seconds; this radially spreading, 6.9-magnitude rupture lasted only 11 seconds.

Had it lasted the expected 20 to 30 seconds, numerous other large buildings and the double-decker Embarcadero Freeway in San Francisco would have failed catastrophically. As it was, the event left 67 people dead or dying, 3,757 injured, and over 12,000 homeless; caused numerous landslides; disrupted transportation, utilities, and communications; and caused about $6 billion in damages.

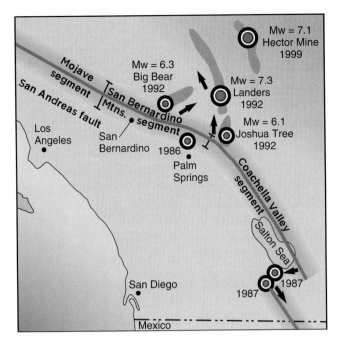

Figure 4.16
Map of major earthquakes near the northern and southern ends of the Coachella Valley segment of the San Andreas fault. The triangular block of crust near the northern end has moved northward.

LANDERS, CALIFORNIA, 1992

New insight on how faults work was provided by the Landers area earthquakes in 1992 and 1999 (Figure 4.16). This earthquake sequence began on 22 April 1992 with the right-lateral movement of the magnitude 6.1 Joshua Tree earthquake. Right-lateral movements along the fault trend resumed two months later at 4:58 a.m. on 28 June with the magnitude 7.3 Landers earthquake. A third earthquake, triggered by the first two, occurred a few hours later. At 8:04 a.m. on 28 June, the magnitude 6.3 Big Bear earthquake came from a left-lateral movement that ruptured northeast. Activity continued on 16 October 1999 with the right-lateral movement of the Hector Mine earthquake in a magnitude 7.1 event. Is this sequence of earthquakes finished? Probably not.

Examining the 1992 Landers earthquake records to see what happened during the 23 seconds of ground shaking associated with this event can teach us a lot about how faults move.

1. Fault movements commonly are restricted to one fault, and the rupture front often stops at large bends or steps in the fault, thus ending the earthquake. The 1992 Landers earthquake was different. It began right-lateral movement on the Johnson Valley fault and travelled northward about 20 km until reaching a right-step, pull-apart zone. The rupture front slowed, but it moved through the step and continued moving

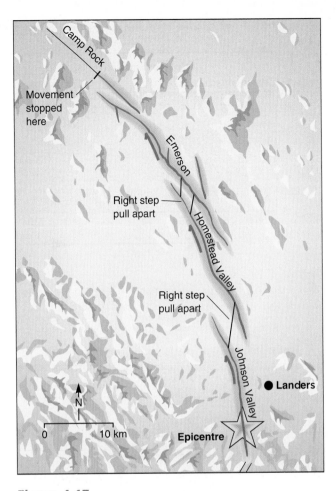

Figure 4.17
Northward-rupturing faults in 1992 Landers earthquake. The rupture front slowed at right steps, then moved onto adjacent faults before stopping in the middle of a straight segment.

northward on successive faults for another 50 km until finally stopping within a straight segment of the Camp Rock fault (Figure 4.17).

2. Figure 4.18 shows the amount of slip on the faults calculated by seismologists Dave Wald and Tom Heaton. It ranges from a few centimetres to 6.3 m. Notice how the amount of fault movement at the ground surface differs from that at depth.

3. Rupture velocity on the Johnson Valley fault was 3.6 km/s, slowing almost to a stop in the right step and then continuing northward at varying speeds. While the rupture front was slowed in a right step, the amount of slip behind the rupture front kept increasing until enough energy built up to cause movement through the step.

4. Fortunately for the Los Angeles megalopolis, the northward-moving fault directed its strongest seismic waves to the north into the sparsely inhabited desert. This phenomenon is known as **directivity,** wherein a rupture moving along a fault sends more energy in the direction it is moving.

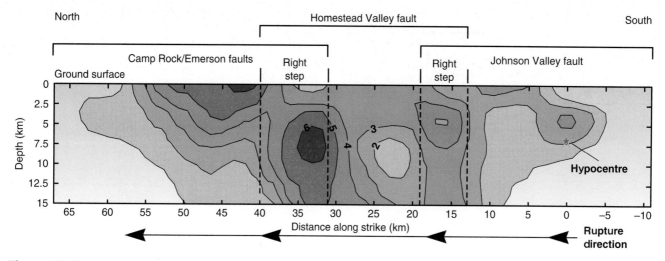

Figure 4.18
Slip on faults varied from centimetres to 6.3 m during movements of 1992 Landers earthquake. Contour interval of slip areas is 1 m.
Source: © Wald and Heaton in Seismological Society of America Bulletin.

5. Fault patches with little or no movement on Figure 4.18 may become the origination points for future earthquakes.

Recording Earth Motions

The study of earthquakes is known as **seismology** (after **seism,** meaning "earthquake"). The earliest earthquake-indicating device known was invented in China in 132 CE by Chang Heng. The modern era of seismologic instrumentation began about 1880. Instrumentation continues to evolve but the basic requirement remains to record the 3-D movement of earthquake waves together with their exact **arrival time** and durations. This is achieved by having instruments detect Earth motions (**seismometers**) and record them (**seismographs**) as north–south horizontal movements, east–west horizontal movements, and vertical movements, and assign them a time stamp.

To accurately record the passage of seismic waves, a seismometer needs to have a part that remains as stationary as possible while the whole Earth beneath it vibrates. The classic way to accomplish this is by building a pendulum seismometer with a heavy mass suspended on a frame (Figure 4.19). The support frame rests on the Earth and moves as the Earth does, but the mass suspended by a wire must have its **inertia** overcome before it moves. The differences between motions of the frame and the hanging mass are recorded as a wiggle trace by a pen on a drum of paper.

A modern seismograph station (Figure 4.20) is equipped with three seismometers, each recording one component of the Earth motion (north–south horizontal, east–west horizontal, and vertical). Most permanent stations are located in vaults to isolate the instruments from traffic vibrations. Seismometers are placed on concrete slabs in direct contact with bedrock for good coupling. Other stations are designed for temporary deployment, often in remote locations. They are powered by solar panels and telemeter data via a satellite link (see photo of chapter opener).

First-order analysis of the seismic records (**seismograms**) allows seismologists to identify the different kinds of seismic waves generated by the fault movement, to estimate the amount of energy released (magnitude), and to locate the epicentre/hypocentre.

Seismic Waves

A GENERAL DESCRIPTION OF WAVES

Throw a rock into a pond, play a musical instrument, or experience a fault movement, and the water, the air, or the Earth will transmit waves of energy that travel away from the initial disturbance. Waves can be described in terms of distance (Figure 4.21). This representation is useful, for example, when mapping the ocean surface and measuring the distance between successive waves. This distance is referred to as the **wavelength** and is expressed in metres. Waves can also be described in terms of time; for example, when measuring the amount of time between successive ocean waves reaching the beach. This length of time is referred to as the **period** and is expressed in seconds. The number of waves reaching a point during one second is called the frequency. Frequency is expressed in **hertz** (Hz) where 1 Hz equals one cycle per second. As mentioned in Chapter 1, period and frequency are inversely related. For example, if five waves passed a given point

Figure 4.19

Pendulum seismograph: The Earth moves, the seismograph framework moves, and the hanging wire vibrates, but the suspended heavy mass and pen beneath it remain relatively steady. Ideally, the pen holds still while the Earth moves beneath the pen to produce an inked line.

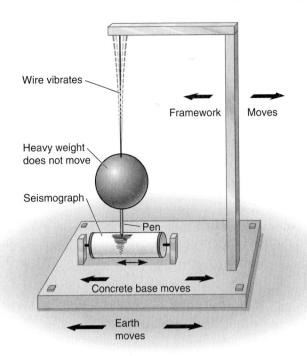

Figure 4.20

Modern seismograph station with three orthogonally aligned seismometers deployed on a large concrete slab in direct contact with bedrock. The seismometer on the right, with all protective covers removed, shows the suspended mass on a boom. The unit on the left has its protective cover in place while the centre unit is fitted with its heat shield. During normal operations, the seismometers are covered by bell jars that are evacuated, further reducing the effects of temperature and protecting against air currents (insert).

Photos: © Claire Samson.

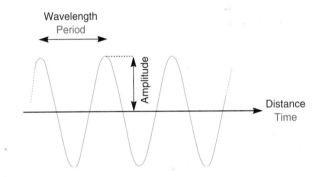

Figure 4.21

Wave motion. The horizontal arrow represents the undisturbed position, that is, the position of the medium when no wave is present. The orange line represents the position of the medium as a wave travels through it. The amplitude is the displacement from the undisturbed position. The section of the wave that rises above or lies below the undisturbed position is called a crest or a trough, respectively. When wave motion is plotted versus time, the length of time between successive crests/troughs corresponds to one period. When wave motion is plotted versus distance, successive crests/troughs are separated by one wavelength.

Source: © Claire Samson.

in 1 second, then the frequency is 5 Hz and the period is 0.2 second.

The **amplitude** of a wave is its displacement above or below the undisturbed position. Waves lose energy as they propagate away from the initial disturbance. Their amplitude decreases with distance, a phenomenon called attenuation. High-frequency waves attenuate over shorter distances than low-frequency waves (Figure 4.22).

The velocity of propagation of a wave in a medium is an intrinsic characteristic of that material. If the material properties change, so will the velocity. Waves will adapt by speeding, slowing, or changing direction.

Each mechanical system, an ocean wave or a guitar string, for example, is characterized by a particular

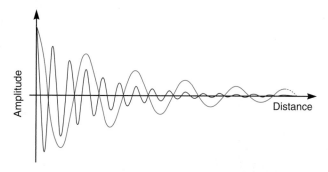

Figure 4.22

Attenuation. The amplitude of high-frequency waves (in blue) decreases closer to the source than that of low-frequency wave (in green).

Source: © Claire Samson.

natural frequency, which is the frequency at which the system vibrates when disturbed. When external forces are imposed on a system at exactly its natural frequency, the energy of these forcing functions are added to the system so that its vibrations are reinforced. Vibrations grow larger and larger, a wave phenomenon called **resonance** (Figure 4.23). As we will see later in this chapter, earthquake waves can induce resonances in earth materials and buildings with dramatic consequences.

BODY WAVES

When Earth shakes, it releases energy in **seismic waves** that pass through the whole body of the planet (**body waves**) and others that move near the surface only (**surface waves**).

Body waves are the fastest and are referred to as either primary or secondary waves. Body waves are most abundant at high frequencies of 0.5 to 20 Hz and are called short-period waves. These waves attenuate over

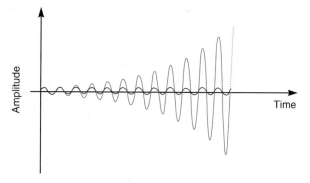

Figure 4.23

Resonance. When a mechanical system is disturbed by a forcing function (in blue) of frequency equal to its natural frequency, it starts to oscillate at progressively higher amplitudes.

Source: © Claire Samson.

short distances and are therefore most energetic close to the hypocentre/epicentre.

Primary Waves

The **primary (P) wave** (also known as the compressional wave) is the fastest and thus is the first to reach a seismograph station. P waves move in a push-pull fashion of alternating pulses of compression (push) and extension (pull) (Figure 4.24a). They travel through any material, be it solid, liquid, or gas. Their speed depends on the density and compressibility of the materials through which they pass. The greater the resistance to compression, the greater the speed of the seismic waves passing through packed atomic structures. Representative velocities for P waves are about 5.0 km/s in igneous rocks (e.g., granite) and 3.0 km/s in sedimentary rocks (e.g., sandstone). P waves in water slow to 1.5 km/s. Because P waves and sound waves are both compressional waves, they can travel through air. P waves may emerge from the ground, and if you are near the epicentre, you may be able to hear those P waves pulsing at around 15 Hz as low, thunderous noises. The arrival of P waves at your home or office is similar to a sonic boom with the rattling of windows.

Secondary Waves

The **secondary (S) wave** (also known as the shear wave) is the second wave to reach a seismograph station. S waves are transverse waves that propagate by shearing particles in their path at right angles to the direction of propagation in the vertical or horizontal plane (Figure 4.24b). S waves travel only through solids. On reaching liquid or gas, the S wave energy is reflected back into rock or is converted to another form. The velocity of an S wave depends on the density and resistance to shearing of materials. Liquids and gases do not have shear strength and thus cannot transmit S waves. Representative velocities for S waves in igneous and sedimentary rocks are about 3 km/s and 1.7 km/s, respectively. With their up-and-down and side-to-side motions, S waves shake the ground surface and can do severe damage to buildings.

SURFACE WAVES

Seismic waves that travel near the Earth's surface are of two main types—Love and Rayleigh waves. Both Love and Rayleigh waves are referred to as L waves (long waves) because they take longer periods of time to complete one cycle of motion and are the slowest moving. The frequencies of surface waves are low, typically between 0.005 and 0.1 Hz. Because of their low attenuation, surface waves carry significant amounts of energy long distances from the epicentre.

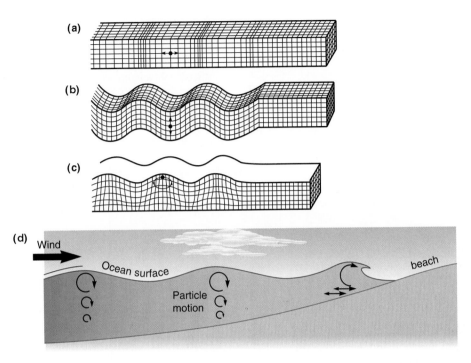

Figure 4.24
Types of seismic waves. (a) P waves move in a push-pull motion parallel to the direction of propagation. (b) S waves move in up-and-down or side-to-side motions perpendicular to the direction of propagation. (c) Rayleigh waves advance in a backward-rotating motion, as opposed to (d) wind-blown ocean waves, which cause water to move in forward-rotating circles.

Love waves were identified on seismograms and first explained by the British mathematician A. E. H. Love. Their side-to-side motion is similar to S waves propagating in a horizontal plane roughly parallel to the Earth's surface. Love waves generally travel faster than Rayleigh waves. Like S waves, they do not move through water or air.

Rayleigh waves were predicted to exist by Lord Rayleigh 20 years before they were actually recognized on seismograms. They advance in a backward-rotating, elliptical motion (Figure 4.24c) similar to the orbiting paths of water molecules in wind-blown waves of water, except that waves in water are forward-rotating (Figure 4.24d). The shaking produced by Rayleigh waves causes both vertical and horizontal movement. The rolling waves pass through both ground and water. The often-heard report that an earthquake feels like one is rocking in a boat at sea well describes the passage of Rayleigh waves.

Figure 4.25 is a three-component seismogram of a large earthquake recorded several thousands of kilometres from the epicentre. The P waves are recorded first, followed by S waves, and finally by the surface waves.

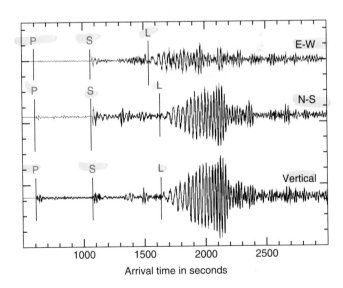

Figure 4.25
The El Salvador earthquake of 13 January 2001 (M_S of 7.8) recorded at Taloyoak, Nunavut. Letters P, S, and L indicate the arrival times of P, S, and surface waves, respectively.
Source: Natural Resources Canada.

In Greater Depth

Seismic Waves and the Earth's Interior

Large earthquakes generate body waves energetic enough to be recorded on seismographs all around the world. Analysis of the travel paths of the seismic waves gives us our models of the Earth's interior (Figure 4.26). The Earth is not homogeneous. Following the paths of P and S waves from the Earth's surface inward, there is an initial increase in velocity but then a marked slowing occurs at about 100 km depth; this is the top of the asthenosphere. Passing farther down through the mantle, the velocities generally increase until 2,890 km depth; there, the P waves slow markedly and the S waves disappear. This is the core–mantle boundary zone. The disappearance of S waves at the core–mantle boundary, due to their reflection or conversion to P waves, indicates that the outer core is mostly liquid. Moving into the core, P wave velocities gradually increase until a jump is reached at about 5,150 km depth, where S waves reappear. These observations suggest that the inner core is solid.

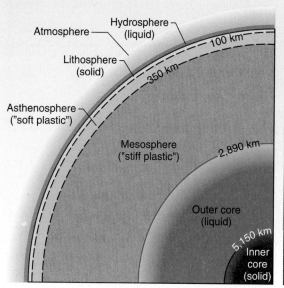

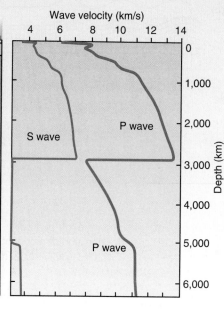

Figure 4.26 Varying velocities of P and S waves help define the internal structure of the Earth.

Note that the amplitudes of the higher-frequency P and S waves are more subdued that those of the surface waves because of stronger attenuation. With its large amplitude and long duration, the surface wavetrain can be particularly destructive.

Locating the Source of an Earthquake

P waves travel about 1.7 times faster than S waves. The method for determining the location of the source of an earthquake exploits the corollary that follows: the farther away from the earthquake origin, the greater is the difference in arrival times between P and S waves (Figure 4.27). Seismograms from three seismograph stations must be available. The method will be described step by step using as example the regional earthquake (magnitude 3.2) that occurred on 1 May 1992 and was recorded by stations Mont-Orford (MOQ), Manicouagan (MNQ), and James Bay (JAQ) in Quebec.

The first step is to determine the arrival times of the P and S waves on the seismograms and to calculate the difference between them (S – P). On Figure 4.28, this arrival time difference is 38 s for station MOQ, 50 s for station MNQ, and 115 s for station JAQ. The second step is to read the corresponding distances on the plot of arrival time versus epicentral distance (Figure 4.29). This yields epicentral distances of 300 km, 375 km, and 800 km for stations MOQ, MNQ and JAQ, respectively. The epicentre will be on the circumference of a circle drawn around each station. The radius of the circle is equal to the epicentral distance. The third and final step consists in plotting the circles on a map (Figure 4.30). The three circles all intersect each other at exactly one point—the epicentre of the earthquake, in this case La Malbaie, in Charlevoix, Quebec. Although located thousands of kilometres away from plate boundaries, the Charlevoix region has been the scene of several destructive earthquakes since the establishment

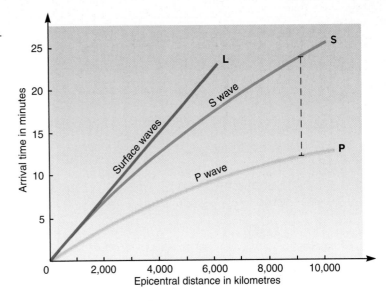

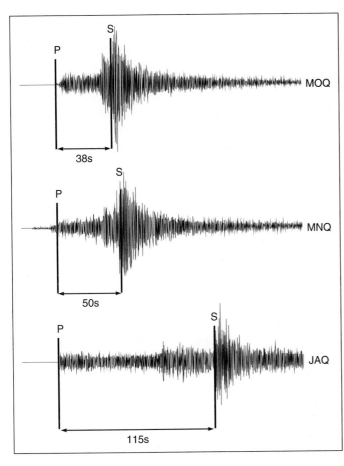

Figure 4.28
Seismograms of the regional 1 May 1992 earthquake (magnitude 3.2) recorded by stations MOQ, MNQ, and JAQ in Quebec.

of New France in the 17th century. We will explore this topic in more detail in the next chapter.

The difference in arrival times of P and S waves actually measures the distance from the seismograph station to the hypocentre of the earthquake, the site of initial fault movement (Figure 4.2). If the hypocentre is at the Earth's surface, then the hypocentre and epicentre are the same. However, if the hypocentre is deep below the surface, it will affect the arrival time of surface waves because these waves do not begin until P waves strike the Earth's surface. The depth to a hypocentre is best determined where an array of seismometers is nearby, thus allowing careful analysis of P wave arrival times.

Magnitude of Earthquakes

Magnitude is an estimate of the relative size or energy release of an earthquake. It is commonly measured from the amplitude of seismic waves on a seismogram.

RICHTER SCALE

Several systems are available to assess the magnitudes of earthquakes. The best-known scheme is the Richter scale. In 1935, Charles Richter of the California Institute of Technology devised a quantitative scheme to describe the magnitude of Californian earthquakes, that is, of events with shallow hypocentres that are located less than 500 km from the seismometers. Richter based his scale on the idea that the bigger the earthquake, the greater the shaking of the Earth and thus the greater the amplitude (swing) of the lines made on the seismogram. To standardize this relationship, he defined magnitude as

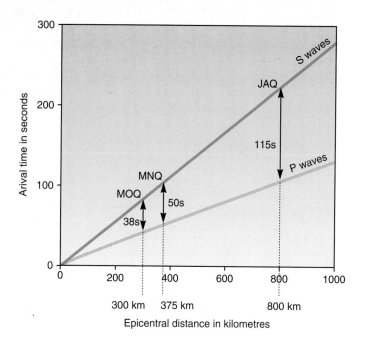

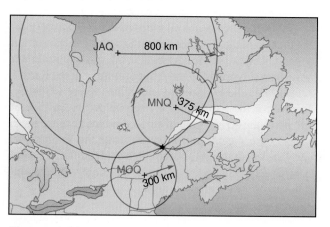

Figure 4.30
Location of the epicentre of the 1 May 1992 earthquake by triangulation. The three circles intersect uniquely at La Malbaie, Quebec.
Source: © Claire Samson.

the logarithm to the base ten of the maximum seismic wave amplitude (in thousandths of a millimetre) recorded on a standard seismograph at a distance of 100 kilometres from the earthquake centre.

Since not all seismometers sit 100 km from the epicentre, corrections are made for distance. Richter assigned simple, whole numbers to describe magnitudes; for every tenfold increase in the amplitude of the recorded seismic wave, the Richter magnitude increases one number, for example, from 4 to 5. The energy released by earthquakes increases even more rapidly than the tenfold increase in amplitude of the seismic wave trace. For example, if the amplitude of the seismic waves increased 10,000 times

$(10 \times 10 \times 10 \times 10)$, the Richter magnitude would move up from a 4 to an 8. However, the energy release from magnitude 4 to 8 increases by 2,800,000 times (Table 4.2).

What does this increase mean in everyday terms? If you feel a magnitude 4 earthquake while sitting at your dinner table, and then a magnitude 8 comes along while you are still at the table, would you really be shaken 2,800,000 times as hard? No. The greater energy of the magnitude 8 earthquake would be spread out over a much larger area, and the magnitude 8 event would dissipate its energy over a time interval about 20 times longer (e.g., 60 seconds as opposed to 3 seconds, as shown in Table 4.3). The actual shaking in earthquakes above magnitude 6 does not increase very much more (maybe three times more for each step up in magnitude). *In effect, the bigger earthquake means that more people in a larger area and for a longer time will experience the intense shaking.*

Computing a Richter magnitude for an earthquake is quickly done, and this is one of the reasons for its great

Table 4.2	
Energy of Richter Scale Earthquakes	
Richter Magnitude	**Energy Compared to Magnitude 4**
4	1
5	48
6	2,050
7	80,500
8	2,800,000

Table 4.3

Magnitude versus Duration of Shaking

Richter Magnitude	Duration of Strong Ground Shaking in Seconds
8–8.9	30 to 90
7–7.9	20 to 50
6–6.9	10 to 30
5–5.9	2 to 15
4–4.9	0 to 5

popularity with the deadline-conscious print and electronic media. Upon learning of an earthquake, usually by phone calls from reporters, one can rapidly measure (1) the amplitude of the seismic waves and (2) the difference in arrival times of P and S waves. Figure 4.31 has reduced Richter's equation to a nomograph, which allows easy determination of magnitude. Take a couple of minutes to determine the magnitude of the earthquake whose seismogram is printed above the nomograph.

Each year, the Earth is shaken by millions of quakes that are recorded on seismometers (Table 4.4). Most are below magnitude 2.5, which is the threshold for detection by humans (you can replicate the feeling of a magnitude 2 "earthquake" by stamping your foot on the floor!). Notice the distinctive "pyramidal" distribution of earthquakes by size, an illustration of the general trend described in Chapter 1—the smaller the magnitude, the higher the

Table 4.4

Earthquakes in the World Each Year

Magnitude	Number of Quakes Per Year	Description
8.5 and up	0.3	
8–8.4	1	Great
7.5–7.9	3	
7–7.4	15	Major
6.6–6.9	56	
6–6.5	210	Strong (destructive)
5–5.9	800	Moderate (damaging)
4–4.9	6,200	Light
3–3.9	49,000	Minor
2–2.9	350,000	Very minor
0–1.9	3,000,000	

frequency. The fewer than 20 major and great earthquakes (magnitudes of 7 and higher) each year account for more than 90% of the energy released by earthquakes. At the upper end of the magnitude scale, the energy increases are so great that more energy is released going from magnitude 8.9 to 9 than from magnitude 1 to 8. These facts underscore the logarithmic nature of the Richter scale; each step up the scale has major significance.

OTHER MEASURES OF EARTHQUAKE SIZE

Although the Richter scale is useful for assessing moderate-size earthquakes that occur nearby, it uses waves with frequencies between 0.5 to 10 Hz that saturate for distant or truly large earthquakes. These waves do not become more intense as an earthquake becomes larger. For example, the Richter scale assesses the 1906 San Francisco earthquake and the 1964 Alaska earthquake as both being of magnitude 8.3. However, using other scales, the San Francisco earthquake is a magnitude 7.8 and the Alaska seism is a 9.2. The Alaska earthquake was at least 100 times bigger in terms of energy.

The Richter scale is now restricted to measuring only local earthquakes with moderate magnitudes (noted as M_L [magnitude—local]). Because earthquakes generate both body waves that travel through the Earth and surface waves that follow the Earth's uppermost layers, two other magnitude scales have long been used: m_b and M_s. The body wave (m_b) scale uses amplitudes of P waves with frequencies between 0.1 and 10 Hz, whereas the surface wave scale (M_s) uses Rayleigh waves with frequencies on the order of 0.05 Hz. Early on, all magnitude scales were considered to be equivalent, but now we know that earthquakes generate different proportions of energy at different frequencies. For example, larger earthquakes with their larger fault-rupture surfaces radiate more of their energy in lower-frequency seismic waves. Thus, for major and great earthquakes, body wave magnitudes (m_b) will significantly underestimate the actual size of the earthquake. Even a composite of these three methods of determining earthquake magnitude (M_L, m_b, and M_s) does not necessarily yield the true size of an earthquake.

Moment Magnitude Scale

Fault-rupture length greatly influences earthquake magnitude (Table 4.5). In an effort to more accurately determine earthquake size, seismologists have developed alternative measures based on parameters describing fault rupture. The seismic moment (M_0) relies on the amount of movement along the fault that generated the earthquake; that is, M_0 equals the shear strength of the rock times the rupture area of the fault times the average displacement (slip) on the fault. Moment is a more reliable measure of earthquake size; it measures the amount of strain energy released by the movement along the whole

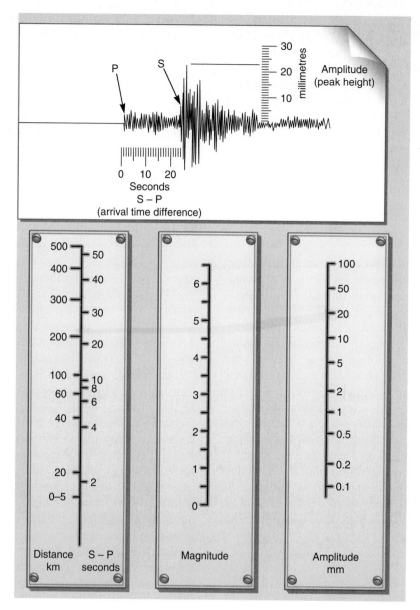

Figure 4.31

Nomograph of the Richter scale allowing earthquake magnitudes to be estimated. On the seismogram, read the difference in arrival times of P and S waves in seconds and plot the value on the left column of the nomograph. Next read the amplitude of the peak height of the S wave and plot this value on the right column. Draw a line between the two marked values, and it will pass through the earthquake magnitude on the centre column. Check your answer in the Questions for review at the end of the chapter.

Table 4.5

Fault-Rupture Length and Magnitude

Rupture Length (km)	Magnitude
0.1	4
1	5
10	6
100	7

rupture surface. Seismic moment has been incorporated into a new earthquake magnitude scale by Hiroo Kanamori, the moment magnitude scale (M_w), where

$$M_w = 2/3 \log_{10}(M_0) - 6$$

The moment magnitude scale is used for big earthquakes. It is more accurate because it is tied directly to physical parameters such as fault-rupture area, fault slip, and energy release.

The three largest moment magnitudes calculated to date are the 1960 Chile earthquake (M_s of 8.5; M_w of 9.5),

1964 Alaska earthquake (M_s of 8.3; M_w of 9.2), and the 2004 Sumatra event (M_s of 8.8; M_w of 9.2 to 9.3). These gigantic earthquakes occurred at subduction zones and triggered deadly tsunami. A variety of energetic events are placed on a scale for comparison in Figure 4.32. The structures of the San Francisco City Hall after the 1906 earthquake and of the Gembaku Dome destroyed by the atomic bomb over Hiroshima in 1945 bear an eerie resemblance (Figures 4.33 and 4.34). The seism, however, generated more than 100 times the amount of energy released by the bomb.

FAULT-RUPTURE LENGTH AND SEISMIC-WAVE FREQUENCIES

Fault-rupture lengths and durations also affect the frequencies of seismic waves produced during earthquakes. Faults that move for short distances and short times

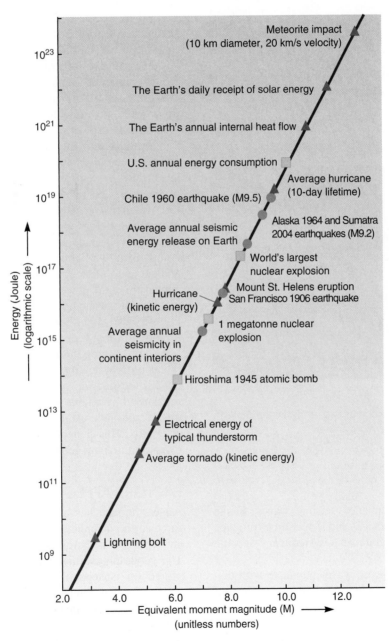

Figure 4.32
Equivalent moment magnitude of a variety of seismic (green dots), human-made (yellow squares), and other phenomena (red triangles).
Source: © A. C. Johnston, US Geological Survey.

Figure 4.33
The San Francisco City Hall two days after the devastating earthquake of 18 April 1906.
Source: Walter Curran Mendenhall.

Figure 4.34
The Gembaku Dome of Hiroshima, Japan, destroyed in 1945 by the first atomic bomb used in warfare.
Courtesy of Tanya Zminkowski.

generate mostly high-frequency seismic waves. Faults that rupture for longer distances and longer times produce increasingly greater amounts of low-frequency seismic waves.

The amplitude of seismic waves attenuate with distance travelled. High-frequency seismic waves die out first—at shorter distances from the hypocentre. Low-frequency seismic waves carry significant amounts of energy farther—through longer distances. High-frequency seismic waves cause much damage at short distances from the epicentre. But at longer distances, it is the low-frequency seismic waves that do most of the damage.

Earthquake Intensity—What We Feel During an Earthquake

During the tens of seconds that a large earthquake lasts, we feel ourselves rocked up and down and shaken from side to side. It is an emotional experience, and the drama of our accounts varies according to our locations during the shaking and our personalities. But for personal narratives to have meaning that can be passed on to succeeding generations, common threads are needed to bind the accounts together. In the late 1800s, descriptive schemes appeared that were based on the intensity of effects experienced by people and buildings. The most widely used scale came from the Italian professor Giuseppi Mercalli in 1902; it was modified by Charles Richter in 1956. The scale has 12 divisions of increasing intensity labelled by Roman numerals (Table 4.6). Mercalli intensities are crucial for assessing magnitudes of historical events before there were instrumented records, thus allowing us to assess the return period between major earthquakes.

Earthquake magnitude scales are used to assess the energy released during an earthquake; earthquake intensity scales assess the effects on people and buildings (Table 4.7). As elegantly phrased by Simon Winchester: "Intensity requires an audience; magnitude requires only the divining powers of machines." The difference between magnitude and intensity can be illuminated by comparison to a light bulb. The wattage of a light bulb is analogous to the magnitude of an earthquake. Wattage is a measure of the power of a light bulb, and magnitude is a measure of the energy released during an earthquake. The intensity of a light bulb and that of an earthquake have in common that they decrease away from the source. A light bulb shining in the corner of a room provides high-intensity light nearby, but the intensity of light decreases toward the far side of the room. The intensity of shaking caused by a fault movement is great near the epicentre, but, in general, it decreases with distance from the epicentre. This generalization is offset by variations in regional and local geology, and building styles.

FACTORS AFFECTING THE MERCALLI SCALE

An earthquake has a unique value of magnitude. The same earthquake, however, has different effects in different areas and is therefore assigned a range of intensities. The geographical distribution of intensities is often presented on **isoseismal maps** where contours outlining areas of equal intensity are drawn (Figure 4.35). The largest contour delineates the **felt area,** the surface over which the earthquake was felt by people.

For a given earthquake, the Mercalli intensity at a given location depends on several factors: (1) earthquake magnitude; (2) epicentre location; (3) distance from the epicentre; (4) hypocentre depth; (5) duration of shaking;

Table 4.6

Modified Mercalli Scale of Earthquake Intensity

I Not felt except by a very few people under especially favourable circumstances.

II Felt by only a few people at rest, especially those on upper floors of buildings or those with a very sensitive nature. Delicately suspended objects may swing.

III Felt quite noticeably indoors, especially on upper floors, but many people do not recognize it as an earthquake. Vibrations are like those from the passing of light trucks. Standing automobiles may rock slightly. Duration of shaking may be estimated.

IV Felt indoors during the day by many people, outdoors by few. Light sleepers may be awakened. Vibrations are like those from the passing of heavy trucks or as if a heavy object struck the building. Standing automobiles rock. Windows, dishes, and doors rattle; glassware and crockery clink and clash. In the upper range of IV, wooden walls and frames creak.

V Felt indoors by nearly everyone, outdoors by many or most. Awakens many. Frightens many; some run outdoors. Some broken dishes, glassware, and windows. Minor cracking of plaster. Moves small objects, spills liquids, rings small bells, and sways tall objects. Pendulum clocks misbehave.

VI Felt by all; many frightened and run outdoors. Excitement is general. Dishes, glassware, and windows break in considerable quantities. Knick-knacks, books, and pictures fall. Furniture moves or overturns. Weak plaster walls and some brick walls crack. Damage is slight.

VII Frightens all; difficult to stand. Noticed by drivers of automobiles. Large bells ring. Damage negligible in buildings of good design and construction, slight to moderate in well-built ordinary buildings, considerable in badly designed or poorly built buildings, adobe houses, and old walls. Numerous windows and some chimneys break. Small landslides and caving of sand and gravel banks occur. Waves on ponds; water becomes turbid.

VIII Fright is general and alarm approaches panic. Disturbs drivers of automobiles. Heavy furniture overturns. Damage slight in specially designed structures; considerable in ordinary substantial buildings, including partial collapses. Frame houses move off foundations if not bolted down. Most walls, chimneys, towers, and monuments fall. Spring flow and well-water levels change. Cracks appear in wet ground and on slopes.

IX General panic. Damage considerable in masonry structures, even those built to withstand earthquakes. Well-built frame houses thrown out of plumb. Ground cracks conspicuously. Underground pipes break. In soft-sediment areas, sand and mud are ejected from ground in fountains and leave craters.

X Most masonry structures are destroyed. Some well-built wooden structures and bridges fail. Ground cracks badly with serious damage to dams and embankments. Large landslides occur on riverbanks and steep slopes. Railroad tracks bend slightly.

XI Few, if any, masonry structures remain standing. Great damage to dams and embankments, commonly over great distances. Supporting piers of large bridges fail. Broad fissures, Earth slumps and slips in soft, wet ground. Underground pipelines completely out of service. Railroad tracks bend greatly.

XII Damage nearly total. Ground surfaces seen to move in waves. Lines of sight and level distort. Objects thrown up in air.

Table 4.7

Comparison of Magnitude, Intensity, and Acceleration

Magnitude		Mercalli Intensity	Acceleration (g)
2 and less	I–II	Usually not felt by people	less than 0.002
3	III	Felt indoors by some people	0.002–0.004
4	IV–V	Felt by most people	0.005–0.019
5	VI–VII	Felt by all; building damage	0.02–0.09
6	VII–VIII	People scared; moderate damage	0.10–0.19
7	IX–X	Major damage	0.20–0.99
8 and up	XI–XII	Damage nearly total	over 1 g

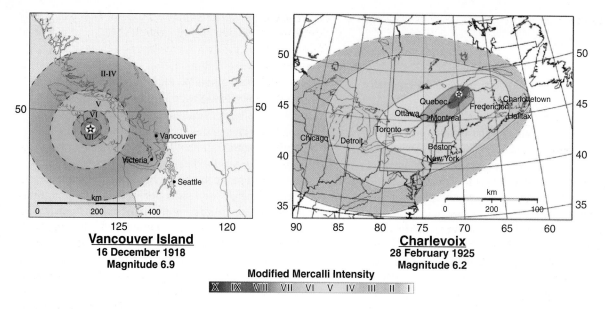

Figure 4.35

Isoseismal maps of the 1918 Vancouver Island and 1925 Charlevoix earthquakes plotted at the same scale.

Source: Natural Resources Canada.

(6) foundation materials; and (7) building style—design, kind of building materials, height. These factors need to be considered in assessing the earthquake threat to any region and even to each specific building.

Earthquake Magnitude

The relation between magnitude and intensity is obvious—the more energy released during an earthquake, the higher the odds for death and damage.

Epicentre Location

Similarly, the relation between epicentre location and intensity is straightforward—densely populated areas are especially vulnerable to fatalities and damage.

Distance from Epicentre

The relation between distance and damage also seems obvious—the closer to the hypocentre/epicentre, the greater the damage. But this is not always the case, as regional geology plays an important role in the spatial distribution of intensities. Consider the isoseismal map of the 1925 Charlevoix earthquake (Figure 4.35). Contours of equal intensity are not concentric circles centred on the epicentre. They are ellipses oriented northeast-southwest in the direction of the St. Lawrence River Valley and the contact between the Canadian Precambrian Shield and the Appalachians. The earthquake was felt with greater intensity (VII) in Montreal, 400 km away from the epicentre in a direction parallel to the geological trend, than in Fredericton (V–VI), 325 km away in a direction perpendicular to the trend. An interesting comparison is

between the 1925 Charlevoix earthquake and the 1918 Vancouver Island earthquake, both seisms of roughly equal magnitude (Figure 4.35). Seismic waves travel efficiently through the rock of the continental interior of eastern North America and carry energy far away from the epicentre. On the other hand, seismic waves travelling through the pervasive fractures and faults of the Canadian cordillera are rapidly attenuated, resulting in a much smaller felt area.

Hypocentre Depth

Seismic waves from shallow hypocentres will induce more violent ground shaking than those originating from great depths, the latter having been significantly attenuated before reaching the Earth's surface. In the previous chapter, we noted that subduction zones are characterized by a wide range of hypocentre depths (Figure 3.13). Shallow earthquakes occurring at the contact between the overriding and down-going plates are of major concern. These earthquakes, termed "**megathrust earthquakes**" both release enormous amounts of energy (large magnitude) and cause widespread destruction in developed areas (high intensity). Eleven of Earth's twelve largest earthquakes listed in Table 3.2 were megathrust earthquakes.

Duration of Shaking

The duration of shaking is underappreciated as a significant factor in damages suffered and lives lost. Consider the shaking times in Table 4.3. For example, if a magnitude 7 earthquake shakes vigorously for 50 seconds, rather than 20, the increase in damages and lives lost can be enormous.

Foundation Materials

Like other mechanical systems, earth materials have a characteristic natural frequency. Hard rock typically vibrates at frequencies higher than 1 Hz. Soft sediments, such as clay or loosely compacted sand, vibrate at frequencies lower than 1 Hz. Their natural frequency is controlled by their thickness: the greater the accumulation of sediments, the lower the natural frequency. During an earthquake, seismic waves act as forcing functions on earth materials. Hard rock foundations are likely to be excited by energetic P and S waves because their frequencies overlap. Soft or water-saturated sediments, with their lower natural frequency, will tend to have their shaking amplified by surface waves.

How strong is the amplification effect? The velocity of a seismic wave depends on the type of rock the wave is travelling through. Seismic waves move faster through hard rock and slower through softer rock and loose sediment. When seismic waves pass from harder rock into softer rock, they slow and thus must increase their amplitude to carry the same amount of energy. Shaking tends to be stronger at sites with softer sediments because seismic waves move more slowly and with greater amplitude. Figure 4.36 shows ground acceleration at four sites in Ottawa, Ontario, during the 2005 Charlevoix, Quebec earthquake (magnitude 4.7) whose epicentre was located 525 km away. Note how seismic waves are preferentially amplified at sites with a thick soil cover.

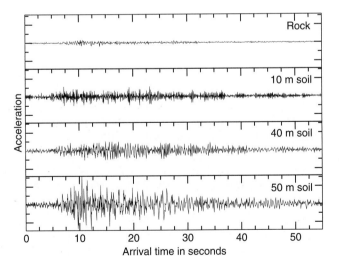

Figure 4.36
Ground acceleration caused by the Charlevoix earthquake of 6 March 2005 recorded at four sites with different foundation materials in Ottawa, Ontario.

Reproduced with the permission of Natural Resources Canada 2008, courtesy of the Canadian Hazards Information Service. http://earthquakescanada.nrcan .gc.ca/hazard/2007/9CCEE/9CCEE_Adams_p1162.pdf.

The case of water-saturated sediments is especially problematic. Under strong ground shaking, the bonds between the sediment grains break and the particles become literally suspended in water. The sediments liquefy and lose strength, leaving unsupported buildings to sink (see In Greater Depth box: Liquefaction).

Building Style

The building style—notably height, construction material, and architecture—is of vital importance.

The concept of natural frequency also applies to buildings. Typical frequencies of swaying for buildings are about 10 Hz divided by the number of storeys. The one-storey bungalow shakes back and forth quickly at about 10 Hz. The 30-storey high-rise building sways much more slowy at a frequency of about 0.3 Hz. The natural frequencies of building are also affected by their construction materials. A building of a given height and architectural style will have a lower frequency if it was built with flexible materials such as wood or steel, or a higher frequency if it was constructed of stiff materials such as brick and concrete.

Buildings have natural frequencies in the same range as seismic waves. The resonance induced by this overlap of frequencies is a common cause of the catastrophic failure of buildings during earthquakes. High-frequency P and S waves will have their vibrations amplified by rigid construction materials and short buildings. Low-frequency surface waves will have their movements increased in tall buildings with low frequencies of vibration. If these tall buildings also lie on soft, water-saturated sand or mud, then disaster may strike.

In his book *Perils of a Restless Planet,* author Ernest Zebrowski draws an interesting comparison between the 1906 San Francisco and the 1908 Messina, Sicily, earthquakes. Both seisms had similar Richter magnitudes (8.3 versus 7.5) and affected societies at the same stage of scientific knowledge and technological development. Although Messina did not experience the ensuing fires, the death toll in the Sicilian city reached 83,000 people, corresponding to a mere 45% survival rate, whereas the survival rate was close to 99% in San Francisco. What happened? Both earthquakes struck in the early morning hours, catching people in their sleep. In Messina, houses were predominantly masonry, with massive stone floors and brick-tile roofs supported by timber set into niches in granite walls. These stiff buildings failed abruptly, crushing people to death. In San Francisco, on the other hand, most homes were small, flexible wooden-frame buildings that swayed during the earthquake and remained relatively intact.

A recent example combining the effects of foundation materials and building style concerns damage to buildings in San Francisco's Marina District inflicted by the 1989 Loma Prieta earthquake, mainly due to (1) amplified shaking, (2) deformation and liquefaction of artificial-fill foundations, and (3) architectural

In Greater Depth

Liquefaction

Liquefaction is a phenomenon in which the behaviour of saturated soils and poorly consolidated sediments transforms from that of a solid material to a liquid.

Soils are a loose assemblage of solid particles with the space between them filled by air and water in various proportions. In saturated soils, all the space between particles is occupied by water. When saturated soils are disturbed—by strong earthquake shaking or rapid loading with excess weight, for example—the particles attempt to move closer to one another but are prevented from doing so by the water trapped between them. Water pressure builds up, which weakens the bonds between particles. Pressure may become so high that many of the soil particles lose contact with each other and become literally free to float in water (Figure 4.37). Under such circumstances, soils lose strength and stiffness, and therefore the ability to support loads. An extreme example occurred during the 1964 Niigata, Japan earthquake. A group of apartment buildings founded on saturated soil sank and tilted severely. Remarkably, they suffered little structural damage (Figure 4.38). Liquefied sediments in the subsurface can also trigger spectacular mass movements in which rafts of earth materials move downslope like floating pieces of ice on a river (Figure 9.31).

Susceptibility to liquefaction depends on soil characteristics and the depth to the water table. This information is often summarized on the form of a regional liquefaction hazard map like that of Victoria, British Columbia, in Figure 4.39.

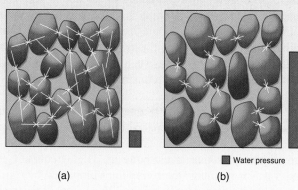

(a)   (b)

■ Water pressure

Figure 4.37 (a) Saturated soil. The length of the arrows represents the size of the binding forces between individual solid particles. The forces are large when water pressure is low. (b) Liquefied soil. Binding forces are weaker due to the increased water pressure.

Sources: J. Johansson, Department of Civil Engineering, University of Washington, 2000.

Figure 4.38 Soil liquefied under the foundations of several apartment buildings in Niigata, Japan, during the 16 June 1964 earthquake (magnitude 7.5).

Source: Courtesy of the National Service for Earthquake Engineering EERC, University of California, Berkeley.

modifications. Much of the Marina District is built on artificial fill dumped onto the wetlands of San Francisco Bay to create more land for development. Ironically, much of the artificial fill is the debris from the buildings ruined by the 1906 earthquake. Seismic waves in 1989 were amplified in this artificial fill. Some fill underwent permanent deformation and settling, and some formed **slurries** as underground water and loose sediment flowed as fluids in the process of liquefaction (Figure 4.40a). The central cause of building failure, however, was design flaws. Because the Marina District is home to many affluent people, they need places to park their cars. But where? The streets are already overcrowded, and basement parking garages would be below sea level and thus flooded. A common solution has been to clear obstructions from first storeys of buildings to make space for car parking. Where are the internal walls, lateral supports, and brac-

ing needed to support the upper one to four storeys? They were removed or sacrificed to make room for cars; thus, during the earthquake, buildings simply pancaked and became one storey shorter (Figure 4.40b).

Mexico City, 1985

On Thursday morning, 19 September 1985, most of the 18 million residents of Mexico City were at home, having their morning meals. At 7:17 a.m., a monstrous earthquake broke loose some 350 km away. Seismic waves travelled far to deal destructive blows to many of the 6- to 16-storey buildings that are heavily occupied during the working day (Figure 4.41). Building collapses killed about 9,000 people.

What caused this earthquake? The Cocos plate made one of its all-too-frequent downward movements. This time, a 200 km long front, inclined 18° east, thrust

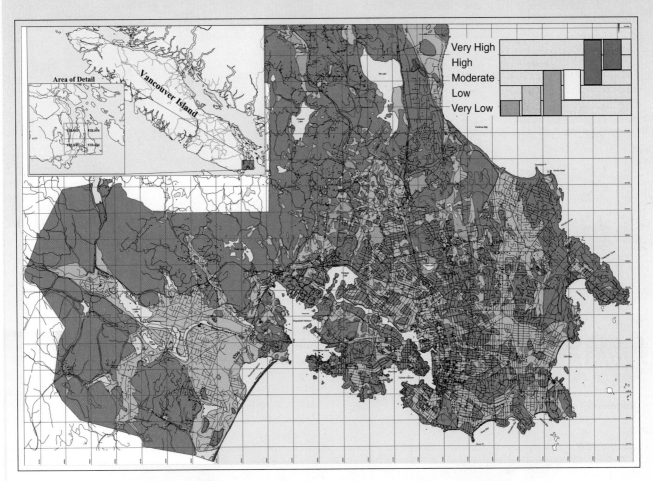

Figure 4.39 Liquefaction hazard map of Victoria, British Columbia. Liquefaction potential is greatest in geologically young beach sand and peat, and in artificial fills.

downward and eastward about 2.3 m in two distinct jerks about 26 seconds apart (Figure 4.42). The mainshock had a surface wave magnitude (M_S) of 8.1. It was followed on 21 September by a 7.5 M_S aftershock and another on 25 October of 7.3 M_S. The earthquakes were not a surprise to seismologists. Before these seisms occurred, the area was called the Michoacan seismic gap, and many instruments had been deployed in the region to measure the expected big event. As Figure 4.42 shows, another large seismic gap waits to be filled by a major movement of the Cocos plate. The Guerrero seismic gap lies near Acapulco and is closer to Mexico City than the Michoacan epicentre.

Many of the coastal towns near the epicentre received relatively small amounts of damage. Yet in Mexico City, over 5,700 buildings were severely dam-aged, with 15% of them collapsing catastrophically. Why did so many buildings collapse and kill so many people when Mexico City lies 350 km from the epicen-tre? It was largely due to resonance between seismic waves, soft lake-sediment foundations, and improperly designed buildings. In addition, the duration of shak-ing was increased due to seismic energy being trapped within the soft sediments.

Mexico City is built atop the former Aztec capital of Tenochtitlan. The Aztecs built where they saw the favour-able omen—an eagle sitting on a cactus and holding a writhing snake in its mouth. The site was Lake Texcoco, a broad lake surrounded by hard volcanic rock. Over time, the lake basin was partially filled with soft, water-saturated clays. Portions of Lake Texcoco have been drained, and

Magnified   **Magnified**

(a)

Figure 4.40

(a) Water-saturated sediment usually rests quietly. However, when seismic waves shake, sand grains and water can form a slurry and flow as a liquid. When earth materials liquefy, building foundations may split and buildings may fail. (b) A typical Marina District building collapse. Three residential storeys sat above a soft first storey used for car parking; now, the four-storey building is three storeys tall.

Drawing and photo: © Dames and Moore.

Figure 4.41

This 15-storey building collapsed during the 1985 Mexico City earthquake, crushing all its occupants as its concrete floors pancaked.

Photo: © M. Celebi, US Geological Survey.

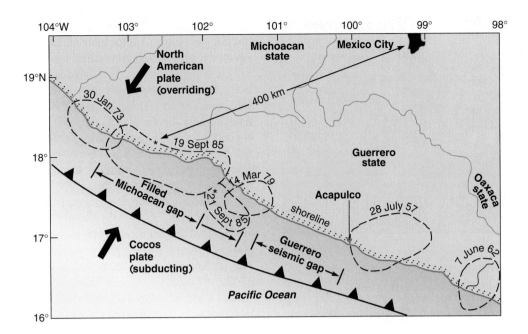

Figure 4.42
Map of coastal Mexico showing dates of earthquakes and fault areas moved (dashed lines) during Cocos plate subduction events. The Michoacan seismic gap was filled by the 1985 seisms. The Guerrero seismic gap is overdue for a major movement.

large buildings have been constructed on the weak, lake-floor sediments.

Building damages were the greatest and the number of deaths the highest where three factors combined and created resonance: (1) the earthquakes sent a tremendous amount of energy in seismic waves in the 1- to 2-Hz frequency band; (2) the areas underlain by thick, soft clays vibrating at 1 to 2 Hz frequencies amplified the seismic waves; and (3) buildings of 6 to 16 storeys vibrated in the 1 to 2 Hz frequency band. Where all three factors were in place, disaster struck. There were design flaws in the failed buildings (Figure 4.43), including soft first storeys, poorly joined building wings, odd-shaped buildings prone to twist on their foundations, and buildings of different heights and vibration frequencies that sat close together and bumped into each other during the earthquake (Figures 4.43c and 4.44).

Building in Earthquake Country

What causes the deaths during earthquakes? Not the shaking of the Earth but our buildings, bridges, and other structures that collapse and fall on us. **Earthquakes don't kill, buildings do.** What can be done to mitigate the risk?

DESIGN CHALLENGES
Ground Motion
Seismic waves radiate outward from a fault movement. The interactions among the various seismic waves move the

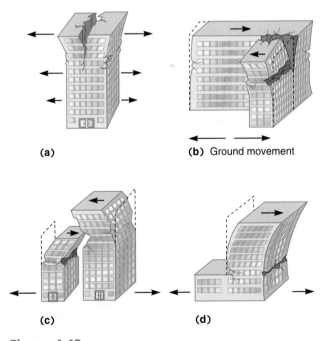

Figure 4.43
Some building-response problems during the Mexico City earthquake. (a) The amplitude of shaking increases up the building. (b) Buildings with long axes perpendicular to ground motion suffer more shaking. (c) Buildings with different heights sway at different frequencies and bang into each other. (d) A building with different heights tends to break apart.

Figure 4.44
Mexico City earthquake damage caused by constructing buildings with different periods of vibration next to each other. The four-storey building on left repeatedly struck the taller Hotel de Carlo (middle building), causing collapse of its middle floors (Figure 4.43c). The taller building on right also was damaged by hammering from the Hotel de Carlo.
Photo: © NOAA.

ground both vertically and horizontally. Buildings usually are designed to handle the large vertical forces caused by the weight of the building and its contents. They are designed with such large factors of safety that the additional vertical forces imparted by earthquakes are typically not a problem. Usually, the biggest concern in designing buildings to withstand large earthquakes is the sideways push from the horizontal components of movement (Figure 4.45).

Acceleration

Building design in earthquake areas must account for **acceleration** (Table 4.7). As seismic waves move the

Figure 4.45
Inadequately braced house failed due to horizontal acceleration during the 1971 San Fernando, California, earthquake.
Photo: © Al Boost.

ground and buildings up and down, and back and forth, the rate of change of velocity is measured as acceleration. As an analogy, when your car is moving at a velocity of 40 km/h on a smooth road, you feel no force on your body. But if you stomp on the car's accelerator and rapidly speed up to 100 km/h, you feel a force pushing you back against the car's seat. Following the same thought, if you hit the brakes and decelerate rapidly, you feel yourself being thrown forward. This same type of accelerative force is imparted to buildings when the ground beneath them moves during an earthquake.

Continuing the analogy further, if you hold your arm upright in front of you and wave it back and forth, you create rapid acceleration and high velocity, but no damage is done because the weight of your arm is small and the inertial forces are low. However, because force is acceleration times mass, if a building weighing thousands of tonnes is subjected to the same acceleration, the acceleration produces large inertial forces that are difficult for the building to withstand. If these forces last long enough, the building may fail.

The usual measure of acceleration is that of a free-falling body pulled by gravity; it is the same for all objects, regardless of their weight. The acceleration due to gravity is 9.8 m/s^2, which is referred to as 1.0 g and is used as a comparative unit of measure. Weak buildings begin to suffer damage at horizontal accelerations of about 0.1 g. At accelerations between 0.1 to 0.2 g, people have trouble keeping their footing, similar to being in the corridor of a fast-moving train or on a small boat in high seas. As an example, buildings in the Vancouver, British Columbia, area are typically designed to tolerate a 0.4 g acceleration. A building able to withstand a sideward pushing force equal to 40% of its own weight is considered earthquake resistant.

Stress

Different building materials respond differently to the stresses imposed on them during an earthquake. Wood is flexible and lightweight, and tends to deform elastically (Figure 2.14a). As stated earlier, these properties saved lives in the 1906 San Francisco earthquake. Steel has ductility and great strength when subjected to tension, but steel columns fail under excess compression (Figure 2.14b). Conversely, masonry and concrete resist well compressional stresses but suffer brittle failure all too easily under tension (Figure 2.14c).

ARCHITECTURAL SOLUTIONS

One of the problems in designing buildings for earthquake country is the need to eliminate the occurrence of resonance. How can this be done? (1) Change the height of the building; (2) move most of the weight to the lower floors; (3) change the shape of the building; (4) change

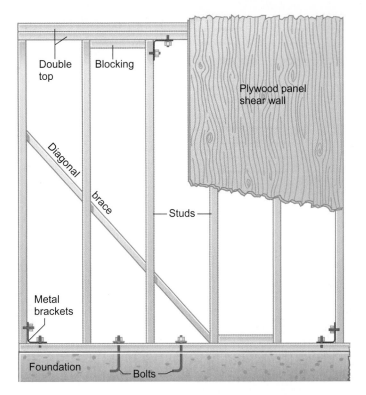

Figure 4.46
How can a house be built to resist seismic waves? Bolt it. Bracket it. Brace it. Block it. Panel it.

the type of building materials; and (5) change the degree of attachment of the building to its foundation. For example, if the earth foundation is hard rock that efficiently transmits high-frequency vibrations, then build a flexible, taller building. Or if the earth foundation is a thick mass of soft sediment likely to couple with low-frequency shaking, then build a stiffer, shorter building.

Ground motion during an earthquake is horizontal, vertical, and diagonal—all at the same time. The building components that must handle ground motion are basic. In the horizontal plane are floors and roofs. In the vertical plane are walls and frames. Modern one and two-storey wood-frame houses typically perform well during seismic shaking as wood is able to handle large accelerations. The ability to withstand Earth movements is enhanced by building shear walls, bracing, and other elements that tie the walls, foundation, and roof together so they do not separate and fail (Figure 4.46).

The process of reinforcing existing buildings to increase their resistance to seismic shaking is known as **retrofitting.** Looking at some newly designed structures and building retrofits allows us to see how seismic strength is given to a building (Figure 4.47).

Braced Frames

Bracing is an effective way to impart seismic resistance to a structure. The bracing gives strength to a building and offers resistance to the up, down, and sideways movements of the ground (Figure 4.48). The bracing should be made of ductile materials that have the ability to deform without rupturing.

Shear Walls

Walls that are designed to receive horizontal forces from floors and roofs and transmit them to the ground are called shear walls. In a building, shear walls must be strong themselves, as well as securely connected to each other and to the horizontal elements. In a simple building, seismic energy moves the ground, producing inertial forces that move the horizontal elements. This movement is resisted by the shear walls, and the forces are transmitted back to the ground.

A "house of cards" is a shear-wall structure, although each "wall" does not have much strength. The walls must be at right angles and preferably in a simple pattern (Figure 4.49). The house of cards is made enormously stronger if horizontal and vertical elements are all securely fastened; for example, by taping them together.

A structure commonly built with insufficient shear walls is the multi-storey parking garage. Builders do not want the added expense of more walls, which then eliminate parking spaces and block the view of traffic inside the parking structure. These buildings are common casualties during earthquakes.

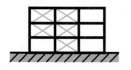
(a) Brace it.

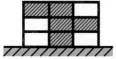
(b) Infill it.

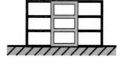
(c) Frame it.

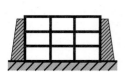
(d) Buttress it.

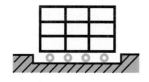
(e) Isolate it.

Figure 4.47
How to strengthen buildings. (a) Add braces. (b) Infill walls. (c) Add frames to exterior or interior. (d) Add buttresses. (e) Isolate building from the ground.
Source: © AIA/ACSA Council on Architectural Research.

Figure 4.48
A six-story building with a braced frame incorporated in its design.
Photo: © Pat Abbott.

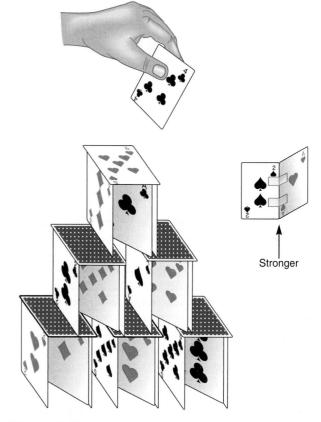

Stronger

Figure 4.49
A "house of cards" is a structure with walls and floors but no strength. Earthquake resistance is greatly increased by tying the walls and floors together with tape.
Source: Federal Emergency Management Agency.

Base Isolation

Some modern designs employ **base isolation** where devices are placed on the ground or within the structure to absorb part of the earthquake energy. Base isolation uses wheels, ball bearings, shock absorbers, "rubber doughnuts," rubber and steel sandwiches, and other creative designs to isolate a building from the worst of the shaking (Figure 4.50). The goal is to make the building react to shaking much like your body adjusts to accelerations and decelerations when you are standing in a moving train or bus. This concept has recently been used in building San Francisco's new airport terminal. The 50 million kilogram building rests on 267 stainless steel sliders that rest in big concave dishes. When the Earth shakes, the terminal will roll up to 50 centimetres in any direction.

Older houses need to have these same resisting elements added to the foundation walls that hold the house above the ground. Additionally, much of the damage, injuries, and even deaths during earthquakes occur inside homes as personal items are thrown about—items such as unsecured water heaters, ceiling fans, cabinets, bookshelves, and electronic equipment. Bolt down or secure with Velcro™ your personal items so they don't become airborne missiles inside your home during an earthquake.

KOBE, JAPAN, 1995

The most expensive earthquake in history ($147 billion in property losses) hit at 5:46 a.m. on 17 January 1995,

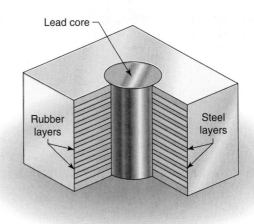

Lead core

Rubber layers

Steel layers

(b)

(a)

Figure 4.50
(a) The Office of Disaster Preparedness in San Diego County, California, is housed in a two-storey, 650 m² building sitting on top of 20 lead-impregnated rubber supports (base isolators) that each weigh 1 tonne (b) An example of a base isolator. Cut-away view into a 1 m wide by 1 m tall sandwich shows alternating layers of rubber (each 15 mm thick) and steel (each 3 mm thick) with a central core of lead. During an earthquake, the rubber and steel flex and the lead absorbs energy.
Photo: © Pat Abbott.

when a right-lateral, strike-slip fault movement began within a right step on the Nojima fault, rupturing simultaneously in both northeast and southwest directions, including through the city of Kobe, Japan. The 50 km long rupture event took 15 seconds to offset the land 1.7 m horizontally and 1 m vertically. The earthquake magnitude was 6.9 (M_W), setting some soft sediment areas of Kobe shaking strongly for 100 seconds. Kobe is a major port, the third busiest in the world. The 1.5 million residents of the city are packed into a narrow belt of land partly reclaimed from the bay with artificial fill. These weak sediments liquefied and performed poorly during the seism. Despite suffering a magnitude 7 earthquake in 1596 and a magnitude 6.1 shaker in 1916, for unknown reasons, Kobe was not considered to have a strong threat of earthquakes.

In the 1995 event, many old wooden buildings with heavy tile roofs and little lateral support collapsed on sleeping residents, causing many of the 6,425 fatalities. The destroyed wooden buildings provided kindling for more than 140 fires, but luckily, the air was calm, and the lack of winds helped firefighters control the blazes. The infrastructure of Kobe was severely impaired as

highways, railways, and port facilities were knocked out and water, sewer, gas, and electrical-power systems were severed. The recovery time for the economy takes years, and there have been increases in suicides, spousal abuse, and alcoholism.

Failed structures included massive bridges, elevated highways, and pillars supporting train tracks (Figure 4.52). The Japanese philosophy has been to build strong, thick columns and pillars meant to stand through ground shaking, analogous to an oak tree. These widespread failures call for designing, in the future, more flexible columns that sway with the shaking, analogous to a reed. Collapses of stiff structures are common occurrences during major earthquakes. Part of the problem comes from different frequencies of movements of vertical supports and horizontal roadbeds, but part comes from the behaviours of different construction materials, where engineers combined steel (for its ductility) with concrete (for its strength). The former leads to a dangerous situation when the joints between roadbeds and support columns are not reinforced properly. The latter might cause support-column failures when concrete cracks and steel deforms simultaneously (Figure 4.53).

In Greater Depth

Torre Mayor

Since 2003, a new 55-storey skyscraper stands on the Paseo de la Reforma in Mexico City. Torre Mayor (which translates in English as "Premier Tower"), the tallest building in Latin America, has been designed by the Toronto firm Zeidler Partnership Architects and developed by Canadian businessman Paul Reichmann (Figure 4.51). The design of Torre Mayor integrates both decorative elements and state-of-the-art earthquake-resistant features.

Torre Mayor is ready to withstand an event larger than the seism that shook Mexico City in 1985. Wrapped in a flexible glass and steel skin, the building is anchored on 26 m-long concrete pillars reaching to the bedrock beneath the soft lake sediments. A look at the glass facade reveals four large diamonds, which are giant brace frames serving as primary structural support. In addition, 98 dampers—devices similar to shock absorbers in automobiles—are located throughout the building. In the event of an earthquake, giant dampers in the basement absorb most of the shock. Any remaining vibrations propagate to higher floors where smaller dampers installed along the elevator shafts gradually dissipate the excess energy. In January 2003, a magnitude 7.6 earthquake tested the system. During the 30 seconds that lasted the shaking, building occupants noticed the dampers moving and experienced only subdued vibrations. No damage was reported.

Figure 4.51 Torre Mayor, located in the centre of Mexico City's business district.

Photo by Aleksu http://www.flickr.com/photos/aleksu/417583367/.

Figure 4.52

Failure of several adjacent supporting pillars along the Hanshin expressway in Kobe, Japan, following the 17 January 1995 earthquake.

Source: Courtesy of the National Information Service for Earthquake Engineering, EERC, University of California at Berkeley.

(a)

(b)

Figure 4.53
Support columns on Freeway 118 in Simi Valley, California. (a) Problem: Column failed during an earthquake in 1994 when brittle concrete cracked and ductile steel rebar buckled. (b) Solution: New columns have (1) vertical steel rebar wrapped by circular rebar, (2) both are encased in concrete, (3) columns are confined by bolted steel jackets that will be (4) encased in concrete.
Photos by Peter W. Wiegand.

Summary

- Earthquakes are shaking ground caused most often by sudden movements along cracks in the Earth called faults. Dip-slip faults have dominantly vertical movements. Normal faults are due to tension. Reverse faults are due to compression. Strike-slip fault types have dominantly horizontal offsets.

- Earthquakes disperse their energy in seismic waves that radiate away from the hypocentre or point of fault rupture. The point on the surface above the hypocentre is the epicentre. Some seismic waves pass through the body of the Earth—the P waves (primary waves with a push-pull motion) and S waves (secondary waves with a shearing motion). Other seismic waves are long wave-trains travelling along the surface (Love and Rayleigh waves).

- P waves travel about 1.7 times faster than S waves, and are the first to be recorded at a seismograph station. The difference in arrival times between P and S is greater farther from the hypocentre. The source of an earthquake can be determined by triangulating epicentral distances.

- Earthquake energy is assessed by its magnitude. Different estimates of magnitude are derived from different methods based on local shaking (Richter scale), body waves (m_b), surface waves (M_s), or seismic moment (M_w). Earth has more than a million earthquakes each year, but more than 90% of the energy is released by the 12 to 18 largest events.

- Earthquake effects on structures and people are assessed via the Mercalli Intensity Scale. The factors affecting the Mercalli Scale are earthquake magnitude, epicentre location, distance from the epicentre, hypocentre depth, duration of shaking, type of rock or sediment foundation, and building style.

- Seismic waves have different frequencies. P waves commonly have a frequency range between 0.5 to 20 Hz; surface waves have a lower frequency range between 0.005 and 0.1 Hz. Where the frequencies of seismic waves match the natural frequencies of foundation materials and buildings, resonance can occur and destruction may be great.

- Deaths from earthquakes are due mostly to building failures.

- Buildings in earthquake areas should be designed to withstand large accelerations. Building components that must stand up to seismic shaking are horizontal (floors, roofs) and vertical (walls, frames). Since horizontal and vertical components move at different frequencies, the horizontal and vertical components must be securely tied together using bolts, brackets, braces, and such. New designs of large buildings utilize energy-absorbing base isolation devices placed between the building and the ground.

Terms to Remember

acceleration   110
aftershock   80
amplitude   93
arrival time   92
base isolation   112
body wave   94
creeping zone   86
cross-section   81
dip   81
dip-slip fault   82
directivity   91
fault   80
felt area   102
footwall   81
foreshock   80
fracture   80

friction   84
hangingwall   81
hertz (Hz)   92
inertia   92
isoseismal map   102
left-lateral fault   83
liquefaction   106
locked zone   86
mainshock   80
map   81
megathrust earthquakes   104
normal fault   82
period   92
primary (P) wave   94
resonance   94
retrofitting   111

reverse fault   82
right-lateral fault   83
secondary (S) wave   94
seism   92
seismic wave   94
seismogram   92
seismograph   92
seismology   92
seismometer   92
slurry   106
strike   81
strike-slip fault   83
surface wave   94
wavelength   92

Questions for Review

Ans. In Figure 4.31, the earthquake magnitude is close to 5.

1. How are foreshocks distinguished from aftershocks?
2. Draw cross-sections of a normal fault and a reverse fault. What are the differing forces that determine which one forms?
3. Sketch a map of a strike-slip and a transform fault. Explain their similarities and differences.
4. Does the Earth always open during an earthquake?
5. Why aren't there earthquake hypocentres at depths greater than approximately 700 km?
6. Evaluate the earthquake hazards in locked versus creeping segments of a fault.

7. How can arrival times of P and S waves be used to determine distance to the epicentre?
8. What are the differences between earthquake magnitude and earthquake intensity?
9. Explain how the various magnitude scales differ.
10. How is surface shaking affected as the depth to a hypocentre increases?
11. Will a tall building be affected more by high or low-frequency seismic waves? Why?

Questions for Further Thought

1. Should we set off controlled explosions to relieve stress in rock and prevent a large earthquake in an area? Make a list of pros and cons.
2. How would you lay out the seismograph stations of a network to most accurately locate earthquake epicentres?
3. What is the quake potential of the Moon (moonquakes)? Does the Moon have similar numbers and magnitudes of quakes as the Earth? Why?

4. If you are in an airplane over the epicentre of a great earthquake, what will you experience?
5. Does a small earthquake mean that a larger earthquake is coming?
6. Is there a maximum magnitude for an earthquake?
7. What do scientists do after an earthquake?

When the Earth Shakes in Canada . . .

Thick dust flew from all sides. Doors opened of themselves. Others, which were open, closed. The bells of all our churches and the chimes of our clocks pealed quite alone, and steeples and houses shook like trees in the wind—all this in a horrible confusion of overturning furniture, falling stones, parting floors, and splitting walls. Amidst all this the domestic animals were heard howling. Some ran out of their houses; others ran in. In a word, we were all so frightened we believed it was the eve of Judgement, since all the portents were to be seen.

—Marie de l'Incarnation, Superior of the Ursuline monastery, Quebec City, describing the Charlevoix earthquake of 5 February 1663 in a letter to her son living in France

Outline

Children at a Vancouver elementary school hide under their desks during an earthquake drill.
Source. © Annie Griffiths Belt / Corbis

Has Canada suffered a great earthquake in historical times? The mythology of the aboriginal people of British Columbia, and the states of Washington and Oregon, is rich with references to earthquakes. Several groups carve earthquake masks representing ancestors who trigger tremors when they feel nature has been abused by humankind (Figure 5.1).

Oral traditions describe a major seism, followed by a tsunami, shortly before contact with the Europeans. The disappearance of the Pachena Bay people living on the West Coast of Vancouver Island, a band of more than 100 people, is attributed to this event. The account below has been transmitted from generation to generation by hereditary chiefs, and gathered in the 1960s by ethnologists of the Canadian Museum of Civilization. Concordant information from various sources—anthropological research, geological evidence, and historical records—points to the 1700 Cascadia megathrust earthquake whose associated tsunami reached the coast of Japan.

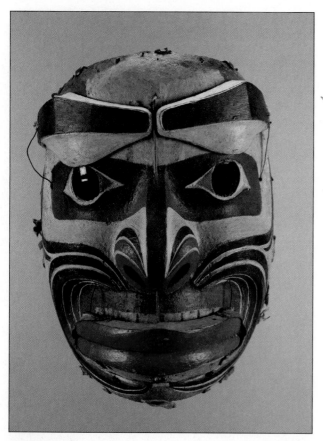

Figure 5.1
Earthquake mask from the Kwakiutl First Nation of northern Vancouver Island, Queen Charlotte Strait and Johnstone Strait, British Columbia.

Source: Used with permission of the Museum of Anthropology at the University of British Columbia.

"This was brought about by the Pachena Bay Chief, brought as dowry for this elder daughter to my grandfather's ancestor before the big earthquake, before the big flood. By that my grandfather's land reached Tsosayi:?at along with all chiefly rights, songs, topa:tis. Many are now today descended from that. Only my grandfather survived who now has many descendants. It is them now who are descendants from the first Pachena Bay people. It is said no one ever knew what happened. I think a big wave smashed into the beach. The Pachena Bay people were lost. Their food was whale meat. That is why they were living there. Nothing was known about what happened and what became of them. But they on their part who lived at Ma:łts'a:s, "House-Up-Against-Hill," the wave did not reach because they were on high ground. Right against a cliff were the houses on high ground at M'a:lsit, "Coldwater Pool." Because of that they came out alive. They did not drift out to sea along with the others."

Canada experiences approximately 3,000 earthquakes per year. Only a few dozen of these, however, are strong enough to be felt. To plan adequately for the larger ones, we need to understand the hazard: where in Canada are earthquakes likely to strike and what are their expected characteristics?

Seismic Risk and Mitigation in Canada

EARTHQUAKES IN CANADA: WHERE AND HOW SEVERE?

Earthquake research in Canada is not focusing on the elusive "When will a major earthquake strike?" but on "Where are earthquakes likely to happen?" and "How strong will the associated ground shaking be?" As discussed in Chapter 1, a general definition of risk is the product of vulnerability and hazard. Let us tailor this definition to seismic risk. With regards to earthquakes, vulnerability is especially high in major urban centres where a large population, numerous high-rise buildings, and critical infrastructure (major bridges and highways, power plants, hospitals, schools, etc.) coexist. Seismic hazard is a more complex parameter to assess. This is due in part to the fact that historical records in Canada do not go back far in time, which makes estimates of return periods of rare, large events very challenging. The earliest records from eastern Canada are accounts of the 1663 Charlevoix earthquake (see quotation with chapter opener). In western Canada, records are limited to a mere 200 years. In 1793, Captain George Vancouver mentioned in his journal a severe earthquake felt near Nookta on the west coast of Vancouver Island. However, plotting

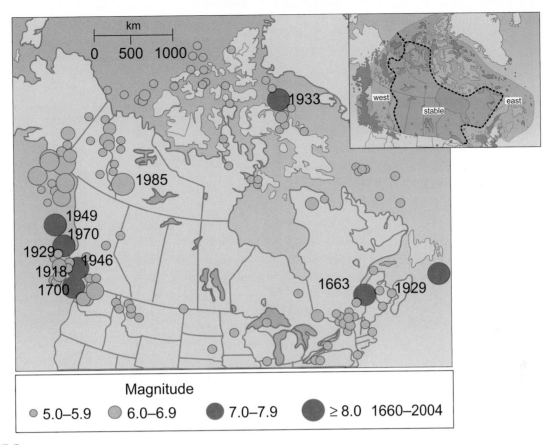

Figure 5.2

Seismicity map of Canada (1660–2004) highlighting the ten largest earthquakes listed in Table 5.1.

Source: Reproduced with the permission of Natural Resources Canada 2008, courtesy of the Canadian Hazards Information Service. http://earthquakescanada.nrcan. gc.ca/historic_eq/top10_e.php.

the epicentres of the earthquakes of magnitude 5 or larger in Canadian history on a map allows a pattern to emerge. Three broad regions can be defined: a central stable region and, in periphery, western and eastern seismically active regions (Figure 5.2). The western region includes a large band of epicentres along the coast of British Columbia, coinciding with the Cascadia subduction zone and the Queen Charlotte transform fault (see In Greater Depth box: Active Tectonic Zones of Western North America in Chapter 3), and a cluster of events along the Richardson Mountains at the border between Yukon and the Northwest Territories. The eastern region includes most of the Arctic Islands, the St. Lawrence River Valley, and the Grand Banks plateau of the Atlantic continental shelf. Table 5.1 lists the 10 largest earthquakes in Canada since 1660. The list is dominated by the events along the tectonically active west coast of British Columbia, yet the list includes events from four provinces and territories. This overview of historical **seismicity** tells us where large earthquakes are more frequent. To complete our seismic hazard assessment we need to understand where large earthquake magnitudes have a destructive impact. A map

of seismic hazard in Canada can be compiled by integrating information about seismic wave propagation and geological trends. The map, shown in Figure 5.3, is based on predicted peak ground acceleration since this parameter is closely related to the behaviour of buildings subjected to shaking. Figures 5.2 and 5.3 generally concord. Sensitive zones, however, are better defined in Figure 5.3.

The product of vulnerability and seismic hazard results in the seismic risk map shown in Figure 5.4. Vulnerability is a difficult parameter to assess in practice; therefore, population was used as the multiplier representing vulnerability in the calculation. Look at the large circles, representing a higher level of risk. They simply correspond to major cities, which are the largest population centres in Canada (from west to east): Victoria, Vancouver, Edmonton, Calgary, Windsor, London, Toronto, Ottawa, Montreal, Quebec City, Fredericton, Halifax, and St. John's. The dominant factor affecting seismic risk is the concentration of people and infrastructure in cities. Urban seismic risk is broken down in more detail in Figure 5.5. With close to two million inhabitants, Vancouver has been attributed

Table 5.1

Ten Largest Earthquakes in Canada since 1660

Magnitude	Date	Seismograph Records	Location	Mass Movements	Tsunami	Damage to Buildings
				Impact		
9.0	26 Jan 1700	NO	British Columbia—Cascadia subduction	YES	YES	YES
8.1	22 Aug 1949	YES	British Columbia—Queen Charlotte Island	NO	YES	YES
7.4	24 Jun 1970	YES	British Columbia—Queen Charlotte Island	NO	NO	NO
7.3	20 Nov 1933	YES	Northwest Territories—Baffin Bay	NO	NO	NO
7.3	23 Jun 1946	YES	British Columbia—Vancouver Island	YES	NO	YES
7.2	18 Nov 1929	YES	Newfoundland—Grand Banks	YES	YES	YES
7.0	26 May 1929	YES	British Columbia—Queen Charlotte Island	YES	YES	YES
7.0	5 Feb 1663	NO	Quebec—Charlevoix	YES	NO	YES
6.9	23 Dec 1985	YES	Northwest Territories—North Nahanni River	YES	NO	NO
6.9	6 Dec 1918	YES	British Columbia—Vancouver Island	NO	NO	YES

Source: Natural Resources Canada (2006).

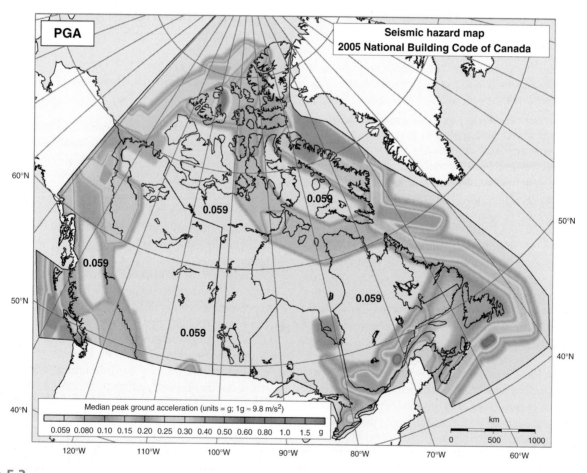

Figure 5.3

Peak ground acceleration (PGA) that has a 2% chance of being exceeded in 50 years, expressed as a fraction of the gravitational acceleration g.

Source: Reproduced with the permission of Natural Resources Canada 2008, courtesy of the Canadian Hazards Information Service. http://earthquakescanada.nrcan.gc.ca/hazard/zoning/images/NBCC2005canPGApdf.pdf.

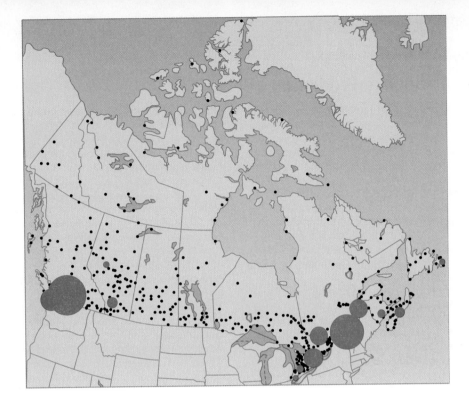

Figure 5.4
Map of seismic risk in Canada. Red circles indicate the areas of largest risk.
Source: Natural Resources Canada.

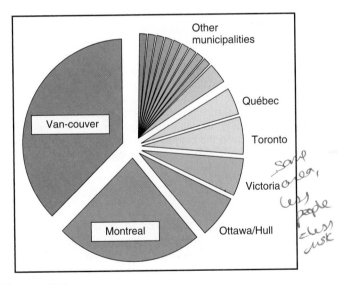

Figure 5.5
Urban seismic risk in Canada.

Source: Adams, J., Rogers, G., Halchuk, S., McCormack, D., Cassidy, J. "The case for an advanced national earthquake monitoring system for Canada's cities at risk." Proceedings of the 7th U.S. National Conference on Earthquake Engineering, Boston, United States. Paper 00042. Reproduced with the permission of the Minister of Public Works and Government Services Canada, 2008.

the highest level of seismic risk of all Canadian cities. Victoria, which is located in the same tectonic environment, is fourth in the ranking because of its modest population of a third of a million (similar hazard, less vulnerability).

THE CANADIAN NATIONAL SEISMOGRAPH NETWORK

The Canadian National Seismograph Network (CNSN) is the cornerstone of earthquake monitoring in Canada. The CNSN is a pan-Canadian infrastructure including more than 100 seismograph stations and 60 **accelerographs** managed by Natural Resources Canada, a department of the federal government. In addition, the CNSN stations are supplemented by stations from local networks, and by stations deployed on a temporary basis. Compare Figures 5.2 and 5.6 and note how the instruments are strategically deployed in seismically active areas.

Looking at the earthquake catalogue for Canada one might get the impression that the number of earthquakes is increasing over time; there are very few earthquakes in the 1600s whereas the CNSN can now locate 3,000 earthquakes annually. Nevertheless, there is no reason to believe that we are experiencing an increase in earthquake activity; what has increased is our capacity to report and to detect earthquakes. The earthquake history of Canada varies significantly across the country due largely to the time lag associated with European exploration (and hence written records). This varies from the early 1600s in eastern Canada to the late 1700s along the British Columbia coast. Northern Canada was covered in

In Greater Depth

Short-Term Earthquake Prediction

Our knowledge of earthquakes is quite impressive. With plate tectonics, we know *why* and *where* they occur, mostly along plate edges. Analyzing the geological record, we can know *how big* and *how often* earthquakes have occurred on any fault. However, many people are not satisfied; they want the same type of short-term prediction for earthquakes that they receive daily for the weather. How close are we to being able to give short-term predictions of earthquakes? We are not close. We don't have a workable theory, and it seems quite possible that the detailed behaviour of faults is too unpredictable to ever allow short-term prediction of earthquakes. There have been theories of earthquake prediction that seem logical, and they still receive coverage in textbooks, but they have all proven disappointing.

A public eager for short-term prediction of earthquakes contains many gullible people. In 1977, Charles Richter commented that "Journalists and the general public rush to any suggestion of earthquake prediction like hogs toward a full trough … [Prediction] provides a happy hunting ground for amateurs, cranks, and outright publicity-seeking fakers." Some people wanting prediction will grasp at almost anything.

Example 1. Fuelled by end-of-the-millennium anxiety, much ballyhoo occurred in the 1990s surrounding the rhymed prophecies published in 1555 by French doctor Michel de Notredame (Nostradamus). Vaguely worded statements by Nostradamus were interpreted to predict a wide range of contemporary events from earthquakes to the end of the papacy. These fantasies seem to appeal to people unable or unwilling to sort fact from fiction.

Example 2. An early 1990s prediction event occurred when dying economist Iben Browning decided to fill his final days with personal excitement by predicting a major intraplate earthquake in the mid–United States similar to the earthquakes that shook the town of New Madrid, Missouri, in 1811–1812. Scientists could readily see that his predictions were based on an old failed hypothesis, but an uncritical print and electronic media went on a binge of emotional coverage as a horde of television crews and reporters descended on New Madrid, eagerly awaiting the earthquake that would never come at the predicted time. In 1993, in the *Bulletin of the Seismological Society of America*, Paula Gori of

the United States Geological Survey published her reflections on the "non-event." She concluded that "The lack of a timely, public rebuttal of the Iben Browning earthquake prediction led to tremendous unnecessary efforts by local, state, and federal governments to respond to the public's demand for information about the validity of the prediction and how to prepare for the predicted earthquake." In the absence of clear official information, charlatans filled media airtime, sending erroneous information to the population.

Example 3. A false lead was followed by fanfare as the United States Geological Survey predicted a magnitude 6 earthquake on the San Andreas fault in the Parkfield area based on the pattern of historical seismicity. Parkfield experienced magnitude 5.5 to 6 earthquakes six times in the historical period—in 1857, 1881, 1901, 1922, 1934, and 1966. There seemed to be a pattern of an earthquake about every 22 years and scientists predicted the next earthquake would occur in 1988, plus or minus five years. Thus, in 1984, the Parkfield Prediction Experiment was launched by deploying an unprecedented array of instruments in the field with a large team of scientists to interpret every detail of the earthquake that would come by January 1993. *Breaking news:* It finally happened! A magnitude 6.0 earthquake occurred on… 28 September 2004 (!), 16 years after the forecast date. With more than 22 years of work and tens of millions of dollars invested, the earthquake was unpredicted. The Parkfield Earthquake Experiment, the best-staffed and best-funded earthquake prediction experiment ever, was a total failure at short-term earthquake prediction. From a longer-term perspective, however, it contributed a wealth of high-quality data, allowing scientists to deepen their understanding of transform-fault earthquakes.

What is our current understanding of the possibilities of short-term predictions of fault movements? First, there is no reason that the fault rupture process must occur with any regularity or predictability. Second, although it may not be hopeless to look for precursors to earthquakes, there clearly is more to earthquake triggering than can be explained simply by the steady loading of plate-tectonic stress onto faults, which rupture in evenly spaced, characteristic earthquakes. Remember that short-term prediction of earthquakes is not forthcoming, so plan accordingly. Organize your home and office to withstand the biggest earthquake possible in your area, and then don't worry about when that day will come.

---

terms of earthquake occurrences only since the introduction of seismographs. In the last 20 years or so, we have definitely had an increase in the number of earthquakes located each year simply because of the tremendous increase in the number of seismograph stations that allow the detection of tiny earthquakes that went unnoticed in the past.

Data acquired by the CNSN contribute to the safety of Canadians in several ways. Seismic events above a certain threshold automatically trigger two tools for rapid response: the Automated Natural Hazard Alert Service (ANHAS) and **shakemaps**. In the longer term, seismicity maps are constantly being updated with new data from the CNSN, leading to an increased understanding of seismic hazard.

The Automated Natural Hazard Alert Service

ANHAS provides information about significant earthquakes anywhere in Canada, usually within 10 minutes of the event. The service is offered under contract to the Canadian railroad industry (five companies totalling more than 50,000 km of track), and hydroelectricity and nuclear energy generators. Clients receive notification of the earthquake characteristics (time, epicentre location, Richter magnitude) via several media links including e-mail, fax, and pagers. Following an alert, trains might be ordered to proceed at restricted speed or even stop along certain track segments until a slope stability inspection has been completed. Utility companies carry out inspections of their infrastructure located within a certain radius from the epicentre.

In Greater Depth

Monitoring Underground Nuclear Explosions

The Comprehensive Nuclear-Test-Ban Treaty calls for a ban on all nuclear explosions in all environments, for military or civilian purposes. The treaty, which was opened for signature in 1996, has been signed by Canada and 70 other states, including five of the eight states that have nuclear capabilities. Canada ratified the treaty in 1998. The commitment of several more states, however, is required before the treaty will enter into force.

Canada's principal contribution to the international monitoring system that will be used to verify compliance with the treaty is the Yellowknife seismological array, a component of the Canadian National Seismograph Network. The array of 19 seismograph stations is situated in the outskirts of the City of Yellowknife, a location as far as possible from ocean coastlines and human sources of seismic noise, such as vehicle traffic. In this quiet environment, instruments can record signals from underground nuclear explosions anywhere on the planet. The use of an array, rather than a single station, allows test locations to be pinpointed with increased accuracy.

The array has been in operation since 1962. Since then it has recorded tens of thousands of seismic events worldwide, including most of the underground nuclear explosions detonated by the nuclear weapons states. Using this extensive data set, Canadian seismologists have developed methodologies to distinguish underground nuclear explosions from earthquakes. The system operates automatically. Data are telemetered to Ottawa, where computers continuously monitor the incoming data stream to search for signals indicative of distant seismic events. When such signals are detected, a time of occurrence, seismic magnitude, and geographical location are assigned to the event.

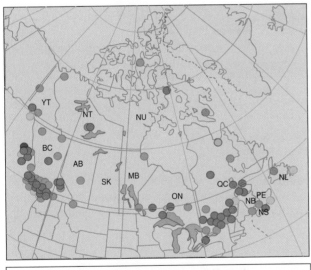

Figure 5.6
Canadian National Seismograph Network.

Source: Reproduced with the permission of Natural Resources Canada 2008, courtesy of the Canadian Hazards Information Service. http://earthquakescanada. nrcan.gc.ca/stnsdata/cnsn/stn_book/index_e.php?tpl_sorting=map.

Shakemaps

Shakemaps (Figure 5.7) are a representation of the ground shaking produced by an earthquake. They might be presented as maps of Mercalli intensity, similar to isoseismal maps (Figures 4.35 and 5.19); however, the source of the information displayed is different. The data plotted on shakemaps are intensities calculated from data recorded by a network of seismographs during an earthquake. The gaps between seismograph stations are filled by predicted intensities. Isoseismal maps, on the other hand, are the product of human input. They are compiled from eyewitness accounts.

Shakemaps are automatically computed and posted within minutes following a moderate or large earthquake, which is their main advantage. They are a critical tool to improve the situational awareness of first responders who need to decide quickly where to provide assistance. Shakemaps are also used to run "what if?" scenarios in planning exercises. Earthquakes with different characteristics are "designed" and their consequences are evaluated.

SEISMIC ZONATION

The National Building Code of Canada is a concrete example of a long-term mitigation effort against seismic risk. The seismic guidelines included in the Code are used to design and construct buildings that are as earthquake-resistant as necessary for the expected seismic hazard of their setting. They are intended as a minimum standard to prevent structural collapse during major earthquakes, without unnecessary, expensive overdesign. They may not, however, prevent serious damage to individual structures. New buildings must adhere to the Code and thus represent less hazard than old buildings. Vintage unreinforced masonry buildings are the most likely to crumble during an earthquake (Figure 5.27). Tall brick chimneys are particularly fragile (Figure 5.8). The Code

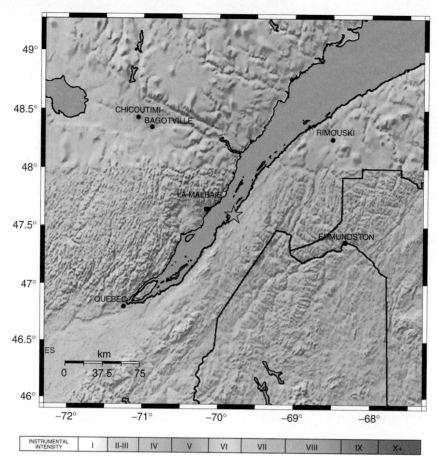

| INSTRUMENTAL INTENSITY | I | II-III | IV | V | VI | VII | VIII | IX | X+ |

Figure 5.7

Shakemap of the 6 March 2005 Riviere-du-Loup, Quebec, earthquake (magnitude 5.4).

Source: Natural USGS http://www.shakemap.carleton.ca/The-Riviere-du-Loup/intensity.html.

outlines principles to be applied when retrofitting existing buildings.

Although the hypocentre of an earthquake might be located hundreds of kilometres away, the propagation of seismic waves in the last 30-m portion of the long path from the source to a particular site has a major impact on ground motion at that site. If there is overlap between the natural frequencies of the seismic waves, foundation materials, and buildings, resonance might occur with destructive consequences. This is why the Code includes provisions for different foundation materials. The foundation materials are classified in the Code according to a scheme developed by the Natural Earthquake Hazard Reduction Program (NEHRP) in the United States. The NEHRP classification is based on the velocity of shear waves in the top 30 m of material (Table 5.2). Amplification effects are more severe at sites characterized by a low shear wave velocity. Class E and F sites are especially problematic.

Several Canadian cities have embarked on programs aiming at mapping foundation materials on their territory (Figure 5.9). This activity is one component of **seismic**

zonation, the process of subdividing a region into areas classified as having similar earthquake hazard characteristics. Seismic zonation can be completed at national,

Table 5.2

NEHRP Site Classification

Site Class	Foundation Material	Shear Wave Velocity V_s in Top 30 m (m/s)
A	Hard rock	$V_s > 1500$
B	Rock	$760 < V_s \leq 1500$
C	Very dense soil and soft rock	$360 < V_s \leq 760$
D	Stiff soil	$180 < V_s \leq 360$
E	Soft soil	$V_s < 180$
F	Soil vulnerable to liquefaction	—

Source: NEHRP site classification source: http://www.nehrp.gov/index.htm.

Figure 5.8
Chimney damage in Port Alberni, British Columbia, caused by the 1946 Vancouver Island earthquake.

Source: Reproduced with the permission of Natural Resources Canada 2008, courtesy of the Canadian Hazards Information Service. http://earthquakescanada. nrcan.gc.ca/historic_eq/20th/1946/images/1946chim.jpg.

regional, and local scales. It conveys important information used by decision makers to direct mitigation efforts.

Earthquakes of Canada's Pacific Coast

The description of several significant earthquakes in Canada's history provides a glimpse of the interactions between Canadian society and its natural environment. Several of the descriptions presented in the next subsections are adapted from the web pages of Natural Resources Canada (http://www.earthquakescanada.ca). Natural Resources Canada recognizes an earthquake as significant when its magnitude exceeds 6 on the Richter scale or when its modified Mercalli intensity is VI or stronger.

Nowhere in Canada are earthquakes more present in the collective minds of communities than along the Pacific coast. The people of British Columbia feel a strong connection with their circum-Pacific neighbours and know their geological environments share many similarities. They maintain a high level of awareness of events occurring around the "Ring of Fire" (Figure 1.11).

Let's take a closer look at the convergence between the oceanic Juan de Fuca plate and the continental North American plate (Figure 5.12), which is one of the science thrusts of the current Neptune oceanographic research project (see In Greater Depth box: Project Neptune in Chapter 8). A cross-section reveals the megathrust fault that marks the contact between the two plates at a depth of approximately 30 km (Figure 5.14). Although a large earthquake shook the region in 1700, there seem to be a deficit of megathrust earthquakes in the Cascadia subduction zone compared to similar tectonic environments around the world. A likely hypothesis is that the megathrust fault is currently locked. The Juan de Fuca plate, however, keeps moving east at a velocity of 4.3 cm per year. The enormous compression results in the buckling and uplift of the continental crust at a rate of 1 to 4 mm, which is directly measurable with using the global positioning system (GPS). As predicted by the elastic-rebound theory (compare Figures 5.13 and 4.8), when stress exceeds the resistive forces locking the fault, the stored elastic energy will be released as seismic waves. The bulge will then collapse and the seaward portion of the continent will spring back, possibly triggering a tsunami (Figure 5.13b).

Megathrust earthquakes are a considerable hazard affecting southern British Columbia. However, seismologists attribute the largest hazard not to these gigantic but infrequent events but to earthquakes associated with the deformation of the plates as they move toward each other. These deformation earthquakes can be quite large (there have been four earthquakes of magnitude 7 or higher in the past 130 years in southwestern British Columbia and north Washington state) and occur frequently, therefore representing the most serious hazard. Note how several shallow hypocentres originating from the North American plate (blue dots in Figure 5.14c) lie directly beneath Victoria, Vancouver, and Seattle.

1700 CASCADIA EARTHQUAKE, BRITISH COLUMBIA

At 9 p.m. on 26 January 1700, a gigantic megathrust earthquake—the largest seism in Canada since 1600—occurred in the Cascadia Subduction Zone. As a result of the convergence between the oceanic Juan de Fuca plate and the continental North American plate, the fault marking the contact between the two plates ruptured suddenly (Figures 5.12 and 5.14). The rupture affected the entire length of the subduction zone from Vancouver Island to northern California, leading to magnitude estimates

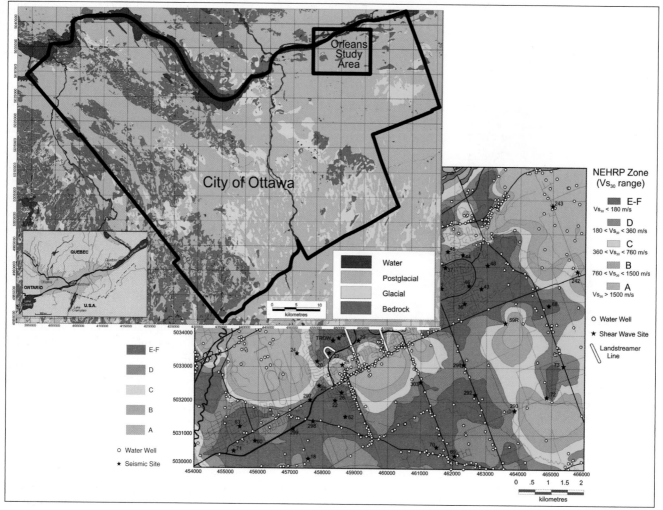

Figure 5.9

(a) Map of sediment thickness in the Ottawa-Gatineau area. At the end of the last glaciation, some 10 000 years ago, a thick blanket of sediment was deposited by an invading shallow sea in the eastern part of Ottawa.

(b) Detailed mapping of NEHRP zones in the suburb of Orleans. Note how the NEHRP classes vary over very short distances. Class E and Class F sites are especially prone to intense ground shaking.

Source: J. Hunter (Natural Resources Canada) and D. Motazedian (Carleton University).

of approximately 9. Native stories describe vividly the event. They report that the shaking was so violent that people could not stand and so prolonged that it made them sick.

How do we know the exact date and time of the earthquake? A recent book, *The Orphan Tsunami of 1700—Japanese Clues to a Parent Earthquake in North America,* written by a group of American and Japanese scholars presents the two converging lines of evidence like a scientific detective story. (1) Several Japanese magistrates, merchants, and peasants recorded in their diaries the arrival of tsunami waves on their shores in the early hours of 27 January 1700 (Figure 5.15). Taking into account the travel time of the waves across the Pacific, their entries correspond with a Cascadia earthquake the

previous evening. (2) The discovery of ghost forests of desiccated red cedars and spruce stumps along the British Columbia, Washington, and Oregon coasts in the 1980s provided additional clues (Figure 5.16). Apparently the ground dropped by one metre during the earthquake and seawater reached the tree roots and killed the forests (Figure 5.17). Detailed examination of tree rings and radioactive carbon (C^{14}) dating of organic material helped to narrow the occurrence of the seism to a 10-month window from August 1699 to May 1700, between the end of one growing season and the beginning of the next one.

The 1700 Cascadia earthquake left unmistakable signatures, from disturbed sediments on the seafloor to sand layers brought far onshore by tsunami waves.

In Greater Depth

Seismic Provisions of the National Building Code of Canada

Seismic provisions—featured modestly in the appendix of the first edition of the National Building Code of Canada in 1941 before moving to the main text in 1953—have become increasingly sophisticated over the years. The provisions are periodically updated to reflect a better understanding of Canadian seismicity, advances in earthquake engineering research, and lessons learned from earthquake damage around the world. In this respect, the 1989 Loma Prieta earthquake (see Chapter 4) was pivotal in revising the Code to better take into account the effects of amplification on soft soil sites. The seismic provisions of the latest edition of the Code in 2005 include estimates of seismic hazard across the country, and a methodology for integrating this information in the design of buildings. The objective is to ensure a uniform level of protection for all structures.

For simplicity, the latest seismic hazard estimates are directly related to the forces that a structure will be subjected to during an earthquake. The estimates are based on the expected ground motion for earthquakes of different magnitudes and epicentral distances. They have been computed for a broad range of frequencies (from 0.1 to 10 Hz), to account for the shaking induced by the different seismic waves. The estimates also include factors reflecting the different foundation materials of the NEHRP classification.

Since buildings are particularly vulnerable to shear stress, the most important factor that civil engineers must estimate in the design stage is the lateral earthquake force. In addition to seismic hazard at the building site, the lateral earthquake force equation includes the natural frequency of the proposed building, the number of storeys, and the flexibility of the structure, important parameters that were examined in Chapter 4. Everything else being equal, direct observations of earthquake damage have shown that buildings regular in shape perform better than irregular buildings, possibly because stresses are more evenly distributed through their structure. For this reason, more stringent seismic provisions apply to buildings with irregular shapes.

The current design standard for buildings is to be able to withstand an earthquake with a return period of 2,500 years. A factor further tailors the design requirements depending on the importance of the buildings to society. Normal buildings are assigned a factor of 1.0, schools and storage facilities containing toxic substances a 1.3, and buildings needed for post-disaster recovery like hospitals, water and sewage treatment facilities, and fire and police stations, a 1.5.

Canada is a world leader in earthquake engineering. This expertise has been captured in the seismic provisions of the National Building Code of Canada and is applied to the design of new, safe buildings. The most pressing demand is now to develop cost-effective strategies for retrofitting existing buildings. Local advocacy groups, like Families for School Seismic Safety of Vancouver, have been instrumental in raising the profile of this important issue. In 2004, B.C. Premier Gordon Campbell made a 15-year, $1.5 billion commitment to ensure that all schools in British Columbia meet acceptable seismic standards. Seismic upgrading is currently underway at 16 schools of the Vancouver School Board.

The recognition of similar signatures in the geological record tells us that the 1700 seism was not a unique event, but has repeated many times at irregular intervals of hundreds of years (Figure 5.18). Geological evidence indicates that 13 great earthquakes have occurred in the last 6,000 years in the Cascadia Subduction Zone. The average return period of large megathrust earthquakes in the region is on the order of 600 years. The last one occurred 300 years ago. Seismologists assign a 10% probability that the next "Big One" will occur in the next 50 years.

1949 QUEEN CHARLOTTE ISLAND EARTHQUAKE, BRITISH COLUMBIA

Canada's largest earthquake (magnitude 8.1) following the 1700 Cascadia earthquake occurred on 22 August 1949 off the coast of the Queen Charlotte Islands in northern British Columbia. The 1949 seism was a classic transform fault earthquake resulting from the abrasive alongside movement of the Pacific and North American plates in the area. Earthquakes along the Queen Charlotte fault share lots of similarities with their southern cousins, the San Andreas fault earthquakes. The Queen Charlotte fault, however, runs mostly offshore. Its related earthquakes affect a largely unpopulated area and therefore do present less risk.

Figure 5.19 shows the isoseismal map of the 1949 Queen Charlotte Island earthquake. The shaking was so severe on the Queen Charlotte Islands that cows were knocked off their feet (intensity VII–VIII)! On the adjacent mainland, standing on the street was described as "like being on the heaving deck of a ship at sea." The fractured rocks of the Canadian cordillera attenuated the seismic waves and the earthquake was hardly felt east of the mountain range.

Intraplate Earthquakes of Eastern Canada

Pushed by the ever-widening Atlantic Ocean, the landmass of Canada drifts slowly to the west as part of the large North American plate. As predicted by plate tectonics, there is notable seismic activity on the edges of the plate: along Canada's Pacific coast to the west, in Iceland, and along the spreading centres of the mid-Atlantic

In Greater Depth

Did You Feel It?

For more than a century, seismologists have sought input from the Canadian public following an earthquake. Data-gathering mechanisms have changed, but the effort continues.

The Dominion Observatory was established in 1905 in Ottawa on the model of the Royal Observatory at Greenwich, England, with the dual mandate of making precise longitude measurements and studying planet Earth (Figure 5.10). When an earthquake was strongly felt, the seismologists of the Dominion Observatory determined the intensity of shaking on Canadian territory. They collected information by sending questionnaires to local postmasters, a clerical process spanning months (Figure 5.11). The process led also to the location of epicentres when the coverage of the network of seismograph stations was sparse.

The tradition remains today as the Observatory and adjacent buildings host a state-of-the-art seismograph station and serve as a telemetry hub as part of the Canadian National Seismograph Network. Seismologists from Natural Resources Canada are now seeking input from the population via a questionaire posted on the web page "Did you feel it?" Sample questions include "Did the earthquake wake you up?," "Did objects fall off shelves?," and "Did you notice the swinging/swaying of doors or hanging objects?" Within minutes, a computer-generated isoseismal map begins taking shape showing Mercalli intensity for each postal code in the region affected.

(http://earthquakescanada.nrcan.gc.ca/dyfi/index_e.php)

Figure 5.10 Dominion Observatory, Ottawa, Ontario.
Photo: © Claire Samson.

---

ridge to the east. Why is there then a cluster of **intraplate earthquakes** along the St. Lawrence River Valley and the Atlantic coast, regions that are thousands of kilometres away from plate boundaries (Figure 5.20)?

The entire crust of the Earth is subjected to stresses (Figure 5.21). Note on the world's stress map the tension (in red) affecting the East African Rift Valley; the compression (in blue) associated with the collision of the Arabian plate against the Eurasian plate in Iran; and the shear stresses (in green) related to the San Andreas and the North Anatolian transform faults. Plate edges are obvious regions of high stress. The influence of deformation forces, however, extends well into the interior of continents. In these intraplate settings, ancient scars in the crust remain as zones of weakness where existing faults are reactivating, failing due to current stress, and generating earthquakes. The geology of eastern Canada features several examples of processes weakening the crust locally, including rifting, impact cratering, and the **intrusion** of igneous rocks in the subsurface.

EARTHQUAKES OF THE ST. LAWRENCE RIVER VALLEY

It is the fate of all continents to be ripped apart from below. Continents are rifted and then drifted and reas-sembled in different patterns. Sometimes the rifting process stops before separating a continent. Figure 5.22 shows some rift arms developed 220 to 180 million years ago as Pangaea was torn apart. Some rift arms succeeded, combining to create today's Atlantic Ocean basin. Other rift arms failed and left behind weakened zones within continents. Other **failed rifts**, from even older plate-tectonic histories, also exist beneath the surface in North America. Failed rifts create zones of weakness in the crust.

The present path of the St. Lawrence River follows an ancient tectonic structure. Some 600 to 500 million years ago, a major rift valley extended through the region. This partially buried rift coincides with most of the large earthquakes in the eastern seismically active region of Canada.

Because some failed rifts are deeply buried, they are often difficult to study. Yet they raise significant questions. What are the frequencies of their major earthquakes? In general, the return period for major earthquakes appears to be from a few hundred to more than a thousand years. How great an earthquake might be produced at each rift? The several magnitude 6 or larger earthquakes that have occurred along the St. Lawrence River Valley in historical times offer a sobering benchmark. Do all the rift-bounding faults have the potential

Figure 5.11 Sample intensity questionnaire response from Lewisporte, Newfoundland, following the 1929 Grand Banks earthquake.

Source: Reproduced with the permission of Natural Resources Canada 2008, courtesy of the Canadian Hazards Information Service. http://earthquakescanada.nrcan.gc.ca/historic_eq/20th/1929/images/1929resp.jpg.

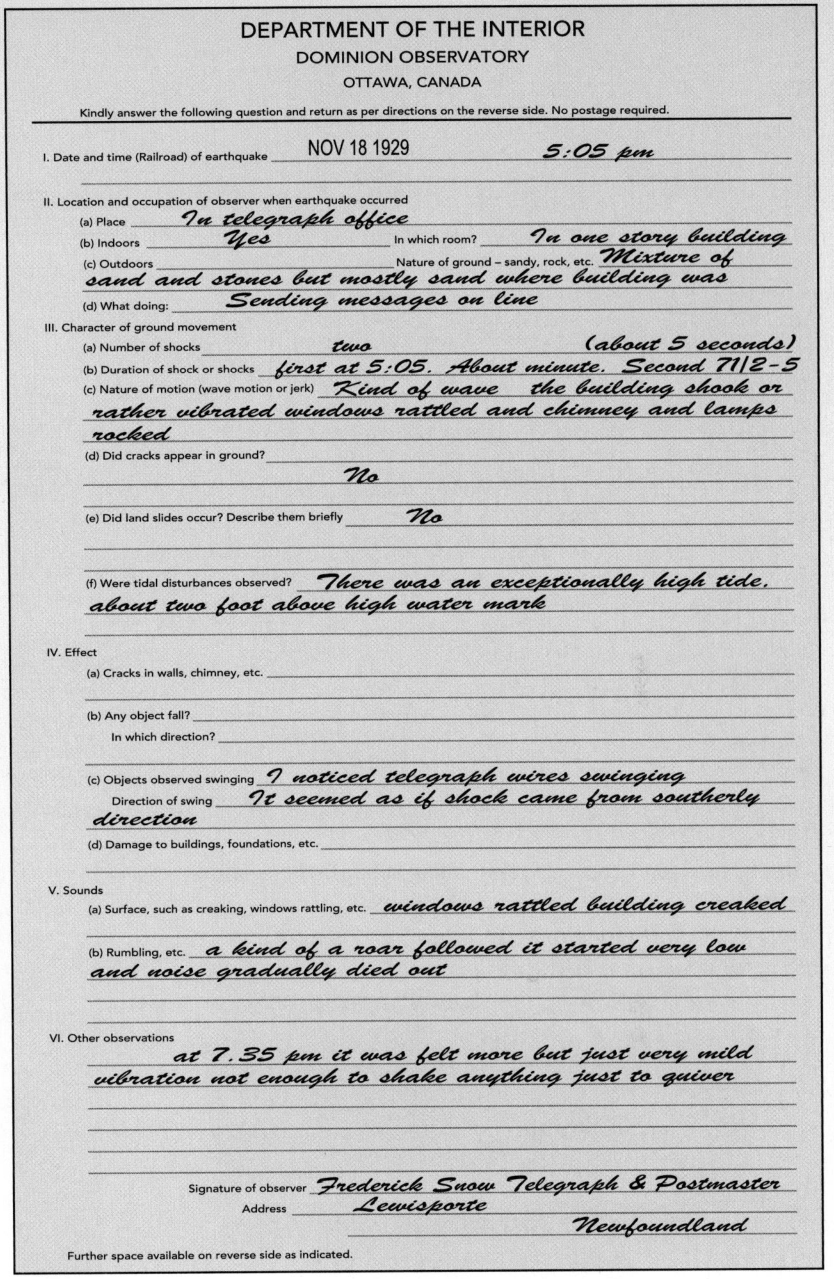

DEPARTMENT OF THE INTERIOR
DOMINION OBSERVATORY
OTTAWA, CANADA

Kindly answer the following question and return as per directions on the reverse side. No postage required.

I. Date and time (Railroad) of earthquake *NOV 18 1929*   *5:05 pm*

II. Location and occupation of observer when earthquake occurred
(a) Place *In telegraph office*
(b) Indoors *Yes*   In which room? *In one story building*
(c) Outdoors _____ Nature of ground – sandy, rock, etc. *Mixture of sand and stones but mostly sand where building was*
(d) What doing: *Sending messages on line*

III. Character of ground movement
(a) Number of shocks *two*   *(about 5 seconds)*
(b) Duration of shock or shocks *first at 5:05. About minute. Second 7½–5*
(c) Nature of motion (wave motion or jerk) *Kind of wave the building shook or rather vibrated windows rattled and chimney and lamps rocked*
(d) Did cracks appear in ground? *No*
(e) Did land slides occur? Describe them briefly *No*
(f) Were tidal disturbances observed? *There was an exceptionally high tide, about two foot above high water mark*

IV. Effect
(a) Cracks in walls, chimney, etc.
(b) Any object fall?
In which direction?
(c) Objects observed swinging *I noticed telegraph wires swinging*
Direction of swing *It seemed as if shock came from southerly direction*
(d) Damage to buildings, foundations, etc.

V. Sounds
(a) Surface, such as creaking, windows rattling, etc. *windows rattled building creaked*
(b) Rumbling, etc. *a kind of a roar followed it started very low and noise gradually died out*

VI. Other observations *at 7.35 pm it was felt more but just very mild vibration not enough to shake anything just to quiver*

Signature of observer *Frederick Snow Telegraph & Postmaster*
Address *Lewisporte*
Newfoundland

Further space available on reverse side as indicated.

for future seismic activity? The historical record is not long enough to properly answer this question. But if the answer is yes, then virtually all the length of the Atlantic coast in Canada and the United States could receive a significant shake sometime. When the next magnitude 6 or greater earthquake strikes eastern North America, the resultant destruction is likely to be proportionately greater than for a similar seism in the western part of the continent. In the East, earthquake energy is transmitted more effectively in the older, less fractured rocks, so damage may be experienced over a wider area. Also consider (1) the population density of the East, (2) the large number of older buildings not designed to withstand earthquake shaking, and (3) the concentration of industrial and power-generating facilities, including nuclear reactors and colossal hydroelectric dams.

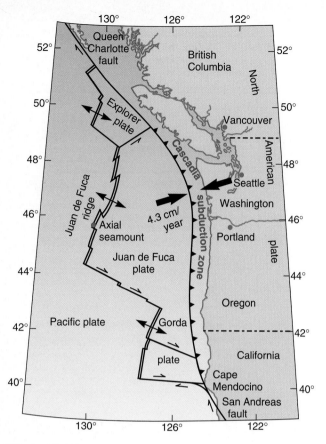

Figure 5.12

Map of small, young oceanic plates being subducted beneath the North American plate along the Pacific coast.

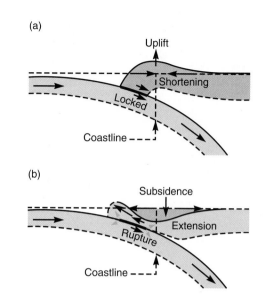

Figure 5.13

(a) The Cascadia megathrust fault is locked, causing the North American plate to bulge up. (b) When the Cascadia megathrust ruptures, the North American plate will rebound violently, triggering a large earthquake and, possibly, a tsunami.

Source: Hyndman et al., Natural Resources Canada.

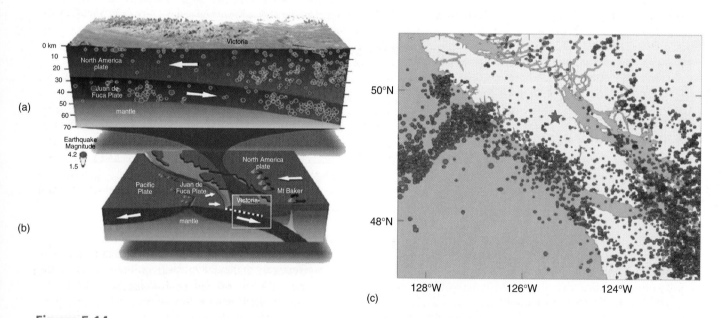

Figure 5.14

Subduction of the Juan de Fuca plate underneath Vancouver Island. (a, b) Cross-section view. The dotted white line shows the megathrust fault at the contact between the Juan de Fuca and the North American plates. (c) Map view of the epicentre distribution. Red and blue dots correspond to epicentres belonging to the Juan de Fuca and North American plates, respectively.

Source: Reproduced with the permission of Natural Resources Canada 2008, courtesy of the Geological Survey of Canada. http://geoscape.nrcan.gc.ca/victoria/eq_e.php.

Figure 5.15

The diary of the Moriai family of Tsugaruishi, Japan. The characters read from top to bottom, right to left, starting at the top of the rightmost column.

Source: Brian F Atwater et al., 2005 The Orphan *Tsunami of 1700 - Japanese Clues to a Parent Earthquake in North America*. Produced by the U.S Geological Survey.

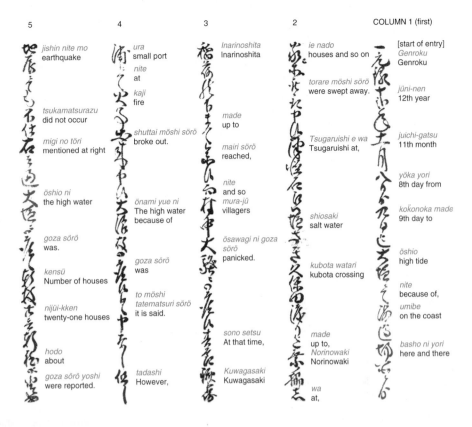

5
jishin nite mo
earthquake

tsukamatsurazu
did not occur

migi no tōri
mentioned at right

ōshio ni
the high water

goza sōrō
was.

kensū
Number of houses

nijūi-kken
twenty-one houses

hodo
about

goza sōrō yoshi
were reported.

4
ura
small port

nite
at

kaji
fire

shuttai mōshi sōrō
broke out.

ōnami yue ni
The high water because of

goza sōrō
was

to mōshi tatematsuri sōrō
it is said.

tadashi
However,

3
Inarinoshita
Inarinoshita

made
up to

mairi sōrō
reached,

nite
and so
mura-jū
villagers

ōsawagi ni goza sōrō
panicked.

sono setsu
At that time,

Kuwagasaki
Kuwagasaki

2
ie nado
houses and so on

torare mōshi sōrō
were swept away.

Tsugaruishi e wa
Tsugaruishi at,

shiosaki
salt water

kubota watari
kubota crossing

made
up to,
Norinowaki
Norinowaki

wa
at,

COLUMN 1 (first)
[start of entry]
Genroku
Genroku

jūni-nen
12th year

juichi-gatsu
11th month

yōka yori
8th day from

kokonoka made
9th day to

ōshio
high tide

nite
because of,

umibe
on the coast

basho ni yori
here and there

Figure 5.16

Ghost forest of Willapa Bay, Oregon.

Source: Brian F Atwater et al., 2005 *The Orphan Tsunami of 1700 - Japanese Clues to a Parent Earthquake in North America*. Produced by the U.S Geological Survey.

1732 Montreal Earthquake, Quebec

Montreal has been assigned the second-highest level of urban seismic risk in Canada (Figure 5.5). What if an earthquake rocked Montreal today? Not only could it happen, it did—recently! Not long ago in terms of geological time, on 16 September 1732, Montreal experienced an earthquake of magnitude 5.8 and intensity VIII–IX.

Mother Duplessis of St. Helen, Superior of the Hotel Dieu in Quebec City, describes, in a letter written a month later, the flow of refugees fleeing Montreal frightened by the numerous aftershocks and seeking refuge in Quebec City: "Many have fled and have come to Quebec having a fear of being buried alive under the ruins of that poor city. What is worse, all is not yet finished. There are no days when it is not felt; some wells are extremely dry and roads appear plowed."

1988 Saguenay Earthquake, Quebec

The 25 November 1988 Saguenay earthquake took everyone by surprise. The epicentre was not located along the St. Lawrence River rift but approximately 100 km further inland, in the Canadian Precambrian Shield, a region assumed until then to be seismically quiet. The earthquake was recorded by modern seismographs and accelerographs, and is the first seism in eastern North America for which we have both ground motion data and liquefaction observations. Its magnitude has been estimated at 5.8 (M_S) or

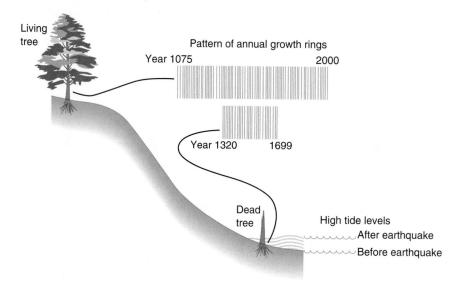

Figure 5.17

Annual growth rings in drowned trees along the British Columbia, Washington, and Oregon coasts tell of their deaths after the 1699 growing season. Seawater flooding occurred as land dropped during a magnitude 9 earthquake.

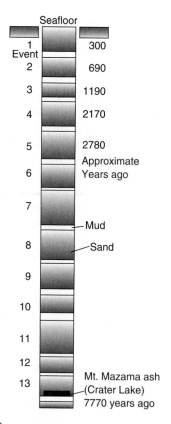

Figure 5.18

A core sample taken from the deep sea floor shows alternating mud and sand layers. The sand layers are interpreted to have been deposited from submarine landslides triggered by great earthquakes.

Source: Modified from Adam et al. 1990 "Giant earthquakes beneath Canada's west coast" (http://gsc.nrcan.gc.ca/geodyn/mega_e.php).

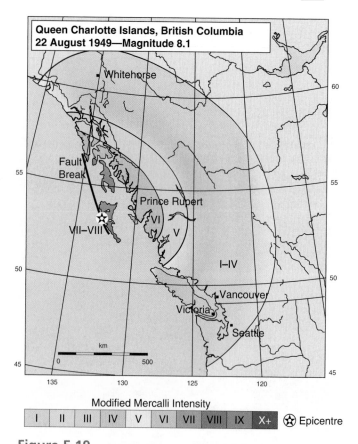

Figure 5.19

Isoseismal map of the 1949 Queen Charlotte Island earthquake.

Source: Reproduced with the permission of Natural Resources Canada 2008, courtesy of the Canadian Hazard Information Service. http://earthquakescanada. nrcan.gc.ca/historic_eq/20th/1949_e.php.

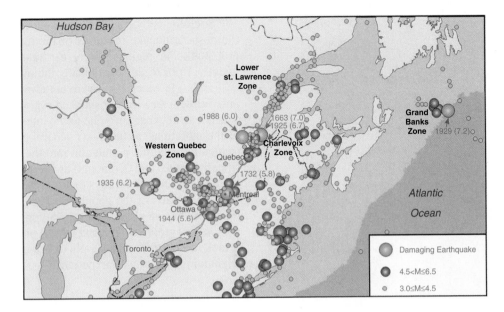

Figure 5.20
Seismicity map of eastern Canada (1568–1998).

Source: *The Atlas of Canada*.

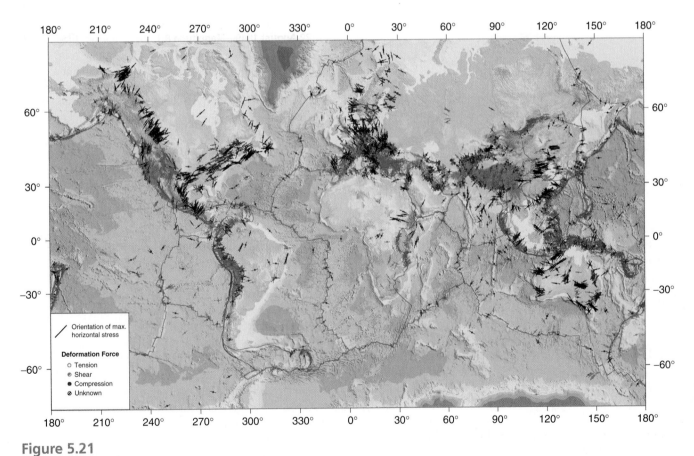

Figure 5.21
World stress map.

Source: Heidbach, O., K. Fuchs, B. Müller, F. Wenzel, J. Reinecker, M. Tingay, and B. Sperner, The World Stress Map, Episodes, 30 (3), 197-202, 2007. Reinecker, J., O. Heidbach, M. Tingay, B. Sperner, and B. Müller, The 2005 release of the World Stress Map, (available online at www.world-stress-map.org), 2005.

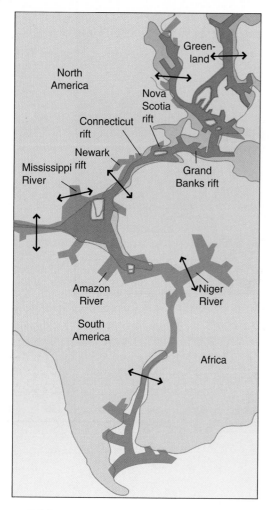

Figure 5.22
Schematic map of rifts that tore apart Pangaea about 220 million years ago. Successful rifts combined to open the Atlantic Ocean basin.

5.9 (Richter, m_b, M_w). Accelerograph data recorded a few tens of kilometres away from the epicentre showed that the maximum measured acceleration of rock was 0.16 g horizontally and 0.10 g vertically. The earthquake was preceded by a single foreshock on 23 November 1988 (magnitude 4.7) and followed by minor aftershock activity.

Only minor damage was reported close to the epicentre: falling masonry blocks (40 km from the epicentre), and embankment failures and landslides (170 km from the epicentre). In fact, the most severe damage occurred 350 km away from the epicentre, in Montreal East, where the masonry cladding of the former City Hall detached from the façade and fell (see photo of chapter opener). The structure was known to be located on a vulnerable site. It is founded on 17 metres of clay and had suffered excessive settlement prior to the earthquake.

Sociologically, the Saguenay earthquake illustrates the post-earthquake reactions of the media and the general public in regions where earthquakes occur infrequently. Prior to this earthquake, the residents, like most eastern North Americans, were not aware of seismic hazards in their area. In the shocked region, the earthquake was a fearful experience due to the intensity and duration of the vibrations, to the quasi-general electrical blackout (which plunged the population into the dark for between fifteen minutes and two hours) and to the noise from falling objects. During the days that followed the earthquake, the fear in parts of the population became more evident. Hundreds of people sought psychological help through personal or group meetings at a local public health clinic. It took months for some people to begin to cope with this frightening and unusual experience.

IMPACT AND EARTHQUAKES IN CHARLEVOIX

The most active area along the St. Lawrence River Valley is an 80 km by 35 km zone near Charlevoix, northeast of Quebec City. Here, earthquakes of magnitudes 6 to 7 occurred in 1663, 1791, 1860, 1870, and 1925 (Figure 4.35). Why the concentration of large seisms in this one relatively small area? Charlevoix was the site of a meteorite impact some 350 million years ago. The northern half of the heavily eroded impact crater still stands out on a satellite image against the fabric of the Canadian Precambrian Shield (Figure 5.23). The southern half lies beneath the waters of the St. Lawrence River. When the epicentres for a 20-year period between January 1978 and September 1999 (including the epicentre of the 1992 earthquake we located in Figures 4.28, 4.29, and 4.30) are superimposed on the image, we can clearly see that the epicentres are not evenly distributed underneath the crater but follow the St. Lawrence River rift. The impact caused intensive fracturing of the area. The impact-caused fractures are probably being reactivated today under the stresses generated by the widening Atlantic Ocean (Figure 5.24).

1633 Charlevoix Earthquake, Quebec

In several cultures and throughout history, observers have tried to interpret natural phenomena as signs from deities. A devout woman, Marie de l'Incarnation, Superior of the Ursuline monastery in Quebec City, wrote a vivid account of the 1633 Charlevoix earthquake, in which religious references and concrete descriptions are intermingled, in a letter to her son. The magnitude 7 earthquake struck on 5 February. In Roman Catholic societies, the beginning of February is a time of merrymaking when people celebrate carnival. Marie de l'Incarnation asks herself if the earthquake is not a sign from God to

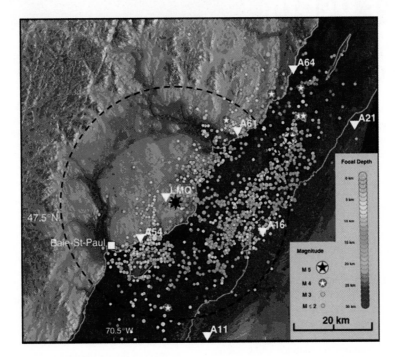

Figure 5.23
Earthquake epicentres from January 1978 to September 1999 superimposed on a satellite image of the Baie-St-Paul area in Charlevoix, Quebec. The black star represents the location of the meteoritic impact. The dashed circle represents the external boundary of the impact structure.

Source: Lamontage, M., Keating, P., and Toutin, T. Complex faulting confounds earthquake research in the Charlevoix Seismic Zone, Quebec. © Copyright 2000, 81, no. 26, p.289–293. Reproduced by permission of American Geophysical Union.

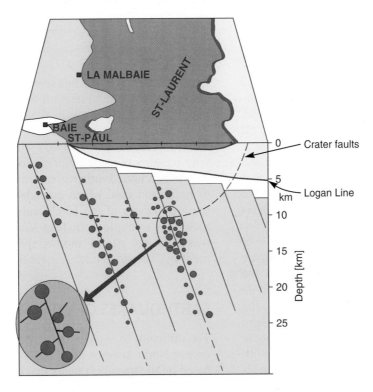

Figure 5.24
Three-dimensional view of the Charlevoix area. Hypocentres (yellow circles) cluster along pre-existing faults (oblique lines) associated with rifting and the opening of the Atlantic Ocean rather than along crater faults (dashed line).

Source: Lamontagne, M. © Her Majesty the Queen in right of Canada 2008.

In Greater Depth

Documenting the First Direct Casualties of a Canadian Earthquake

As of 2008, no loss of life has been directly attributed to an earthquake in Canada. A direct loss of life is defined as a death caused by the consequences of seismic ground motions or by surface rupture of a fault. Examples of events causing direct losses of life are partial or total collapses of buildings, and mass movements such as rockfalls, mudslides, and avalanches. Indirect losses of life are those related to physical, technological, or human consequences derived from earthquakes. The best Canadian example of an earthquake causing indirect loss of life is the 1929 Grand Banks earthquake, which sent a tsunami to the southern coast of Newfoundland.

In a letter describing the 1732 Montreal earthquake, Mother Duplessis of St. Helen from Quebec City mentions that one girl was killed in the event. Since there was no casualty reported by hospitals in Montreal, historians consider the remark an unfounded rumour.

According to recent investigations by Maurice Lamontagne, seismologist at Natural Resources Canada, the 20 October 1870 magnitude 6.5 earthquake, centred in the Charlevoix region of Quebec, may have caused direct casualties.

Quebec City's *Quebec Daily Mercury* of 22 October 1870 reported: "At Eboulements, ten houses were completely thrown down, besides that of Mr. Clement, M.P.P., for Charlevoix, and Dr. Laterriere. Two children are reported killed in this parish, but a letter from there today does not mention the fact. It appears that all the houses within an area of a mile, in this locality, were more or less damaged and there would have been great loss of life had not the people hurriedly quitted their residences."

Quebec City's *Morning Chronicle—Commercial and Shipping Gazette* of 22 October 1870 reported: "At les Eboulements the church and ten houses were injured, and two children killed." The newspaper *Le Canadien* of 24 October 1870 says of the village Les Éboulements: "*Il y a eu deux enfants de tués en cet endroit.* [There were two children killed at that place]."

The parish registry of Les Éboulements reports two deaths of children on 24 October 1870. The first is Joseph Tremblay, 6 years old, "mort l'avant veille [who died the day before yesterday]," which would mean on 22 October. The other is Marie-Élizabeth Miville, 4 months old, "décédée depuis quatre jours et déjà inhumée [dead for four days and already put to earth]." The latter would have died on 20 October 1870, the date of the earthquake. The causes of the deaths are not mentioned. There are no other sources of information in existence.

From a lack of text mentioning explicitly the causes of the deaths of these two children, we cannot be certain that the earthquake was really the cause. In fact, deaths of children in their early years were quite common in those days. On the other hand, the severity of the earthquake in Les Éboulements (landslide, soil liquefaction, and damage to most houses, including complete destruction of some dwellings) makes it a likely source of the deaths of these two children. As a footnote, it is interesting to note that the village name "Les Éboulements" translates to "landslides" in French. Les Éboulements acquired its name when a huge landslide was triggered by the 1663 Charlevoix earthquake. The debris flow is still visible today as a tongue of earth advancing in the St. Lawrence River.

---

boisterous youth: "So unexpected a calamity, when the young people were preparing to spend the carnival season in excesses, was a clap of thunder on everyone's head, they expecting nothing less." She notes that, in his mercy, God did not punish humankind but merely issued a warning: "But the wondrous thing is that amidst so great and universal a wreckage, no-one has perished or even been injured. This is quite visible sign of God's protection of his people, which gives us just cause to believe that he is angry with us only to save us."

The 1633 Charlevoix earthquake was felt all over eastern North America, an area of two million square kilometres. It triggered landslides that changed the landscape in several localities. In her letter, Marie de l'Incarnation refers to "...a great many crevices in the earth, new torrents, new springs and new hills, where they had never been before; the earth leveled where there had formerly been mountains..." About the St. Lawrence River, she writes: "...nothing astonished us more, I say, than to see this river change and assume the colour of sulphur and retain it for a week." This coloration is probably the result of numerous landslides on the river banks. An account of a spectacular display of soil liquefaction was reported by the Jesuit missionaries who were meticulous observers of life in New France: "...whence issued either great clouds of smoke or jets of muds and sand which ascended to a lofty height in the air." Traces of the 1663 landslides are still visible today, for example in St-Jean-Vianney, Quebec, which was to be the site of another spectacular mass movement two centuries later (Figure 9.30).

EARTHQUAKES OF WESTERN QUEBEC

The difficulty of explaining the causes of earthquakes in eastern North America has led to a speculative hypothesis based on the transform faults that offset the mid-Atlantic

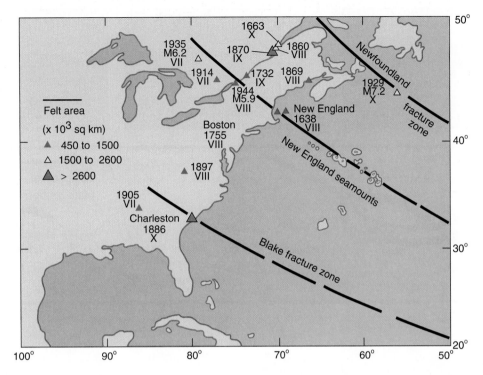

Figure 5.25
Location of earthquake epicentres in eastern North America and fracture-zone extensions of transform faults on the mid-Atlantic spreading centre.

Ocean spreading centre. The transform faults continue northwestward as great **fracture zones** that seem to line up with some onland seismic zones (Figure 5.25). If the fracture zones continue beneath the North American continent, they would be linear trends of weakness. The ongoing westward spreading of the North Atlantic plate could cause earthquake-producing movements on the fracture zones beneath eastern North America.

In Figure 5.25, notice how the northernmost fracture zone lines up with the epicentre of the 1929 Grand Banks earthquake (Figure 5.20). The southernmost fracture zone lines up with the epicentre of the 1886 Charleston, South Carolina, earthquake. The central fracture zone projects toward the New England seamounts and the Western Quebec seismic zone. Could there be a relation between the two?

The Western Quebec seismic zone is a cluster of intraplate earthquakes whose epicentres are located in a linear zone branching out from the St. Lawrence rift west of Montreal (Figure 5.20). Western Quebec has been the site of three earthquakes of intensity higher than VII in the 20th century. A working hypothesis is

that seismic activity in western Quebec, the Monteregian Hills, and the New England seamounts results from remnants of the passage of the North American plate over the Great Meteor hot spot.

The Great Meteor hot spot is a long-lived thermal anomaly over which the westward drifting North American plate has been migrating, as is the Pacific plate over the Hawaiian hot spot (Figure 3.11). Some 150 million years ago, the Great Meteor hot spot was underneath the present-day Ottawa River Valley. Molten rocks rose from deep in the mantle, were trapped in the crust, and crystallized in the subsurface. Several fractures developed in the crust to accommodate the intrusive bodies, creating local zones of weakness. These fractures might be reactivating and controlling present-day seismicity in the area. Since then, erosion has gradually removed the rocks surrounding several of these intrusive bodies, leaving them exposed. They form a chain of small mountains, the Monteregian Hills, the most famous being Mount Royal after which the city of Montreal has been named (Figure 5.26). Approximately 100–80 million years ago, the plate continued its migration and

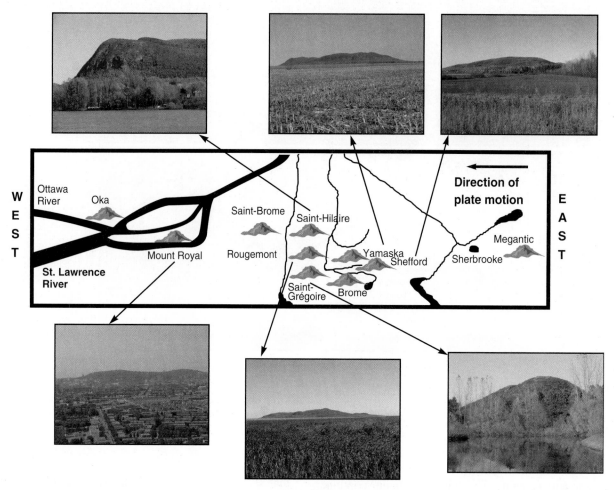

Figure 5.26
The ten Monteregian Hills of Ontario and southern Quebec formed by the passage of the North American plate over the Great Meteor hot spot 150 million years ago. Can you infer which hill is the oldest?
Photos: © Claire Samson.

Figure 5.27
Masonry damage caused by the 1944 Cornwall-Massena earthquake.
Source: Reproduced with the permission of Natural Resources Canada 2008, courtesy of the Canadian Hazards Information Service. http://earthquakescanada.nrcan.gc.ca/historic_eq/20th/1944_e.php

In Greater Depth

Reservoir-Induced Seismicity

Building a large dam and impounding a deep reservoir of water may trigger earthquakes. Contrary to our intuition, the weight of the water in the reservoir is not the main trigger of these earthquakes, technically called RIS, Reservoir-Induced Seismicity. The earthquakes are primarily associated with water seeping through the floor of the reservoir and flowing slowly underground, pushed by the large body of reservoir water above it. The underground water moves downward and outward as an advancing front of high pressure along pre-existing faults or fractures. When the shear resistance is sufficiently low, the sides of the fault move abruptly, giving rise to an earthquake.

The Province of Quebec, with its large hydroelectric infrastructure, has experienced many cases of RIS. The first case was reported in 1975 under the reservoir created by the Manic-3 dam. The earthquake had a magnitude of 4.1 on the Richter scale and caused quite a surprise. In months to follow, hundreds of smaller shocks occurred, closely monitored by portable seismographs. Later, a permanent seismograph station was added to closely monitor the activity, which eventually died down. Most earthquakes were shallow (about 1 km depth) and located along one of the numerous fractures of the Canadian Precambrian Shield in the area. Surprisingly, a much larger reservoir upstream from the Daniel-Johnson dam (formerly the Manic-5 dam; Figure 5.28), which made the Manicouagan crater visible from space (Figure 16.10), did not cause any RIS. Other cases of RIS were observed in other large reservoirs in Quebec, but none approached the magnitude of the earthquake recorded at Manic-3. The small magnitude of most reservoir-induced seismicity makes it a minor risk to large dams.

Figure 5.28 The Daniel-Johnson dam on the Manicouagan River, Quebec. The dam, the largest multiple-arch-and-buttress dam in the world, was completed in 1968.
Source: Hydro-Quebec.

molten material from the hot spot punctured the ocean floor to form the New England seamounts. The process continues today at the Great Meteor seamount in the Atlantic ocean, south of the Azores.

1944 Cornwall-Massena Earthquake, Ontario and New York State

Both Canada and the United States claim the 1944 Cornwall-Massena earthquake whose epicentre lay under the St. Lawrence River at the border between the two countries. Although the earthquake was only of magnitude 5.6, it caused considerable damage, illustrating the vulnerability of traditional brick construction to vibrations (Figure 5.27). About 2,000 chimneys were reported to be damaged in Cornwall alone.

A Lot Still to Be Learned...

Large efforts are deployed in Canada to better understand and assess seismic hazards, from the maintenance of a complex infrastructure of monitoring instruments to geological fault mapping. Canadian society is addressing seismic risk by a series of concrete measures for short-term response (for example, alert services and shakemaps) and long-term mitigation (for example, the seismic provisions of the National Building Code of Canada and seismic zonation). The instrumental recording of earthquake signals, however, started less than a century ago, a short time compared to the return period of large earthquakes. Earthquake seismology is still in its infancy.

In Greater Depth

What to Do Before, During, and After an Earthquake

Before

We have seen that earthquakes don't kill us: it is our own buildings and belongings that fall during the shaking and harm us. What should you do? *First,* walk into each room of your house, assume strong shaking has begun, and carefully visualize what might fall (for example, ceiling fan, chandelier, mirror, china cabinet, gas water heater). Now reduce the risk. Nail them. Brace them. Tie them. Velcro™ them. Lower them. Remove them.

Second, walk outside, assume strong shaking, and visualize what might fall (for example, trees, power lines, brick chimney). Now reduce the risk. Trim them. Chop them. Replace them.

Third, repeat the visits inside and outside your home. This time, locate safe spots where protection exists, for example, under a heavy table, beneath a strong desk, under a bed. Remember these safe spots so you can use them quickly when shaking begins. Drop, cover, and hold on.

During

After examining your home, prepare yourself to stay composed during the shaking. Remember that the severe shaking probably will last only 5 to 60 seconds. So, be calm and protect yourself for one minute. In most places, if you are inside, you should stay inside; if you are outside, stay outside.

After

Expect aftershocks. If you feel aftershocks, stay where you are until they stop.

Do a safety check around your property. Check for fire hazards such as gas leaks and damaged electrical wiring. Check for structural damage to your home. Approach chimneys with caution. Turn on a battery-powered radio for information and damage reports.

Summary

- The seismicity map reveals that Canada can be divided into a stable central region, flanked by seismically active regions in the west and the east.

- The seismically active western region coincides with active tectonic environments. The subduction of small oceanic plates underneath the North American plate has triggered several megathrust earthquakes in the Cascadia Subduction Zone in the last few thousand years. Vancouver is the Canadian city where seismic risk is highest. In northern British Columbia, the along-side movement of the Pacific and North American plates along the Queen Charlotte fault has produced several transform fault earthquakes in the past. These large earthquakes, however, affect a largely unpopulated area.

- The earthquakes of the seismically active eastern region occur far from plate boundaries. The causes of these intraplate earthquakes are more enigmatic. The seisms seem to be related to pre-existing zones of weakness in the crust that are reactivated under current stresses. Ancient rifting, the Charlevoix meteoritic impact, and intrusions have left scars in the crust where rocks are more susceptible to fail. The continued opening of the Atlantic Ocean has been invoked as the source of present-day regional stress.

- Seismicity patterns, seismic wave propagation data, and geological trends are integrated to produce a national seismic hazard map for Canada. At the local level, several cities are compiling maps of foundation materials to identify zones more vulnerable to seismic amplification effects.

- In Canada, seismic risk is mitigated in the long term by the design of a better earthquake-resistant infrastructure. In the event of an earthquake, automated alert services and shakemaps would contribute to an effective short-term response.

Terms to Remember

Questions for Review

1. Sketch a plate-tectonic map along western North America from Alaska through Mexico. Label the spreading centres, subduction zones, and transform faults. What type of earthquakes are expected along the coastal zones?
2. Where do earthquakes occur in Canada? Where do megathrust earthquakes occur? Why?
3. Do damaging earthquakes occur in Canada?
4. What is the largest earthquake ever felt in Canada? The largest ever recorded?
5. What other natural disasters can be associated with earthquakes?

Questions for Further Thought

1. On the basis of the map presented in Figure 5.9b, where in Orleans would you build bungalows? High-rise apartment buildings?
2. Which would be the better of two bad choices for the Vancouver area: a magnitude 6.5 to 7 earthquake every 15 years or a magnitude 8 every century?
3. How earthquake safe is your home or office? What are the nearest faults? What kind of earth materials is your home or office built upon? How will your building size, shape, and materials react to shaking? What nearby features could affect your home? What hazards exist inside your home?
4. If the return period of magnitude 7 earthquakes in a particular urban area is 1,000 years, which buildings should be built to withstand it? Should we go to a lot of expense to make houses withstand it? Nuclear power plants? Refineries? Schools? Explain in each case why or why not.
5. How should the Canadian federal government split limited funds for seismic risk analysis and mitigation between western and eastern Canada?

Tsunami

Whence came the voice. To the sea-beaten shore
We looked, and saw a monstrous wave that soared
Into the sky, so lofty that my eyes
Were robbed of seeing the Scironian cliffs.
It hid the isthmus and Asclepius rock.
Then seething up and bubbling all about
With foaming flood and breath from the deep sea,
Shoreward it came to where the chariot stood.

—*Euripides, 428 BCE, The Hippolytus*

Outline

An onrushing tsunami sets some people fleeing while others stay and stare at the building being destroyed in Koh Raya, Thailand, on 26 December 2004. This tsunami is the leading edge of a massive sheet of water, and it poured inland for several minutes, causing destruction and death. Standing and watching a tsunami was a life-ending decision for thousands of people. When tsunami approach, run fast and gain elevation—up a hill, upstairs in a strong building, or up a tree.

Source: © John Russell/AFP/Getty

Mid-December 2004 found Tilly Smith, a 10-year-old English schoolgirl, watching video of a tsunami in her geography class in Oxshott, south of London. Two weeks later, the Smith family was on vacation on the island of Phuket in Thailand. On the morning of 26 December 2004, the family was walking along the beach near their hotel. Tilly remembers the morning:

"I saw this bubbling on the water, right on the edge, and foam sizzling just like in a frying pan. The water was coming in, but it wasn't going out again. It was coming in, and then in, and then in, towards the hotel."

She recognized the unusual phenomena as signs that powerful tsunami were on their way. Tilly told her mother, Penny:

"Mum, I know there's something wrong. I know it's going to happen—the tsunami."

Her father, Colin, recalls that *"Tilly went hysterical."*

Tilly, mum, dad, and little sister Holly returned to the hotel. While Colin Smith alerted the hotel staff to his daughter's observations, Tilly ran back to the beach to spread her tsunami warning to about 100 people. Tilly was convincing and the beach was evacuated before the killer tsunami arrived. The beach near the Marriott Hotel was a rarity in Phuket—no one was killed or seriously injured. Tilly's story is a simple reminder that education can make a difference between life and death.

Indian Ocean Tsunami, 26 December 2004

On 26 December 2004, a killer tsunami swept through the Indian Ocean and crossed Asian and African shorelines, causing death and destruction in 13 countries (Figure 6.1). The estimated death total is 245,000, but the true number is almost certainly higher and will never be known. Countries hit especially hard were Indonesia (about 198,000 dead), Sri Lanka (about 30,000 killed), India (about 11,000 dead), and Thailand (about 6,000 dead). Five Canadians are confirmed to have died in the event; 146 are missing.

What did the Earth do to cause so many deaths? The Indian-Australian plate moves obliquely toward western Indonesia at 5.3 to 5.9 cm/yr. The enormous, ongoing collision results in subduction-caused earthquakes that are frequent and huge (Figure 6.2). Many of these earthquakes send off tsunami. On 26 December 2004, a 1,200 km long fault rupture began as a 100-km long portion of the north-south oriented plate-tectonic boundary ruptured and slipped for a minute. The rupture then moved northward at 3 km/s for four minutes, then slowed to 2.5 km/s during the next six minutes. This fault movement created the second-largest earthquake in the world in the last 100 years (Table 3.2). The rupture began 30 km below the seafloor and caused movements up to 20 m that shifted the

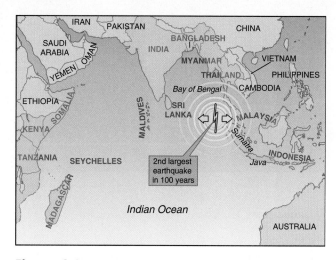

Figure 6.1
A huge earthquake on 26 December 2004 split the seafloor off northern Sumatra and sent tsunami throughout the Indian Ocean, killing about 245,000 people in 13 countries (red names).

positions of some Indonesian islands and tilted other ones. It abruptly raised the seafloor by 10 m, thus charging the water column with energy. Waves rapidly moved outward in an east-west direction, perpendicular to the fault. The huge earthquake must have collapsed many nearby buildings that fell and killed many thousands of people, but the evidence of earthquake damage was largely erased by the powerful tsunami that swept across the land minutes later (Figure 6.3). The most powerful tsunami moved east to kill people in Indonesia and Thailand, and west to slaughter people in Sri Lanka and India.

On 28 March 2005, the subduction zone broke again and this time ruptured 400 km southward from the southern end of the 2004 rupture. Was this second rupture event, just 92 days later, a continuation of the earlier earthquake? It appears that a bend or scissors-like tear in the subducting plate may have delayed the full rupture in December 2004. The 2005 earthquake did cause widespread panic but overall was a "false alert." Fault movements this time were largely strike-slip movements not accompanied by the vertical displacements required to set the water column in motion. The history of the region tells us more big earthquakes are coming; there are more seismic gaps to fill.

An overwhelming event such as this far-reaching tsunami results in many dramatic stories. A common heart-wrenching scene occurred when parents fought to withstand the tsunami and hold onto their children. Too many times, the children were pulled from their grasp and killed. In Sri Lanka, about 40% of the dead were children.

In Sri Lanka, the train known as the Queen of the Sea left Colombo at 7:30 a.m. with more than 1,000 passengers. The train chugged slowly up the palm-fringed coast until about 9:30 a.m., when the tsunami struck. It knocked the railroad cars off the track and rolled them

Figure 6.2
Subduction of Indian-Australian plate beneath Indonesia was the cause of the huge earthquakes in 2004 and 2005. The region has a long history of large earthquakes, and more will occur.

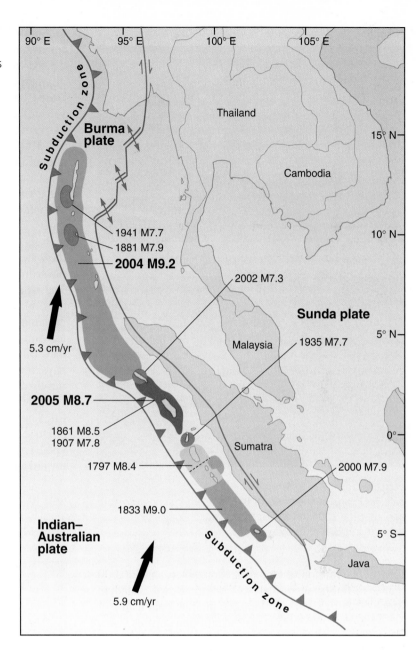

into a thick marsh, killing more than 800 passengers. The force of the tsunami was so great that wheels were torn off and tracks were twisted into odd shapes.

In India, it was Full Moon Day and many Hindus were at the ocean's edge doing ritual bathing when they were pulled out to sea by the tsunami.

In Thailand, at the peak of the tourist season, the tsunami pushed snorkellers across sharp coral reefs only to pull them back out to sea along with sunbathers. Meanwhile, farther offshore, scuba divers enjoyed the sights in deeper water, unaware of the tsunami that raced past them. On their way back to shore, they were sickened by the sight of floating corpses but did manage to rescue some people far offshore.

Immediately following this great natural disaster, people and countries of the world mobilized to bring aid to the survivors. The relief funds pledged worldwide reached between US$3 and 4 billion. Australians were particularly generous to their Indonesian neighbours and contributed more than $1 billion. People needed shelter, food, clean water, and sanitary installations. One of the big concerns was the outbreak of diseases. Without outside help, diseases such as cholera, typhoid, hepatitis A, and dysentery could conceivably have killed more people than the tsunami did.

Canadians were deeply moved by the live television images of this tragedy, which contrasted so strongly with the festive themes of the end-of-year celebrations. They responded generously. The federal government contributed $95 million to the relief effort, and Canadian non-governmental organizations another $65 million. The public Health Agency of Canada sent concrete help in the

Before

After

Figure 6.3
Satellite image of the town of Banda Aceh, Indonesia, before and after the 2004 Indian Ocean tsunami.

Photos: DigitalGlobe/Getty Images.

form of one million water purification tablets and 200,000 blankets. Ten forensic analysts from the Royal Canadian Mounted Police worked alongside international teams of experts in the gruesome task of identifying corpses.

For Canadians who might have experienced a small earthquake or observed minor slope failures, tsunami seem to be a very foreign hazard, bringing destruction to faraway lands. Most Canadians do not know that a tsunami struck Newfoundland not that long ago.

1929 Grand Banks Earthquake and Tsunami

At 5:02 p.m. on 18 November 1929, an earthquake of magnitude 7.2 M_w occurred offshore the Maritime Provinces (Figure 6.4). In fact, the "Grand Banks" earthquake is somewhat of a misnomer since its epicentre was located south of the Grand Banks, 18 km away from the continental slope, where the water is 2 km deep. The earthquake triggered the submarine movement of a sediment mass

with an estimated volume of 200 km³, which ruptured 12 transatlantic telegraph cables in its path. Direct damage caused by the earthquake was limited to a few cracked chimneys on Cape Breton Island and minor landslides. Based on questionnaires returned by local postmasters, seismologists later assigned a maximum intensity of VI to the event (Figure 5.11).

This was the first earthquake ever felt by the inhabitants of the Burin Peninsula of Newfoundland. Quoted by Janet Looker who wrote a description of the event, merchant George Bartlett of the village of Burin commented, "People gathered in little knots and discussed the occurrence, and went home to their tea. That night the moon rose with its silvery light and it died out calm, not a ripple on the water." People were unaware that the kinetic energy of the sediment mass moving downslope had set off tsunami. The tsunami began arriving about 2.5 hours later (Figure 6.5); the waves came in three major pulses during a 30-minute interval. The long narrow bays caused 1 m high tsunami to build to 3 m in many inlets and to 7 m in Taylor's Bay. When tsunami reached the heads of inlets and bays, they had so much energy and momentum that their run-up onto land reached 13 m elevation in some areas.

The tsunami ripped boats from their moorings and lifted houses from their foundations, dragging everything out to sea (Figures 6.6 and 6.7). People scrambled for survival. One story tells of a man swept out to sea. He swam toward a house, its upper windows bobbing just above the waves. Breaking through a window, he climbed inside, only to discover he was in his own home.

Help was slow to arrive. Because the telegraph cables were severed, villagers were cut off from the outside

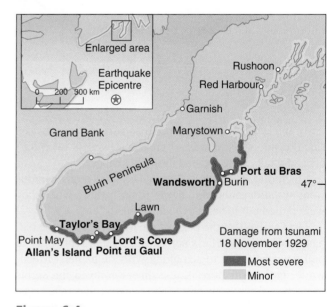

Figure 6.4
The irregular coastline of the Burin Peninsula in Newfoundland focuses the energy of tsunami. Deaths occurred in the bold-lettered villages.

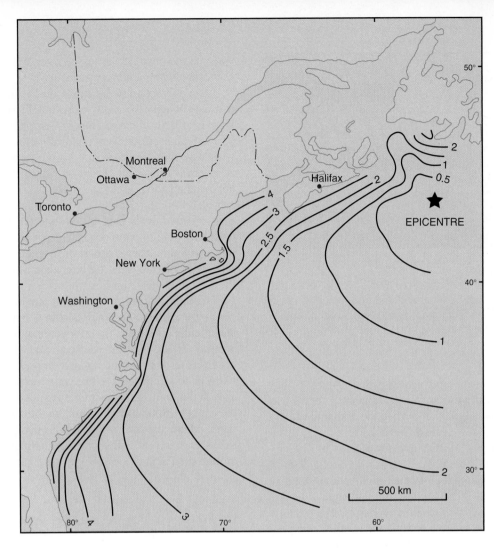

Figure 6.5
Travel times for the 1929 Grand Banks tsunami. Contour interval is half an hour. Note how the tsunami waves travel slower in the Grand Banks plateau than in the open ocean because of seafloor friction.

Source: Reproduced with the permission of Natural Resources Canada 2008, courtesy of the Geological Survey of Canada (GSC Bulletin 548).

Figure 6.6
Remnants of a destroyed dwelling, Port au Bras, Newfoundland.

Photo: The Rooms Provincial Archives, A2-146/S.H. Parsons & Sons.

Figure 6.7
The home of Steven Henry Isaacs of Port au Bras, Newfoundland, which was swept out to sea by the tsunami. The house was anchored to a fishing schooner and towed back to shore.
Photo: The Rooms Provincial Archives, A2-149/S.H. Parsons & Sons.

world and unable to send a SOS signal. At first, they could count on only themselves to organize relief. Their fate was discovered two days after the tsunami when a coastal steamer made a scheduled stop.

In total about 40 villages were affected by the tsunami, where 500 buildings, 100 fishing boats, and 26 schooners were damaged. Twenty-eight people died in what is Canada's most devastating earthquake-related loss of life recorded in written documents. The tsunami also disturbed the seabed ecosystem, resulting in poor fish catches in the following years. It dealt a crippling blow to the local fishing industry and almost drove Newfoundland to bankruptcy.

The Newfoundland tsunami is not an isolated event. Beneath the Atlantic Ocean off the east coast of North America, new images of the seafloor show significant scars where big submarine landslides occurred. Similar landslides in the future will generate tsunami.

Tsunami

The biggest, most feared waves pass mostly unnoticed across the open sea and then rear up and strike the shoreline with devastating blows. The country with the most detailed history of these killer waves is Japan, and the waves are known by the Japanese word *tsunami* (*tsu* = harbour; *nami* = waves). The reference to harbour waves emphasizes the greater heights that waves reach in inlets and harbours because the narrowed topography focuses the waves into smaller spaces. For example, an 8 m high wave on the open coast may be forced to heights of 30 m as it crowds into a narrow harbour.

A deadly example hit Japan on 15 June 1896, a summer day when fishermen were out to sea and beaches were crowded with vacationers. An offshore earthquake swayed the seafloor; then about 20 minutes later, the sea withdrew, only to return in 45 minutes with a sound like a powerful rainstorm. Tsunami hit all the beaches hard but reached their greatest heights of 29 m where they crowded into narrow inlets. The tsunami destroyed more than 10,000 homes, and killed over 27,000 people. The fishermen on the open ocean did not feel the earthquake or the tsunami; they learned of it when they sailed back into a bay littered with the wreckage of their houses and the bodies of their families.

Tsunami are most commonly created at subduction zones by earthquakes with shallow hypocentres, more specifically by subsea fault movements with pronounced vertical offsets of the seafloor that disturb the deep ocean-water mass. Not being compressible, water acts like a piston (Figure 6.9). The water column cannot easily absorb the fault-movement energy; therefore, it transmits the energy throughout the ocean in the waves we call tsunami. Major tsunami occur about once per decade. Historical data reveal that more than half of them occurred around the Pacific Ocean (Figure 6.10 and Table 6.1).

Waves in Water and on the Coastline

Water waves are pulses of energy that move through a water mass, causing water particles to rotate in place, similar to the passage of Rayleigh seismic waves (compare Figures 4.24 and 6.11). You can feel the orbital motion within waves by standing chest-deep in the ocean. An incoming wave will pick you up and carry you shoreward and then drop you downward and back as it passes. At the water surface, the diameter of the water-particle orbit is the same as the wave height. The diameters of water orbits decrease rapidly as water deepens; wave orbital motion ceases at a depth of about one-half the wavelength (Figure 6.11).

WHY A WAVE BREAKS

Waves undergo changes when they move into shallow water—at depths less than one-half their wavelength. Wave friction on the floor of the shallow ocean interferes with the orbital motions of water particles, thus waves begin slowing (Figure 6.12). Friction with the bottom

In Greater Depth

An Interview with Joseph Mitchell, Witness to the 1929 Tsunami in Wandsworth, Burin Peninsula (March 2008).

Can you describe Wandsworth at the time of the tsunami?

Wandsworth was a small fishing community on the east coast of the Burin Peninsula (Figure 6.8). The name Wandsworth was borrowed from a town in England and was chosen by English settlers who came there many years before. It was the community where my family lived for five generations before it was closed down by the government in the 1960s.

In the 1920s, there were about 120 people living in 30 households in Wandsworth. Each family had its own wharf, colloquially known as a "stage." The houses were built fairly close to each other and there was a main road and footpath connecting the houses to each other.

Fishing was the mainstay of the community. In addition, most families harvested a few crops such as potatoes, carrot, and turnip to support themselves. They grew fruit such as apples and plums in order to make preserves for use in the winter months.

Did you feel the earthquake?

At the time of the tsunami I was nine years old. I felt the earthquake while I was walking home from a neighbour's house with my mother and older sister. The earth shook violently, enough to cause damage to a few homes. During the tremor I was initially very frightened and confused about what was happening. Most everyone else felt the same way—including my family and our neighbours. Nothing like this had ever happened before. Some thought that a large airplane had passed overhead while others believed that the world was coming to an end. This all took place around 5:00 pm while many families were sitting down to their suppers.

What happened when the tsunami struck?

Wandsworth was a sheltered harbour, protected by various points and islands, which prevented the massive wave from fully reaching the community. The water level did rise about 3 m higher than usual, causing some slight damage to stages but not to the homes, since they were built farther up on the hillside.

The tsunami was completely unexpected by the people and the community was in turmoil as it struck. Children were crying, women were screaming, and everyone began to scramble to reach higher ground. The whole situation was chaotic. This was about three hours after the earthquake, around 8:00 pm.

A few people did make the connection between the earthquake and the tsunami; however, most were confused about what had happened to them.

What happened in the aftermath of the tsunami?

There was virtually no communication at the time, even between communities that were close together. The only method of transportation was by boat, and the next day people began travelling around to other places to see the extent of the damage. News spread mainly by word of mouth.

Help was mainly organized for the affected communities when word of the disaster reached St. John's. Food, supplies, and clothing were all distributed to those who had been hit the hardest by the disaster. Although people who were spared any damage were too poor to help those less fortunate, they tried to do anything they could to help, such as helping to clean up.

Although it took quite a while to repair the damage, most people stayed in their communities and rebuilt their lives. A few did leave, as the government relocated them since they had lost their homes and possessions.

Most people who are still alive that survived the tsunami disaster vividly remember the event, since it was so unexpected and frightening. Children such as my grandson have done research projects about the disaster for school, which also helps keep the memories alive.

Figure 6.8 Wandsworth, Burin Peninsula, Newfoundland, in the 1950s (left) and at present (right).
Photos: © Dr. Ian Hammond.

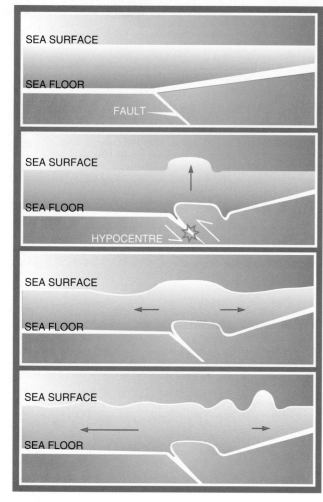

Figure 6.9
Vertical sea floor movements act like a piston to give an initial impulsion to the water column.

Source: Based on UNESCO http://portal.unesco.org/ci/en/ev.php-URL_ID=1657&URL_DO=DO_TOPIC&URL_SECTION=201.html.

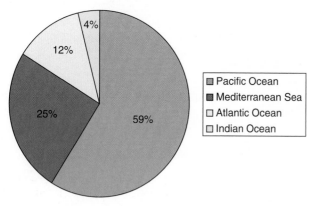

■ Pacific Ocean
■ Mediterranean Sea
□ Atlantic Ocean
□ Indian Ocean

Figure 6.10
Geographical occurrence of tsunami.

Source: Based on http://www.prh.noaa.gov/ptwc/faq.php#8.

flattens the circular motions of the water into elliptical movements.

As waves slow, their wavelengths decrease, thus concentrating water and energy into a shorter length, resulting in waves growing higher, a phenomenon known as **shoaling**. When the wave height-to-wavelength ratio (H:L) reaches about 1:7, the wave–front has grown too steep, and it topples forward as a breaker (Figures 6.13 and 6.14). Note that the 1:7 ratio is reached by changes in both wave height and wavelength; wave height is increasing at the same time that wavelength is decreasing. The depth of water beneath a breaker is roughly 1.3 times the wave height as measured from the still-water level. At this depth, the velocity of water-particle motion in the wave crest is greater than the wave velocity, thus the faster-moving wave crest outraces its bottom and falls forward as a turbulent mass.

Tsunami versus Wind-Caused Waves

PERIODS AND WAVELENGTHS

Wind-caused waves are created by the friction between wind and the ocean surface. Controlling factors are the velocity, duration, and consistency of the wind, together with the length of the body of water across which the wind blows. Although the periods and wavelengths of wind-caused waves vary by storm and season, they are distinctly different from those of tsunami (Table 6.3).

The familiar wind-caused waves rise up as they near the beach, roll forward, run up the beach for several seconds, and then withdraw (Figure 6.15a). Wind-caused waves not only come and go quickly, but the water run-up and retreat is confined to the beach (Figure 6.15b). Even huge wind-blown waves are different from tsunami. For example, at Waimea on the north shore of Oahu Island in Hawaii, the world-famous surfing waves may reach 15 m in height, but each wave is a solitary unit. These huge waves have short wavelengths and brief periods, meaning that each wave is an entity unto itself; there is no additional water mass behind the wave front. These waves are spectacular to view or ride, but what you see is what you get; the wave is the entire water mass.

Tsunami are different. Tsunami arrive as the leading edge of an elevated mass of water that rapidly runs up and *over* the beach and then floods inland for many minutes (Figures 6.15c and d). Tsunami are dangerous because their tremendous momentum carries water and debris far inland. They may be no taller than the wind-blown waves we see at the beach everyday, but they are much more powerful. Even a knee-high tsunami can kill

Table 6.1

Notable Tsunami in Recent Times

Date		Cause	Height	Site	Deaths
1 November	1755	Earthquakes	10 m	Lisbon, Portugal	30,000
21 May	1792	Volcano avalanche	10 m	Japan (Unzen)	>14,000
11 April	1815	Volcano eruption	10 m	Indonesia (Tambora)	>10,000
27 August	1883	Volcano eruption	35 m	Indonesia (Krakatau)	36,000
15 June	1896	Earthquake	29 m	Japan	27,000
11 October	1918	Subsea landslide	6 m	Puerto Rico	116
2 March	1933	Earthquake	20 m	Japan	3,000
1 April	1946	Earthquake	15 m	Alaska	175
22 May	1960	Earthquake	10 m	Chile	>1,250
27 March	1964	Earthquake	6 m	Alaska	125
1 September	1992	Earthquake	10 m	Nicaragua	170
12 December	1992	Earthquake	26 m	Indonesia	>1,000
12 July	1993	Earthquake	31 m	Japan	239
2 June	1994	Earthquake	14 m	Indonesia	238
17 July	1998	Subsea landslide	15 m	Papua New Guinea	>2,200
26 December	2004	Earthquake	10 m	Indonesia, Sri Lanka, India	>245,000
17 July	2006	Earthquake	7 m	Indonesia	>600

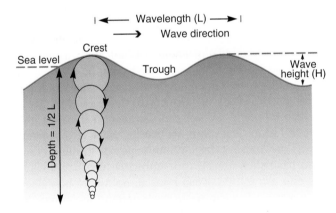

Figure 6.11
Waves are energy fronts passing through water, causing water particles to rotate in place. Rotational movement becomes insignificant at depths greater than one-half the wavelength.

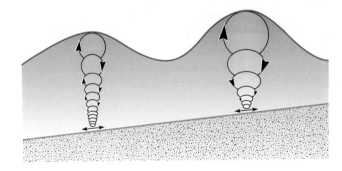

Figure 6.12
As a wave moves into shallower water, it rises higher. Circular rotating water touches bottom, causing a flattening into a back-and-forth motion.

you; the power of the fast-moving water can knock you down, then beat your body and head with debris, and drown you.

The vastly different periods and wavelengths of wind-caused versus tsunami waves can be further appreciated by looking at islands. Huge wind-caused waves such as at Waimea, Hawaii, hammer the north shore of Oahu, the windward shore. The relatively short wavelengths and periods of the Waimea waves prevent them from affecting the other shores, the leeward or protected shores.

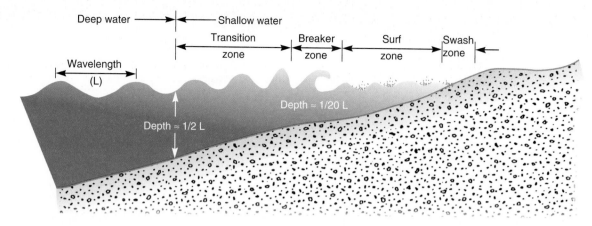

Figure 6.13
Schematic cross-section of deep-water waves entering shallow water. Wavelengths decrease and wave heights increase, leading to pitching forward as breakers.

Figure 6.14
A breaking wave. Circular rotating water is slowed at the base but rolls forward on top.
Source: © Royalty-Free/Corbis

The long wavelengths and periods of tsunami allow them to bend around many islands and hit all shores with high waves. Tsunami wavelengths are typically longer than the dimensions of an island. During the 2004 Indian Ocean tsunami, the island nation of Sri Lanka was hit by 4 to 7 m high tsunami at sites on all shores (Figure 6.16). The tsunami were directed at the east shore, where more than 14,000 people were killed, but more than 10,000 were killed on the south shore and more than 6,000 were killed on the north shore. Nearly 100 people were killed in the capital city of Colombo on the "protected" west shore.

VELOCITIES

The contrasts in velocities of wind-caused waves versus tsunami are also great. In deep water, the velocities of the wind-caused waves are about 8 m/s for a 5-second wave

and about 31 m/s for a 20-second wave (Table 6.3). The velocity of tsunami may be calculated from

$$v = \sqrt{gD}$$

where v equals wave velocity, g equals acceleration due to gravity (9.81 m/s^2), and D equals depth of ocean water. The Pacific Ocean has an average depth of 5,500 m. Calculating the square root of g times D yields a tsunami velocity of 232 m/s.

The calculated velocities of tsunami are faster than those typically measured. The energy pulse that makes the wave also puts the water into a forward rotating motion to depths of about one-half the wavelength (Figure 6.11). Tsunami wavelengths can be as great as 840 km (Table 6.3), meaning that ocean water would be disturbed to depths of 420 km. But the ocean's average depth is only 3.7 km and the deepest trenches just exceed 11 km. Therefore, the energy pulse of a tsunami moves the entire water column it passes through. Tsunami have such long wavelengths that they are always dragging across the ocean bottom, no matter how deep the water. The ocean basin has enough topography on its bottom to slow most tsunami to the 185–215 m/s range. Still, this figure converts to 725 km/h, the speed of a jet!

A tsunami of 1 m height in the deep ocean may be moving at nearly 200 m/s. As the tsunami enters shallower water, the increasing friction with the seafloor and internal turbulence of water slow its rush, but it still may be moving at highway speeds. Shoaling then compresses the wave and increases its amplitude. Water behind it begins to build up. The visible tsunami wave is only the leading edge of a tabular sheet of water that will flow on land for minutes.

Tsunami arrive as a series of several waves, with successive peaks and troughs, separated by periods in the

In Greater Depth

Velocity, Wavelength, Period, and Energy of Deep-Water Wind-Caused Waves

Waves moving through water deeper than one-half their wavelength are essentially unaffected by friction with the bottom. The waves move as low, broad, evenly spaced, rounded swells with velocities related to wavelength by

$$v = 1.25\sqrt{L}$$

where v equals wave velocity and L equals wavelength. A swell with a wavelength of 64 m would have a velocity of the square root of 64 (e.g., 8) times 1.25, or 10 m/s. The equation is telling us that wave velocity in deep water depends upon the wavelength—as wavelength increases, so does velocity.

The period (T) is the amount of time it takes for two successive wave crests to pass a given point. Since the distance between successive wave crests is the wavelength, there must be a relationship between period (T) in seconds and wavelength (L) in metres. This relationship may be defined by

$$v = \text{distance travelled/time} = L/T$$

which may be rewritten as

$$L = 1.56\ T^2$$

Higher-velocity waves carry more energy, but how much more? Wave energies can be computed with the following relationship:

$$E = 0.125\rho\ g\ H^2 L$$

where E equals wave energy, ρ equals density of water, g equals gravitational acceleration, H equals wave height, and L equals wavelength. Some representative values computed from this equation are listed in Table 6.2. Notice that doubling the wavelength will double the wave energy, but that doubling the wave height will quadruple the wave energy.

Table 6.2

Typical Energies of Wind-Caused Waves

Period (T)	Wavelength (L)	Wave Height (H)	Energy in Joules $\times 10^5$
10 seconds	156 m	1 m	2.39
		2 m	9.57
		3 m	21.54
14.1 seconds	312 m	1 m	4.79
		2 m	19.15
		3 m	43.08

Table 6.3

Representative Periods and Wavelengths

	Period (second)		Wavelength (metres)	Velocity (metres/second)
Wind-caused waves	Short:	5	39	8
	Medium:	10	156	16
	Long:	20	624	31
Tsunami	**Very long:**	**3,600**	**837,000**	**232**

10- to 60-minute range. Sometimes the trough reaches the coast first. When this happens, the ocean draws down water away from the coastlines, a foreboding sign of approaching tsunami.

Tsunami waves are typically a metre high in the open ocean and 6 to 15 m high on reaching shallow water, except where topography, such as bays and harbours, focuses the energy to create much taller waves. A tsunami wave rushes inland, causing destruction for about 30 minutes before the water is pulled back to help form the next wave. A view of the aftermath of the 1960 Chilean tsunami at Hilo, Hawaii, shows that the powerful tsunami was able to charge upslope, through the city for a long distance and a long time before receding to help form the next tsunami wave (Figure 6.17).

TSUNAMI AT THE SHORELINE

What does a tsunami look like when it comes onshore? Does it resemble the animation in the Hollywood movie *Deep Impact*, where a beautiful symmetrical wave curves high above the buildings of New York City? No.

(a)

Figure 6.15
Ocean waves. (a) A wind-blown wave rolls onto the beach in Natal, South Africa. (b) Daily wind-blown waves break on the beach and do not flood higher areas. (c) Tsunami pour across the beach and flood inland for many minutes. Even small tsunami can knock you down, batter your body with debris, and kill you. (d) A tsunami flows as a long-lasting sheet of water through Maddampegama, Sri Lanka, on 26 December 2004.

Source (a): © Digital Vision/PunchStock D)
© Gemunu Amarasinghe/AP Photos

Water rotates in circles

(b)

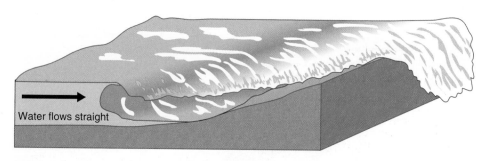

Water flows straight

(c)

(d)

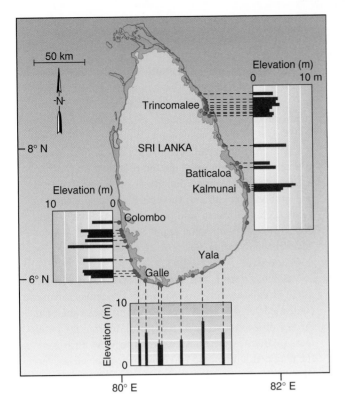

Figure 6.16
Tsunami from 4 to 7 m high were common all around Sri Lanka. The long wavelengths of the tsunami allowed them to encircle the island.

Source: *Science*, v. 308 (2005). © Science, v. 308 (2005).

Figure 6.17
Tsunami damage to Hilo, Hawaii, following the magnitude 9.5 Chile earthquake, 22 May 1960. Notice the Pacific Ocean in the background and how far inland the tsunami travelled.

Photo: © NOAA.

A tsunami arriving at the shoreline does not look like a gigantic version of the breaking waves we see every day. A typical tsunami hits the coastline like a very rapidly rising tide or whitewater wave, but it does not stop on the beach; it keeps rushing inland (Figure 6.15c).

Some well-written accounts by eyewitnesses give us insight into the flow of tsunami across shorelines.

Earthquake and Tsunami in Chile, 8 August 1868

Several ships were moored in the harbour at Arica (then part of Bolivia), including the *USS Wateree*, a two-masted sidewheeler with a broad, flat bottom. About 4 p.m., the ship began vibrating and chains rattled as a huge earthquake shook down houses in Arica. Despite worries about tsunami, the desire to help people ashore caused the *Wateree* captain to drop extra anchors, close the hatches, lash the guns, rig lifelines, and then send a yawl with 13 men to go to the jetty to help. From Lieutenant L. G. Billings, who remained aboard the Wateree:

> . . . survivors were coming down the beach and crowding on the little jetty, calling to the crews . . . to carry them to the apparent safety of the anchored vessels. . . . all at once a hoarse murmuring noise made us look up; looking towards the land we saw, to our horror, that where a moment before there had been the jetty, all black with human beings, there was nothing: everything had been swallowed in a moment by the sudden rising of the sea, which the *Wateree*, floating upon it, had not noticed. At the same time we saw the yawl carried away by the irresistible wave towards the lofty, vertical cliff of the Morro, where it disappeared in the foam as the wave broke against the rock.
>
> . . . there was another earthquake shock. Once more we saw the ground move in waves. This time the sea drew back from the land until we were stranded and the bottom of the sea was exposed, so that we saw what had never been seen before, fish struggling on the seabed and the monsters of the deep aground. The round-hulled ships rolled over on their sides, while our *Wateree* sat down upon her flat bottom; and when the sea came back, returning not as a wave, but rather like a huge tide, it made our unhappy companion [ships] turn turtle, whereas the *Wateree* rose unhurt on the churning water.
>
> It had been dark for some time when the lookout hailed the deck and said that a breaking wave was coming. Staring into the night, we first made out a thin phosphorescent line which, like a strange kind of mirage, seemed to be rising higher and higher in the air: its crest, topped by the baleful light of that phosphorescent glitter, showed frightful masses of black water below. Heralded by the thunder of thousands of breakers all crashing together, the wave that we had dreaded for hours was at last upon us.

Of all the horrors, this seemed the worst. We were chained to the bed of the sea, powerless to escape . . . We could only hold on to the rails and wait for the catastrophe. With a terrifying din, our ship was engulfed, buried under a half-liquid, half-solid mass of sand and water. We stayed under for a suffocating eternity; then, groaning in all her timbers, our solid old *Wateree* pushed her way to the surface, with her gasping crew still hanging on to the rails.

Our survival was certainly due to the construction of the ship . . . which allowed the water to pour off the deck almost as quickly as if she had been a raft. The ship had been carried along at a very great speed, but all at once she became motionless. . . . we lowered a lantern over the side and discovered that we had run aground. . . . The sun rose upon such a spectacle of desolation as can rarely have been seen. We were high and dry, three miles from our anchorage and two miles inland. The wave had carried us at an unbelievable speed over the sand dunes which line the shore, across a valley, . . . leaving us at the foot of the coastal range of the Andes.

Note several items in this thrilling account: (1) after the first earthquake, the initial seawater reaction was a deadly onrushing mass of water that killed people on the jetty; (2) after the second earthquake, the initial seawater reaction was a huge withdrawal of the sea, leaving ships sitting on the seafloor; (3) the biggest tsunami occurred hours after the earthquakes; (4) the phosphorescent glow of the huge incoming tsunami is a commonly reported phenomenon due to bioluminescence of small sea life caught up in the monster wave; and (5) a large U.S. warship was carried 3 km inland.

Tsunami at Hilo, Hawaii, 1 April 1946

As 1 April 1946 began in the Aleutian Islands, two large subduction movements occurred and shook the area severely. The five workers in the Scotch Gap lighthouse were shaken awake and wondered what lay ahead during the dark night. The lighthouse was built of steel-reinforced concrete, and its base sat 14 m above mean low-water level (Figure 6.18a). About 20 minutes after the second earthquake, a tsunami approximately 30 m high swept the lighthouse away (Figure 6.18b). This time, *the first wave was the biggest;* it killed all five men.

Tsunami are not only local events; these waves raced across the entire Pacific Ocean. The April Fool's Day tsunami travelled about 215 m/s in the deep ocean, slowing to about 15 m/s as it neared shore in Hilo, Hawaii, where 159 people were killed. Humans are no match for these massive waves. The long wavelengths allow the wave front to rush onland for long distances; there is no trough immediately behind, waiting to pull the water back to the ocean.

U.S. oceanographer Francis P. Shepard described the tsunami that arrived in Hilo, Hawaii:

. . . we were sleeping peacefully when we were awakened by a loud hissing sound, which sounded for all the world as if dozens of locomotives were blowing off steam directly outside our house. Puzzled, we jumped up and rushed to the front window. Where there had been a beach previously, we saw nothing but boiling water, which was sweeping over the ten-foot [3 m] top of the beach ridge and coming directly at the house. I rushed and grabbed my camera, forgetting such incidentals as clothes, glasses, watch, and pocketbook. As I opened the door, I noticed with some regret that the water was not advancing any farther, but, instead, was retreating rapidly down the slope.

By that time I was conscious of the fact that we might be experiencing a tsunami. My suspicions became confirmed as the water moved swiftly seaward, and the sea dropped a score of feet [6 m], leaving the coral reefs in front of the house exposed to view. Fish were flapping and jumping up and down where they had been stranded by the retreating waves . . .

In a few minutes as I stood at the edge of the beach ridge in front of the house, I could see the water beginning to rise and swell up around the outer edges of the exposed reef; it built higher and higher and then came racing forward with amazing velocity. "Now," I said, "here is a good chance for a picture" (Figure 6.19).

One of the ironies of this tragedy is that some of the deaths were people who were warned. After being told a tsunami was coming, some folks laughed, said they knew it was April Fool's Day, and ignored the warning.

Causes of Tsunami

Powerful tsunami are caused when a water mass is hit with a massive jolt of energy. Common causes are earthquakes, volcanoes, mass movements, and impacts.

In earthquake-caused tsunami, movement is initiated along an active fault on the seafloor. The energy released tends to move in a direction perpendicular to this linear source, with little attenuation. The 2004 Indian Ocean tsunami, for instance, was generated by a north-south oriented fault and propagated mainly in an east-west direction across the ocean basin with still enough power to strike hard the faraway shores of east Africa (Figure 6.1). In contrast, volcano-caused and landslide-caused tsunami originate from point sources—similar to a stone dropped in a pond. Their energy flows away radially from the source point, and as it does so, the energy "spreads out"

(a)

(b)

Figure 6.18
The Scotch Gap lighthouse in the Aleutian Islands of Alaska (a) before and (b) after the tsunami unleashed by a magnitude 7.3 earthquake on 1 April 1946.
Photos: © NOAA.

Figure 6.19
Tsunami rushing across the shore and heading into Hilo, Hawaii, on 1 April 1946.
Photo: © Francis P. Shepard, NOAA.

along the wavefront, which gets longer as the wave moves. This increased loss of energy results in attenuation over shorter distances. Waves from volcano-caused and landslide-caused tsunami might locally be higher than those generated by earthquake-caused tsunami. However, they do not carry energy as far.

The biggest tsunami are caused by the rarest of these events, the impact of high-velocity asteroids and comets. Consider the amount of energy injected into the ocean when a 10 km diameter asteroid hits at 13,000 m/s. These events will be discussed in Chapter 15 on mass extinctions and Chapter 16 on hazards from space.

Earthquake-Caused Tsunami

Fault movements of the seafloor that generate large earthquakes also may cause powerful tsunami. In general, the fault movements need to be vertical and result in uplifting or down-dropping the seabed in an earthquake with a magnitude of at least $7M_w$ (Table 6.4).

CHILE, 22 MAY 1960

The most powerful earthquake ever measured occurred in Chile on 22 May 1960. Tsunami generated by this magnitude 9.5 subduction movement killed people throughout the Pacific Ocean basin. In Chile, the main seism broke loose at 3:11 p.m. on Sunday. Chileans are familiar with earthquakes, so many people headed for high ground in anticipation of tsunami. About 15 minutes after the seism, the sea rose like a rapidly rising tide, reaching 4.5 m above sea level. Then the sea retreated with speed and an incredible hissing and gurgling noise, dragging broken houses and boats out into the ocean. Some people took the "smooth wave" as a

Table 6.4

Fault Displacements of Seafloors

Earthquake Magnitude (M_w)	Fault Slip (metres)	Rupture Duration (second)	Vertical Movement of Seafloor (metres)
7	0.6	23	0.2
8	2.7	70	0.7
9	9	200	2.3
9.5	27	330	7

Source: © *Science*, v. 78 (1997).

sign that these tsunami could be ridden out at sea, thus remaining on their boats. About 4:20 p.m., the second tsunami arrived as an 8 m high wave travelling at 55 m/s. The wave crushed boats and their terrified passengers, as well as wrecked coastal buildings. But *the third wave was the largest;* it rose 11 m high, but it travelled at only half the speed of the second wave. Over 1,000 Chileans died in these tsunami.

Since 1960, Hawaiians are given warnings before tsunami arrive. The Chilean tsunami was predicted to travel 14 hours across the Pacific and arrive in Hawaii at 9:57 a.m.; it arrived at 9:58 a.m (Figure 6.20). But 61 people drowned anyway, including sightseers attracted to the shore to watch the tsunami roll in. The tsunami raced on to Japan, where it killed another 185 people, 22.5 hours after the earthquake. The energy in this set of tsunami was so great that it was recorded on Pacific Ocean tide gauges for a week as the energy pulses bounced back and forth across the entire ocean basin.

ALASKA, 27 MARCH 1964

Saint Matthew's account of the first Good Friday included, "And, behold . . . the earth did quake, and the rocks rent." His words applied again, over 1,900 years later, on Good Friday, 27 March 1964. At 5:36 p.m., in the wilderness at the head of Prince William Sound, a major subduction movement created a gigantic earthquake. This was followed in sequence by other downward thrusts at 9, 19, 28, 29, 44, and 72 seconds later as a nearly 1,000 km long slab of 400 km width lurched its way deeper into the mantle. Hypocentre depths were from 20 to 50 km. The earthquake magnitude was 9.2 M_w. The duration of strong ground shaking was lengthy—more than 4 minutes; it induced many avalanches, landslides, ground settlements, and tsunami. Of the 131 lives lost, 122 were due to tsunami.

The tsunami reached Port Alberni on Vancouver Island three hours after the earthquake (Figure 6.20). Residents had received warning and retreated to high ground, and no one was killed. They returned home, however, to a scene of destruction. The over 6 m high tsunami had destroyed no less than 58 buildings in the small town and damaged 320 others (Figure 6.21). Thanks to advance warning, the Crescent City, California, waterfront area was also evacuated, and residents waited upslope while tsunami arrived and did their damage. After watching four tsunami and seeing their sizes, many people could no longer stand the suspense of not knowing the condition of their properties. Some people went down to check—a big mistake. At that location, *the fifth wave* in the tsunami series was the biggest; it was 6.3 m high, and it killed 12 of the curious people.

Tsunami arrive as a series of several waves. Which wave in the series will be the biggest? It is unpredictable; in the 1946, 1960, and 1964 case histories above, the biggest wave was the first, third, and fifth, respectively.

TSUNAMI HAZARD IN COASTAL BRITISH COLUMBIA

Nowhere in Canada is tsunami hazard highest than along the coast of British Columbia due to the earthquake activity around the Pacific "Ring of Fire" (Figure 1.11). Three types of tsunami threaten coastal British Columbia on the basis of the size of the area affected. Basin-wide tsunami are energetic enough to travel across the Pacific Ocean. The 1960 Chile tsunami is an example (Figure 6.20). Depending on the point of origin of the tsunami, British Columbia residents have between 5.5 and 18 hours to take preventive measures. Regional tsunami originate from the active tectonic zones of western North America (Figure 3.23). Because of the size and frequency of its earthquakes, and the flow direction of ocean currents, Alaska is the most frequent source. Regional tsunami can strike anytime between 0.5 and 5 hours after a large earthquake, as in the case of the Alaska tsunami, which ravaged Port Alberni in 1964. Finally, local tsunami may be triggered by earthquakes occurring offshore British Columbia or in the inner waters separating Vancouver Island from the mainland. The most devastating tsunami would result from a megathrust earthquake in the Cascadia Subduction Zone, similar to the event of 1700 (Figure 5.13b). In such a case, the areas most affected would be the west coast of Vancouver Island, which is facing the open ocean, where wave heights up to 9 m are predicted. The long-wavelength tsunami waves would circle around Vancouver Island and also hit its eastern shores and the continental coast. Fortunately, the cities

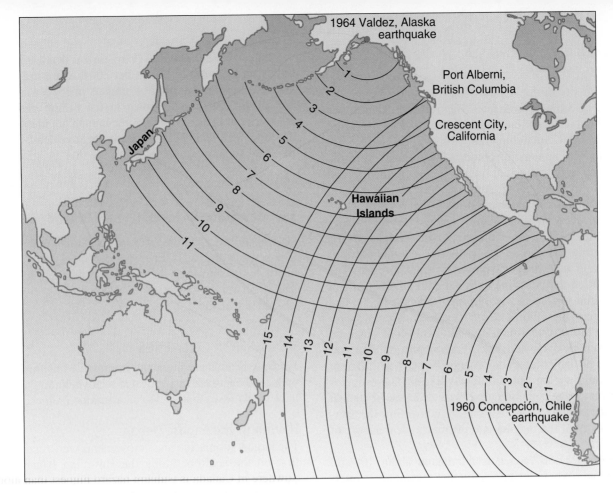

Figure 6.20
Tsunami travel times in hours.
Data source: © Kious, W.J. and Tilling, R.I., The Dynamic Earth, p. 77, US Geographical Survey

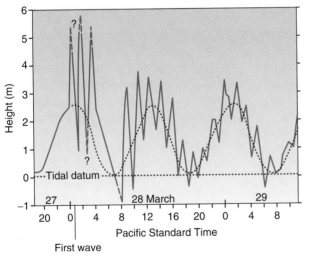

Figure 6.21
Tidal records for Port Alberni, British Columbia, 27–29 March 1964. The three main waves of the Alaska tsunami arrived between 12:20 a.m. and 3:30 a.m. on 28 March, forcing the tide gauge offscale. Normal tidal heights are shown by a dotted line.

Source: Reproduced with the permission of Natural Resources Canada 2008, courtesy of the Geological Survey of Canada (GSC Bulletin 548).

of Victoria and Vancouver are in sheltered waters. Wave heights of only 1 m are expected in these areas.

In the event of a Cascadia megathrust earthquake triggering a local tsunami, there might not be enough time for formal warnings due to the proximity between the epicentre and the shore. In such a case, authorities give one simple, potentially life-saving advice: "Persons in coastal areas who experience a large earthquake with shaking lasting a minute or more should assume that a tsunami will arrive within a few minutes and take immediate action to evacuate to safer high ground."

Volcano-Caused Tsunami

Volcanic action can create killer tsunami (Table 6.1). Volcanoes can put jolts of energy into a water body in several ways: they can explode, they can collapse, and they can send avalanches of debris into the water. It seems likely that tsunami were generated by all three mechanisms during the eruption of Krakatau in 1883.

KRAKATAU, INDONESIA, 26–27 AUGUST 1883

Krakatau sits in the sea between the major Indonesian islands of Sumatra and Java (Figure 6.22). One of the most famous eruption sequences in history occurred here in 1883, including the killing events of 26–27 August. On Sunday afternoon, 26 August, volcanic eruptions and explosions increased in frequency and strength. In the evening, some of the eruptions blasted large volumes of gas-charged rocky debris downslope into the sea. These volcanic masses flowed rapidly downslope, across the shoreline, and collided with the sea, putting energy into the water that radiated outward as tsunami that ravaged villages on the shoreline. The highly irregular coastline in this region affects tsunami height and run-up in the various harbours, inlets, and peninsulas (Figure 6.22).

On Monday morning, gigantic explosions occurred around 5:30, 6:45, and 8:20. Each explosion sent tsunami with their maximum energy focused in different directions, wiping out different villages. These explosions may have been due to seawater coming in contact with the magma body and rapidly converting the thermal energy of the magma into the mechanical energy of tsunami.

The eruption sequence culminated about 10 a.m. with an overwhelming explosion that commonly is interpreted as being due to the volcano mountain collapsing into the void formed by its partly emptied magma chamber. The resulting blast was heard for thousands of kilometres. Tsunami pushed into harbours and ran up and over some coastal hills up to 40 m high. The tsunami during this 20-hour period destroyed 165 villages and killed more than 36,000 people. This tsunami death total was not exceeded until 26 December 2004, again in Indonesia. The world population of humans in 1883 was about 1.6 billion, but it had grown to 6.4 billion people in 2004. The dramatic growth of the human population during those 121 years helped lead to the huge death total in the 2004 tsunami.

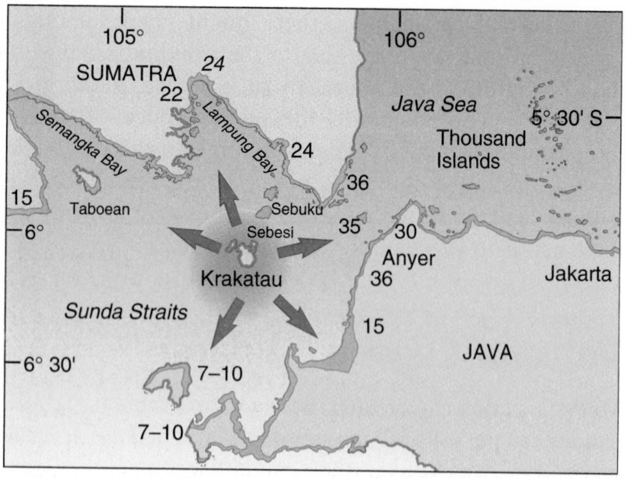

Landslide-Caused Tsunami

Gravity pulls a variety of rock and sediment masses into and beneath the seas. Energy from these mass movements is transferred to the water, locally causing higher and larger run-ups of water than caused by earthquake-generated tsunami.

VOLCANO COLLAPSES

Volcanic islands are huge and impressive features. Their bulk and beauty are inspiring and overwhelming, but they have weaknesses that lead to catastrophic failures.

Hawaii in the Pacific Ocean

The largest submarine mass movements were recognized first on the seafloor along the Hawaiian Islands volcanic chain. Slump and debris-avalanche deposits there cover more than five times the land area of the islands (Figure 6.23). Some individual debris avalanches are over 200 km long with volumes greater than 5,000 km^3,

Figure 6.22
Many killer tsunami were sent off by the eruptive behaviours of Krakatau Volcano in Indonesia on 26–27 August 1883. Tsunami run-up heights are shown in metres. Tsunami flooded areas are coloured.

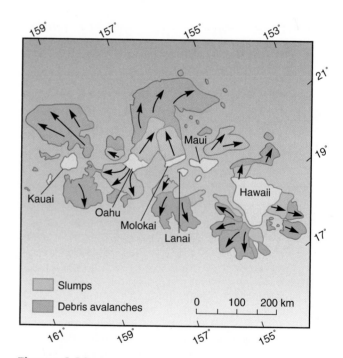

Figure 6.23
The Hawaiian Islands cover less surface area than the slumps and debris avalanches that have fallen from them.

making them some of the largest on Earth. These events are not just loose debris sliding down the side of the volcano; they are catastrophic **flank collapses** where the whole side of an oceanic volcano breaks off and falls into the sea (Figure 3.38). There have been at least 70 flank collapses from the Hawaiian Islands in the last 20 million years.

Pause and think about this a moment: each Hawaiian Island has major structural weaknesses that lead to massive failures. The not-so-solid earth here betrays us; it can fail rapidly and massively. For example, the island of Molokai has no volcano. Where did it go? Apparently, the northern part of the island fell into the ocean (Figure 6.23), leaving steep cliffs behind.

What happens to the ocean when a gigantic chunk of island drops into it and flows rapidly underwater? Huge tsunami are created. For example, prehistoric giant waves washed coral, marine shells, and volcanic rocks inland, where they are found today as gravel layers on Lanai lying 365 m above sea level and on Molokai over 2 km inland and more than 60 m above sea level. Tsunami of this size would not only ravage Hawaii but also cause death and destruction throughout the Pacific Ocean basin.

Islands in the Atlantic Ocean

After it was recognized in Hawaii that large volcanic islands experience major collapses that generate powerful tsunami, the search began to find other sites where flank collapses have occurred. A similar history was found in the Canary Islands in the Atlantic Ocean off the coast of northwest Africa at about 28° north latitude. At least three of the Canary Islands—Tenerife, La Palma, and Hierro—have had mega-collapses. The last known major event happened on Hierro just 15,000 years ago. When the next collapse occurs, powerful tsunami could hit coastal cities along the east coasts of North and South America and along the west coasts of Europe and Africa. Although these events are rare, they are real and can be destructive.

A computer simulation was made by Steven Ward and Simon Day assuming a 500 km³ flank collapse from Cumbre Vieja Volcano on La Palma in the Canary Islands. The model forecast that tsunami waves could travel across the Atlantic Ocean and strike the east coasts of the Americas with heights of 3 to 18 m at the shoreline (Figure 6.24).

Flank collapses are not unique to Hawaii and the Canary Islands; they can occur around the world. As oceanic volcanoes grow, they tend to develop internal weaknesses and sides that are too steep, and thus, they collapse in gigantic events. Worldwide, approximately one flank collapse occurs every 10,000 years.

EARTHQUAKE-TRIGGERED MOVEMENTS

As illustrated by the 1929 Grand Banks event, earthquakes not only generate tsunami directly, but also their

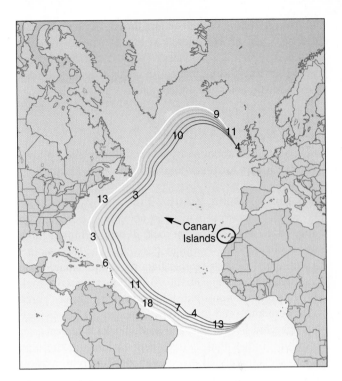

Figure 6.24
Tsunami wave amplitude six hours after a flank collapse in the Canary Islands. Tsunami striking the east coast of North America could locally be 13 m high.
Source: © Ward and Day.

energy can trigger the movement of large masses of rock or sand whose kinetic energy causes tsunami.

Papua New Guinea, 17 July 1998

At 6:49 p.m. on Friday evening, the north shore of Papua New Guinea was rocked by a 7.1 magnitude earthquake occurring about 20 km offshore. As the shaking ended, witnesses describe seeing the sea rise above the horizon and shoot spray 30 m high. Sounds were heard like distant thunder, and then the sea slowly pulled back. About four to five minutes later, a rumbling sound was heard and a tsunami about 4 m high was seen approaching. But if you can see the wave coming, it is too late to escape. Many people living on the barrier beach were washed into the lagoon.

Several minutes later, a second wave approached, but this one was about 14 m tall and measured 4 to 5 km across. A tsunami does not have the shape of a typical wave; it is more like a pancake of water. Visualize this thick pancake of water pouring over the heavily populated beach at 7 m/s for over a minute. This tsunami event was a three-wave sequence that washed thousands of people and their homes into the lagoon. A barrier beach that hosted four villages was swept clean. The estimated 2,200 fatalities were mostly those least able to swim—the children.

The Papua New Guinea tsunami apparently was not caused directly by the earthquake but by a submarine landslide triggered by the shaking. This event has caused a global rethinking of the tsunami threat. Big tsunami can no longer just be considered as events caused by giant earthquakes in distant places. Tsunami can be created by smaller local faults that cause unstable sand and rock masses to slip and slide under water.

IN BAYS AND LAKES

The constricted topography of bays and lakes allows some landslides to create huge tsunami of local extent.

Lituya Bay, Alaska, 9 July 1958

The largest historical wave run-up known occurred on 9 July 1958, when a massive rockfall dropped into Lituya Bay in Glacier Bay National Park, Alaska. It was after 10 p.m. when the Fairweather fault moved in a magnitude 8 earthquake, causing about 90 million tonnes of rock and ice to drop more than 900 m into the water. Three boats were anchored in the bay. One was a 12 m fishing boat operated by a father and son who later reported an earsplitting crash that caused them to look up the bay, only to see a huge wall of water about 30 m high roaring toward them faster than 45 m/s. They had only enough time to turn the bow (front) of the boat toward the wave. The onrushing tsunami swept over 54 m high Cenotaph Island and then hit them. Their anchor chain snapped, and the boat soared near vertically upward like a high-speed elevator in a tall building. Reaching the crest of the wave, they dropped down the back side and survived. The second boat was carried across the sandbar beach into the ocean, and the crew survived. The third boat fired up its engine and tried to outrun the tsunami; this was a bad decision. The wave hit that boat on the stern (backside), flipped it, destroyed it, and killed the crew.

Looking at beautiful Lituya Bay after the traumatic evening showed that the rockfall impact sent a surge of water up the opposite slope, stripping away mature trees up to 525 m above sea level. The tsunami destroyed and stripped away mature trees along both walls of the bay, all the way to the open ocean.

Seiches

Seiches are oscillating waves that slosh back and forth within an enclosed body of water such as a sea, bay, lake, or swimming pool. The process was observed and named in Lake Geneva, Switzerland, in 1890. The word "seiche" (pronounced "SAY-sh") comes from a Swiss-French word that means to sway back and forth.

The energy to cause a seiche can come from a variety of sources. Winds blowing across a lake can cause the water body to oscillate at some natural frequency. Seiches are common in the Great Lakes of Canada and the United States, where they may be called sloshes. For example,

with its elongate shape and relatively shallow water, Lake Erie can experience seiches when strong winds blow. The oscillating water mass can form seiches up to 5 m high, alternating from one end of the lake to the other.

Earthquakes frequently cause seiches. People living in seismically active areas commonly get to watch seiches during an earthquake when the water in swimming pools sloshes back and forth and overflows the sides.

HEBGEN LAKE, MONTANA, 17 AUGUST 1959

Shortly before midnight on 17 August 1959 two faults running beneath the northern end of Hebgen Lake moved in magnitude 6.3 and 7.5 earthquakes. These two normal faults had their southwestern sides drop 7 and 7.8 m, also dropping the northern end of Hebgen Lake. The foreman at the Hebgen Lake Dam was awakened by the earthquake, dressed, and went outside for a look. He became eyewitness to a spectacular seiche event where lake water sloshed back and forth for 11.5 hours. In foreman Hungerford's own words:

> The dust was so intense you could hardly see. You could hardly breathe, or anything. It obscured the moon. We went to the river gauge. . . . Just as we got to it, we heard a roar and we saw this wall of water coming down the river. . . . We thought the dam had broken. . . . Then we went up to the dam. When we got there we couldn't see much, but I walked over to the edge of the dam and all we could see was blackness. There was no water. No water above the dam at all, and I couldn't imagine what had become of it. By that time the dust had started to clear, and the moon had come out a little. And then here came the water. It had all been up at the other end of the lake. . . . We rushed back when we heard the water coming. We could hear it before we could see it. When it came over the dam, it was a wall of water about three to four feet [0.9–1.2m] high completely across that dam, and it flowed like that for what seemed to me to be 20 minutes, but possibly it could have been 5 or 10. I have no idea of time. It flowed for a while, and then it started to subside. Then it all cleared away, and no water again. The lake was completely dry as far as we could see. All we could see down the dam was darkness again. It seemed like a period of maybe 10 to 15 minutes, and the water came back, and then it repeated the same thing over again.

Surviving a Tsunami

When confronted to a tsunami, the best strategy is avoidance. Recent tsunami tragedies show how important it is to broadcast widely this simple message to populations living in coastal areas (Figure 6.28).

TSUNAMI WARNINGS

Nagging questions arose about the lack of warning about the approaching 2004 Indian Ocean tsunami. For example, the first tsunami arrived in Sri Lanka two hours after the earthquake. Couldn't warnings have been spread to alert people in time to save thousands of lives?

In the aftermath of the 1960 Chilean tsunami, the circum-Pacific nations were first to coordinate efforts toward an integrated warning system, leading to the creation in 1949 of the Pacific Tsunami Warning Center (PTWC). The PWTC receives data from seismograph stations deployed around the globe and screens earthquakes as they occur. An earthquake with the following characteristics could potentially generate a tsunami: (1) Richter magnitude of 7.0 or greater; (2) epicentre on the ocean floor; (3) hypocentre shallower than 100 km. When an earthquake meeting these criteria is identified, computers calculate the travel times to coastal communities and a regional "tsunami watch" is issued. A "tsunami watch" is an advance alert to areas that could be impacted by destructive tsunami waves, based on seismic information alone, without confirmation that a tsunami is underway. When sea-level data from buoys and tidal gauges detect tsunami waves, the threat is confirmed and a "tsunami warning" is broadcast across the entire Pacific Ocean basin. National authorities are responsible to take appropriate actions, which could include the evacuation of low-lying coastal areas and ordering ships out of harbour to deep water.

The 2004 Indian Ocean tsunami cruelly made the case for an infrastructure similar to the PTWC in other parts of the world. The establishment of warning systems in the Indian Ocean and Caribbean Sea is currently underway. The design of effective warning systems in these smaller bodies of water is particularly challenging because of the shorter travel times between the earthquake epicentre and coastal areas.

BUOYS AND SEAFLOOR SENSORS

The first seafloor sensors designed to warn people of approaching tsunami were activated in October 2003 by the U.S. National Oceanographic and Atmospheric Administration (NOAA). The sensors exploit a fundamental feature of tsunami waves—the fact that they disturb all the water column down to the ocean floor as opposed to wind-caused waves, which create turbulence only a few tens of metres below the water surface. Each instrument consists of a tsunameter and a surface buoy (Figures 6.25 and 6.26). The tsunameter is anchored securely on the ocean floor. Its pressure sensor is sensitive to the passage of tsunami waves. When anomalous pressure variations are detected in this otherwise very quiet environment, the tsunameter sends a signal to the surface buoy, which relays it to the PTWC via a satellite link.

Figure 6.25
DART™ (Deep-ocean Assessment and Reporting of Tsunami) tsunami warning system.

Source: DART tsunami warning system http://nctr.pmel.noaa.gov/Dart/Jpg/DART-II_05x.swf NOAA/PMEL.

Figure 6.26
Tsunami-warning buoy in Pacific Ocean.
Photo: © NOAA.

On 16 November 2003, a magnitude 7.5 earthquake rocked the seafloor in the Aleutian Islands of Alaska. In 25 minutes, a seafloor sensor triggered a tsunami warning for U.S. coastal areas. But in another 40 minutes, computer analysis predicted that the tsunami would be only 19 cm high at Hilo, Hawaii. The tsunami warning was cancelled in Hawaii, saving $68 million, the economic impact of a statewide coastal evacuation—an impressive start for a new warning system.

Before the 2004 Indian Ocean tsunami, NOAA operated a six-buoy warning system in the northern Pacific Ocean. After the 2004 disaster, funding was provided to install an extensive network. As of March 2007, there are 28 seafloor sensors in operation, mostly deployed near the subduction zones around the Pacific Ocean, and in the Caribbean Sea (Figure 6.27). Several more are planned, including three in the Indian Ocean. Also, new tidal gauge stations and seismometers will be placed along the coastlines of several countries. Canada is participating in this effort. With the 1929 Grand Banks tsunami in mind, the federal government announced in 2007 an upgrade of several Atlantic sea-level gauges and seismic-data transmission links. The goal is to provide real-time warnings before tsunami hit the shorelines of Atlantic Canada.

IF YOU FEEL THE EARTHQUAKE

If you are near the coast and feel an earthquake, then think about the possibility of tsunami (Figure 6.28). The earliest warning of a local tsunami is the strong shaking of the ground, and people near the shoreline should evacuate immediately without waiting for an official warning (Figure 6.28). Other clues can alert you to the possibility of powerful tsunami. Before the first big wave of a tsunami, the sea either may withdraw significantly far from shore, or it may suddenly rise. Sometimes the ocean water changes character or makes different sounds, or something out of the ordinary may happen. Notice these changes in ocean behaviour.

If you think tsunami might be coming, seek high ground immediately. If no high ground is available, then go upstairs in a well-built building or climb a tree—the so-called vertical evacuation (Table 6.5). It doesn't matter how strong a swimmer you are; it is not only the water that can hurt you but also the debris it carries.

Simuele Island, Indonesia, 26 December 2004

Simuele Island is the inhabited land closest to the epicentre of the magnitude 9.2 earthquake in 2004. When the destructive seismic shaking stopped, the residents did not

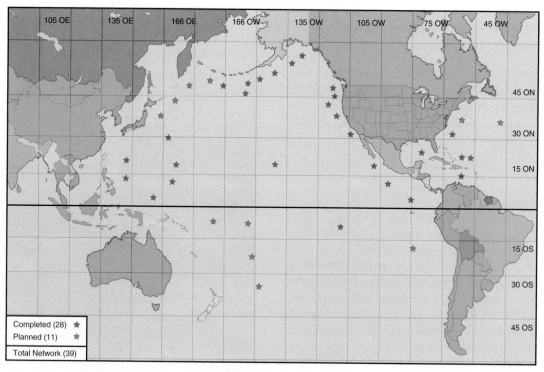

Figure 6.27
Geographical distribution of DART™ tsunami warning systems as of March 2007.
Source: Geographical distribution of DART http://nctr.pmel.noaa.gov/Dart/Jpg/buoylocations-mar08.jpg NOAA/PMEL.

Figure 6.28
International tsunami warning sign.
Source: The McGraw-Hill Companies/John A. Karachewski, photographer.

Table 6.5

Surviving a Tsunami

Abandon your belongings.

Many lives are lost while trying to save possessions.

Head for high ground—and stay there.

If there is no high ground nearby, then

Climb to an upper floor or roof of a strong building.

If there is no sturdy building, then

Climb a tree.

If there are no climbable trees, then

Grab onto something that floats.

Look for something to use as a raft.

take time to check their houses or talk with their neighbours; they fled to the hills. Within 30 minutes of the earthquake, tsunami 10 m high ravaged the earthquake-damaged coastal villages and destroyed much of what remained. After the earthquake and tsunami, a counting of the residents found that only 7 out of 75,000 inhabitants were killed. Why were so few people killed? The islanders remembered the stories passed down as oral history from their ancestors: when the ground shakes, run to the hills before the giant waves arrive.

COASTAL MAPS

In the long term, a sensible mitigation strategy against tsunami comprises identifying and managing vulnerable coastal areas. Centrally located in the earthquake-prone Pacific Ocean, Hawaii has experienced tsunami generated in all parts of the Pacific. The broad-scale threats to homeowners and businesses are presented in a tsunami hazard map for the Big Island of Hawaii (Figure 6.29). The map predicts the effect of local topography on the heights and run-ups of tsunami at the shoreline. Notice how the large bay of Hilo is particularly vulnerable. Following the 1946 tsunami, the citizens of Hilo have rebuilt their city centre several blocks inland from the shoreline. The waterfront area of Hilo is now recreational parkland.

Mapping of coastlines in Indonesia, India, and Sri Lanka following the killer tsunami of 2004 showed how human activities increased the damages and life loss in some areas. The coastal areas where forests had been removed suffered more extensive damages than neighbouring areas with the natural vegetation intact. Trees and shrubs reduce the amplitude and energy of incoming waves. With the forest gone, only houses, bridges, and other human-built structures were left to absorb the tsunami energy.

In Sri Lanka, many of the hardest-hit coastlines were ones where coral reefs had been removed. Coral reefs there are mined for souvenirs to sell, removed to open beaches for tourists, and blown up to stun and catch the fish inside them. With coral barrier reefs removed, tsunami could charge farther inland and with greater energy.

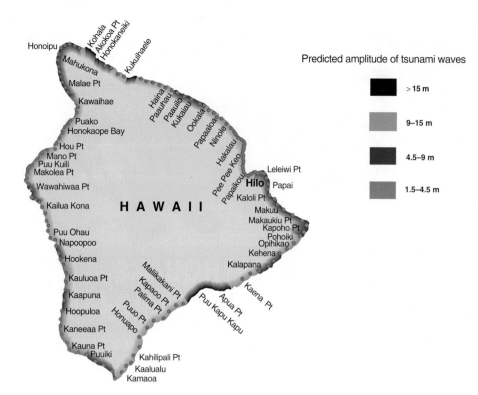

Predicted amplitude of tsunami waves

> 15 m

9–15 m

4.5–9 m

1.5–4.5 m

Summary

- Wind-caused waves are induced by the friction between wind and the water surface. They typically have periods of a few seconds and wavelengths ranging between a few tens to several hundreds of metres. Wind-caused waves are solitary waves that curl over at the shore, run partway up the beach, and then pull back to the sea.
- Tsunami waves are created when the entire water column of the ocean is disturbed. They commonly travel at 200 m/s in the open ocean and may be spaced as much as 60 minutes apart. Tsunami waves are the leading edge of a tabular mass of water that may keep running onshore for 5, 10, or even 30 minutes before being pulled back to the sea. Their long period and momentum make tsunami dangerous.
- Tsunami are most often triggered by large earthquakes. Other causes include volcanic eruptions, terrestrial and subsea mass movements, and asteroid impacts.
- Earthquakes that could potentially generate tsunami have the following characteristics: (1) large magnitude; (2) epicentre on the ocean floor; and (3) shallow hypocentre. They are especially dangerous if associated with large vertical displacement of the ocean floor.
- Seiches are oscillating waves that slosh back and forth within an enclosed body of water such as a bay or a lake. The energy for a seiche commonly comes from strong winds, seismic waves, or ground movements.
- If a tsumani is coming: Abandon your belongings. Head for high ground and stay there. If there is no high ground, climb to an upper floor of a strong building. If no building is nearby, climb a tree. If there are no trees, grab something that floats.

Terms to Remember

flank collapse   161   seiche   163   shoaling   150

Questions for Review

1. What is the energy source of (a) everyday waves at the beach? (b) tides (see Chapter 2)? (c) tsunami?
2. What are four major causes of tsunami? Make two rank-order lists (from #1 to #4) completing these statements: Tsunami are most frequently caused by _____? Tsunami are largest when caused by _____?
3. How fast can tsunami travel? (a) in the deep ocean? (b) in shallow water? What are typical tsunami wavelengths and periods?
4. How many wavetrains occur in a tsunami event?
5. Which wave is the biggest in a tsunami event?
6. How does a tsunami behave as it approaches land? Are tsunami more dangerous along a straight coastline or in a V-shaped harbour or inlet?
7. How do tsunami differ from seiches?
8. Do all oceans have tsunami?

Questions for Further Thought

1. Is there any way to prevent a tsunami?
2. Are tsunami similar to seismic waves? What are major similarities or differences?
3. What are the additional challenges of designing a tsunami warning system for the smaller Indian Ocean than for the large Pacific Ocean?
4. What features should tsunami-resistant houses have?
5. If you were at the beach and felt an earthquake lasting 30 seconds, what would you do?

Volcanic Eruptions: Plate Tectonics and Magma

Past civilizations are buried in the graveyards of their own mistakes.

—*Lord Ritchie-Calder, 1970,* Mortgaging the Old Homestead

Outline

View over the harbour city of Catania, Sicily, toward Mount Etna. The city has been buried seven times by lava from Etna. Each time, the city has been rebuilt on top of its predecessor to await its turn to be buried.

Photo: © Pat Abbott.

Volcanoes deal out overwhelming doses of energy no human can survive. The most famous of all volcanoes probably is Vesuvius in Italy, and the most famous of all eruptions must be those of 79 CE. It was then that the cities of Pompeii and Herculaneum were buried and forgotten for over 1,500 years. A reminder of the natural hazards near Vesuvius arrived on 5 February 62 CE, when a major earthquake destroyed much of Pompeii and caused serious damage in Herculaneum and Neapolis (Naples). Earthquakes, although not as large, were a common occurrence for the next 17 years. Pompeii had been a centre of commerce for centuries. In 79 CE, the city had a population of about 20,000 people, 8,000 of whom were slaves. Robert Etienne described it as

> An average city inhabited by average people, Pompeii would have achieved a comfortable mediocrity and passed peacefully into the silence of history, had the sudden catastrophe of the volcanic eruption not wiped it from the world of the living.

The 24th of August 79 CE was a warm summer day, but then Vesuvius began erupting and the day became even hotter. Vesuvius blew out 4 km³ of volcanic material. About half of the old volcanic cone was destroyed. A modern example of a similar eruption occurred in 1991 at Mount Pinatubo in the Philippines (Figure 7.1). In Pompeii, great clouds of hot gas and volcanic ash flowed across the city, killing the people who had not fled (Figure 7.2). Today, the excavated city is a major attraction for tourists (Figure 7.3).

In 79 CE, the fine volcanic ash settling out from the great heights of the eruption cloud affected a large region. Pliny the Younger was at Misenum and wrote

Figure 7.1
First big explosive blast from Mount Pinatubo, 15 June 1991.
Photo: © R. S. Culbreth, US Geological Survey.

And now came the ashes, but at first sparsely. I turned around. Behind us, an ominous thick smoke, spreading over the earth like a flood, followed us. "Let's go into the fields while we can still see the way," I told my mother—for I was afraid that we might be crushed by the mob on the road in the midst of darkness. We had scarcely agreed when we were enveloped in night—not a moonless night or one dimmed by cloud, but the darkness of a sealed room without lights. To be heard were only the shrill cries of women, the wailing of children, the shouting of men. Some were calling to their parents, others to their children, others to their wives—knowing one another only by voice. Some wept for themselves, others for their relations. There were those who, in their very fear of death, invoked it. Many lifted up their hands to the gods, but a

Figure 7.2
Body cast of man killed by a flow of hot gas and volcanic ash from Vesuvius in late August in the year 79 CE.

Figure 7.3
Tourists walk through the heart of Pompeii toward Vesuvius, the volcano that destroyed the city in 79 CE.
Photo: © Pat Abbott.

Figure 7.4
Feet of a child killed by an eruption from Vesuvius in 79 CE. The flexed toes and feet were an involuntary contraction when surrounded by 500°C volcanic material. Death was instantaneous.
Photo: © Mastrolorenzo, G., Petrone, P., Pagano, M., Incoronato, A., Baxter, P., Canzanella, A., Fattore, L., in *Nature,* 410:769, 2001.

great number believed there were no gods, and that this was to be the world's last eternal night.

In the coastal city of Herculaneum, 300 skeletons were found in lifelike positions in boat chambers at the beach. The skeletons of these people killed by the eruption testify to the lethal energy they experienced. The people had not been battered or suffocated; they did not display any voluntary self-protection reactions or agony contortions. In other words, their vital organs stopped functioning in less than a second, in less time than they could consciously react. The types of bone fractures, tooth cracks, and bone coloration indicate the victims were covered by volcanic material at about 500°C. At this temperature, their soft tissues vaporized; their feet flexed in an instantaneous muscle contraction (Figure 7.4).

The timing of major eruptions of Vesuvius offers an interesting lesson. Apparently Vesuvius did not have a major eruption from the 7th century BCE until 79 CE. People had at least 700 years to lose their fears and yield to the allure of the rich agricultural soils on Vesuvius. After 79 CE, large eruptions occurred more often: in 203, 472 (ash blown over much of Europe), 512, 685, 993, 1036 (first lava flows in historical time), 1049, and 1138–1139. Then nearly 500 years passed; time to forget

the past and recolonize the mountain. But in 1631, Vesuvius poured out large volumes of lava that destroyed six towns; mudflows ruined another nine towns, and about 4,000 people perished. The long periods of volcanic quiescence in the last 2,700 years, one about 700 years long and another of nearly 500 years, seem like long times to short-living, land-hungry humans, but this is the time schedule of an active volcano. A lack of appreciation for the time involved between eruptions leads to many dormant volcanoes being falsely regarded as extinct.

Between 1631 and 1944, there were 18 eruption cycles; each lasted from 2 to 37 years with quiet intervals ranging from 0.5 to 6.8 years (Figure 7.5). Since 1944, Vesuvius has been quiet. Is this interval of calm setting the stage for another major eruption? It is not known for

Figure 7.5
Lava dome growing in the crater of Mount Vesuvius, a few weeks before the eruption of 1767. This fascinating illustration is one of 54 hand-coloured plates by artist Pietro Fabris found in *Campi Phlegraei*, a scientific treatise on the late-18th-century eruptions of Vesuvius written by Sir William Hamilton, Britain's envoy to the Spanish Court at Naples.
Source: Glasgow University Library, Department of Special Collections.

sure, but consider that almost three million people live within reach of Vesuvius today, including about one million people living on the slopes of the volcano.

THE HAZARDS OF STUDYING VOLCANOES

The dangers of volcanic eruption are obvious, but the quiet spells between active volcanism are seductive. Some people are lured to volcanoes like moths to a flame, even those who should know better. On 14 January 1993, volcanologists attending a workshop in Colombia, as part of the international decade of natural disaster reduction, hiked into the summit crater of Galeras Volcano to sample gases and measure gravity. They were looking for ways to predict imminent eruptions. The volcano had been quiet since July 1992, but during their visit, an unexpected, gas-powered secondary eruption killed six in the scientific party—four Colombians, a Russian, and an Englishman. Their deaths were not an unusual event (Table 7.1). They serve as a small-scale example of the larger drama played out when a volcano suddenly buries an entire city. During long periods of volcanic quiescence, people tend to build cities near volcanoes. For example, 400,000 people live on the flanks of Galeras Volcano, defying the inevitability of a large, life-snuffing eruption.

An individual volcano may be active for millions of years, but its eruptive phases are commonly separated by centuries of inactivity, lulling some into a false sense of security. Around 410 BCE, Thucydides wrote, "History repeats itself." We know well that those who do not learn the lessons of history are doomed to repeat them.

HOW WE UNDERSTAND VOLCANIC ERUPTIONS

Two primary building blocks of knowledge are paramount to understanding volcanic eruptions:

1. Plate tectonics has given us great insight into understanding earthquakes; now it will help us understand volcanoes.

Table 7.1

Volcanologists Killed by Eruptions

Year	Volcano	Total Deaths	Dead Volcanologists
1951	Kelut, Indonesia	7	3
1952	Myojin-sho, Japan	31	9
1979	Karkar, Papua New Guinea	2	2
1980	Mount St. Helens, United States	62	2
1991	Unzen, Japan	44	3
1991	Lokon-Umpong, Indonesia	1	1
1993	Galeras, Colombia	9	6
1993	Guagua Pichincha, Ecuador	2	2
2000	Semeru, Indonesia	2	2

2. Magma (liquid **rock**) varies in its chemical composition, ability to flow easily, gas content, and volume. These variations govern whether eruptions are peaceful or explosive.

First, we take a brief look at plate tectonics and volcanism. Second, we examine magma variations and how they control eruptive style. Third, we apply this knowledge globally to understand why volcanoes occur where they do and why only some volcanoes explode.

Plate-Tectonic Setting of Volcanoes

Over 90% of volcanism occurs at the edges of tectonic plates, more specifically at spreading centres and subduction zones (Figures 1.11 and 7.6). Over 80% of Earth's magma extruded through volcanism is found at the oceanic spreading centres. Solid, but hot and ductile, mantle rock rises upward into regions of lower pressure, where up to 30 to 40% of the rock can melt and flow easily as lava on the surface (Figure 7.7). The worldwide rifting process releases enough magma to create 20 km^3 of new oceanic crust each year. Virtually all this volcanic activity takes place below sea level and is thus difficult to view.

Subduction zones cause the tall and beautiful volcanic mountains we see at the edges of the continents,

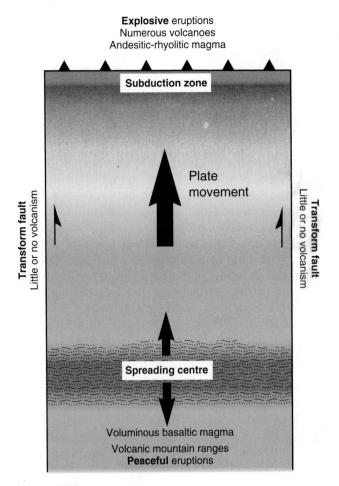

Figure 7.6
Map view of an idealized oceanic plate showing styles of volcanism.

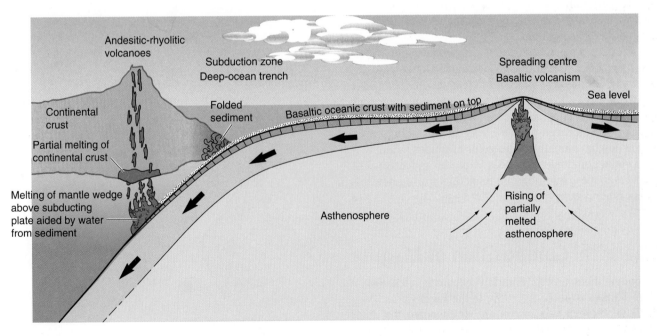

Figure 7.7
Idealized cross-section showing production of basaltic magma at spreading centres. Plates pull apart, and some asthenosphere liquefies and rises to fill the gap. Andesitic-rhyolitic magmas are created above subduction zones, where rising magma partially melts the continental crust on its way up, thus altering the melt by increasing SiO_2 content and viscosity.

but the volume of magma released at subduction zones is small compared to that of spreading centres. Subduction zones account for the eruption of approximately 10% of all magma. The downgoing plate carries oceanic-plate rock covered with water saturated sediment into much hotter zones (Figure 7.7). The presence of water lowers the melting point of rock. Rising magma melts some of the continental crust it passes through. This adds new melt of different composition to rising plumes of magma. Each rising plume has its own unique chemical composition.

Most other volcanism occurs above hot spots, accounting for the remaining 10% of all extruded magma (Figure 3.11).

Transform faults and continent–continent collision zones have little or no associated volcanism. Thinking three-dimensionally, this is understandable. At a transform fault, the two plates simply slide past each other in a horizontal sense and at all times keep a quite effective "lid" on the hot asthenosphere some 100 km below. At continent–continent collision zones, the continental rock stacks into extra-thick masses that deeply bury the hot mantle rock, making it difficult for magma to rise to the surface.

People commonly speculate upon whether an individual volcano is **active, dormant,** or **extinct.** Because of the strong hope that a volcano is extinct and the nearby land is thus available for use, many dormant volcanoes are misclassified. But consider this: A subduction zone commonly lasts for tens of millions of years, and its province of volcanoes is active for the entire time. An individual volcano may be active for hundreds of thousands to several million years, despite "slumbers" of centuries between eruptions. As a general rule, if a volcano has a well-formed and aesthetic conical shape, it is active. A pretty shape is dangerous.

From a volcanic disaster perspective, the differences are clear. Oceanic volcanoes are relatively peaceful, whereas subduction-zone volcanoes are explosive and dangerous. Ironically, humans tend to congregate at the seaward edges of the continents, where the most dangerous volcanoes operate. Why do spreading-centre volcanoes have relatively peaceful eruptions? And why do subduction-zone volcanoes explode violently? The answers to these questions are found in knowing how different magma behaves.

Chemical Composition of Magma

Although there are 92 naturally occurring elements, a mere 8 make up more than 98% of the Earth's crust (Figure 7.8). Oxygen and silicon are so abundant that their percentages dwarf those of all other elements. Oxygen atoms carry negative charges (-2), while silicon atoms are positively charged ($+4$). As magma begins cooling, some silicon and oxygen atoms will bond. A central silicon atom ($+4$) links up with four oxygen atoms ($4 \times -2 = -8$) to form the silicon-oxygen tetrahedron (SiO_4) (Figure 7.9). The SiO_4 tetrahedron presents a -4 charge on its exterior that attracts and ties up positively charged atoms. After negatively charged oxygen, the seven elements of greatest abundance are all positively charged (Figure 7.8); they are attracted to, and bound up by, oxygen. This process is so common and voluminous that elemental abundances in the crust are usually listed in combination with oxygen (as oxides). The weight percentages of elements are quite different for continental versus oceanic crust (Figure 7.10). Marked differences in oxide percentages produce magma of variable composition and behaviour.

A working understanding can be gained while considering only three magma types and the three clans of igneous rocks that form from them. The rock types are based on their silicon and oxygen (SiO_2) percentages (Table 7.2). If the magma cools and solidifies below the surface, it crystallizes as **plutonic rocks,** named for Pluto, the Greek god of the underworld. If the magma reaches the surface, it forms **volcanic rocks,** named for Vulcan, the Roman god of fire.

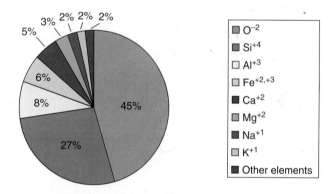

Figure 7.8
Common elements of the Earth's crust (weight percentages).

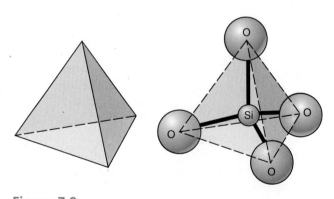

Figure 7.9
A silicon atom with +4 charge is linked to four oxygen atoms each with a −2 charge.

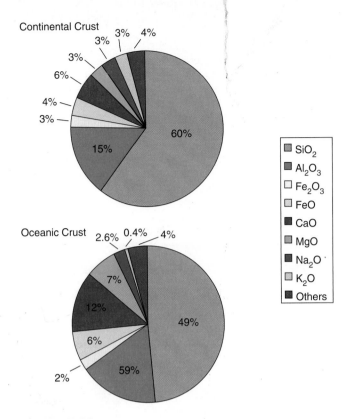

Continental Crust

3% 3% 4%
3%
6%
4%
3%
15%
60%

Oceanic Crust

2.6% 0.4% 4%
7%
12%
6%
2%
49%
59%

Legend:
- ■ SiO₂
- ■ Al₂O₃
- ☐ Fe₂O₃
- ☐ FeO
- ■ CaO
- ■ MgO
- ■ Na₂O
- ☐ K₂O
- ■ Others

Figure 7.10
Crustal elements in oxides (weight percentages).

Table 7.2

Igneous Rock Types

Magma Type	Plutonic Rock	Volcanic Rock
$SiO_2 < 55\%$	Gabbro	Basalt
$SiO_2 = 55$–65%	Diorite	Andesite
$SiO_2 > 65\%$	Granite	Rhyolite

Viscosity, Temperature, and Water Content of Magma

Liquids flow freely; their volumes are fixed but their shapes can change. Liquids vary in how they flow; some flow quickly, some flow slowly, and some barely flow at all. A liquid's internal resistance to flow is measured by its viscosity; viscosity may be thought of as a measure of fluid friction. The lower the viscosity, the more fluid is the behaviour. For example, tilt a glass of water and watch it flow quickly; water has low viscosity. Now tilt the same glass filled with honey and watch the slower flow; honey has higher viscosity. Low-viscosity magma flows somewhat like ice cream on a hot day. High-viscosity magma barely flows.

The viscosity of magma is changed by various means.

1. Higher temperature lowers viscosity; it causes atoms to spread farther apart and vibrate more vigorously, thus atomic bonds break and deform more, resulting in increasing fluidity. Consider the great effect of temperature on magma. At 600°C, magma viscosity is five orders of magnitude (100,000 times) more viscous than at 900°C.
2. Silicon and oxygen (SiO_2) increase the viscosity of magma because they form abundant silicon–oxygen tetrahedra (Figure 7.9) that link up in chains, sheets, and networks, creating more joints and bonds between atoms, which in turn make flow more difficult.
3. Increasing content of **mineral** crystals increases viscosity. Magma is a mixture of liquid and minerals that have crystallized from the liquid fraction. Mineral content in magma varies from none to being the majority of the mass.

Magma contains dissolved gases held as **volatiles;** their solubility increases as pressure increases and as temperature decreases. You can visualize the pressure–temperature relations with a bottle of carbonated soft drink as an analogy. Carbon dioxide (CO_2) gas is dissolved in the soft drink and kept under pressure by the bottle cap. Pop the cap off the bottle, reducing pressure, and some volatiles escape. As the uncapped bottle warms, more volatiles are lost.

A good grasp of volcanic behaviour can be gained by considering the properties of three types of magma and the rocks they become—**basalt, andesite,** and **rhyolite** (Table 7.3). Basalt is mainly composed of dark minerals crystallizing first in a cooling magma; andesite is the intermediate case; rhyolite is principally formed from the light-coloured minerals last to crystallize. Notice that the highest temperatures and lowest SiO_2 contents are in basaltic magma, giving it the lowest viscosity and easiest fluid flow. The lowest temperatures and highest SiO_2 contents occur in rhyolitic magma, material so viscous that it commonly does not flow. Table 7.3 also states that about 80% of the magma reaching Earth's surface is basaltic, with only about 10% andesitic and 10% rhyolitic. Why the difference? Basaltic magma is produced in great abundance by partial melting of the mantle. The lower viscosity of basaltic magma helps it reach the surface, especially at spreading centres and other oceanic settings. Much basaltic magma also is produced at subduction zones, but as it rises through continents, its composition changes due to incorporating continental rock with its high SiO_2 content. During the process of rising, the magma compositions become more andesitic or rhyolitic. The more viscous rhyolitic magma is so sluggish that it tends to be trapped deep below the surface where it cools, solidifies, and grows into the larger mineral crystals of plutonic rocks, such as granite.

In Greater Depth

Volcanoes and the Origin of the Ocean, Atmosphere, and Life

The elements in volcanic gases are dominated by hydrogen (H), oxygen (O), carbon (C), sulphur (S), chlorine (Cl), and nitrogen (N). These gaseous elements combine at Earth's surface to make water (H_2O), carbon dioxide (CO_2), sulphur dioxide (SO_2), hydrogen sulfide (H_2S) with its rotten-egg smell, carbon monoxide (CO), nitrogen (N_2), hydrogen (H_2), hydrochloric acid (HCl), methane (CH_4), and numerous other gases. The dominant volcanic gas is water vapour; it commonly represents more than 90% of total gases.

The elements of volcanic gases (C, H, O, N, S, Cl) differ from the elements of volcanic rocks: oxygen (O), silicon (Si), aluminum (Al), iron (Fe), calcium (Ca), magnesium (Mg), sodium (Na), and potassium (K). The elements of volcanic gases make up the oceans, the atmosphere, and life on Earth, but they are rare in rocks. The 4.5 billion years of heat flow from Earth's interior have "sweated" out many lightweight elements and brought them to the surface via volcanism. Billions of years of volcanism on Earth go a long way to explaining the origin of the continents, the oceans, the present atmosphere, and the surface concentration of the CHON elements (carbon, hydrogen, oxygen, nitrogen) of which all life on Earth is composed and on which it depends.

Table 7.3

Comparison of Three Types of Magma

	Volcanic Rock Types		
	Basalt	**Andesite**	**Rhyolite**
Rock description	Black to dark grey	Medium to dark grey	Light-coloured
Volume at Earth's surface	80%	10%	10%
SiO_2 content	45–55%	55–65%	65–75%
	— increasing SiO_2 →—————————		
Temperature of magma	1,000–1,300°C	800–1,000°C	600–900°C
	←———— increasing temperature ————		
Viscosity	Low		High
	———— increasing viscosity ————————→		
Water dissolved in magma	~0.1–1 wt. %	~2–3 wt. %	~4–6 wt. %
	———— increasing water ————————→		
Gas escape from magma	Easy		Difficult
	———— increasing difficulty ————————→		
Eruptive style	Peaceful		Explosive
	———— increasing explosiveness ————————→		

In magma, water is the most abundant dissolved gas. As magma rises toward the surface and pressure decreases, water dissolved in the hot magma becomes gas and forms steam bubbles. Basalt magma is low in dissolved water content, helping make eruptions peaceful. Rhyolitic magma has dissolved water contents up to 6%; as it rises and steam bubbles form, they have difficulty escaping from the high-viscosity magma and have to burst their way out.

When the basaltic volcanoes of Hawaii begin to erupt, it is a touristic event. Although such an eruption makes a thrilling show, it is a relatively peaceful happening. Why is it safe? Because it does not contain much dissolved water, and the dissolved gases escape from the low-viscosity magma with relative ease (Figure 7.11). Compare this behaviour to the eruption of a rhyolitic magma of lower temperature, greater dissolved water content, higher percentage of SiO_2, and very high viscosity. When rhyolitic magma oozes out onto the ground surface, the pressure within the magma is reduced and the dissolved gases expand in volume. But how do gases escape from their entrapment in sticky magma? By exploding (Figure 7.12). Spectators at the eruption of rhyolitic magma frequently die. When it comes to volcanic hazards, the greatest problem is how much gas is in the magma and how easily the dissolved gases can escape from the magma. As Frank Perret stated: "Gas is the active agent, and magma is its vehicle."

Figure 7.11 ~ Basalt

Peaceful eruption of low-viscosity magma with easy separation of volatiles by magma, Surtsey, Iceland.

Photo: © Pat Abbott.

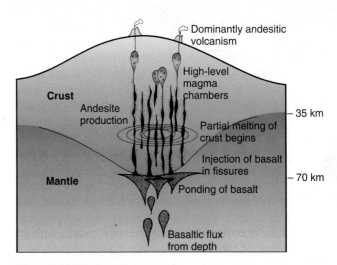

Figure 7.13

Schematic cross-section of magma rising from a subduction zone and being contaminated en route.

Figure 7.12 ~ Rhyolitic

Explosive eruption of high-viscosity magma and trapped volatiles by Paricutin Volcano, Michoacan, Mexico.

Photo: © US Geological Survey.

ERUPTIVE STYLES AND PLATE-TECTONIC SETTING

Knowing about magma viscosity and volatile content allows us to revisit our earlier questions about plate tectonics and volcanism. Why does the vast majority of Earth's magma pour out at spreading centres and in relatively peaceful eruptions? And why does the magma above subduction zones commonly explode violently? Spreading centres operate in oceanic crust, and subducting plates commonly are pulled beneath continental crust. The chemistry of oceanic crust and continental crust are different (Figure 7.10), their magmas are different, and their volcanic behaviours differ.

Spreading centres are ideal locations for volcanism because (1) they sit above the high-temperature

asthenosphere, (2) the asthenosphere rock has low percentages of SiO_2, and (3) the oceanic plates pull apart, causing hot asthenosphere rock to rise, experience lower pressure, and change to magma that continues to rise. This magma is high-temperature, low SiO_2, low-volatile content, low-viscosity basalt allowing easy escape of gases. Spreading centres combine all the factors that promote the peaceful eruption of magma.

When a subducting oceanic plate reaches a depth of about 100 km, magma is generated and rises toward the surface (Figure 7.7). The subducting plate stirs up the mantle, causing the hotter rock at depth to rise and then melt as pressure decreases. A significant reason that magma forms here is because the subducting plate carries a cover of sediment, water, and hydrated minerals down with it. Water, even in slight amounts, promotes partial melting by lowering the temperature necessary for rock to melt. However, the partial melting process affects only those minerals with lower melting temperatures. As this partial melt rises upward, it in turn melts part of the overlying crust to produce magma of highly variable compositions (Figure 7.13). Magma composition depends on the amount of crustal rock melted and incorporated into the rising magma. In general, in the subduction-zone setting, magma temperature decreases while SiO_2, water content, and viscosity increase. All these changes in magma add to its explosive potential.

How a Volcano Erupts

The Earth's internal energy flows outward as heat (see Chapter 2). The eruptions of volcanoes are rapid means for Earth to expel some of its internal heat.

A volcanic eruption begins with heat at depth. Super-heated rock will rise to levels with lower pressure, and some solid rock may change phase to liquid magma, resulting in volume expansion leading step by step to eruption.

Magma is generated by the melting of existing rock. Rock may melt by (1) lowering the pressure on it, (2) raising its temperature, or (3) increasing its water content. How do most rocks melt? The two most effective melting agents are reductions in pressure (decompression) and increases in volatile content (mostly water).

Most magma is generated by decreasing the pressure on hot rock. For example, as the solid, but mobile, hot rock of the mantle rises upward, it experiences progressively less pressure and spontaneously melts, without the addition of more heat. Melting caused simply by a decrease in pressure is called **decompression melting.** The process of decompression melting is so important it is worth restating: most of the rock that melts to form magma does so because the pressure on it decreases, not because more heat is added.

The largest nearby reservoir of superhot, ready-to-melt rock exists in the nearly molten asthenosphere; this rock, hot enough to flow without being liquid, is the main source of magma. As this superheated rock rises, the pressure on it decreases, allowing some rock to melt. The hot, rising rock-magma mixture also raises the temperature of rock it passes through, thus melting portions of the overlying rocks.

If pressure in the asthenosphere or lithosphere is decreased, some rock melts with a resultant increase in volume that causes overlying rocks to fracture. The fractures allow more material to rise to lower pressure levels, causing more rock to liquefy. For example, at a depth of 32 km, basaltic rock melts at 1,430°C, but this same rock will melt at only 1,250°C at Earth's surface. Since upward-moving rock/magma reaches ever-lower pressures, rising rock can liquefy and magma can increase in fluidity, which in turn causes more superheated rock to become magma.

Magma at depth does not contain gas bubbles because the high pressure at depth keeps volatiles dissolved in solution. But as magma rises toward the surface, pressure continually decreases, and gases begin to come out of solution, forming bubbles that gradually expand (Figure 7.14). The added lift of the growing volume of gas bubbles helps propel magma upward through fractures toward an eruption. Gas bubbles continue increasing in number and volume as magma keeps rising upward to lower pressures. At one point, the gas overwhelms magma, fragmenting it into pieces that are carried up and out by a powerful gas get (Figure 7.15). Upon escape from the volcano, the gas jet draws in air, which adds to buoyancy in the turbulent, rising plume (Figure 7.14).

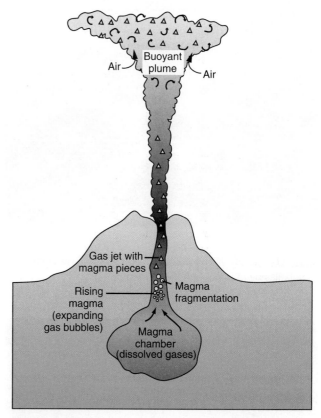

Figure 7.14

Anatomy of an eruption. As magma rises to levels of lower pressure, gas comes out of solution, forming bubbles that overwhelm magma and create a gas jet, leading to a buoyant plume.

Figure 7.15

Remarkable view into the crater of Mount Pinatubo just as a major explosive eruption was beginning its upward blast, 1 August 1991.

Source: © NOAA

ERUPTIVE STYLES AND THE ROLE OF WATER CONTENT

Whether a volcanic eruption is peaceful or explosive depends significantly on the concentration of water in the magma. For example, if all magma contained low concentrations of water (such as 0.3 weight percentage; Table 7.3), there would be no highly explosive eruptions. Even a high-viscosity rhyolitic magma with a low concentration of water leads only to slow flows or no flow as the magma oozes upward and builds a dome.

The most important requirement for explosive eruptions is a high concentration of volatiles, mainly water. Volatiles drive explosive eruptions. Given a high concentration of water, even a basaltic magma can erupt violently. Rhyolitic magma is often associated with explosive eruptions because of its high content of water (Table 7.3). Water concentration in magma plays a controlling role, and viscosity a secondary role, in determining the peaceful versus explosive style of eruption.

Volcanoes erupt in a variety of different types (Figure 7.16). This classification is just for general purposes; each volcano varies in its eruptive behaviour over time. Non-explosive eruptions are commonly subdivided into *Icelandic* and *Hawaiian* types. *Strombolian* types are somewhat explosive. Explosive eruptions can be described as *Vulcanian* and *Plinian* types.

SOME VOLCANIC MATERIALS

Magma (from the Greek word "ointment") changes name to lava (from the Latin verb "to wash", becoming "torrent" in Italian) when it reaches the Earth's surface. Low–water content and low-viscosity magma that reaches the surface typically moves as lava flows, with easy gas escape yielding non-explosive eruptions. High–water content and high-viscosity magma holds its volatiles, making gas escape difficult. Gas is forced to burst out of the magma, yielding explosive eruptions. Gas blasting into the atmosphere takes along chunks of magma and older rock known collectively as **pyroclastic** debris (*pyro* = fire; *clastic* = fragments).

Magma is rich in magnesium and iron from its origin, deep in the asthenosphere. On its way up, it becomes enriched in the elements that are abundant in the crust like aluminium, calcium, potassium, and sodium (Figure 7.10). When exposed on the surface of Earth, volcanic materials gradually break down, releasing these elements into the ground where they, especially potassium, act as excellent fertilizers. In tropical areas, revegetation of areas buried under lava can begin less than one year after the eruption, given enough rainfall. Volcanic soils are

Figure 7.16
Some types of volcanic eruptions.

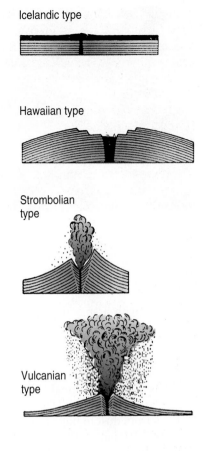

Icelandic type

Hawaiian type

Strombolian type

Vulcanian type

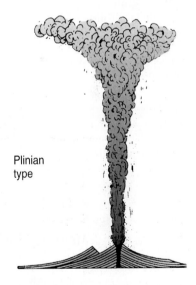

Plinian type

among the most fertile on the planet, and have nurtured civilizations for thousands of years (Figure 7.42).

Non-explosive Eruptions

Lava flows are especially typical of basaltic magma and exhibit a variety of textures (Table 7.4). Highly liquid lava

Figure 7.17
Small-scale pahoehoe near Halemaumau, Hawaii.
Photo: © Pat Abbott.

Figure 7.18
Aa flow in Hawaii.
Photo: © Pat Abbott.

may cool with a smooth, ropy surface called **pahoehoe** (Figure 7.17). Slower-flowing, more viscous lava commonly has a rough, blocky texture called **aa** (Figure 7.18).

Explosive Eruptions

Gaseous explosions break rock and tear apart magma and older rock into pyroclastic debris with a wide range of sizes from dust to huge blocks and bombs (Table 7.4; Figures 7.19 and 7.20). Airborne pyroclasts have their coarsest grains fall from the atmosphere first, closest to the volcano, followed by progressively finer material at greater distances. An air-fall deposit can be recognized by its layering and the sorting of pyroclasts into layers of different sizes. Pyroclastic debris also can be blasted out over the ground surface as high-speed, gas-charged flows that dump material quickly, producing indistinct layering and little or no sorting of the various-size particles.

Magma reaching the surface can solidify so quickly that **crystallization** cannot take place because there is no time for atoms to arrange themselves into the ordered atomic structures of minerals. When magma cools this quickly, it produces glass (Table 7.4). Cooled volcanic glass is known as **obsidian** (Figure 7.21a). Obsidian is a valued product, sought after and traded extensively

Table 7.4

Volcanic Materials

Lava	Aa	Rough, blocky surface
	Pahoehoe	Smooth, ropy surface
	Pillow	Ellipsoidal masses formed in water
Pyroclastic	Air-fall fragments	
	Fine ash (dust)	Flour-size material
	Coarse ash	Sand size
	Cinders	Marble to golf-ball size
	Blocks	Big angular fragments, solid while airborne
	Bombs	Big fragments often of an aerodynamic shape, liquid while airborne
	Volcanic tuff	Rock made of smaller fragments, e.g., deposit of a hot, gas-charged flow
	Volcanic breccia	Rock made of coarse, angular fragments, e.g., deposit of a water-charged debris flow
Glass	Obsidian	Non-porous glass
	Pumice	Porous froth

(a)

Figure 7.19a
Large blob of magma cooled while airborne and fell as a pyroclastic bomb, Irazu Volcano, Costa Rica.

Photo: © Pat Abbott.

(b)

Figure 7.19b
Pyroclastic bombs kill people every year.

Drawing: © Jacobe Washburn.

Figure 7.20
Volcanic ash covers a house near Mount Pinatubo in the Philippines, June 1991.

Photo: © R. P. Hoblitt, US Geological Survey.

throughout the ages (Figure 7.22). People from early civilizations broke obsidian into sharp fragments to make arrowheads and sword blades. They polished it to make mirrors. Obsidian was also used as a gemstone, a tradition that continues today.

When gas escapes quickly and violently from lava, it may produce a frothy glass full of holes left by former gas bubbles; this porous material, known as **pumice,** contains so many holes that it can float on water (Figure 7.21b).

(a)

(b)

Figure 7.21
Volcanic glass. (a) Obsidian—dense and dark. (b) Pumice—porous and light.

Photos: © Jacques Cornell and Ken Cavanagh, the McGraw-Hill Companies.

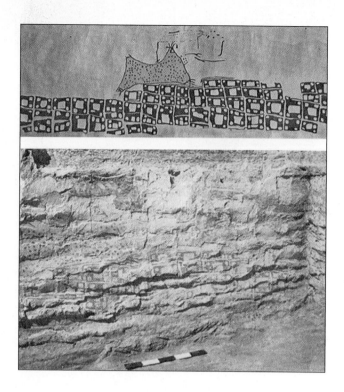

Figure 7.22
Painting from a shrine in the ruins of the Stone Age town of Çatal Hüyük in Turkey (top: reconstruction drawing; bottom: original wall-painting). The painting, which features volcano Hasan Dağ with stylized houses in the foreground, is the earliest known depiction of a volcanic eruption. Abundant obsidian has been found at this archeological site, which suggests that Çatal Hüyük had the monopoly of the obsidian trade within a large region reaching as far as Cyprus and the Middle East.

Source: J. Mellaart, *Early Civilizations of the Near East,* 1965.

The Three Vs of Volcanology: Viscosity, Volatiles, Volume

We can understand volcanoes anywhere in the world using *the three Vs of volcanology: viscosity, volatiles, volume. Viscosity* may be low, medium, or high; and it controls whether magma flows away or piles up. *Volatile* content may be low, medium, or high; and volatiles may ooze out harmlessly or blast out explosively. *Volume* of magma may be small, large, or very large. Volume correlates fairly well with eruption intensity; the greater the volume, the more intense the eruption.

Consider the five eruption types in Figure 7.16 in terms of volatile content and viscosity (Table 7.5). The lower the volatile content and the viscosity, the more peaceful the eruption. As the volatile content increases, so can the explosiveness of the eruptions.

Applying what we have learned about magma allows us to see links between eruptive behaviours and the landforms built by volcanic activity. By mixing and matching

Table 7.5

Eruptive Styles, Eruption Types, and Explosiveness

Eruptive Style and Eruption Type		Magma Characteristics									Volcanic Explosivity Index
		Composition			Volatile Content			Viscosity			
		Basalt	Andesite	Rhyolite	Low	Medium	High	Low	Medium	High	
Peaceful	Icelandic	√			√			√			0–1 (very low)
	Hawaiian	√			√			√			0–1 (very low)
Explosive	Strombolian	√	√			√		√	√		1–3 (low)
	Vulcanian	√	√	√		√	√		√	√	2–5 (high)
	Plinian		√	√			√			√	3–8 (high)

How a Geyser Erupts

The eruption of water superheated by magma is called a geyser. The name is drawn from the Icelandic word *geysir*, meaning "to gush or rage." Areas of geyser activity include Iceland, Chile, Yellowstone Park in the United States, North Island of New Zealand, and Kamchatka Peninsula of Russia. All of these sites share common characteristics: subsurface water is present and heat is abundant. Water from snow, rain, streams, and lakes is pulled below the ground surface by gravity, where it slowly moves through the network of voids presented by fractures and cavities in rocks. The downward-circulating water encounters heat from a near-surface body of magma, absorbs some of that heat, and then erupts (Figure 7.24).

This simple description ignores the complex interplay of temperature and pressure, which combine to set off an eruption. Water boils at 100°C at sea level. Water circulating at thousands of metres below the surface, however, can be heated to temperatures far above 100°C without boiling because the pressure of the overlying groundwater body is so great (Figure 7.23). When some of this superheated water does boil, its volume expands as liquid changes to steam, helping lift surrounding water upward to lower pressure levels. There, at lesser depths and lower pressures, some of the water flashes to steam; this helps lift more superheated water to lower pressure levels, and so on. Thus, superheated water rises into successively lower pressure levels, making geysers erupt.

What triggers the gushing of a geyser? Reduction of pressure on superheated water causes it to change from liquid to gas, triggering the geyser eruption, analogous to the reduction in pressure that causes hot rock to change from solid to liquid, triggering a volcano eruption. A geyser eruption usually follows this sequence of events: (1) at depth, superheated water flows out of tiny pressurized cracks into geyser reservoirs of larger volume; (2) as water temperature rises, some water will flash to steam; (3) the steam bubbles rise to lower pressure levels, expanding continuously; (4) steam and bubbles become so abundant that they overwhelm the water, carrying it upward to levels of lower pressure, causing continual conversion to steam along the upward route; and (5) finally—the spectacular eruption.

Figure 7.23 Eruption of geyser at Rotorua, North Island, New Zealand.
Photo by Pat Abbott.

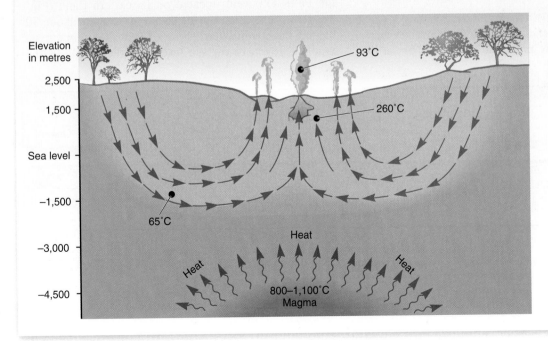

Figure 7.24 Surface water is pulled below ground by gravity, flows through holes in rocks, is superheated by magma, and through complex reductions in pressure, erupts at the surface as geysers.

Table 7.6

Volcanism Control by the Three Vs (Viscosity, Volatiles, Volume)

Viscosity	+	Volatiles	+	Volume	=	Volcanic Landforms
Low		Low		Large		Shield volcanoes
Low		Low		Very large		Flood basalts
Low/medium		Medium/high		Small		Scoria cones
Medium/high		Medium/high		Large		Stratovolcanoes
High		Low		Small		Lava domes
High		High		Very large		Calderas

the values among the three Vs, we can define volcanic landforms (Table 7.6) and forecast the eruption types styles that occur at each of them.

SHIELD VOLCANOES: LOW VISCOSITY, LOW VOLATILES, LARGE VOLUME

The rocks of **shield volcanoes** are formed mostly from the solidification of lava flows of basalt. These lava flows are low viscosity, contain less than one weight-percent volatiles, and are so fluid that they travel for great distances, somewhat analogous to pouring pancake batter on a griddle. Each basaltic flow cools to form a gently dipping, relatively thin volcanic rock layer. Many thousands of these lava flows must cool on top of each other over a long time to build a big volcano. A shield volcano, such as Mauna Loa in Hawaii, has a great width compared to its height, whereas a volcano built of high-viscosity magma, such as Mount Rainier in northern Washington State, has a great height compared to its width (Figure 7.25).

Hawaiian-type Eruptions

As with virtually all volcanic eruptions, Hawaiian-type eruptions commonly are preceded by a series of earth-quakes as rock fractures and moves out of the way of swelling magma (Figure 3.37). When these fractures split the ground surface, they suddenly reduce pressure, allowing gas to escape from the top of the magma body. This can create a beautiful "curtain of fire" where escaping jets of gases form lines of lava fountains up to 300 m high. Also common in the Hawaiian eruption type is the formation of a low cone with high fountains of magma. After the initial venting of gas, great floods of basaltic lava spill out of the fissures and flow down the mountain slopes as red-hot rivers (Figure 7.26). These eruptions may last from a few days to a year or more. Although few lives are lost to Hawaiian volcanism, the ubiquitous lava flows engulf and incinerate buildings, bury highways, cause drops in property value of homes near the latest flow, and cause some homeowners to lose their peace of mind (Figure 7.27).

Kilauea on the island of Hawaii is the only volcano of the Hawaiian chain currently erupting. Since 1983, voluminous amounts of lava continue to outpour from the Pu'u 'O'o vent, located on its eastern flank (Figure 7.28). The island-to-be Loihi is located about 30 km off the southeastern shore of Hawaii. Loihi's peak is about 969 m below sea level, and the weight of the

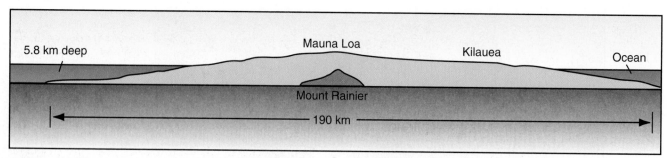

Figure 7.25

A shield volcano, such as Mauna Loa in Hawaii, has a great width compared to its height. A stratovolcano, such as Mount Rainier in northern Washington State, has a great height compared to its width.

Source: © Tilling, R. I., et al., Eruptions of Hawaiian Volcanoes, US Geological Survey, 1987.

In Greater Depth

Volcanic Explosivity Index (VEI)

Combining the historical record with the geological information stored in the rock record, the major volcanic eruptions occurring between the years 1500 to 1980 were studied to develop a semiquantitative estimate of their magnitude, the volcanic explosivity index (VEI). Factors evaluated include (1) volume of material erupted, (2) how high the eruption column reached, and (3) how long the major eruptive burst lasted (Table 7.8). The VEI ranges from 0 to 8. Vulcanian- and Plinian-type eruptions have the highest VEI values.

How frequent are eruptions at specific VEIs? Somewhere on Earth, a VEI 2 event occurs every few weeks, a VEI 3 event happens several times a year, a VEI 4 event erupts once or twice a year, a VEI 5 event happens about once per decade, and a VEI 6 event blasts forth once or twice a century. The bigger the eruptions, the less frequently they occur, another example of the inverse relation between magnitude and frequency. This trend has been confirmed for the last 10,000 years (Table 7.7).

Does the total energy involved in a volcanic eruption correlate well with the number of deaths? Not necessarily. Table 7.9 lists VEIs for some of the deadly events we will be discussing in Chapter 8. Some had low VEIs but nevertheless killed thousands with melted glacier ice (Nevado del Ruiz) or gas without magma (Lake Nyos).

Table 7.7

Volcanic Eruptions in the Last 10,000 Years

VEI	Number of Eruptions in Last 10,000 Years
7	4
6	39
5	84
4	278
3	868
2	3,477

Source: After Newhall and Self (1982).

Table 7.8

Volcanic Explosivity Index (VEI)

	VEI 0	1	2	3	4	5	6	7	8
Volume of material erupted (m³)	$<10^4$	10^4–10^6	10^6–10^7	10^7–10^8	10^8–10^9	10^9–10^{10}	10^{10}–10^{11}	10^{11}–10^{12}	$>10^{12}$
Eruption column height (km)	<0.1	0.1–1	1–5	3–15	10–25	>25			
Eruption type	<---Hawaiian--->		<----Vulcanian---->						
		<-----Strombolian----->			<-----------Plinian---------->				
Duration of continuous blast (hours)	<-----<1-----> <-----1–6----->			<-----6–12----->		<------->12- ------>			

Source: Based on U.S. Geological Survey http://volcanoes.usgs.gov/Products/Pglossary/vei.html.

Continued

overlying ocean water suppresses the explosiveness of the eruptions for now, but the volcano is building upward impressively.

Icelandic-type Eruptions

The most peaceful eruptions are the Icelandic type. They are referred to as **fissure** eruptions because lava pours out of linear vents or long fractures (cracks) up to 25 km long. Eruptions can be beautiful to watch as an elongated "curtain of fire" shoots upward with varying intensity and height (Figure 7.29). Icelandic eruptions of low-viscosity, low-volatile lava flows can be so peaceful that their movement is almost waterlike. Over time, the lava flows build up and create wide volcanic plateaus of nearly horizontal volcanic rock layers.

FLOOD BASALTS: LOW VISCOSITY, LOW VOLATILES, VERY LARGE VOLUME

Flood basalts are the largest volcanic events known on Earth. All have occurred in the distant geological past. Two important descriptive facts are (1) the immense amounts of mass and energy they pour onto Earth's surface, and (2) in the geologically brief time of 1 to 3 million years.

Table 7.9

VEIs of Notable Volcanic Disasters

VEI	Fatalities	Volcanic disaster	Date	Location
8	—	Yellowstone	600,000 years ago	USA
7	92,000	Tambora	1815	Indonesia
6	700	Pinatubo	1991	Philippines
6	36,000	Krakatau	1883	Indonesia
6	18,000	Vesuvius	79	Italy
5	57	Mount St. Helens	1980	USA
4	29,000	Pelee	1902	Martinique, France
4	3	Paricutin	1943	Mexico
3	24,000	Nevado del Ruiz	1985	Columbia
3	1	Vestmannaeyjar	1973	Iceland
2	9	Galeras	1993	Columbia
1	—	Stromboli	Daily eruptions	Italy
0	17,000	Lake Nyos	1986	Cameroon

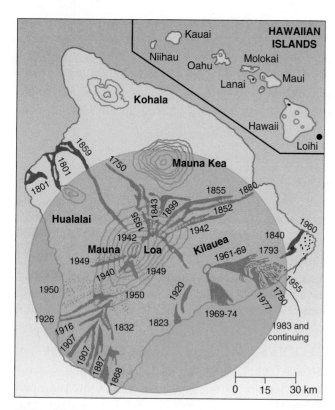

Figure 7.26

Map of Hawaii showing some historical lava flows. Colour overlay shows the boundaries of the mantle plume rising from the hot spot at depth.

Hot spots also bring up huge volumes of magma but do so over a long time; for example, 100 million years.

The numbers that describe the volumes of magma flood basalts erupt and the surface areas they bury with lava are so large they are hard to visualize. For example, over one billion years ago, a failed rift developed in

Figure 7.27

Lava flows caused the Wahalua Visitors' Center in Hawaii Volcanoes National Park to burn to the ground in 1989.

Photo: © J. D. Griggs, US Geological Survey.

Figure 7.28
Volcanic gases escape from the crater floor of the Pu'u 'O'o vent at Kilauea volcano on the island of Hawaii. The crater is approximately 400 m in diameter.

Photo: © Deanne Van Rooyen.

Figure 7.29
Fissure eruption generating a "curtain of fire" on Kilauea Volcano, Hawaii, in 1992. Icelandic-type eruptions do not occur only in Iceland!

Photo: Kilauea East Rift Zone Eruption, 1983-1, FIG0182.jpg USGS.

the mid-continent region of North America, accompanied by flood basalt eruptions. It is estimated that 1.3 million km^3 of basalt flowed out along a long network of fissures, extending from Kansas to Lake Superior. There are more than 15 km of basalt beneath the centre of Lake Superior, the thickest accumulation of volcanic rock anywhere on the planet. Some of these rocks are exposed on the lake shore. They exhibit features similar to present-day basalts like holes left by gas bubbles and pahoehoe (Figure 7.30).

Flood basalt eruptions obviously devastate a region, but can they have global effects? Yes, not from the lavas directly, but from the climate-modifying volatiles such as carbon dioxide (CO_2) or sulphur dioxide (SO_2) they release into the atmosphere. Is it a coincidence that some mass extinctions occurred at the time of flood basalt eruptions? Probably not. We will revisit this hypothesis in Chapter 15 on the great dyings.

(a)

(b)

Figure 7.30
Precambrian flood basalts from eastern Lake Superior. (a) The top of the lava flows still exhibit holes left by gas bubbles more than a billion years ago; (b) pahoehoe (compare this photo with Figure 7.17).

Figure 7.31
Group of scoria cones at Kilauea Volcano on the island of Hawaii with aa lava flows in the foreground.
Photo: © Claire Samson.

SCORIA CONES: MEDIUM VISCOSITY, MEDIUM VOLATILES, SMALL VOLUME

Scoria cones (Figure 7.31) are conical hills, typically of low height, formed of basaltic to andesitic pyroclastic debris piled up next to a volcanic vent. Scoria cones are commonly produced during a single eruptive interval lasting from a few hours to several years. The scoria or **cinder cone** has a summit **crater,** the basin on top of the cone that usually is less than 2 km in diameter. The summit crater may hold a lava lake during eruption. After the excess gas has been expelled from the magma body, the lava may drain and emerge from near the base of the cone. When eruption ceases, scoria cones usually do not erupt again. Being made of poorly consolidated debris, they degrade rapidly when subjected to rain and wind.

Strombolian-type Eruptions

Scoria cones are built mainly by Strombolian-type eruptions. The volcano Stromboli, offshore from southwestern Italy, has had almost daily eruptions for millennia. Its central lava lake is topped by a cooled crust. Even the tidal cycle disrupts the lava-lake crust, thus triggering eruptions. Gas pressure builds quickly beneath the crust, and eruptions occur as distinct and separate bursts up to a few times per hour. Each eruption tosses pyroclasts tens to hundreds of metres into the air. For many centuries, tourists have climbed Stromboli to thrill at the explosive blasts, but almost every year, a few of those tourists die when hit by large pyroclastic bombs. Strombolian eruptions are not strong enough to break the volcanic cone.

On 20 February 1943, a new volcano was born as eruptions blasted up through a cornfield near the village of Paricutin in the state of Michoacan, Mexico. Farmer Dionisio Pulido was first to witness the event:

"At four o'clock in the afternoon, I had left my wife Paula beside the fire in the kitchen when I noticed a fissure had opened in the ground, in one of the corrals of my farm. The fissure was only half a metre deep. I looked around again when I heard what sounded like loud thunder. The trees were shaking and I turned back to talk to Paula. It is at this moment that I saw the ground in the hole swell and rise by 2 or 2.5 metres. A fine, grey powder, like ash, was starting to come out of a portion of the fissure I had not seen until then. Smoke continued to come out

Figure 7.32
The façade of the church of Paricutin, engulfed in a field of aa lava flows. Paricutin Volcano and its secondary Sapichu cone are seen in the background.
Photo: © Alana M. Hinchey.

with a whistling noise. It smelled like sulphur. I was very frightened . . ."

Over the following weeks, a scoria cone grew at an amazing rate, reaching 30 m in the first day, 60 m after 3 days, 120 m after a week, and 150 m after a month. The volcano erupted for nine years, reaching a final height of 450 m above the plain and developing a secondary cone on its northeast flank. No lives were loss but pyroclastic debris and lava flows buried about 260 km² of land and destroyed the towns of San Juan de Parangaricutiro and Paricutin where only the façade of the church survives today (Figure 7.32).

STRATOVOLCANOES: HIGH VISCOSITY, HIGH VOLATILES, LARGE VOLUME

Stratovolcanoes, or **composite volcanoes,** commonly are steep-sided, symmetrical volcanic peaks built of alternating layers of pyroclastic debris successively capped by high-viscosity andesitic to rhyolitic lava flows that solidify to form protective caps. Stratovolcanoes may show marked variations in their magma compositions from eruption to eruption, and their eruption types include Vulcanian and Plinian. Some of Earth's most beautiful mountains are stratovolcanoes, for example, the Popocatepetl in Mexico, Mount Kilimanjaro in Tanzania, and Mount Fuji in Japan (Figure 7.33).

Vulcanian-type Eruptions
All volcanoes take their name from Vulcan, the Roman god of fire and blacksmith for the gods. The prototypical volcano is one of the Aeolian Islands in the Tyrrhenian Sea north of Sicily. The fire and smoke emitted from the top of the mountain reminded observers of the chimney of Vulcan's forge, so the mountain was named Vulcano. Vulcanian-type eruptions alternate between thick, highly viscous lava and masses of pyroclastic material blown out of the volcano. Some Vulcanian-type eruptions are more violent blasts of high-viscosity magma loaded with trapped gases. The material blown out during eruptions covers wide areas. A Vulcanian-type eruption commonly corresponds to the early phase of an eruptive sequence leading to a Plinian-type eruption. In this case, the volcano

Figure 7.33
Mount Fuji, a symmetrical stratovolcano rising 3,776 m above sea level, Honshu, Japan. Last major eruptions were in 1707–1708.
Photo: © CORBIS.

merely "clear its throat" during the Vulcanian-type eruption before emitting a larger eruption.

Plinian-type Eruptions

Plinian eruptions are named after the 17-year-old Pliny the Younger in honour of his detailed written observations of the 79 CE eruptions of Vesuvius that claimed the life of his well-known uncle Pliny the Elder. In Plinian eruptions, "the volcano's throat is now clear," and incredible gas-powered vertical eruption columns carry pyroclastic debris, including lots of pumice, up to 50 km into the atmosphere. The Plinian eruption is a common final phase in a major eruptive sequence. About two to three Plinian eruptions occur each century. For a recent example of a major Vulcanian-type eruption, see Figure 7.1.

Vesuvius, 79 CE

Vesuvius began as a submarine volcano in the Bay of Naples. It grew greatly in size, and its rocky debris filled in the waters that once separated it from mainland Italy. What is the cause of the volcanism at Vesuvius and the neighboring volcanoes of Stromboli, Vulcano, Etna, and others? It is

the subduction of Mediterranean seafloor beneath Europe to make room for the northward charge of Africa.

In 79 CE, when Mount Vesuvius began erupting, most residents fled from Pompeii. Those who stayed first experienced volcanic ash clouds dropping pumice. Pompeii lay downwind and was buried by pumice fragments accumulating up to 3 m deep. It is thought that about 60% of the people who remained in Pompeii survived the first flows of ash and pumice. About half of the survivors then fled, but many of them died when they were caught outside during later flows of ash and pumice. The people still inside houses remained alive only to suffocate from breathing hot particles and gases seeping out of the volcanic debris. Death was not always quick. Some bodies were found inside houses on top of thick layers of pumice, giving evidence of hours of struggle by people fighting to stay alive. Their hands held cloths over their mouths as they tried to avoid asphyxiation from gases seeping out of the pumice.

Many other people were found near the sea. They escaped the falling pumice, but ground-hugging **pyroclastic flows,** full of hot gases, finished them off. About 4,000 people died. The more-distant town of Stabiae was also mostly destroyed. It was here that Pliny the Elder died; the weak heart of the overweight man failed at age 56 under the stress of the farthest-reaching gas-rich flow.

Testing of rocks formed during the 79 CE eruption, as well as roof tiles from Pompeii, indicates that the cloud of volcanic ash and pumice that smothered Pompeii erupted out of Vesuvius at about 850°C and then cooled to less than 380°C by the time it reached the city. Roof tiles in Pompeii were heated to maximum temperatures of 340°C, while some walls on the partially protected down-flow side of houses reached temperatures only around 180°C, presumably because cooler air mixed into the volcanic ash cloud.

Following the Vulcanian-type eruption, the volcano entered a second phase, the Plinian phase, where it blew immense volumes of pyroclasts up to 32 km high in the atmosphere. The height of the eruption column varied as the volcanic energy waxed and waned. During weakened intervals, the great vertical column of ash would temporarily collapse, sending surges and pyroclastic flows down the volcano slopes. Pompeii was buried under an additional 2 metres of pyroclastic debris. These were the flows that finished off the surviving Pompeiians.

Some volcanic eruptions create their own "weather." A Plinian eruption not only blows ash to great heights but also volcanic gases. Water, as abundant steam, can be blown high into the atmosphere, cooling and condensing and then falling back down as rain—heavy rain. Rain falling on thick piles of pyroclastic debris, sitting unstably on the steep slopes of Vesuvius, set off thick volcanic mudflows (Figure 7.34). Any gravity-pulled mass movements of muddy volcanic debris are known as **lahars,** an

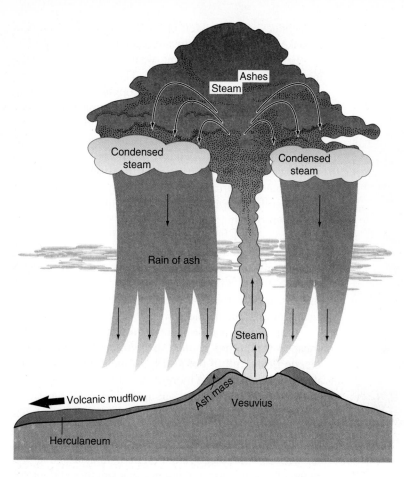

Figure 7.34

"Volcano weather" and formation of lahars. Prolonged vertical eruption leads to accumulation of debris on steep slopes of the volcano. Steam blown upward into cold, high altitudes condenses and falls back as rain. The stage is set: steep slopes + loose volcanic debris + heavy rain = lahars.

Indonesian word. Lahars buried the city of Herculaneum up to 20 m thick in pumice, ash, and volcanic rock fragments jumbled together in a confused mass. However, this was during the second phase of the eruption, and most people had used the day or two before to clear out of the area, so the loss of life was not nearly as great as at Pompeii. Today, the town of Ercolano lies on top of the mudflows burying Herculaneum. The lessons of history have not been well learned here.

Recent seismic surveys have helped define the magma body underlying Vesuvius today. Seismic waves with lowered velocity define a 400 km^2 horizontal, broad sheet of partially molten rock. This magma body lies at 8 km below the surface. Assuming a magma body thickness of 0.5 to 2 km, the volume of magma is about 200 to 800 km^3. This magma reservoir is fed from below, and it can supply magma to smaller layers closer to the surface, as it has in fuelling past eruptions. The millions of people around the Bay of Naples live in real danger.

LAVA DOMES: HIGH VISCOSITY, LOW VOLATILES, SMALL VOLUME

Lava domes form when high-viscosity magma with a low-volatile content cools quickly, producing a hardened dome or plug a few metres to several kilometres wide and a few metres to one kilometre high. Lava domes can

form in as quickly as a few hours, or they may continue to grow for decades. The formation of lava domes can be visualized as part of a larger eruptive process. When a large volume of magma rises and undergoes decompression melting, dissolved volatiles are freed. Much of the freed gases rise and accumulate at or near the top of the magma mass. When a major eruption occurs, these gases power the initial Vulcanian-type blast and then the succeeding Plinian-type eruption, which lasts until the excess volatiles have escaped. The type of magma remaining is often a low-volatile, high-viscosity paste that oozes upward slowly and cools quickly, forming a plug in the throat of the volcano. Figure 7.35 shows the lava dome emplaced in Mount Katmai in southern Alaska following its 1912 eruption, the biggest eruption of the 20th century.

Lava domes can provide spectacular sights. After the 1902 eruptions of Mont Pelée in the Caribbean killed more than 30,000 people (see Chapter 8), a lava dome formed as a great spine that grew about 10 m/day and rose above the top of the volcano. The spine of hardened magma was forced upward by the pressure of magma below until it stood over 300 m higher than the mountaintop, like a giant cork rising out of a bottle.

Do lava domes present hazards? Yes, in the 1990s, they were responsible for 129 deaths: 19 from Soufriere Hills Volcano on Montserrat in 1997, 66 from Mount

Figure 7.35
Novarupta lava dome formed as hardened magma plugged the central magma pipe of the 1912 eruption of Mount Katmai in southern Alaska. The dome is 244 m across and 61 m high.
Photo: © US Geological Survey.

Figure 7.36
Volcanic landscape from the Kamchatka Peninsula, Russia. Foreground: A crater (under 2 km across) formed atop the volcano during eruptions. Background: The large caldera (over 2 km across) at low elevation formed when the volcano collapsed during a massive eruption.
Photo: © US Geological Survey.

Merapi in Indonesia in 1994, and 44 from Mount Unzen in Japan in 1991. The hardened, brittle lava dome rock can fail in a gravity-pulled landslide from the mountain, or magma trapped below the brittle lava dome can break out in a violent eruption.

A Typical Eruption Sequence

A common pattern for a major eruptive episode is that gas-rich materials shoot out first as a Vulcanian blast quickly followed by a longer-lasting, gas-driven Plinian eruption. When the gas is depleted, then gas-poor, high-viscosity magma slowly oozes out to build a lava dome over an extended period of time. The volcanic sequence could be described as a Vulcanian precursor, a Plinian main event, and a lava dome conclusion.

CALDERAS: HIGH VISCOSITY, HIGH VOLATILES, VERY LARGE VOLUME

Caldera-forming eruptions are the largest of the violent, explosive volcanic behaviours. Calderas are large volcanic depressions formed by roof collapse into partially emptied magma reservoirs. Calderas differ from volcanic craters. Both are topographic depressions, but a crater is less than 2 km in diameter and forms by *outward explosion*. Calderas are larger; they range from 2 to 75 km in diameter and form by *inward collapse* (Figure 7.36).

Calderas form in different settings: (1) at the *summits of shield volcanoes* such as Mauna Loa and Kilauea on the island of Hawaii; (2) at the *summits of stratovolcanoes* such as Krakatau in Indonesia (following a series of sustained Plinian eruptions, the final cataclastic eruption

opened a void space that caused the volcano to collapse into its magma chamber); (3) as *giant continental calderas,* which are huge negative landforms such as Lake Yellowstone in Wyoming, United States, where a broad and deep depression formed following the rapid eruption of 2,000 km³ of pyroclasts. In the latter case, huge volumes of magma pour out over short periods as **ultra-Plinian** eruptions with extra-high ash columns and widespread sheets of outward-flowing ash and pumice.

The most recent example of an ultra-Plinian eruption occurred 74,000 years ago at Toba, on the island of Sumatra in Indonesia. The caldera at Toba is 30 km by 100 km long and has a central raised area inside it over 1 km high. The raised area formed during the millennia following the giant eruption; this resurgent topography inside the caldera gives these features their name—**resurgent calderas.**

Crater Lake (Mount Mazama), Oregon

Crater Lake is one of the jewels in the United States national park system. Its intense blue waters are pure and lie cradled in a high-rimmed, nearly circular basin. Crater Lake is about 9.5 km across and as deep as 589 m (Figures 7.37a and 7.38).

Several thousand years ago, the stratovolcano Mount Mazama stood about 3,660 m high as one of the Cascade Range volcanoes (Figure 8.7). Over 7,600 years ago, a major eruption began blowing sticky magma out of the mountain as glassy, gas-bubble-filled pumice and ash (Figure 7.39b). The magma had too high a viscosity to flow as a liquid, so it erupted as pyroclastic flows and Plinian columns. As the erupted material grew in volume,

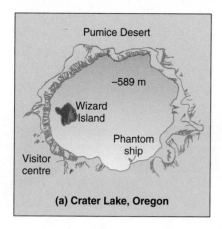

(a) Crater Lake, Oregon

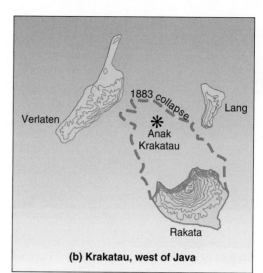

(b) Krakatau, west of Java

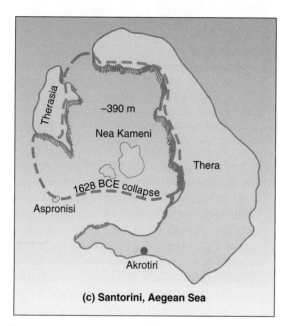

(c) Santorini, Aegean Sea

Figure 7.37
Map of some collapse calderas. (a) The nearly circular caldera of Crater Lake, Oregon, formed about 5677 BCE. (b) Nearly circular outline of old Krakatau Volcano; crudely ovoid shape of the 1883 collapse; and the new and growing volcano, Anak Krakatau. (c) Caldera in Volcano Santorini that collapsed into the Aegean Sea about 1628 BCE.

its debris covered much of the Northwest United States and part of Canada with a thick, distinctive ash layer that is easily recognizable (Figure 5.18). Mazama ash is found in the Greenland glacier within the ice layer formed during the snowfall season of the year 5677 BCE. About 40 km³ of magma was ejected. Evacuation of this immense volume of magma left so tremendous a void below the surface that the weakened mountain peak collapsed and moved down in pistonlike fashion into the emptied magma chamber (Figure 7.39c). The collapse produced a caldera about 10 km across that has collected the water for Crater Lake and hosted the growth of a 1,000-year-old successor volcanic cone called Wizard Island (Figure 7.39d).

The eruption of Mount Mazama affected American Indians as evidenced by moccasin tracks and artifacts found beneath the distinctive ash layer. What have caldera-forming collapse events wrought elsewhere?

Krakatau, Indonesia, 1883
Today, Krakatau (Krakatoa) is a group of Indonesian islands in the Sunda Strait between Sumatra and Java. It is part of the grand arc of volcanoes built above the subducting Indian-Australian plate. Krakatau is a big stratovolcano that builds up out of the ocean and then collapses. Its larger outline is still distinguishable (Figure 7.37b).

From the ruins of an earlier collapse, magmatic activity built Krakatau upward through the 17th century. After

Figure 7.38
Crater Lake, Oregon, fills the caldera of Mount Mazama, which collapsed in the year 5677 BCE.
Photo by Robert Glusic/Getty Images.

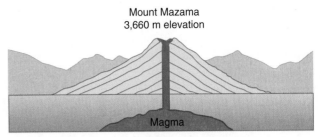

(a)

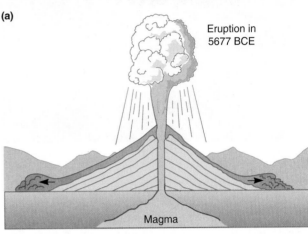

(b)

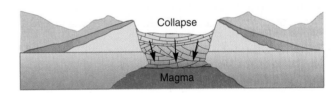

(c)

(d)

Figure 7.39
How Crater Lake formed. (a) Mount Mazama stood high. (b) Gaseous eruption in the year 5677 BCE emptied a huge volume of viscous magma. (c) The gigantic eruption left a void inside the weakened mountain, and the unsupported top fell into the emptied magma chamber. (d) The waters of Crater Lake now fill the caldera, and a small new volcanic cone (Wizard Island) has built above lake level.

two centuries of quiescence, volcanic activity resumed on 20 May 1883. By August 1883, moderate-size Vulcanian eruptions were occurring from about a dozen vents. At 2 p.m. on 26 August, a large blast shot volcanic ash and pumice 28 km high as one of the cones collapsed into the sea, setting off huge tsunami. Eruptions were so noisy that night that sleep was not possible in western Java, including the capital city of Djakarta (then called Batavia). The early morning hours of 27 August were rocked by more ear-hammering eruptions, and further volcanic collapses sent more giant tsunami to wrack the coastal villages. Day was turned to night-like darkness as heavy clouds of volcanic ash blocked the sunlight. At 10 a.m., a stupendous blast rocketed a glowing cloud of incandescent pumice and ash 80 km into the atmosphere, and sent tsunami higher than 35 m sweeping into bays along the low coastlines of Java and Sumatra (Figure 6.22). The eruption sequence blew out 18 km^3 of material (95% fresh magma and 5% pulverized older rock), creating a subterranean hole into which 23 km^2 of land collapsed (Figure 7.37b). Where islands with elevations of 450 m had stood, there now was a hole in the seafloor 275 m deep.

The Krakatau blast was distinctly heard 5,000 km away but, in the figurative sense, the event resonated much beyond that distance. Only 13 years earlier, a submarine telegraph cable had been laid to connect the island of Java to the international telegraph network. Via telegraph, the Krakatau eruption was the first great natural disaster to be broadcast to the "global village," a fact captured in the title of a recent book by Simon Winchester: *Krakatoa— The day the world exploded: August 27, 1883.*

In 1927, Krakatau began rebuilding a new volcanic cone called Anak Krakatau—"child of Krakatau"; it is still growing (Figure 7.37b). We will hear more from Krakatau.

Figure 7.40
The dark silhouette of the reborn volcano Nea Kameni, meaning "New Burnt," in the centre of the Santorini caldera. Nea Kameni has raised 450 m from the sea floor in the last 3,000 years.
Photo: © Claire Samson.

Santorini and the Lost Continent of Atlantis

As the Mediterranean oceanic plate subducts beneath Europe, it causes numerous volcanoes. One of the biggest is the stratovolcano Santorini in the Aegean Sea. Today, Thera is the largest island in a circular group centred on the new volcanic cone Nea Kameni and marking the sunken remains of Santorini (Figures 7.37c and 7.40). Thera is one of the most popular tourist sites in the Greek Islands (Figures 7.41 and 7.42), but around 1628 BCE, Santorini underwent an explosive series of eruptions that buried the Bronze Age city of Akrotiri on Thera to depths of 70 m in four distinct phases.

The eruption phases were determined by volcanologists Floyd McCoy and Grant Heiken (Figure 7.43).

Phase 1 volcanic activity is represented by a 6 m thick layer of air-settled pumice that gently entombed and preserved the buildings and artwork in Akrotiri. Pumice is produced when there is no water reacting with magma, so the eruption must have been from above sea level. The settling of pumice is not necessarily fatal and usually provides time for the wise to heed the warning and evacuate. When the eruptions began, most Akrotirians picked up their most prized possessions and left. All the "brave" people who were not scared away and remained with their homes and valuables died in the second phase.

In Phase 2, several-metre-thick deposits formed from rapidly flowing hot water that scoured the area. This occurred when seawater reached the exposed magma chamber, escaping as destructive steam blasts.

Figure 7.41
Picturesque whitewashed Greek homes on the cliff of the Santorini caldera. Note, in the foreground, the troglodyte dwellings excavated in soft ash layers.
Photo: © Claire Samson.

Figure 7.42
Terraced gardens in Santorini, Greece. Note the dark colour of the soil, enriched with volcanic ash.
Photo: © Claire Samson.

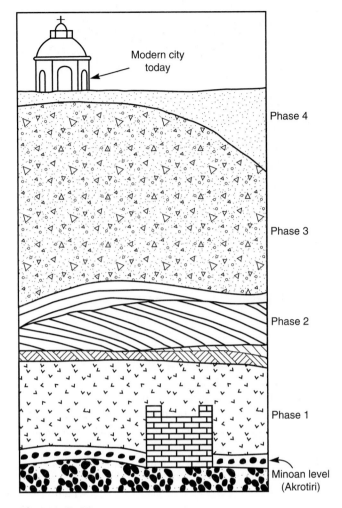

Figure 7.43
The Minoan city of Akrotiri on the volcanic island Thera was buried about 70 m deep by a four-phase eruption about 1628 BCE.

Source: McCoy and Heiken (1990).

Phase 3 deposits are a pyroclastic mass of jumbled ash, pumice, and large rock fragments that fell from the air, accumulating up to 56 m thick. This massive mess was produced by collapse of volcanic cones in the centre of Santorini.

Phase 4 deposits are layers of ash and small rock fragments formed during the final degassing of the magma body as it spit out ground-hugging, hot gaseous clouds. Where there had been a large island made of several volcanic cones, there now existed a huge caldera with depths of 390 m below sea level. What were the effects of this eruption on the Mediterranean world?

Akrotiri was an important city, a part of the Minoan civilization based in Crete. The Minoans created an advanced civilization. In 1628 BCE, Akrotiri had three-storey houses; paved streets with stone-lined sewers beneath them; advanced ceramic and jewellery work; regular trade with the Minoans' less-advanced neighbours in Cyprus, Syria, Egypt, and mainland Greece; and colourful

wall frescoes that depicted their wealthy and comfortable lifestyle. In short, the Minoans had a higher standard of living than many people in this part of the world today, over 3,600 years later.

The dramatic collapse of this piece of the Minoan civilization must have made an indelible impression on the people of that time. In fact, this may be the event passed down to us by Plato as the disappearance of the island empire of Atlantis, which after violent earthquakes and great floods "in a single day and night disappeared beneath the sea." Plato lived in Greece from 427 to 347 BCE. He told the tale in the dialogues of Critias, the historian, who recounted the visit of Solon to Egypt, where he learned the account of Atlantis from the Egyptian priests in their oral histories. About 1,200 years after the event, Plato wrote a reasonably good description of a caldera-forming collapse with attendant earthquakes, floods (steam surges or tsunami), and a landmass sinking below the sea in a day and a night.

The eruption and caldera-forming collapse into the sea at Santorini seem similar to the events at Krakatau 3,500 years later, except the Santorini event was bigger. The Santorini eruption is estimated to have blown out 30 km^3 of rhyolitic magma; Krakatau blew out 18 km^3. Krakatau sent out ocean waves 35 m high; Santorini must have done as much. The Aegean Sea region is one of the most island-rich areas on Earth. Tsunami in this region must have had a devastating effect on coastal towns and people, as well as leaving profound impressions on survivors, who passed these memories down to succeeding generations. The tales of Plato, the excavations by archaeologists, and the reconstructions by volcanologists all point to a remarkably consistent story.

Historians also note that the Minoan civilization declined some 150 years after the Santorini eruption, and was gradually replaced by the Mycenaean culture from mainland Greece with no sign of hostilities. They speculate that the Minoan suffered a loss of collective knowledge when skilled people living near the sea—sailors, shipwrights, sailmakers—died in the tsunami. Over a few generations, this loss caused a deterioration of their commercial fleet and undermined their domination of Mediterranean trade routes.

The Yellowstone Continental Caldera

A resurgent caldera exists in Yellowstone National Park, Wyoming, United States, above a hot spot, a long-lived mantle plume over which the North American continent is drifting. The hot spot occupies a relatively fixed position above which the North American plate moves southwestward about 2 to 4 cm/yr. Plate movement over the hot spot during the last 15 million years is recorded by a trail of surface volcanism. At present, Yellowstone National Park sits above the hot spot, and a large body of rhyolitic magma lies about 5 to 10 km beneath the surface.

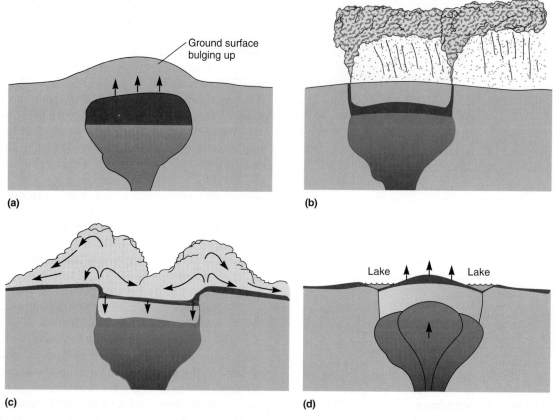

Figure 7.44
Stages in formation of a giant continental caldera. (a) Rising mass of magma forms low-density cap rich in SiO_2 and gases, bulging the ground surface upward. (b) Plinian eruptions begin from circular fractures surrounding the bulge. (c) Magma pours out in pyroclastic flows of tremendous volume, causing the ground surface to sink into a giant caldera. (d) Removal of magma decreases the crustal pressure, causing new magma to bulge up the caldera floor.

In the last 2 million years, three catastrophic ultra-Plinian eruptions have occurred at Yellowstone at 2 million, 1.3 million, and 0.6 million years ago. Such mega-eruptions do not come often, but in a few short weeks, they pour forth virtually unimaginable volumes of rhyolitic magma, mostly as pyroclastic flows. The oldest event erupted 2,500 km^3 of magma, the middle one emptied 280 km^3, and the youngest dumped out 1,000 km^3, creating a giant caldera 75 km long and 45 km wide.

Eruptive Sequence of a Resurgent Caldera

These giant caldera-forming eruptions go through a characteristic sequence. They begin when a very large volume of rhyolitic magma rises to a few kilometres below the surface, bowing the ground upward (Figure 7.44a). The magma body accumulates a cap rich in volatiles and low-density components such as SiO_2.

After a few hundred thousand years, a mega-eruption begins with a spectacular circular ring of fire as Plinian columns jet up from circular to ovoid fractures surrounding the magma body (Figure 7.44b). The escaping magma erodes the fractures, thus increasing the size of the eruptive vents so more and more magma escapes.

As greater volumes of gas "feel" the lessening pressure, the magma begins gushing out of the fractures in mind-boggling volumes (Figure 7.44c). The outrushing magma is too voluminous to all go airborne, so most just pours away from the vents as pyroclastic flows, the fastest way to remove gas-laden, sticky magma.

As the subsurface magma body shrinks, the land surface sinks as well, like a piston in a cylinder, creating a giant caldera (Figure 7.44d). The removal of 1,000 km^3 of magma creates a void, an isostatic imbalance, that is filled by a new mass of rising magma that bows up the caldera floor to create **resurgent domes.** Resurgent domes may be viewed as the reloading process whereby magma begins accumulating toward the critical volume that will trigger the next eruption.

Summary

- Volcanism is a rapid mechanism by which the Earth dissipates its internal energy. Hot rock at depth rises buoyantly. This rock may melt and become magma due mainly to decreased pressure and/or increased water content, and to a lesser extent to increased temperature. When magma nears the surface, gases come out of solution and help its upward progression.

- Viscosity is the most important property controlling magma behaviour and therefore eruptive style. Factors affecting viscosity are temperature, the percentage of SiO2, and mineral content.
  - Beneath the ocean basins, magma is basaltic in composition with low contents of SiO_2 and water, and high temperatures producing low viscosity, easy escape of volatiles, and peaceful eruptions.
  - Beneath continents, rising basaltic magma is contaminated by melting continental-crust rocks, thus altering magma compositions. The resultant andesitic-to-rhyolitic magma has high contents of SiO_2 and water, and relatively low temperatures producing high viscosity, difficult escape of volatiles, and explosive eruptions.

- Most volcanic eruptions occur at the edge of tectonic plates.
  - Eighty percent of magma reaching the Earth's surface is extruded under water at oceanic spreading centres.

- Magma rises to fill the gap between pull-apart plates in relatively peaceful eruptions.
  - Ten percent of extruded magma builds up tall volcanic mountains at the edge of subduction zones.
  - Ten percent of magma erupts above hot spots.
  - Transform faults and continent-continent collision zones have little or no volcanism associated with them.

- Magma viscosity, volatiles, and volume shape volcanic landforms.
  - Low-viscosity lava flows may build shield volcanoes much wider than they are tall (for example: the Hawaiian volcanoes).
  - If gas is high and is trapped in magma, then explosions blast pyroclastic debris into the air. They accumulate around the volcanic vent, gradually building up a scoria cone (for example, Paricutin).
  - Tall symmetrical volcanic peaks are usually stratovolcanoes built of alternations of lava and pyroclastic material (for example, Vesuvius).

- The volcanic explosivity index (VEI) measures size of volcanic eruptions on a scale of 0 to 8. The largest explosive eruptions (VEI = 7–8) occur when stratovolcanoes collapse in their rapidly emptied magma chambers, creating resurgent calderas.

Terms to Remember

aa   180
active volcano   174
andesite   175
basalt   175
caldera   193
cinder cone   189
composite volcano   190
crater   189
crystallization   180
decompression melting   178
dormant volcano   174
extinct volcano   174

fissure   185
flood basalt   185
lahar   191
lava dome   192
mineral   175
obsidian   180
pahoehoe   180
Plinian eruption   191
plutonic rock   174
pumice   181
pyroclastic   179
pyroclastic flow   191

resurgent caldera   193
resurgent dome   198
rhyolite   175
rock   173
scoria cone   189
shield volcano   184
stratovolcano   190
ultra-Plinian   193
volatile   175
volcanic rock   174

Questions for Review

1. Sketch a map of an idealized tectonic plate and evaluate the volcanic hazards along the different plate edges.
2. What changes in temperature, pressure, and water content will cause hot rock to melt? What are the two most effective melting agents?
3. Contrast the differences between basaltic, andesitic, rhyolitic magma in terms of SiO_2 percentage, water content, temperature, viscosity, and mode of gas escape.
4. What determines whether volcanic activity will be a lava flow or a pyroclastic eruption?
5. Play the three Vs game. Pick various low, medium, and high values for viscosity, volatiles, and volume, and then describe the resultant eruptive styles, eruption types, and volcanic landforms.
6. Draw a cross-section showing the difference between a shield volcano and a stratovolcano.

7. Which volcanic landform degrades faster due to erosion: a scoria cone or a stratovolcano? Why?
8. Explain the factors controlling the volcanic explosivity index (VEI).
9. Draw a cross-section and describe the collapse of an oceanic volcano, such as Krakatau. What usually is the biggest killer in this process?

10. Explain the eruptive behaviour of a hot spot–fed volcano on a continent.
11. Name two islands formed by volcanism.

Questions for Further Thought

1. What kind of volcanic rocks are found in your area? How old are they? How did they form?
2. Why do people keep rebuilding cities in the vicinity of an active volcano, such as Vesuvius?
3. List the beneficial aspects of volcanoes and volcanism.
4. How do volcanoes change the landscape?

5. When will the Atlantic ocean floor start to subduct underneath eastern North America? What kind of volcanoes will be created by this process?
6. Have some major volcanic eruptions changed the course of history?
7. Evaluate this message: Plate boundaries are bad news.

Killer Events

"An incredible black cloud was cascading down the mountain-side, fed by the billowing columns soaring upwards into a huge mushroom cloud. 'Nuée ardente' immediately came to mind as it became obvious nothing would stop it—not even the deep river valley that lay between us and the mountain."

—Canadian volcanologist Catherine Hickson, eyewitness to the
1980 Mount St. Helens eruption
(excerpt from her book Mt. St. Helens—Surviving the Stone Wind*)*

Outline

- Volcanism at Spreading Centres
- Volcanism at Subduction Zones
- Volcanism at Hot Spots
- Canada's Sleeping Volcanoes
- Killer Events and Processes
- Volcano Monitoring and Warning
- Summary

High-temperature pyroclastic flow rolling down the side of Mount St. Helens, 7 August 1980.

Photo: © US Geological Survey.

The explosive eruption of Krakatau Volcano in Indonesia on 27 August 1883 seems to have influenced the world of art. Edvard Munch created his famous painting *The Scream* (Figure 8.1) from an experience he had while walking in Oslo, Norway. Munch's journal entry states: "All at once the sky became blood red . . . and clouds like blood and tongues of fire hung above the blue-black fjord and the city . . . and I felt alone, trembling with anxiety . . . I felt a great unending scream piercing through nature." *The Scream* is thought to be his reaction to the skies made blood red in Europe by the Krakatau eruption.

In this chapter, we tour the world, describing volcanism in different tectonic environments, and discover that Canada has examples of almost every type of volcanoes found on the planet. We then examine the historical record of volcano-related fatalities to understand the specific processes that kill people. Lastly, we look at issues in volcano monitoring and warning.

Volcanism at Spreading Centres

Most of the volcanism on Earth takes place along the oceanic ridge systems where seafloor spreading occurs. Solid, but hot and ductile, mantle rock rises upward into regions of lower pressure, where up to 30 to 40% of the rock melts and flows as basaltic magma. Virtually all of this volcanic activity takes place below sea level and is thus difficult to view. In 1979, the submersible *Alvin* gave scientists a first glimpse at the newly formed, still-hot oceanic crust on the seafloor. *Alvin*'s photographs unveiled high-temperature vents—called black smokers because they resemble chimneys—spewing dark, mineral-rich fluids, and surrounded by a thriving ecosystem with abundant lifeforms (Figure 8.2). Sunlight does not reach these organisms, which rely on the chemical reactions associated with the hydrothermal fluids for energy. The study of these extremophiles gives biologists clues about the different environments that might support extraterrestrial life. In a more down-to-earth pursuit, geologists are keen to find remnants of black smokers in the geological record in the search for economic ore deposits.

The worldwide rifting process releases enough magma to create 20 km^3 of new basaltic oceanic crust each year. We see and are impressed by the tall and beautiful volcanic mountains on the edges of the continents, but the volume of magma they release is small compared to that of spreading centres.

ICELAND

Iceland is a volcanic plateau built of basaltic lava erupted from a hot spot below the mid-Atlantic spreading centre (Figure 3.26). About 13% of the country's surface is covered by glaciers, and one-third comprises active volcanoes. During the nearly 1,000 years of human records, volcanic eruptions have occurred about every five years, on average. Most Icelandic eruptions do not cause deaths, but exceptions do occur (see description of the famine of 1783 later in this chapter).

Lava Flows of 1973

The recent story of Iceland shows that humans can make enough adjustments to live profitably and happily next to active basaltic volcanism. The 1973 eruptions on the small island of Heimaey on the southern coast of Iceland illustrate the "peaceful" nature of these eruptions. The town of Vestmannaeyjar is built next to the premier fishing port in Iceland. The safe harbour is itself a gift of volcanism; it was formed between ancient lava flows. On 23 January 1973, a fissure opened up only 1 km from the town of 5,300 people (Figure 8.4). By early July, the eruption had emitted 230 million m^3 of lava (Figure 8.5) and 26 million m^3 of pyroclastic material. The lava flows increased the size of the island by 20%. Gases vented during the eruptive sequence, other than water vapour, were dominantly CO_2 with lesser amounts of H_2, CO, and CH_4. The only fatality was a person asphyxiated in a gas-filled building.

Figure 8.1
The Scream, painting by Edvard Munch (1863–1944).

In Greater Depth

Project Neptune: Revolutionizing Ocean Science

Project Neptune, launched in 2003 as a collaborative effort between Canada and the United States, aims to address fundamental questions in ocean science with high-tech instruments reminiscent of space exploration. When the project is fully operational, the Neptune "tool box" will include seafloor rovers, robots, high-definition cameras, seismometers, and different sensors to monitor the movements of sea creatures (Figure 8.3).

What could be a better natural laboratory for the project than the Juan the Fuca plate (Figure 5.12)? The plate, one of the smallest of the world, features a large variety of tectonic environments in a relatively small geographical area and an active underwater volcano, the Axial seamount. The innovative concept of Project Neptune is to equip the plate with an array of sensors linked by optical cables. These sensors will be interactive: via the Internet, scientists will control their configuration to adapt to changing conditions like storms, earthquakes, plankton blooms, and fish migration.

Six seafloor locations have been chosen for study. Among them, the Cascadia Subduction Zone will be monitored by an array of ocean-bottom seismometers. A practical goal is to give advance warning quickly enough so that utility companies turn off gas and electricity in time to limit the spread of fire in the case of a megathrust earthquake. Microbial incubators will be deployed in and around the high-temperature vents of the Axial seamount while other sensors monitor environmental changes (Figure 8.2). Conditions near the vents may vary very quickly, and biologists are keen to understand how the deep sea ecosystem adapts to change by correlating several data sets.

Currently, a first 800-km section of optical cable has been laid on the continental shelf and deep ocean, offshore of Vancouver Island. The next step is to connect more than 200 sensors to the cable with the objective of acquiring the first live data stream in late 2008.

Figure 8.2 This black smoker (in the background) from the Juan de Fuca ridge supports a lush colony of tube worms.
Image courtesy of University of Washington.

Figure 8.3 Project Neptune will monitor seafloor processes on the northern portion of the Juan de Fuca plate with high-tech equipment. (1) Sonar imager; (2) high-definition camera; (3) rover; (4) seismometer; (5) microbial incubators; (6) optical cable; (7) control system; (8) self-propelled gas collection system; (9) cable sensor; (10) service robot.
Source: *Wired*.

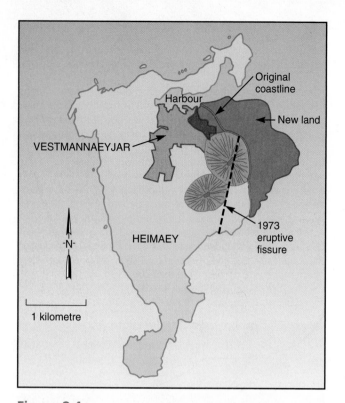

Figure 8.4
The island of Heimaey with the old coastline shown as an orange line. Dark-grey area is new land formed by 1973 lava flows. Note that the new harbour is bigger and better protected.

Source: Williams, R. S., Jr., and Moore, J. G.

The early lava flows on Heimaey began filling in the harbour and destroying about 300 buildings; pyroclastic fallout buried another 70 buildings. But the volume of lava was not overwhelming, so the Icelanders took over. Pyroclastic material was bulldozed to create barriers that diverted and controlled the flow of later lavas and even controlled the flow paths of the dense volcanic gases. To save their harbour and economic livelihood, the Icelanders sprayed seawater on the lava flows, causing rapid cooling and hardening into wall-like features that forced the lava to flow off in another direction (Figure 8.6). This action prevented the harbour from being filled and closed. Now, with its new shape and larger size, the harbour is better than before the 1973 eruptions (Figure 8.4).

When the eruptions stopped, the people set up a pipe system that poured water into the 100 m thick mass of slowly cooling lava. Return pumps were installed to bring the water, which had been heated to 91°C, back to the surface and into town, where it was used to heat buildings. Basaltic eruptions do not have to be killers. Humans and volcanoes can coexist in harmony, with luck and with some exceptions.

Jokulhlaup of 1996

An earthquake episode began in southeastern Iceland on 30 September 1996 as fissuring opened along the mid-Atlantic spreading centre beneath the thick Vatnajokull glacier, which covers 10% of Iceland. In two days, magma rising through the fissure melted through the 600 m thick ice

Figure 8.5
An aa lava flow stopped against and between two fish-factory buildings in Vestmannaeyjar, 23 July 1973.

Photo: © US Geological Survey.

Figure 8.6
Seawater is being sprayed on the lava front to cool, harden, and stop it from closing off Vestmannaeyjar harbour, 4 May 1973.

Photo: © US Geological Survey.

cap, sending steam and other gases several kilometres into the atmosphere. Meltwater flowed under the glacier to the ice-covered Grimsvotn Volcano, where it accumulated in the volcano caldera. The meltwater volume reached an estimated 4 km³, but on 5 November, the rising water lifted the glacier and poured forth as an enormous **jokulhlaup,** a flood flowing at 45,000 m³/s. For two days, the water flowed as the second largest river in the world, behind only the Amazon River, and then it died out, stranding blocks of ice up to 1,000 tonnes on the bed of the short-lived stream. The jokulhlaup water and ice blocks destroyed Iceland's longest bridge, key telephone lines, and a road.

Volcanism at Subduction Zones

Through newspapers and television, we learn of death-dealing volcanic eruptions at Galeras Volcano in Colombia, Mount Unzen in Japan, Mounts Pinatubo and Mayon in the Philippines, and Soufriere Hills on Montserrat. These are all subduction-zone volcanoes, and they have the biggest impact on humans. A similar situation exists in southern British Columiba where Canada's most explosive volcanoes are found—Mount Garibaldi and Mount Meager—at the northern end of a **volcanic belt** extending along the Pacific coast all the way to Northern California, the Cascade Range.

Worldwide, many of the regions around subduction-zone volcanoes are heavily populated and feel the wrath of the eruptions. Also, because these volcanoes erupt directly into the atmosphere, they can affect weather worldwide (see Chapter 11).

CASCADE RANGE, SOUTHERN BRITISH COLUMBIA AND NORTHWESTERN UNITED STATES

Explosive eruptions are frequent happenings at the numerous volcanoes in southern British Columbia and in the Pacific Northwest region of the United States (Figure 8.7). The plate-tectonic process responsible for these volcanoes is identical to the cause of the region's great earthquakes—subduction. The melting of part of the asthenosphere wedge above the subducting plate is aided by water released from sediment on top of the subducting plate. The rising basaltic magma partially melts overlying crustal rock, increasing its contents of SiO_2 and water. Much of the magma changes its composition to andesite or rhyolite and increases its viscosity as it rises (Figure 8.8). Some collects in great pods and cools underground, forming plutonic rocks, but some erupts explosively at the surface.

How often do major eruptions occur? Forty-nine eruptions have been documented in the Cascade Range in the last 4,000 years (Figure 8.9). How are prehistoric

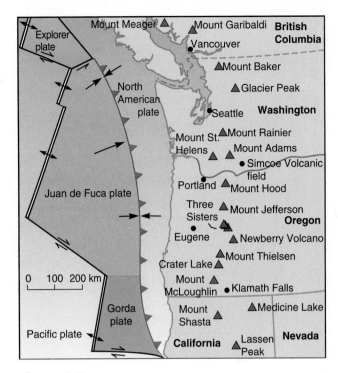

Figure 8.7
Tectonic map of Cascade Range volcanoes. Volcanoes are subparallel to the subduction zone and are spaced somewhat regularly.

eruptions documented? The process is the same as that used to work out dates of prehistoric earthquakes. The slopes near a volcano reveal the remains of trees knocked down by volcanic blasts (Figure 8.10). These trees may be buried by volcanic ash, incorporated in lahars, or otherwise preserved. Radiocarbon determinations of the dates when trees died also tell the dates of the volcanic eruptions that killed them. Notice the distribution of ages along the chain of Cascade Range volcanoes (Figure 8.9). Basically, the volcanoes are all the same age; they sit above subducting plates and are active now. Volcanoes built above hot spots also line up, for example, Hawaii (Figure 3.11). In contrast to subduction-zone volcanoes, the ages along chains of hot-spot volcanoes range from young to old in orderly progressions.

Note the exceptional activity of Mount St. Helens, which has experienced major eruptions every century or two and has never been free from major volcanism for longer than 500 years (Figure 8.9). In their 1975 study, Dwight Crandell and colleagues stated, "Although dormant since 1857, St. Helens will erupt again, perhaps before the end of this century." The geological analysis was prophetic (Figure 8.11).

Mount St. Helens, Washington State, 1980
In late March 1980, Mount St. Helens awoke from a 123-year-long slumber. Dozens of magnitude 3 earthquakes occurred each day as magma pushed its way toward the

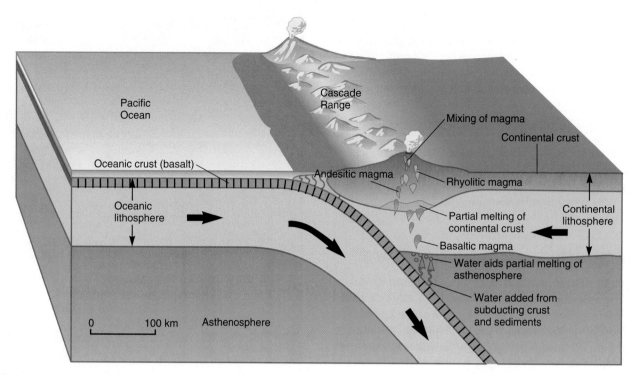

Figure 8.8
Subduction-zone volcano factory. Basaltic magma forms in upper asthenosphere where subducted water aids partial melting. Rising magma partially melts some continental crust, forming water-rich andesitic to rhyolitic magmas that erupt explosively.

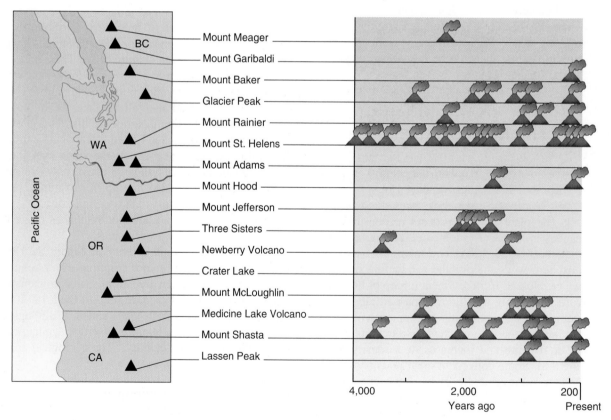

Figure 8.9
Eruption histories of Cascade Range volcanoes.

Figure 8.10
A mature forest is now fallen trees pointing in the direction travelled by the volcanic blast from Mount St. Helens on 18 May 1980.

surface. On 27 March, small explosions began as groundwater and magma came in contact. The spectacle of an erupting volcano was a tremendous lure for sightseers. People flocked to Mount St. Helens. The weekend traffic was so jammed that it reminded people of rush hour in big cities. But this was an explosive giant just warming up its act, and all nearby life was in grave danger. The governor of Washington ordered blockades placed across the roads to Mount St. Helens to keep people away. Her action was unpopular. Then, at 8:32 a.m. on 18 May 1980, the volcano blew off the top 400 m of its cone during a spectacular blast that generated about 100 times the power of all electrical power plants in the United States combined. Most of the 62 people killed had found ways around the barricades to get a better view of an erupting volcano. A look at the eruptive sequence provides a good example of how an explosive volcano operates (Figure 8.12).

First, Mount St. Helens achieved its beautiful conical shape during the mid-1800s (Figure 8.12a). In 1843, a SiO_2-rich lava dome grew at the volcano peak. In 1857, andesitic lava flows cooled high on the slopes. But these events also set up discontinuities, or weaknesses, within the volcanic cone.

Second, in 1980, rising magma began changing the shape of the volcano (Figure 8.12b). Earthquake hypocentres were abundant at 1 to 3 km depth. The seisms were recording the injection and pooling of magma. With magma forcing its way upward, the northern side of the volcano began rising. The increasing volume of magma also caused the groundwater body to expand its volume. The effect on the volcano was dramatic. By 12 April, a 2 km² area on the north flank had risen upward and outward by 100 m. This unstable situation grew worse as the "mega-blister" kept growing about 1.5 m per day.

Third, at 8:32 a.m. on 18 May 1980, a magnitude 5.1 earthquake rocked the volcano. It triggered a gigantic

landslide as 2.5 km³ of the north side of the mountain fell away at speeds up to 250 km/h (Figure 8.12c). The avalanche was a roiling mass of fragmented rock that once was the mountaintop and side, combined with ice blocks, snow, magma, soil, and broken trees; the internal temperature of the mass was about 100°C. The resulting deposit was a chaotic mixture of broken rocks and loose debris that averaged 45 m in thickness and had a hummocky surface relief of 20 m. Only a short time earlier, this material had been the top of the mountain. At the same time as the avalanche occurred, lahars were forming and flowing down the river valleys as rock particles mixed with water derived from melting snow and ice, from a neighbouring lake, and from within the avalanche. These slurries continued to form and flow for many hours after the eruption began. Lahars moved long distances at speeds up to 40 km/h, carrying huge boulders and flowing with a consistency like wet concrete.

Fourth, as the landslide began to pull away, the dramatic drop in pressure on the gaseous magma and superheated groundwater caused a stupendous blast (Figure 8.12d). The blast and surge roared outward at speeds up to 400 km/h. The blast overtook and passed the fast-moving avalanche, racing over four major ridges and scorching an area of 550 km² with 0.18 km³ of volcanic rock fragments and swirling gases at about 300°C. The blast was a pyroclastic flow (see chapter opening photo). It was denser than air, flowing along the ground as a dark cloud with turbulent volcanic gases keeping solid rock fragments, magma bits, and splintered trees in suspension; it behaved as a very low-viscosity fluid. This menacing cloud is what Dr. Catherine Hickson, an earth science student at the University of British Columbia at the time, describes as the "stone wind" (see chapter opening quotation). Dr. Hickson had been spending the two nights preceding the eruption camping 15 km east of Mount St. Helens and enjoying a panoramic view of the volcano. Her idyllic weekend came abruptly to an end. On Sunday morning, 18 May, caught directly in the turmoil of the eruption, she was fleeing for her life, driving through a maze of back roads in very poor visibility. This experience was clearly a defining moment for Dr. Hickson, who has since then devoted her professional career to the study of volcanoes.

Fifth, the big blast opened up the throat of the volcano, exposing an effervescing magma body. Rapidly escaping gases blew upward, carrying small pieces of magma to heights greater than 20 km during the Plinian phase, which lasted about nine hours (Figure 8.12e). The boiling gases carried about 1 km³ of ashes up and away. About 0.25 km³ of ash was blown across the United States and Canada by westerly wind systems. Another 0.25 km³ formed pyroclastic flows by either spilling out of the volcano or falling from the eruption cloud. These pyroclastic

(a)

Figure 8.11
Mount St. Helens, Washington State.
(a) *Before:* View to the northeast of the beautiful cone of Mount St. Helens on 25 August 1974. Mount Rainier is in the distance. (b) *After:* Same view on 24 August 1980, after the volcano had blown off its top 400 m.
Photos: © John S. Shelton.

(b)

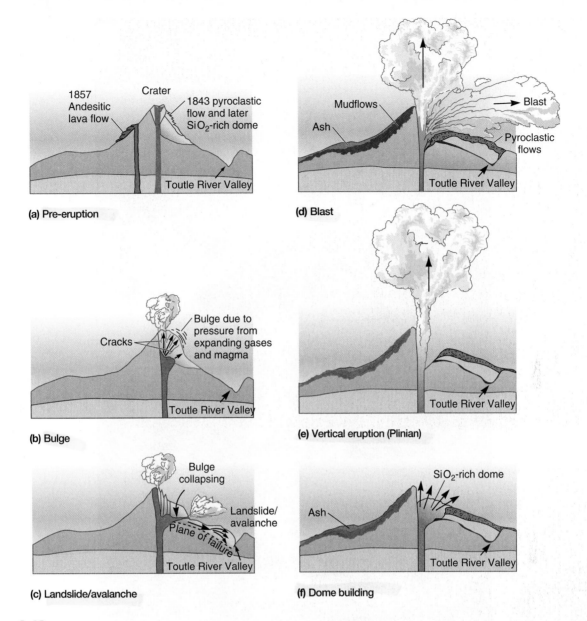

Figure 8.12
Eruptive sequence (VEI = 5) of Mount St. Helens in 1980. (a) The symmetrical volcanic cone was shaped in 1843 and 1857. (b) In late March, rising magma and expanding gases caused a growing bulge on the northern side. (c) At 8:32 a.m. on 18 May 1980, a magnitude 5.1 earthquake caused the bulge to fail in a massive landslide/avalanche. (d) The landslide released pressure on the near-surface body of magma, causing an instantaneous blast of fragmented rock and magma. (e) The "throat" of the volcano was now clear, and the vertical eruption of gases and small blobs of magma shot up to heights of more than 20 km for nine hours. (f) Today, the mountain is slowly rebuilding with a volcanic dome of low–water content, SiO_2-rich magma.

flows had temperatures of 300°C to 370°C and moved at speeds up to 100 km/h.

Sixth, the volcano now slowly repairs the damage done to its once-symmetrical cone as it builds an SiO_2-rich lava dome (Figure 8.12f). The magma building the lava dome has not erupted explosively probably because it lost most of its volatiles during the big eruption on 18 May 1980. The growth of this lava dome continues in the 21st century (Figure 8.13).

Mount St. Helens looks very different these days (Figure 8.11b). Gone are the mountaintop, snowfields, forests, and lakes. The once tree-lined river valleys are now clogged with volcanic debris (Figure 8.14). But recovery is progressing well. Bacteria have eaten sludge from dirty lakes, leaving pure water that has been stocked with trout. Plants have sprouted anew in devastated ground, and animals have returned to feed on them and each other. Life is erasing the effects of the volcanic events.

Figure 8.13
Lava dome of high-viscosity, low-volatile magma growing in the central magma pipe of Mount St. Helens since its big eruption in 1980.
Photo: © PhotoLink/Photodisc/Getty Images.

Volcanism at Hot Spots

Hot spots are shallow magmas or plumes of slowly rising mantle rock that create volcanism on the Earth's surface. The temperature of the rising rock is hotter than the surrounding rock by about 300°C in the plume centre and only 100°C along the outer margin of the plume head. But this temperature difference lowers viscosity enough to start the rise toward the surface.

Most hot spots operate for about 100 million years. They do not move as much as tectonic plates and are used as reference points to help chart plate movements

(Figures 3.11 and 5.26). They occur under the oceans and under the continents, in the centre of plates, and as part of spreading centres (Figure 8.15). There is only one hot spot in Canadian territory, the Anahim hot spot, fuelling volcanism in central British Columbia.

The explosiveness of volcanic eruptions above hot spots varies. They are relatively peaceful above oceanic hot spots, such as Hawaii, where low-volatile, low-viscosity, large-volume magma flows easily and builds shield volcanoes. A hot spot below a spreading centre means a much greater volume of basaltic magma can erupt. For example, in Iceland, the magma of the

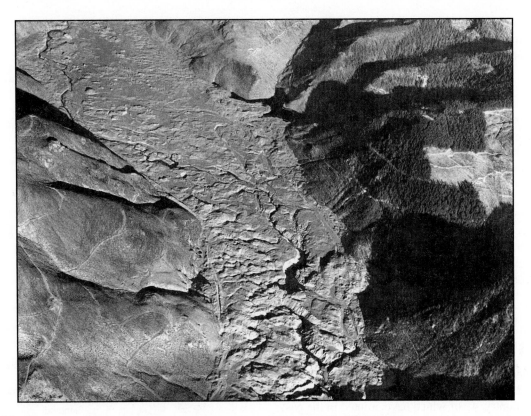

Figure 8.14
The Toutle River Valley, at the foot of Mount St. Helens, choked with eruption debris.
Photo: © John S. Shelton

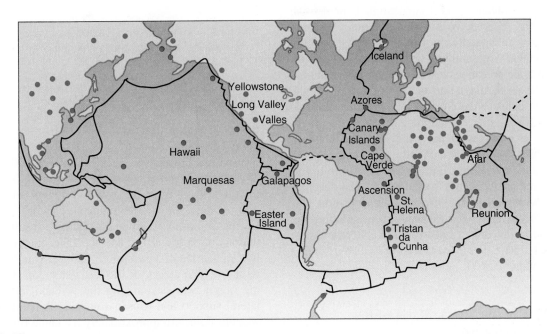

Figure 8.15
Hot spots active in the last 10 million years. Antarctica is not shown but lies above 11 hot spots, raising questions about the effects of melting massive volumes of ice.

spreading process is augmented by deeper mantle magma to create an immense volume of basaltic rock. The mantle plume beneath Iceland is the most vigorous hot spot on Earth today.

Above continental hot spots, such as at Yellowstone National Park in the United States, the eruptions may be incredibly explosive because the rising magma breaks off and absorbs so much continental rock that it creates a volatile-rich, high-viscosity, very-large-volume magma. These mega-eruptive centres occur where large volumes of basaltic magma intrude upward to shallow depths. While rising, they encounter continental rocks that melt at lower temperatures. The resultant mixture of melts creates magmas with lower temperature, higher percentages of SiO_2, high viscosity, and high content of volatiles. The buoyant, sticky magma accumulates as very large masses a few kilometres below the surface.

Canada's Sleeping Volcanoes

Although there is currently no volcanic eruption in Canada, there are more than 200 potentially active volcanoes in the country, 49 of which have erupted in the past 12,000 years. Several Canadian volcanoes are "dormant," a word derived from the French verb *dormir*, meaning "to sleep."

Canada's volcanoes are concentrated in British Columbia and Yukon. Within these regions, a large variety of volcanic landforms exists and three tectonic environments are represented (Figure 8.16). There are subduction-zone volcanoes in southern British Columbia and southwestern Yukon due to the subduction of the Pacific plate beneath the North American plate. In central British Columbia, the alignment of several volcanoes along an east-west trend is the surface expression of the Anahim hot spot track. Finally, in northern British Columbia and Yukon, the Earth's crust is subjected to stretching and thinning in association with the development of a continental rift (Figure 3.29c). Several volcanoes lie in the zone of weakened crust, including the three Canadian volcanoes that erupted in historical times: Lava Fork (1750 ± 100), Tseax Cone (1730 ± 150) and Ruby Mountain (1898?).

GARIBALDI VOLCANO, SOUTHERN BRITISH COLUMBIA

The Garibaldi volcanic belt, the northern extension of the Cascade Range into Canada, contains the most explosive volcanoes in the country: Garibaldi Volcano and Mount Meager, both uncomfortably located in the shadow of the Vancouver metropolitan area. Consider that Mount Meager experienced an eruption similar to

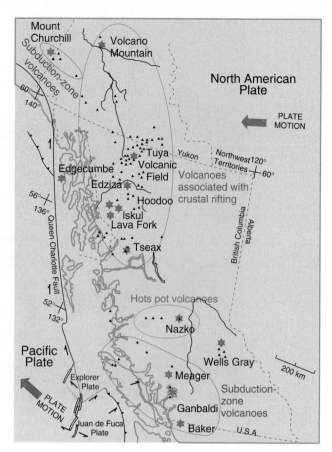

Figure 8.16

Map of Canadian volcanoes. Stars indicate young volcanoes that have erupted less than 12,000 years ago, and triangles correspond to older volcanoes that have erupted between 12,000 and 1.8 million years ago.

Source: Reproduced with the permission of Natural Resources Canada 2008, courtesy of the Geological Survey of Canada (GSC Bulletin 548).

that of Mount St. Helens in 1980 (VEI = 5), only 2,350 years ago.

Garibaldi Volcano itself formed 300,000 years ago. The stratovolcano is a complex structure, damaged and rebuilt several times in a succession of violent eruptions (Figure 8.17). The rugged volcanic landscape at Garibaldi Volcano and in its vicinity results from the interaction between fire and ice. The most recent eruption of Garibaldi Volcano, 13,000 years ago, coincided with the final stages of the last glaciation. Rapid melting of glaciers surrounding the volcano left it without lateral support and caused a catastrophic collapse of its western flank. At approximately the same time, two lava flows erupted from Mount Price, to the north. They were blocked in their progression by glaciers, causing them to pond and gradually solidify behind a wall of ice up to a thickness of 250 m. The resulting steep cliff of volcanic rocks, called "The Barrier" (Figure 8.18), has been the site of several mass movements, most recently in 1855–1856. The small village of Garibaldi located at the

Figure 8.17

Four volcanoes in the Garibaldi volcanic belt, southern British Columbia. Garibaldi Volcano, which includes three different mountain peaks (Mount Garibaldi, Atwell Peak, and Dalton Dome), is the large stratovolcano in the background. Table Mountain is a flat-topped steep-sided volcano that erupted under glacial ice. Clinker Peak and Mount Price are the volcanoes in the foreground. Prominent levees are visible emanating from Mount Price. These levees demarcate the edges of a lava flow that erupted about 10,000 years ago.

Photo: Reproduced with the permission of Natural Resources Canada 2008, courtesy of the Geological Survey of Canada (Photograph by C.J. Hickson). http://gsc.nrcan.gc.ca/volcanoes/cat/feature_garibaldi_e.php.

Figure 8.18

The Barrier, Garibaldi volcanic belt. The Barrier is a steep cliff of volcanic rocks formed when lava solidified behind an ice dam.

Photo: Reproduced with the permission of Natural Resources Canada 2008, courtesy of the Geological Survey of Canada (Photograph by C.J. Hickson). http://gsc.nrcan.gc.ca/volcanoes/cat/feature_garibaldi_e.php.

foot of the cliff has been closed permanently as a preventive measure. Table Mountain, a classic tuya, dates from the same time. Tuyas are subglacial volcanoes with a characteristic flat top (Figure 8.19). A nascent subglacial volcano is completely buried under ice. It produces pillow lavas, similar to those extruded on the seafloor (Table 7.4), as the ice confining it melts. If the volcano grows to an extent that it pierces through the ice and

Figure 8.19

Development of a tuya. The eruption occurs (a) initially below the ice, and (b) then subaerially. (c) Lava pools and solidifies on the surface of the ice. (d) The ice later melts, exposing a volcano with a distinctive flat top.

Source: Reproduced with the permission of Natural Resources Canada 2008, courtesy of the Geological Survey of Canada (GSC Bulletin 548). http://gsc.nrcan.gc.ca/volcanoes/images/fig23_e.gif.

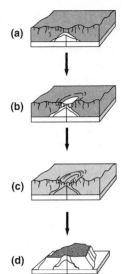

erupts subaerially, then lava flows pool and form a flat cap, giving it the distinctive tuya shape.

NAZKO CONE, CENTRAL BRITISH COLUMBIA

The Anahim hot spot is believed to have been active for over 23 million years. As the North American plate moves westward relative to the Anahim hot spot, a chain of volcanoes, progressively younger to the east, have been created along its track. The two oldest volcanoes, heavily eroded, lie on the Pacific coast. The youngest volcano, Nazko Cone, born 340,000 years ago, occupies a central location in British Columbia (Figure 8.20). Nazko Cone has had a mixed eruptive history, including

Figure 8.20

The Nazko cinder cone shines in the sunset on a winter's day.

Photo by M.C. Kelman, Geological Survey of Canada.

quiet lava eruptions and explosive pyroclastic eruptions. The last eruption at Nazko Cone, some 7,200 years ago, may have started forest fires because charcoal is found within pyroclastic deposits at the site. Today, some of the unconsolidated pyroclastic material from the volcano is mined for landscaping and agricultural applications (Figure 8.21). Before being mined into oblivion, Nazko Cone showed signs of renewed activity in October 2007 (see In Greater Depth box: Is Nazko Cone Reawakening?).

TSEAX CONE, NORTHERN BRITISH COLUMBIA

The weakened crust of northern British Columbia and southern Yukon is host to the largest concentration of volcanoes in Canada. There are more than 100 volcanoes in the area, most of them small cinder cones erupting basaltic lavas.

The very young Tseax Cone is of particular significance as being the cause of Canada's worst natural disaster. Its eruption in the 18th century caused the death of 2,000 people of the Nisga'a First Nation by asphyxiation, most likely from carbon dioxide (CO_2). Lava flows, travelling as far as 22 km from the cone, covered a large plain and transformed the landscape into barren lands, forcing people to relocate (Figure 8.22).

The Nisga'a house system is composed of four main families: Wolf, Raven, Killer Whale, and Eagle. Each family owns stories and passes them on to the next generation. The oral tradition of the Nisga'a tells of a prolonged period of disruption by the volcano, and includes reference to earthquakes, rivers of molten rock glowing red, and poisonous smoke. A well-known legend mentions that children had shown disrespect to the life-giving

Figure 8.21
Pyroclastic material being mined at Nazko Cone, central British Columbia.

Photo: Reproduced with the permission of Natural Resources Canada 2008, courtesy of the Geological Survey of Canada (Photograph by C.J. Hickson). http://gsc. nrcan.gc.ca/volcanoes/cat/volcano_e.php?id=avb_ncn_032.

Figure 8.22
Lava flows from Tseax Cone, northern British Columbia.

Photo: Reproduced with the permission of Natural Resources Canada 2008, courtesy of the Geological Survey of Canada (Photograph by C.J. Hickson). http://gsc. nrcan.gc.ca/volcanoes/cat/volcano_e.php?id=svb_tsx_107.

salmon by putting stones and burning sticks into their backs and watching them swim. The elders warned the children repeatedly to stop but they did not listen. Soon the ground began to rumble. The volcano erupted and lava flows covered the valley bottom, redirected a river, and destroyed two villages.

VOLCANIC HAZARDS IN CANADA

With several dormant subduction-zone volcanoes in the Cascade Range, an explosive volcanic eruption is a significant hazard in British Columbia. The densely populated Vancouver and Victoria areas are most at risk from Mount Baker, Washington State, located very close to the international border (Figure 8.26). Mount Baker, which last erupted in 1880, is handsomely capped by a thick blanket of glacial ice and snow. Volcanic activity could induce a meltdown and send lahars reaching all the way to the Fraser River Valley. Less dramatically, Mount Baker could also produce large quantities of volcanic ash. Southwestern British Columbia experiences significant accumulations of ash every few hundred years (Figure 8.27). Ash fallout would cause respiratory problems for people and disrupt technological systems. Airplane jet engines are particularly sensitive to abrasive ash (see In Greater Depth box: British Airways Flight 9). In fact, the Geological Survey of Canada estimates that the threat of airborne ash in Canadian airways constitutes the most important short-term impact of volcanoes on the Canadian public (Figure 8.28). The International Civil Aviation Organization (ICAO), headquartered in Montreal, has developed colour codes to inform pilots and air-traffic controllers about volcanic-ash hazards (Table 8.1). Depending on the circumstances, flights are rerouted, planes are supplied with extra fuel, or higher vigilance is recommended.

Diamonds and Volcano Roots

Diamonds were born some three billion years ago more than 100 km below the Earth's surface (Figure 8.23a). At these depths, temperature and pressure are high enough to pack carbon atoms into dense three-dimensional crystals where each atom is connected to four others by strong chemical bonds. Diamond is the hardest mineral known. Its rigid atomic structure gives diamond its extreme hardness and distinguishes it from its "cousin" graphite, a mineral also composed of pure carbon, but made of loosely bound sheets of atoms.

Relatively recent (some 55 million years ago), strong volcanic events have brought diamonds to the surface of the Earth in rising magma plumes supplying small volcanoes. The roots of these volcanoes eventually solidified as carrot-shaped intrusive bodies known as kimberlite pipes (Figure 8.23b). Although some diamonds have been dispersed in the environment by water and ice erosion, most are still found in their original kimberlite pipes. More than 500 kimberlite pipes have been identified in Canada. Only a very few, however, contain economic concentrations of diamonds.

The first economic discovery of diamonds in Canada dates from the 1990s. There are currently three diamond mines in operation in the Northwest Territories (Figure 8.24) and one in Nunavut. Another mine is under construction in northern Ontario. In fewer than two decades, Canada has become the third largest international producer, behind Botswana and Russia (Figure 8.25).

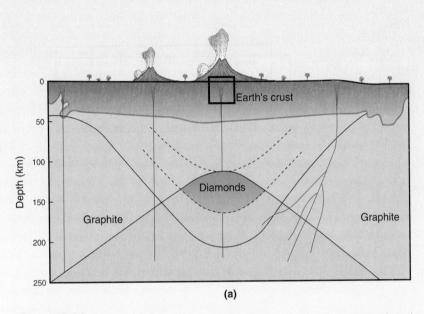

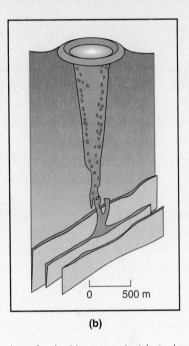

Figure 8.23 Formation of diamonds. (a) Generated at great depths, diamonds were brought near the surface by rising magma in violent volcanic events. (b) (enlarged boxed area) Kimberlite pipes, typically a few hundred metres in diameter, are the roots of ancient volcanoes where most diamonds are hosted.

Source: Diavik Diamond Mine Inc.

Figure 8.24 The Diavik Diamond Mine is located on a 20 km² kilometre island in Lac de Gras, approximately 300 kilometres northeast of Yellowknife. Dikes had to be built to hold back the waters of the lake to allow open-pit mining of the diamondiferous kimberlite pipe. During its projected 20-year life, the mine is expected to produce six to eight million carats a year, about 5 percent of the world's total supply.

Photo: © A. Snider.

Figure 8.25 Rough diamonds from the Ekati Mine, Northwest Territories, harvested during one day of production.

Photo: © Claire Samson

Figure 8.26
Mount Baker, northern Washington State, looming over the City of Victoria, British Columbia.
Photo: © Daves Photography.

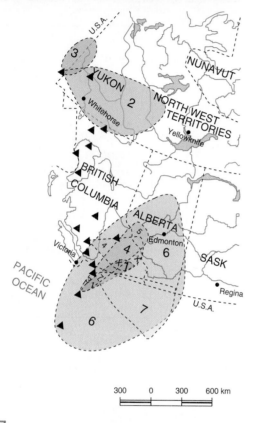

	Volcano	Eruption Date
1	Mount St Helens, Oregon	508 years ago
2	White River, Alaska	1,200 years ago
3	White River, Alaska	1,500 to 1,900 years ago
4	Bridge River, British Columbia	2,360 years ago
5	Mount St Helens, Oregon	3,400 years ago
6	Mazama, Washington	6,800 years ago
7	Glacier Peak, Washington	11,200 years ago

300 0 300 600 km

Figure 8.27
Significant accumulations of volcanic ash in western Canada. Cones represent volcanoes less than 12,000 years old.
Source: Reproduced with the permission of the Minister of Public Works and Government Services 2008.

Killer Events and Processes

Volcanoes can kill in numerous ways (Figure 8.29). They can burn you with a pyroclastic flow, slam and suffocate you with a lahar, batter and drown you with tsunami, poison you with gas, hit you with a pyroclastic bomb, fry you with a lava flow, and kill you with indirect events such as famine.

THE HISTORICAL RECORD OF VOLCANO FATALITIES

Volcanoes operate all around the world. How many people do they kill? Which volcanic processes claim the most lives? The lack of written records for some time intervals and in some parts of the world makes these questions difficult to answer. Volcanologists Tom Simkin, Lee Siebert, and Russell Blong have studied the questions and made approximate answers. About 275,000 people have been killed by volcanic action during the last 500 years (Figure 8.30). A dozen or so volcanic processes have done the killing (Table 8.2). We will now individually examine the killer processes and, in so doing, cover each multi-thousand-death event named in Figure 8.30.

PYROCLASTIC FLOWS

Few events on Earth are as frightening as having a super-hot, turbulent cloud of ash, gas, and air come rolling

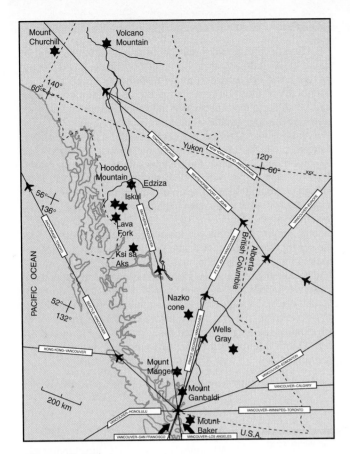

Figure 8.28
Several major air routes over western Canada could potentially be affected by volcanic ash.

Source: Reproduced with permission of the Minister of Public Works and Government Services Canada, 2006 and Courtesy of Natural Resources Canada, Geological Survey of Canada.

Table 8.2

Volcanic Causes of Deaths

	275,000 Deaths	530 Volcanic Events
Pyroclastic flow	29%	15%
Tsunami	21%	5%
Lahar	15%	17%
Indirect (famine)	23%	5%
Gas	1%	4%
Lava flow	<1%	4%
Pyroclastic fall (bombs)	2%	21%
Debris avalanche	2%	3%
Flood	1%	2%
Earthquake	<1%	2%
Lightning	<1%	1%
Unknown	7%	20%

Source: © Simkin, T., Siebert, L., and Blong, R., "Volcano Fatalities" in *Science*, 291:255, 2001.

Table 8.1

International Colour Codes for Volcanic Ash Hazards to Aviation

	Volcano is in normal, non-eruptive state.
GREEN	*or, after a change from a higher level:*
	Volcanic activity considered to have ceased, and volcano reverted to its normal, non-eruptive state.
	Volcano is exhibiting signs of elevated unrest above known background levels.
YELLOW	*or, after a change from a higher level:*
	Volcanic activity has decreased significantly but continues to be closely monitored for possible renewed increase.
	Volcano is exhibiting heightened unrest with increased likelihood of eruption,
ORANGE	*or,*
	Volcanic eruption underway with no or minor ash emission *[specify ash-plume height if possible].*
	Eruption is forecast to be imminent with significant emmission of ash into the atmosphere likely.
RED	*or,*
	Eruption is underway with significant emission of ash into the atmosphere *[specify ash-plume height if possible.]*

Source: http://volcanoes.usgs.gov/Products/Warn/WarnSchemes.html.

In Greater Depth

British Airways Flight 9

On 24 June 1982, 247 people on British Airways Flight 9 boarded a Boeing 747 for a night flight from Kuala Lumpur, Malaysia, to Perth, Australia. The night was moonless but clear, and the weather forecast was good. The crew took the airplane up to its cruising altitude of 11,000 m and then relaxed. Weather radar showed that outside conditions were normal. But the pilot noticed puffs of "smoke" and an acrid or electrical odor. As he peered through the front windscreens, the atmosphere seemed to be on fire as intense electricity danced about. Out the side windows, the engines were glowing as if they were lit inside. Then the flight engineer called out: "Engine failure number 4," followed shortly by "Engine failure number 2."

"Three's gone."

"They've all gone."

The pilot thought, "Four engines do not fail." The instrument panel was contradictory, with some gauges reading normal while others told of problems with a confusing lack of pattern.

Meanwhile, the plane was descending slowly. At 8,000 m, the oxygen masks were released but some didn't work; a steep descent was initiated to get down to atmospheric levels with more oxygen. When the plane reached 4,200 m, the pilot said:

"Good evening, ladies and gentlemen. This is your captain speaking. We have a small problem. All four engines have stopped. We are doing our darnedest to get them going again. I trust you are not in too much distress." His words could not have brought much comfort to those passengers in window seats who had been watching the engines that seemed to be on fire.

What to do? Land on the ocean during a dark night? Too dangerous. Finally, at 3,500 m, engine number 4 started, and 90 seconds later, the other three engines started. The pilot set the plane to climbing to avoid hitting the mountainous Indonesian topography, but at 4,500 m, the bad atmospheric problems began again. Descent was once again initiated. Permission was granted for an emergency landing at Jakarta, but the approach was hazardous. The front and side windows were frosted and opaque, so the copilot had to look out a little side window and give instructions to the pilot landing the huge, fast-moving plane. At last, the landing was smooth, and the passengers cheered and clapped.

What happened that night to BA9? It flew during an eruption of Mount Galunggung and passed through its seething cloud of hot volcanic ash and larger pyroclastic debris. The volcanic ash clogged the engines, frosted the windscreen, and turned BA flight 9 into a terror-filled flight. Airplanes must avoid volcanoes in eruption.

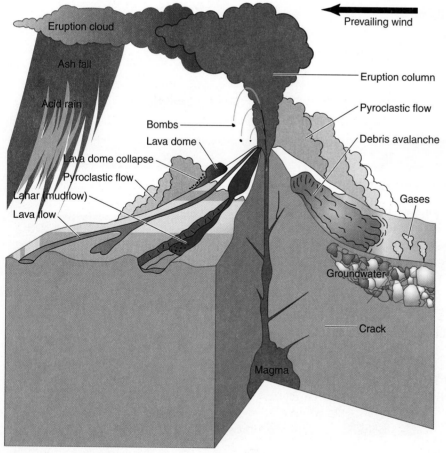

Figure 8.29

Volcanoes create many life-threatening natural hazards.

Source: © US Geological Survey *Fact Sheet* 002–97 (1997).

Figure 8.30
Cumulative fatalities from volcanoes during 500 years, 1500–2000.

Source: © Simkin, T., Siebert, L., and Blong, R., "Volcano Fatalities" in *Science*, 291:255, 2001.

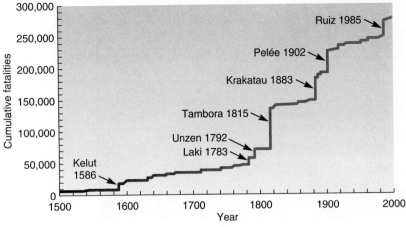

toward you at high speed. History records numerous instances of these pyroclastic flows killing thousands of people at each event. Pyroclastic flows begin in a variety of ways (Figure 8.31). Case histories teach us more about pyroclastic flows.

Mount Mayon, Philippines, 1984

Since 1616, more than 1,500 people have been killed during 40 recorded deadly eruptions of the subduction-caused stratovolcano Mount Mayon. In 1984, a series of Vulcanian eruptions sent eruption clouds 10 km into the atmosphere several times. Partial collapses of the eruption columns sent pyroclastic flows down the mountain slope at velocities ranging from 50 to 100 km/h (Figures 8.31d and 8.32).

Is Mount Mayon at its deadliest when it is erupting most energetically? No, it is deadliest in weaker intervals during the eruption. At its most powerful, the volcano is sending its eruption column of hot pyroclastic material, hot gas, and inter-mixed air up into cooler air, providing time for heat to dissipate and for pyroclasts to cool and be spread far and wide. The most dangerous phase of the eruption occurs in those moments when less energy is fed into the eruption column and the column begins to collapse, sending clouds of hot gases, ash, and pumice flowing as ground-hugging deadly pyroclastic flows.

El Chichón, Mexico, 1982

Can pyroclastic flows travel down all sides of a volcano simultaneously? Yes, especially if they are the variety known as **pyroclastic surges**, ring-shaped base surges that occur when more steam and less pyroclastic material combine to produce a more-dilute, less-dense, high-velocity flow. The deadliest pyroclastic surge in modern time occurred in Mexico on 4 April 1982.

El Chichón Volcano sits in a remote part of Chiapas, the southernmost state in Mexico. The volcano had been dormant for at least 550 years and was not considered an imminent hazard. March 1982 was a month of numerous

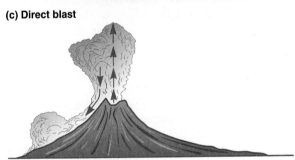

(a) Dome collapse

(b) Overspilling crater rim

(c) Direct blast

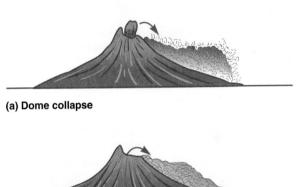

(d) Eruption column collapse

Figure 8.31
Ways of generating pyroclastic flows. (a) Dome collapse as at Mount Unzen, 1991; (b) Overspilling of crater rim as at Mont Pelée, 1902–1903; (c) Direct blast as at Mount St. Helens, 1980, and Mount Pinatubo, 1991; (d) Eruption column collapse as at Mount Mayon, 1968.

Figure 8.32
Formation of pyroclastic flows as collapses from the vertical eruption column flow downhill, Mount Mayon, Philippines, 1984.

Photo: © US Geological Survey.

earthquakes leading up to 29 March, when an unexpected six-hour-long Plinian eruption blasted 1.4 km³ of rock and magma into the atmosphere. The eruption was surprising and the pyroclastic debris settling from the atmosphere was uncomfortable, but the Plinian event was not enough to drive the rural farmers and villagers from their land. The next five days were calming for the residents as only minor volcanic activity occurred. But suddenly on 4 April, a pyroclastic surge flowed radially outward for 8 km, over-running nine villages and killing 2,000 people. Everyone within 8 km of the volcano, in any direction, was killed by the base surge. Following the surge, a Plinian column shot up 20 km. On the same day, there were two more base surges and Plinian columns, but the last two base surges did not matter; everyone was already dead. However, the Plinian columns injected sulfur dioxide (SO_2) into the upper atmosphere, and the whole world felt the effect as global weather changed. The impact of volcanism on weather will be explored further in Chapter 11.

Mount Unzen, Japan, 1991
Mount Unzen's growing lava dome provides a unique combination of steady magma supply and the upward lift of unstable, overhanging topography. Big hunks of lava dome frequently break off and create pyroclastic flows (Figure 8.31a). How frequent are the pyroclastic flows at Unzen? Between 1991 and 1994, more than 7,000 were recorded before this volcanic violence slowed in 1995.

Does being the world's most active creator of pyroclastic flows cause people to avoid building and living in the area? No, cities and towns lie along the coastline near the volcano, and farming villages are built on its lower slopes. In May 1991, the lava dome in Mount Unzen began a growth spurt that attracted international attention. As the unstable lava dome grew and towered 90 m above the crater rim, 15,000 residents were evacuated from villages and tea plantations around the mountain's base. As residents left, journalists and volcanologists arrived to record the numerous collapses of 60 to 90 m high masses from the lava dome and watch them run downslope as glowing pyroclastic flows. At 4:09 p.m., on 3 June 1991, a much larger than usual mass fell off the lava dome and rolled downslope at about 100 km/h, killing 44 observers, including the famed French volcano photographers Maurice and Katya Krafft. All the deaths occurred in previously evacuated areas.

Mont Pelée, Martinique, 1902
The Caribbean island of Martinique in the West Indies was colonized by the French in 1635. The tropical climate was superb for growing sugar cane to help satisfy the world's growing appetite for the sweetener. On the north end of Martinique is a 1,350 m high volcano with a pronounced peak. The French called the volcano Pelée, meaning "peeled" or "bald," to describe the bare area where volcanism had destroyed all plant life during the eruptions of 1792 and 1851. By coincidence, the pronunciation of the French word *Pelée* is the same as the Polynesian word *Pele* used in Hawaii as the name of the goddess of volcanoes and fire.

In early spring of 1902, Vulcanian activity began. The crater atop Mont Pelée began filling with extremely viscous magma, displacing boiling lake waters through a V-shaped notch. The extraordinarily sticky magma kept plugging the crater. At times, superhot pyroclastic flows would gush out of the crater; at other times, they would blast out. By late April, it was obvious to most people that this trouble might worsen. About 700 rural people migrated each day into St. Pierre, a city of picturesque, early-17th century buildings that normally was home to 25,000 residents. Another 300 people a day were leaving St. Pierre, which lay only 10 km from Mont Pelée (Figure 8.33). At a little past noon on 5 May, a large pyroclastic flow sped down the Rivière Blanche, destroying the sugar mill and killing 40 people. This further increased the anxiety level in St. Pierre. But there was an election coming up on 10 May, and the governor did not want everyone scattered from the island's largest city; it was likely to change the election results. Governor Mouttet and his wife went to St. Pierre and used the militia to preserve order and halt the exodus of fleeing people. Bad decision. There was no election on 10 May anyway; all the voters, including the governor, died on 8 May (Figure 8.34).

On the morning of 8 May 1902, a massive volume of gas-charged, ultra-sticky magma had risen to the top of the crater. At about 7:50 a.m., there were sharp blasts that sounded like thousands of cannons being fired as trapped gas bubbles exploded and shattered magma into

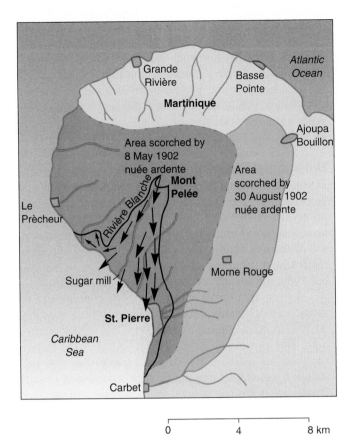

Figure 8.33
Map of Mont Pelée showing areas scorched by the largest pyroclastic flows of 1902.

Figure 8.34
The pyroclastic flow–charred remains of St. Pierre, May 1902. Mont Pelée is in background.

Photo: © Underwood and Underwood, Library of Congress.

fine pieces. This spectacular pyroclastic flow moved as a red-hot avalanche of incandescent gases and glowing volcanic fragments (then called ***nuée ardente***, which is French for "glowing cloud.") The mass moved as solid particles of magma suspended in gas. Its energy came from (1) the initial blast, (2) gravity, and (3) gas continuing to escape from the pieces of airborne magma, creating a "popcorn" effect. The momentum of the flow was aided and its friction was reduced by internal turbulence and air mixed into the flow as it moved downward and outward. The temperature at the crater is estimated to have been about 1,200°C, and the glowing cloud was still hotter than 700°C when it hit St. Pierre. The coarsest and heaviest part of the pyroclastic flow moved down the Rivière Blanche. The associated gas-ash clouds expanded in width and overwhelmed St. Pierre (Figure 8.34).

What happened to St. Pierre? The pyroclastic flow moved with hurricane speeds of about 190 km/h, but it was much denser than a hurricane because it contained ash. The flow lifted roofs, knocked down most walls perpendicular to its path, twisted metal bars, and wrapped sheets of metal roofing around the scorched trunks of trees. Within the space of a couple of minutes, St. Pierre turned from a verdant tropical city to burned-out ruins covered by a foot of grey ash and with muddy ash plastered on those walls and tree trunks that were still standing.

What killed the people? Death was quick and came from one of three causes: (1) physical impact, (2) inhaling superhot gases, or (3) burns. The refugee-swollen population of St. Pierre was more than 30,000; only two people are known to have survived. One was Auguste Ciparis, a 25-year-old murderer locked in a stone-hut jail without windows and with only a small barred grating in his door. When hot gases entered his cell, he fell to the floor, suffering severe burns on his back and legs. Four days later, he was rescued; he then spent the rest of his life showing his scarred body at circus sideshows as "the prisoner of St. Pierre." The other survivor was a man inside the same house where his family members died.

Was it safe to be on a boat in the harbour? No. The fiery hot cloud did not stop when it hit the water. Of 18 boats in the harbour, only the British steamship *Roddam* survived, though it was badly burned and two-thirds of its crew were dead.

Pyroclastic flows continued rolling out of Mont Pelée. St. Pierre was overwhelmed again on 20 May, but it no longer mattered. On 30 August, a pyroclastic flow moved toward the southeast and scorched Morne Rouge and four other towns, killing another 2,000 people. Despite these tragic events, at present the area is fully settled once again.

Krakatau, Indonesia, 1883

Can a pyroclastic flow travel across a body of water to kill you? A body of water does not eliminate the hazard. During the 1883 eruptions of Krakatau leading up to the volcano collapse, one remarkable blast on 27 August sent out a hot gaseous pyroclastic flow that raced across the sea surface of the Sunda Straits for 40 km to reach the coastal province of Katimbang on Sumatra. It flowed onshore with enough heat to fatally burn more than 2,000 people.

TSUNAMI

The Krakatau eruption and caldera collapse in 1883 killed more than 36,000 people. The volcanic eruptions directly killed less than 10% of the people; over 90% of fatalities were due to volcano-caused tsunami.

Mount Unzen, Japan, 1792

Can a pyroclastic flow or lava-dome avalanche cause tsunami? Yes. On 21 May 1792, an earthquake triggered a collapse from the lava dome in Mount Unzen. The avalanche volume of 0.3 km^3 was not impressively large. However, after it flowed 6.4 km to the sea, it hit the water with enough impact to create tsunami that killed 15,000 people in the surrounding region. The tragedy inspired the construction of the Anyoji Temple and Buddhist sanctuary in memory of those killed. In 1991, the temple served as a temporary morgue for the 44 people slammed and burned to death by the 3 June pyroclastic flow.

LAHARS

Viscous lahars cause many deaths and major damages, as we saw in the case history of Vesuvius in 79 CE. Many other lahar disasters have occurred and will continue to occur.

Kelut, Indonesia, 1586, 1919

Indonesia is a nation of volcanoes—Krakatau, Tambora, and Toba are part of a lengthy rogue's gallery of serial killers. Figure 8.30 shows that one of the seven deadliest volcanic events of the last 500 years was at another Indonesian stratovolcano—Kelut in 1586. It was the deadly events at Kelut that brought us the Indonesian word *lahar* to describe volcanic mudflows. Why does Kelut kill so many people? The volcano supplies fresh pyroclastic materials to its slopes, and they quickly decompose under the tropical climate to produce fertile soil, and that attracts people. The slopes of Kelut are intensely cultivated and densely populated. How does Kelut kill? Kelut has a large crater lake at its summit, and Kelut erupts often—15 eruptions in the last 200 years. In 1919, a surprise eruption forced 40 million m^3 of lake water onto the slopes covered with loose pyroclastic debris. The combination of water with loose pyroclasts and steep slopes produced three major lahars flowing down three sides of the volcano at velocities of 65 km/h—and more than 5,000 people died. The longest-travelled lahar went 38 km. What can be done? The 1919 disaster caused Dutch engineers

to dig a set of tunnels to reduce the size of the crater lake by over 95%. Did that solve the problem? No. A 1951 eruption deepened the crater floor, allowing another large lake to form. Then a 1966 eruption dumped 20 million m^3 of water onto the pyroclast-covered slopes to again form lahars; this time, they killed 282 people. Will people cease coming to this dangerous volcano to live and farm its fertile soils? Probably not.

Nevado del Ruiz, Colombia, 1985

Is a huge eruption required to kill a lot of people? Consider this story. Nevado del Ruiz rises to an elevation of 5,400 m, up where the air is cold. The Spanish word *nevado* means snow-covered, and year-round a 19 km^2 area on top of the mountain is covered by an ice cap 10 to 30 m thick with a volume of about 337 million m^3. In November 1984, the volcano awoke with small-scale activity.

A year later, on 10 November 1985, continuous harmonic tremors (earthquakes) foretold a coming eruption. At 9:37 p.m., a Plinian column rose several kilometres high. Hot pyroclastic debris began settling onto the ice cap, causing melting. By 10 p.m., condensing volcanic steam, ice melt, and pyroclastic debris combined to send lahars down the east slopes into Chinchina, destroying homes and killing 1,800 people.

But the worst was yet to come. Increasing eruption melted more ice, sending even larger lahars flowing down the canyons to the west and onto the floodplain of the Rio Magdalena (Figure 8.35). At 11 p.m., the first wave of cool lahars reached the city of Armero and its 27,000 residents. These lahars had travelled 45 km from the mountaintop, dropping over 5,000 m in elevation. In the steep-walled canyons, the lahars moved at rates up to 45 km/h, slowing as they flowed out onto the flatter land below.

A few minutes after 11 p.m., roaring noises announced the approach of successive waves of warm to hot lahars. Most of Armero, including 22,000 of its residents, ended up buried beneath lahars 8 m thick (Figure 8.36). The 22,000 unlucky people were either crushed or suffocated by the muddy lahars.

But 5,000 people did escape. How? They were higher on the slopes. A memorable video showed a man's talking head, which appeared to be resting on top of the mudflows; the man was caught by lahars and buried to his chin as he tried to escape upslope. One step slower and he would have been completely buried and suffocated. But with a bit of digging, he was freed, shaken but unharmed.

The volcanic eruption at Nevado del Ruiz was actually rather minor. Had there not been an ice cap to melt, no harm would have been done. Danger was well known from historical records. In fact, a hazards map published just one month before the tragic events of November 1985 clearly indicated the potential danger for the town of Armero. The 1985 lahars were a virtual rerun of the events of 1845, themselves a repeat of those of 1595. The same

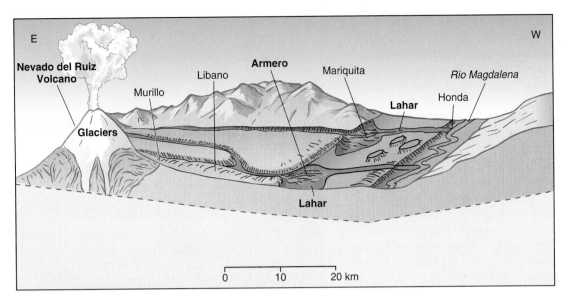

Figure 8.36
Most of the town of Armero, Colombia, and 22,000 of its residents lie beneath lahars up to 8 m thick.
Photo: © US Geological Survey.

places were buried by the same types of lahars. In 1845, the death toll was about 1,000, but because Colombia's population has grown, the dead in 1985 numbered about 24,000. Faced with pressing demands for basic needs like health services and education, poor countries often do not prioritize mitigation against natural hazards.

GAS

It is not just gas-powered magma that kills; gas can be deadly by itself.

Killer Lakes of Cameroon, Africa

Cameroon sits near the equator in western Africa. It hosts a string of crater lakes running in a northeasterly trend.

Prolific rainfall fills the lakes and combines with the hot temperatures to cover the countryside with greenery. Lake Nyos is one of these crater lakes filled with beautiful, deep-blue water. This topographically high crater is only several hundred years old. It was blasted into the country rock by explosions of volcanic gases and is 1,925 m across at its greatest width and as deep as 208 m.

At about 9:30 p.m. on 21 August 1986, a loud noise rumbled through the Lake Nyos region as a gigantic volume of gas belched forth from the crater lake and swept down the adjacent valleys (Figure 8.37). The dense, "smoky" rivers of gas were as much as 50 m thick and moving at velocities up to 70 km/h. The ground-hugging cloud swept outward for 25 km. Residents of four villages overwhelmed by the gaseous cloud felt fatigue, light-headedness, warmth, and confusion before losing consciousness. After 6 to 36 hours, about half a dozen people awoke from their comas to find themselves in the

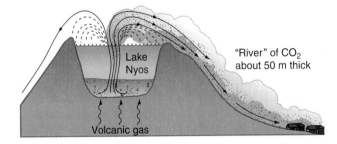

Figure 8.37
Schematic cross-section of Lake Nyos. Volcanic gas is absorbed by a deep-water layer. In 1986, when bottom water was disturbed, 0.15 km³ of CO_2 gas erupted out of the lake and poured down river valleys for an hour or more in a 50 m thick cloud. Virtually all animal life was killed; plants were unaffected. Solid lines show gas flow; dashed lines are water drops.
Diagram after Y. Zhang, 1996, *Nature*, 379, 57–59.

midst of death: 1,700 asphyxiated people; 3,000 dead cattle; and not a bird or insect alive, nor any other animal. Yet the luxuriant plants of the region were unaffected.

This shocking event raises numerous questions. What was the deathly gas? After a lot of effort to identify some exotic lethal gas or toxic substance as the cause of the tragedy, the killer gas turned out to be simply carbon dioxide. This is the same gas we drink in sparkling spring water, soft drinks, and champagne. Its toxicity at Nyos is explained by the principle set forth in 1529 by German physician Theophrastus von Hohenheim (Paracelsus). *The principle of Paracelsus states: the dose alone determines the poison.* A gas does not have to be poisonous, just abundant. Life in the Nyos region was subjected to the same conditions we recreate inside the fire-extinguisher cylinders in our buildings. Fire extinguishers are loaded with carbon dioxide, which does not put out flames directly; because CO_2 is heavier than air, it deprives fire of oxygen, thus causing flames to die out. Animal life in the Nyos area was extinguished in the same fashion.

What was the origin of the gas? It had a volcanic origin, leaking upward from underlying basaltic magma. A 1,600 km–long string of volcanoes, the Cameroon volcanic line, trends northeastward through several Atlantic Ocean islands and then on land through northeastern Nigeria and northwestern Cameroon. Interestingly, this is the location of the triple junction of spreading centres that ripped apart this section of Gondwanaland, helping give the distinct outlines to the Atlantic margins of South America and Africa (Figure 8.38). The two successful spreading arms are still widening the South Atlantic Ocean. The failed rift is occupied by the line of volcanism that includes the crater that forms Lake Nyos; it is not a volcanic mountain but a crater blasted through bedrock by largely gaseous explosions. The volcanic activity is not seafloor spreading per se; rather, it is a "wannabe" ocean basin that never made it but has not given up totally.

How did the gas accumulate into such an immense volume? Lakes by their nature are stratified bodies of water. Their water layers differ in density, one stacked on top of another. (This is a smaller-scale example of the density differentiation discussed for the whole Earth in Chapter 2.) Carbon dioxide, given off by basaltic magma at depth, rises into the bottom waters of Lake Nyos, is dissolved into the heavier, lower water layer, and is held there under the pressure of the overlying water (Figure 8.37). As the amount of CO_2 in the lake-bottom water increases, the arrangement becomes more unstable. When CO_2 bubbles form, they rise with increasing speed, setting off a positive feedback chain of events leading to more and more bubble formation and rise. Volcanologist Youxue Zhang calculated that the gas eruption was moving about 325 km/h when it reached the lake surface. The event of 21 August 1986 released about 0.15 km³ of

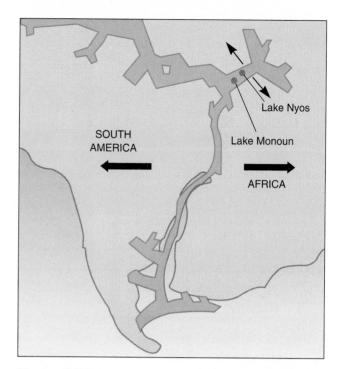

Figure 8.38
Schematic map of Africa and South America splitting apart 135 million years ago. Note the third rift that extends into Africa.

gas in about one hour. It was like a large-scale erupting champagne bottle, where removal of the cork causes a decrease in pressure, allowing CO_2 to escape in a gushing stream. About 66% of the dissolved gases escaped. After the event, the lake level was 1 m lower, and the water was brown from mud and dead vegetation stirred up from the bottom (Figure 8.39).

What triggered the gas avalanche? Many suggestions have been made, including volcanic eruption, landslide, earthquake, wind disturbance, or change in water

Figure 8.39
Water of Lake Nyos is still muddy 10 days after a huge volume of gas escaped in 1986.
Photo: © US Geological Survey.

temperature with resultant overturn of lake-water layers. It is interesting to note that a similar event occurred two years earlier at Lake Monoun on 15 August 1984. This was a smaller event, but it killed 37 people. Both events were in August, the time of minimum stability in Cameroon lake waters. Is this a coincidence, or is this a normal overturning of lake water during the rainy season?

Is this event likely to happen again? Definitely. The Lake Nyos gas escape left behind 33% of the CO_2, and more is constantly being fed through the lake bottom. In about 20 years, the lake water could again be oversaturated with CO_2. The same loss of life will occur again unless remedial actions are taken. Degassing pipes have been installed to allow high-pressure gas to shoot out of the lake as a fountain of gassy water. This could prevent the CO_2 concentrations from building up to dangerous levels.

As this situation has become better known, other similar lakes have been recognized. For example, the giant Lake Kivu that straddles the border between Rwanda and Congo holds 1,000 times as much CO_2.

LAVA FLOWS

Lava flows are common and impressive, but are they big killers? No (Table 8.2). Why don't lava flows kill more people? Usually they move too slow, but not always.

Nyiragongo, Democratic Republic of the Congo, 1977, 2002

As East Africa slowly rifts away from the African continent (Figure 3.28), magma rises to build stratovolcanoes such as Mounts Kilimanjaro and Nyiragongo in the East African Rift Valley. Mount Nyiragongo has a long-lived lava lake in its summit crater. On 17 January 2002, lava flowed rapidly down the slopes of the volcano, killing more than 45 people living on the mountain. Upon reaching flatter ground, the lava flows slowed but moved relentlessly toward Lake Kivu. The city of Goma lay in the path of the oncoming lava: 500,000 residents plus uncounted thousands of civil war refugees from Rwanda lived there. Lava reached the lake, but it first flowed through the heart of Goma, destroying about 25% of the buildings, and the war refugees were forced to flee again.

How were the lava flows able to catch and kill so many people? The lava had unusually low viscosity. In 1977, Nyiragongo lava flows had exceptionally low SiO_2 content, about 42% (compare this value to those listed in Table 7.3). The low-viscosity lava in 1977 flowed down the volcano slopes at about 60 km/h, killing an estimated 300 people.

INDIRECT—FAMINE

Volcanoes affect humans not only directly, but also indirectly by changing the atmosphere and weather, and by harming the plants and animals we depend upon.

Laki Fissure Eruption, Iceland, 1783

During the summer of 1783, the greatest lava eruption of historical times poured forth near Laki. After a week of earthquakes, on the morning of 8 June 1783, a 25 km–long fissure opened and basaltic lavas gushed for 50 days. The Laki event was a textbook fissure eruption where the magma typically flowed at 5,000 m³/s. To better appreciate this volume of magma, consider that North America's mightiest river, the Mississippi, empties into the Gulf of Mexico at about three times this volume. When the eruption ended, an area of 565 km² was buried beneath 13 km³ of basaltic lavas. The volume of ash and larger airborne fragments totalled another 0.3 km³.

The 50 days of eruption were accompanied by the release of an enormous volume of gases that enshrouded Iceland and much of northern Europe in a "dry fog" or blue haze. This haze was rich in SO_2 (one of the visible components of today's urban smog) and an unusually large amount of fluorine. The gases slowed the growth of grasses and increased their fluorine content. An Icelandic farmer named Jon Stein-Grimmson wrote

> The hairy sand-fall and sulfurous rain caused such unwholesomeness in the air and in the earth that the grass became yellow and pink and withered down to the roots. The animals that wandered around the fields got yellow-covered feet with open wounds, and yellow dots were seen on the skin of the newly shorn sheep, which had died.

The volcanic gases helped kill 75% of Iceland's horses and sheep and 50% of the cattle. The resulting famine weakened the Icelandic people, and about 20% of the population (10,000 people) died. In today's world of instant communication and rapid air transport, these deaths would have been avoided.

Tambora, Indonesia, 1815

The most violent and explosive eruption of the last 200 years was another Indonesian event; it was Tambora Volcano on Sumbawa Island in April 1815. After three years of moderate activity, on 5 April, a Plinian eruption column shot up 33 km and carried out 12 km³ of pumice in just two hours. On 10 April, an even more powerful Plinian eruption blasted up to 44 km high for three hours. The magma exited with so much force that it eroded and widened the vent in the volcano, thus cutting off the focused energy that drove the Plinian column. The eruption column stopped and the widened vent lay open; the volcano now had its insides exposed and it spilled its guts. On 11 April, about 50 km³ of magma poured out of the caldera in overwhelming pyroclastic flows. The week-long eruption saw about 150 km³ of magma burst forth. Tambora once stood 4,000 m high, but now its elevation was reduced to 2,650 m with a 6 km wide caldera over

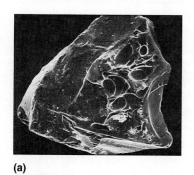

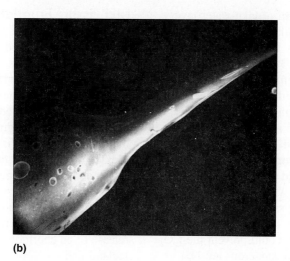

(a) (b) (c)

Figure 8.40

Volcanic ash under the high magnification of a scanning electron microscope (SEM) is seen to be sharp, jagged, angular pieces of glass and rock. (a) Broken glass droplet from Mount Etna, Sicily (size ≈ 2 microns); (b) Tail of cooled droplet from Kilauea, Hawaii (size ≈ 10 microns); (c) Angular glass fragment, Mount Mayon, Philippines (size ≈ 10 microns).

Photos: © SEM photos from Grant Heiken, *Atlas of Volcanic Ash,* Smithsonian Press.

1 km deep (Figure 11.46). The volcanic explosions were audible 2,600 km away, and volcanic ash fell 1,300 km from Tambora. On Sumbawa Island, pyroclastic flows killed at least 10,000 people, and destroyed the feudal kingdoms of Sanggar and Tambora, leading to the erasure of the Tambora language, the easternmost Austro-Asiatic language.

The eruption of Tambora was responsible for an estimated 117,000 deaths; about 10% killed by the eruption and 90% dying slowly at the end of a chain reaction. Pyroclastic fallout devastated crops, which led to famine. Inhalation of volcanic ash over long periods of time caused respiratory problems (Figure 8.40). Weakened people became more susceptible to disease, and then the diseases killed them. But Tambora was not just an Indonesian disaster; the Plinian eruptions of April 1815 so affected global weather patterns that 1816 is known as "the year without a summer."

Volcano Monitoring and Warning

Can we monitor the activity of a volcano and provide advance warning before a large eruption? There have been failures and successes.

Mount Pinatubo, Philippines, 1991

A volcano-warning success story occurred in the Philippines in 1991 before the climactic eruption of Mount Pinatubo on 15 June 1991. The volcanic eruption was the largest in the 20th century to occur near a heavily populated area. Nearly one million people lived in the danger zone.

In March 1991, Mount Pinatubo awoke from a 500-year-long slumber as magma moved upward from a depth of 32 km, causing thousands of small earthquakes, creating three small steam-blast craters, and emitting thousands of tonnes of sulfur dioxide–rich gas. Volcanologists and seismologists began an intense monitoring program to anticipate the size and date of a major eruption. On 7 June, magma reached the surface but had lost most of its gas (like a stale glass of sparkling water), so the magma simply oozed out to form a lava dome. Then on 12 June (Philippine Independence Day), millions of cubic metres of gas-charged magma reached the surface, causing large explosive eruptions. The message to speed the evacuation was spread quickly and loudly. Virtually everyone, and every movable thing, left hurriedly. On 15 June, the cataclysmic eruption began (Figure 7.1). It blew more than 5 km³ of magma and rock up to 35 km into the atmosphere, forming an ash cloud that grew to more than 480 km across. The airborne ash blocked incoming sunlight and turned day into night. Pyroclastic flows of hot ash, pumice, and gas rolled down the volcano flanks and filled valleys up to 200 m deep. Then, as luck would have it, a typhoon (hurricane) arrived and washed tremendous volumes of volcanic debris downslope as lahars.

How successful was the advance warning? Although almost 300 people died, it is estimated that up to 20,000 people might have died without the forceful warnings. The scorecard for the monitoring program from March to June 1991 shows that a monitoring expense of about

In Greater Depth

Is Nazko Cone Reawakening?

On 9 October 2007 seismometers started to detect signals from a swarm of small earthquakes whose epicentres were located 20 km west of Nazko Cone in central British Columbia. Eight earthquakes of magnitude 2–3 occurred the following day. Was Nazko Cone reawakening after a dormant period of more than 7,000 years?

State-of-the-art equipment was rapidly deployed to monitor the situation from different perspectives. Nine portable seismograph stations were installed to gather the data necessary to pinpoint the hypocentres with enhanced accuracy. To complement the seismic recordings, an infrasound station was put in place to capture pressure waves, which have a higher frequency content than seismic waves but are still below the threshold of human hearing. Geologists also measured concentrations of carbon dioxide that might be linked to subsurface magmatic activity. Very importantly, they re-examined lava flows and pyroclastics deposits from ancient eruptions to better predict the characteristics of future events.

Analysis of the data indicates that seismic activity is probably caused by magma movement some 25 km below the surface. Earth scientists from Natural Resources Canada conclude, "There is no evidence at this time to suggest that a volcanic eruption is likely. It is possible that magma intruding at depth may stall without immediately rising towards the earth's surface, and swarms of small magmatic earthquakes may occur at volcanoes without being followed by eruptive activity. If magma were to ascend towards the surface in the Nazko region, it is anticipated that the size and number of earthquakes would increase significantly, providing a warning in the very unlikely event of an eruption. If an eruption were to occur, it is our expectation that it would be a small cinder cone building event, similar to the Nazko eruption that took place about 7,000 years ago."

After a swarm of more than 1,000 small earthquakes over a few months, seismic activity in the area has ceased . . . at least for the time being . . .

$1.5 million saved 20,000 lives and $500 million in evacuated property, including airplanes. What a dramatic and cost-effective success!

SIGNS OF IMPENDING ERUPTIONS

Several phenomena are being evaluated as signs of impending eruption. We need to determine if they are reliable enough to justify evacuation of people from a volcanic-hazard zone. Phenomena being studied include seismic waves, ground deformation, and gas measurements.

Seismic Waves

As magma rises toward the surface, it causes rocks to snap and break, thus sending off short-period seismic waves in an SP event. These short-period waves typically have periods of 0.02 to 0.06 seconds. Magma on the move through an opened conduit generates longer-period seismic waves in LP events. Long-period waves usually have periods of 0.2 to 2 seconds. In 1991, during the two weeks before Mount Pinatubo erupted, there were about 400 LP events a day coming from about 10 km deep. Apparently, the LP events were recording the arrival of new magma moving in and loading the volcano for eruption.

Ground Deformation

The ground surface rises up and sinks down as magma moves up or withdraws. Ground deformation can be measured by tilt meters or strain meters placed in the ground and by electronic distance meters. In recent years, satellite radars and global positioning system (GPS) stations have been used to measure movements of the ground over time. The more the ground rises, the more likely it is that some magma will break through to the surface and erupt.

Gas Measurements

As magma rises toward the surface, the pressure on it drops and dissolved gases escape. In that respect, gas release can signal an impending eruption. However, this interpretation can be misleading. In 1993, at Galeras Volcano in Colombia, a decrease in gas emissions was interpreted as meaning an eruption was less likely. But, in fact, it meant that the volcano had become plugged by its sticky magma and gas pressure was building toward the eruption that killed six volcanologists. So, either an increase or a decrease in gas emissions can be bad. More research needs to be done.

Summary

- Spreading centres sit on top of the asthenosphere, which yields basaltic magma that rises to fill fractures between diverging plates. Eruptions are usually peaceful and basaltic volcanoes may be successfully colonized.
- Subduction-zone eruptions involve basaltic magma contaminated by crustal rock to yield water-rich, highly viscous magma containing trapped gases. Their explosive eruptions pose the greatest risk to humans.
- Hot-spot volcanism can exhibit a range of explosiveness depending on the amount of crustal rock incorporated in magma.

- In the last 500 years, the most devastating direct volcanic causes of deaths have been pyroclastic flows, tsunami, and lahars. Volcanoes also kill indirectly via famine.
  - Gas-powered scorching-hot pyroclastic flows move at speeds up to 250 km/h, for distances up to tens of kilometres.
  - Pyroclastic debris and water can combine and flow downslope as lahars.
- It is possible to monitor seismic activity, ground deformation, and gas releases at a volcano and give advance warning of a major eruption.

Terms to Remember

jokulhlaup   205
nuée ardente   221

pyroclastic surge   219
tuya   213

volcanic belt   205

Questions for Review

1. Explain why it is relatively safe to watch the eruption of a Hawaiian volcano but dangerous to watch the eruption of a Cascade Range volcano.
2. Draw a cross-section and explain how a jokulhlaup forms.
3. Draw a tectonic map and explain the origin of the Cascade Range volcanoes.
4. What volcanic processes have killed the most people in the last 500 years?
5. Are severe earthquakes associated with volcanic activity?
6. Why do pyroclastic flows travel so fast? How do they kill?

7. Draw a cross-section and explain how lahars form and move. How do they kill?
8. Explain the hazard that Mount Baker presents to Vancouver.
9. Draw a cross-section and explain the sequence of events at an African killer lake, such as Nyos.
10. Can an eruption with a low VEI rating kill thousands of people? How?
11. How do the ages vary along a chain of subduction-zone volcanoes versus along a chain of hot-spot volcanoes?

Questions for Further Thought

1. Is it likely that there will be a volcanic eruption in Canada in your lifetime? Are there more volcanoes expected in Canada in the future?
2. A volcano can have effects beyond the borders of the country where it is located. How can neighbouring nations collaborate to mitigate volcanic hazards?

3. What action can governments take to discourage people from living in areas where lahars and pyroclastic flows are likely to be a hazard?
4. Could a major volcanic eruption anywhere in the world affect Canadian weather?

and Snow Avalanches

The town of Frank might exist on its present site uninjured for ages, but there will always be a possibility of a second destructive slide . . . A succession of seasons with unusually heavy precipitations and rapid changes of temperature, a slight earthquake shock, which is by no means an impossibility, or the closing of the chambers in the mine after the coal has been drawn, perhaps long after the inhabitants have lost all dread of the mountain, may snap the supports which retain this mass in place and start it on a career of destruction.

R.G. McConnell and R.W. Brock, 1904,
Report on the Great Landslide at Frank, Alta., 1903,
Geological Survey of Canada

Outline

- The Role of Gravity
- External Conditions of Slope Instability
- Internal Conditions of Slope Instability
- Triggers of Mass Movements
- Classification of Mass Movements
- Falls
- Slides
- Flows
- Complex Events
- Subsidence
- Snow Avalanches
- Mitigation
- Summary

A glider's view of the Frank slide, Canada's deadliest mass movement, killing 70 people in 1903. Glider pilots use the scarred Turtle Mountain as a landmark to orient themselves.
Photographer: Gerald Ince.

In the early morning of Saturday 9 January 1965, four people in three vehicles were driving in the isolated Nicolum Valley, a few kilometres southeast of the village of Hope in British Columbia when a small snow avalanche blocked the highway. As people debated what course of action to take, a massive landslide engulfed them. In a few seconds, more than 46 million m³ of rock from the high mountain ridge forming the north side of the valley crashed down, filling up the valley floor with up to 70 m of debris. Water from the nearby Outram Lake was splashed violently onto the mountain wall on the opposite side of the valley and the lake was completely buried (Figure 9.1) Two of the victims were never found.

Local seismograph stations recorded the vibrations associated with the event. First, scientists assigned them to two minor earthquakes (at 11:56 and 14:59 Universal Time), the second of which triggered the event. A re-examination of the data some 30 years later by Dieter Wiechert and co-investigators reversed the cause and the effect! They reinterpreted the seismic signals as the signatures of two mass movements, a small "precursor" landslide, followed three hours later by the main Hope slide.

Today, the site of the Hope slide looks amazingly fresh, with a large field of angular boulders scattered at the foot of Johnson Peak, a reminder of the briefness of the human experience in relation to geological processes like erosion (Figure 9.2). The Hope-Princeton highway has been rebuilt at an elevation 38 m higher than the original road.

Large volumes of material move downslope under the pull of gravity, and some do so catastrophically as we will explore in this chapter. Thousands of small mass movements occur every year in Canada, most often in the spring and fall, highlighting the role of water as a contributing factor. Due to their high frequency, mass movements are Canada's most destructive geological hazard, costing between CDN$100–200 million annually. Snow avalanches are most frequent in the Rockies where they have a significant economic impact: the closure of the Trans-Canada Highway through mountain passes results in estimated economic losses of CDN$1 million per hour. Historical records show that mass movements and snow avalanches together have been responsible for over 630 deaths in Canada since 1840 (Table 9.1). Major mass movements, displacing in excess of 1 million m³ of material, that is, a volume equivalent to 1,000 m long by 100 m wide by 10 m deep, occur on average once every 10 years. A large array of mitigation measures, however, is deployed against mass movements and snow avalanches in an effort to reduce risk.

The Role of Gravity

Gravity is relentless. It operates 24 hours a day, every day of the year. The constant pull of gravity is the immediate power behind the agents of erosion (see Chapter 2). Rain falls, water flows, ice glides, wind blows, and waves break under the influence of gravity. But gravity can also accomplish major changes working largely by itself, without the help of any erosive agent. It is the solo work of gravity that is the subject of this chapter.

Given enough time, gravity would pull all the land into the seas. Over the great lengths of geological time, all slopes can fail; all slopes should be viewed as inherently unstable. Slope failures may be overpowering, catastrophic events, as when the side of a mountain breaks loose and roars downhill. Or hill slopes may just quietly deform and yield to the unrelenting tug of gravity in the very slow-moving process known as **creep.**

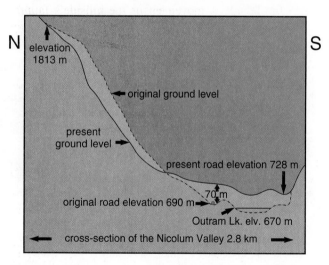

Figure 9.1
North-south cross-section through the Nicolum Valley at the Hope slide site, British Columbia.

Figure 9.2
Panoramic view of the Hope slide site, British Columbia.
Photo: © James Hall.

Table 9.1

Ten Deadliest Mass Movements and Snow Avalanches in Canada 1840–2006

Fatalities	Date	Event	Location
75	23 Apr 1903	Rock avalanche	Frank, AB
62	5 Mar 1910	Snow avalanche	Rogers Pass, BC
56	22 Mar 1915	Rock avalanche	Jane Camp, BC
50	19 Sep 1889	Rock fall	Quebec City, QC
35	6 Jul 1891	Debris flow	North Pacific Cannery, BC
33	26 Apr 1908	Lateral spread	Notre-Dame-de-la-Salette, QC
32	17 May 1841	Rock fall	Quebec City, QC
31	4 May 1971	Lateral spread	Saint-Jean-Vianney, QC
28	18 Nov 1911	Submarine mass movement and tsunami	Grand Banks, NF
26	18 Feb 1965	Snow avalanche	Grandduc Mine, BC

Source: Ten deadliest mass movements and snow avalanches in Canada 1840–2006, Atlas of Canada at http://atlas.nrcan.gc.ca/site/english/maps/environment/naturalhazards/
naturalhazards1999/majoravalanches/avalanches_stats_new.html. Reproduced with the permission of the Minister of Public Works and Government Services, 2008.

Gravity pulls materials downslope with a measurable force. For example, consider a boulder of a mass equal to 1 kg resting upon a 30° slope (Figure 9.3). Gravity pulls the boulder toward the centre of the Earth with a force equal to its mass times the gravitational acceleration (1 kg × 9.8 m/s² = 9.8 Newton), but the ground is too solid to allow the boulder to move down vertically. Trigonometric relations allow the force acting on the boulder to be decomposed into a component parallel to the slope and a component perpendicular to the slope. The parallel component, the driving force, is calculated as 9.8 N × sine 30° = 4.9 N. The driving force is directed downslope, toward open space.

Before the boulder moves downhill, or before the whole hillside begins to move, these masses must overcome inertia and friction. Inertia is the tendency of a body to remain at rest until an external force is applied. Friction is the resistance to motion of a body that keeps it from moving over another body. Friction comes in large part from the roughness of surfaces that make sliding, flowing, or rolling difficult. The surface could be the ground or some weak rock layer at depth. All that is needed is some initial energy to overcome inertia and friction to begin the boulder's movement or the hillside's failure. Initial energy could come from an earthquake, a heavy rain, a bulldozer, or the footstep of a sheep.

External Conditions of Slope Instability

In a typical mass movement, the centre of gravity of a portion of the land surface has moved downward and outward (Figure 9.4). There is a tear-away zone upslope where material has pulled away and a pileup zone downslope where material has accumulated.

External conditions that increase the odds of a slope failure include (1) adding mass high on a slope, as in sediment deposition, (2) steepening the slope, as by fault movements, and (3) removing support from low on a slope, as by stream or wave erosion (Figure 9.5).

WATER IN ITS EXTERNAL ROLES

Water plays many important roles in mass movements, both externally and internally. Rainfall is an external factor; rain falls from the atmosphere. Rain runoff causes external erosion that sets masses moving on slopes, and it undercuts bases of slopes, causing hillsides to fail and move.

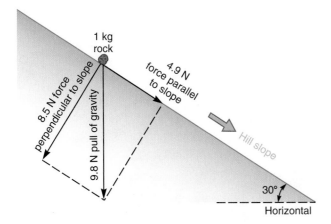

Figure 9.3
Gravitational forces acting on a 1 kg boulder sitting on a 30° slope.

Internal Conditions of Slope Instability

Beneath the surface, inside the materials underlying a slope, long-term processes are weakening Earth and preparing it for failure. Internal conditions of slope instability include (1) inherently weak materials, (2) water in different roles, (3) decreases in cohesion, and (4) adverse geological structures.

INHERENTLY WEAK MATERIALS

The materials most commonly associated with earth failures are the clay minerals. Clays are the most abundant

(a)

Figure 9.4
(a) Rotational slide showing downward-and-outward movement. and (b) associated topographic features.
Photo and drawing: © US Geological Survey.

Figure 9.5
Overhanging limestone block, Bruce Peninsula, Ontario. For several thousands of years following the end of the last glaciation, waves from Lake Huron have eroded the base of the block. Present-day water levels are several metres lower than they were at the time.
Photo: © Claire Samson.

of all sediments. They form during **chemical weathering** as rocks exposed at the surface decompose and form new minerals under conditions of low temperature and pressure. Weathering occurs when acidic fluids, such as CO_2–charged water and organic acids, decompose silicate minerals. These minerals are likely to transform into new atomic structures to achieve equilibrium.

Clay crystals are very small—too small to be seen with a typical microscope. Clay minerals are built like submicroscopic books (Figure 9.6). From a top view, they are nearly equidimensional. But a side view shows a much thinner dimension that also is split into even thinner subparallel sheets, like the pages in a book. The book-like structure typically forms in the soil zone where water strips away elements, leaving many unfilled atomic positions in crystal structures. This is like building a Tinker Toy or Lego structure, then having a tremendous number of pieces removed.

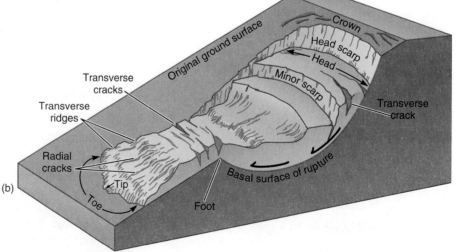

(b)

Transverse cracks

Transverse ridges

Radial cracks

Tip

Toe

Original ground surface

Crown

Head scarp

Head

Minor scarp

Transverse crack

Basal surface of rupture

Foot

Top view **Side view**

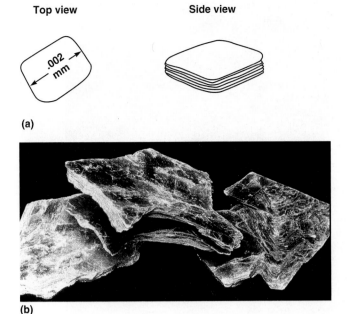

(a)

(b)

Figure 9.6
(a) Schematic views of the exceedingly small size and structure of a clay mineral. (b) Ultrathin individual sheets have relatively large lengths and widths as seen in these magnified views of the mineral mica.

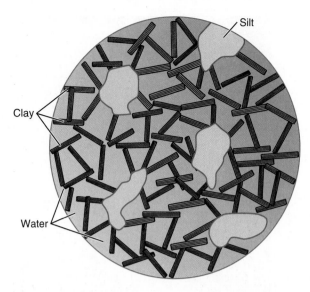

Figure 9.7
A "house of cards" structure occurs in quick clay. Platy clay minerals are stacked in an unstable configuration with silt grains and much water.

As clay minerals take in new elements and lose others, they increase and decrease in strength, they expand and contract, and they may absorb water and later have it removed. The constantly changing conditions cause variations in the strength of clay minerals from month to month and year to year. Thus, there are certain times when a hill containing clay minerals is weaker, and then gravity has a better chance of provoking a slope failure.

The mechanical or strength characteristics of a rock are usually governed by the 10 to 15% of the rock with the finest grain size, which is often the clay fraction. Clay minerals may have their strength lessened by water (1) adsorbed to the exterior of clays, thus spreading the grains apart, and (2) absorbed between the interlayer sheets, with resultant expansion.

A spectacular type of mass movement, the **lateral spread**, is associated with **sensitive clays**, known also as "quick" clays. Sensitive clays are abundant in eastern and northern Canada, Alaska, and Scandinavia as their formation is closely related to glacial processes. Sensitive clays begin as fine rock flour scoured off the landscape by massive glaciers and later deposited in nearby seas. The clay and silt sediments sit in a loosely packed "house of cards" structure filled with water and some sea salts that help hold it together as a weak solid (Figure 9.7). When glaciers retreat, the Earth's surface rebounds (see Chapter 2), lifting these clay sediments above sea level where they become exposed to rain. Freshwater passing through the uplifted sediments dissolves and removes much of the sea salt "glue," leaving sensitive clay with (1) weak structure, (2) grains mostly less than 0.002 mm diameter, (3) water contents commonly in excess of 50%, and (4) a low salt content. In short, the house of cards structure can be collapsed by a jarring event, such as a dynamite blast or vibrations from construction equipment.

What has been solid earth can literally turn to liquid and flow away. The collapse of the house of cards with its high water content creates a muddy fluid. To really believe this, you need to see it. Check out the video entitled "The Rissa Landslide," 1998, Norwegian Geotechnical Institute, 24 minutes; it is mind boggling to watch solid earth suddenly turn to fluid and flow off, carrying houses with it.

The Ottawa and St. Lawrence River Valleys have extensive deposits of sensitive clay, known locally as Leda clay (Figure 9.8). Leda clay formed in the Champlain Sea, a body of water that occupied the depression surrounding the massive glaciers present in the area during the last glaciation, between 13,000 and 10,000 years ago. When the glaciers retreated, the land rebounded and the Champlain Sea gradually shrank, leaving the marine clays exposed above the surface, vulnerable to leaching by rainwater. Leda clay deposits have experienced several liquefaction events and triggered dramatic lateral spreads as will be described later in this chapter (Figure 9.9).

WATER IN ITS INTERNAL ROLES

Water weakens earth materials in several different ways; it does so by (1) its weight, (2) interplay with clay minerals, (3) decreasing the cohesion of rocks, (4) subsurface erosion, (5) increasing pressure in pores, and (6) raising the water table.

Figure 9.8
Leda clay (light grey) and sand lenses (dark grey), Ottawa River Valley, Ontario.

Photo: Reproduced with the permission of Natural Resources Canada 2008, courtesy of the Geological Survey of Canada.

Figure 9.9
Mass movements in Leda clay of the Champlain Sea in eastern Ontario (red dots). The maximum extent of the Champlain Sea is indicated in light blue.

Source: Reproduced with the permission of Natural Resources Canada 2008, courtesy of the Geological Survey of Canada (Map by J.M. Aylsworth). http://geoscape.nrcan.gc.ca/ottawa/landslides_e.php.

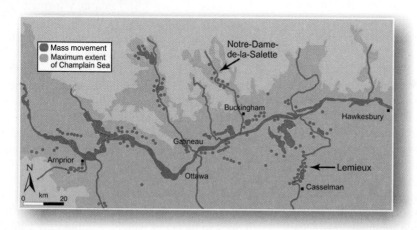

1. **Weight of Water:** Water is heavier than air. Sedimentary rocks commonly have porosities of 10 to 30%. If these void spaces are filled with water, the weights of materials are dramatically increased, thus the driving forces acting upon slope materials are also increased and mass movements may begin.

2. **Absorption and Adsorption by Clay Minerals:** Water is both absorbed (internally) and adsorbed (externally) by clay minerals with resultant decreases in strength. Water attaches easily to clay minerals because of its unique distribution of charges. Water is a molecule formed by two hydrogen (H^+) atoms linking up with one oxygen (O^{--}). The two positive charges from the hydrogen atoms should cancel the two negative charges from the oxygen atom to create an uncharged or neutral molecule. But water is a bipolar molecule (Figure 9.10a) with its hydrogen atoms on one side (a positive side) and its oxygen on the other side (a negative side). Thus, water molecules can attach their positive sides against clay minerals because clay surfaces are negatively charged (Figure 9.10b).

3. **Cement Dissolution:** Water flowing through rocks can dissolve some of the minerals that bind the rock together. The removal of cementing material decreases the cohesion of rocks.

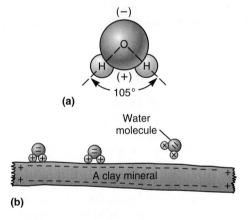

(a)

(b)

Figure 9.10
(a) Water is a bipolar molecule. Two hydrogen atoms (each H^+) attach to one oxygen atom (O^{--}), creating an electrically neutral molecule. However, the asymmetry of the molecule makes one side slightly negative and the other side positive. (b) The positive side of water molecules attaches to the negatively charged surface of clay minerals.

4. **Piping:** Water flowing underground can not only chemically dissolve minerals but also physically erode loose material. Subsurface erosion (**piping**) can create extensive systems of caverns (Figure 9.11). A network of caves obviously makes a hill weaker.

5. **Pore-Water Pressure:** Pressure builds up in water trapped in pores of rocks being buried deeper and deeper. As sediments pile up on the surface, their weight puts ever more pressure on sediments and pore water at depth. Sediment grains of sand and mud pack into smaller and smaller volumes, while water, which is nearly incompressible, simply stores built-up pressure. When a pile of sediment sits on top of over-pressurized pore water, the entire mass becomes less stable. The build-up of pressure within pore water has been referred to as a "hydraulic jack" that progressively "lifts up" sediment until the pull of gravity can start a massive failure. Many mass movements and slope failures are due to abnormally high **pore-water pressures**.

Quicksand occurs where sand grains are supersaturated with pressurized water. For example, if water flows upward through sands, helping lift the sand grains, then the pull of gravity on the sand grains can be effectively cancelled, leaving the sand with no strength or ability to carry a load (Figure 9.12).

If water-pressurized sand was on a slope, it would flow away; but if it sits on a flat surface, it will be quicksand. Despite what some old movies show, quicksand does not suck people or other objects down. It is rather like stepping in a high-viscosity liquid. Stand there long enough and you will sink below the surface (Figure 9.12b). What should you do if you get caught? If the water is not too deep, fall backward and spread your arms out; this distributes your weight broadly, like a boat on water, and you will not sink. If you can float on water, you surely will float on the denser quicksand. Then call to your companions to pull you out, or if alone, slowly slide your way backward, keeping your weight broadly distributed as you pull your legs from the quicksand's grasp. Quicksand holds tightly, so do not panic and flail wildly to get yourself out. Slow and easy, with a broad spreading of your body weight, is the answer.

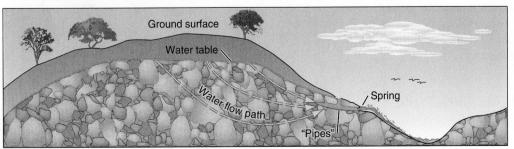

Figure 9.11
Schematic cross-section of groundwater flowing through poorly consolidated rocks. Water will carry sediment to the surface at springs. This erosion creates a network of caverns that seriously weakens a hill.

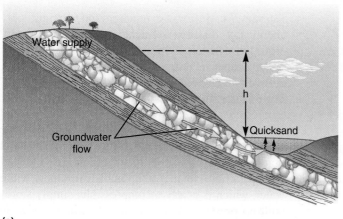

(a)

(b)

Figure 9.12
(a) Schematic cross-section showing groundwater pushed by a high column of water (h) and reaching the surface through loose sands. The uplifting force of the escaping water equals the weight of the sand grains, thus making quicksand. (b) Quicksand!
Source: © Jacobe Washburn.

6. **Water Table Height:** Rain, streams, and lakes all supply water to the subsurface. Gravity pulls surface water down to saturate open spaces in subsurface rocks with **groundwater.** A groundwater body is not a lake or pond-like volume of water. Instead it is water that saturates a zone of subsurface rock by filling fractures in rocks, pores between sand grains, voids left after shells are dissolved, and other holes. The top of the groundwater body is the **water table.** Below the water table is the saturated zone, and above is the unsaturated zone where groundwater is sparse.

During droughts, water tables may drop hundreds of metres below the ground. During rainy intervals, the water table may reach the ground surface. As water tables rise higher, they trigger increasing numbers of mass movements.

DECREASES IN COHESION

When rocks are buried to depths of hundreds, thousands, and tens of thousands of metres, they are compressed into smaller volumes by the weight of the overlying materials. But this process also works in reverse. When deeply buried rocks are uncovered by erosion and exposed at the surface, the removal of great weight allows the compressed rocks to relax and expand. The expansion in volume produces fractures and increases in porosity. The stress-relaxation process reduces the strength of rocks, opening up passageways and storage places for water to attack and further weaken the rocks.

ADVERSE GEOLOGICAL STRUCTURES

Many hill slope masses are weak due to pre-existing geological conditions.

Ancient Slip Surfaces

Ancient slip surfaces are weaknesses that tend to be reused over time. When a mass first breaks loose and slides downslope, it tends to create a smooth, slick layer of ground-up materials beneath it. The slick layers become especially slippery when wet. It is wise to avoid building on these sites, but if building is necessary, then these slick slip surfaces need to be recognized, dug up, and destroyed. Otherwise, they commonly are reactivated when wetted, causing major financial losses and much heartache for building owners. Replays of this scenario are found in the news with a saddening frequency.

Orientation of Rock Layers

The orientation of rock layering within a hill may create either a strong or a weak condition. Where rock layers are subparallel to the slope or where they dip at angles less than that of the hill slope, then the stage is set for slippage and mass movement (Figures 9.12a, 9.27, and 9.43). Conversely, where rock layers dip into the hill at a steep angle, it is difficult for a slide to initiate and break free. The two situations are commonly observed on both sides of the same valley (Figure 9.13). On which side of the valley would you recommend selecting a building site?

Figure 9.13
Dipping layers create a less-stable condition on the side of the valley where they are subparallel to the slope than on the side where they are subperpendicular to the slope.
Source: © Claire Samson.

Structures within Rocks

Rocks have weaknesses that set up slope failure. Examples include where (1) crumbly rocks are not well cemented together, (2) a clay layer may provide a basal slip surface, (3) soft rock layers may slide off strong materials, (4) fractures split and separate rock, or (5) an ancient fault may act as a slip surface.

Triggers of Mass Movements

Slopes usually do not fail for just one reason; most failures have complex causes. Over the long intervals of time a slope exists, gravity is constantly tugging, and water keeps soaking in and sapping its strength. On numerous occasions, a slope almost fails. Then along comes another stress for the slope, such as heavy rains, and the slope finally fails in a massive event. Did the last stress, the saturation by heavy rains, cause the slide? Or was it just the trigger for the movement, the proverbial straw that broke the camel's back? Clearly the rains were simply the trigger, or immediate cause, for the mass movement.

It is useful to distinguish between immediate causes and underlying conditions of instability. The sum of all the underlying conditions of instability pushes the slope to the brink of failure, and then an immediate cause triggers the movement. Common triggers for mass movements include heavy rains, earthquakes, thawing of frozen ground, and more and more frequently, the construction projects of humans.

Classification of Mass Movements

Speed of movement and water content vary markedly in different types of mass movements (Figure 9.14). Slow-moving masses cause tremendous amounts of destruction and property damage, but rapidly moving masses not only destroy, but also kill. Rapidly moving mass movements have been responsible for large numbers of deaths worldwide (Table 9.2).

The main types of mass movement are downward, as in falling or subsiding, or downward and outward, as

Figure 9.14
Mass-movement speed versus water content.

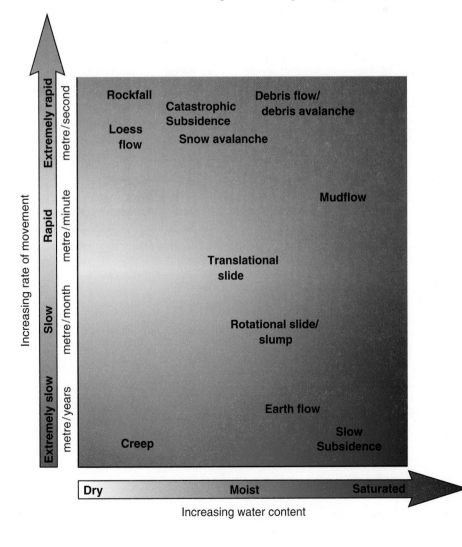

Table 9.2

Twenty-Five Most Catastrophic Mass Movements of the Twentieth Century

Date	Country	Event or Location	Type of mass movement	Trigger	Volume of displaced material or area affected	Fatalities
1911	Tadzhikistan	Usoy	Rock slide	Earthquake	2,000 million m³	54
1919	Indonesia	Kalut	Lahars	Volcanic eruption	185 km²	5,110
1920	China	Haiyuan	Landslides	Earthquake	?	100,000
1921	Kazakhstan	Alma-Ata	Debris flow	Snowmelt	?	500
1933	China	Deixi	Landslides	Earthquake	150 million m³	9,300
1939	Japan	Mount Rokko	Slides, mudflows	Heavy rain	?	505
1949	Tadzhikistan	Khait	Rock slide	Earthquake	?	12,000–20,000
1953	Japan	Arita River	Slides, debris/mud flows	Heavy rain	?	460
1953	Japan	Minamiy-amashiro	Slides, debris/mud flows	Heavy rain	?	336
1958	Japan	Kanogawa	Slides, debris/mud flows	Heavy rain	?	1,094
1962	Peru	Nevados Huascaran	Complex event	?	13 million m³	4,000
1963	Italy	Vaiont Reservoir	Rock slide	?	250 million m³	2,000
1964	United States	Alaska	Landslides	Earthquake	?	0
1965	China	Yunnan	Rock slide	?	450 million m³	444
1966	Brazil	Rio de Janeiro	Slides, avalanches, debris/mud flows	Heavy rain	?	1,000
1967	Brazil	Serra das Araras	Slides, avalanches, debris/mud flows	Heavy rain	?	17,000
1970	Peru	Nevados Huascaran	Complex event	Earthquake	100 million m³	18,000
1974	Peru	Mayunmarca	Rock slide, debris avalanche	?	1,600 million m³	450
1980	United States	Mount St. Helens	Rock slide, debris avalanche	Volcanic eruption	2,500 million m³	5–10
1983	United States	Thistle	Debris slide	Snowmelt, heavy rain	21 million m³	0
1983	China	Saleshan	Landslide	?	35 million m³	237
1985	Columbia	Nevado del Ruiz	Lahars	Volcanic eruption	?	22,000
1986	Papua New Guinea	Bairaman	Rock slide, debris avalanche	Earthquake	200 million m³	0
1987	Ecuador	Reventador	Landslides	Earthquake	75–110 million m³	1,000
1994	Columbia	Paez	Landslides	Earthquake	250 km²	1,971
1998	Honduras, Guatemala, Nicaragua, El Salvador	Hurricane Mitch	Landslides, debris flows	Hurricane	?	10,000

Source: Modified from Schuster, 1996.

in sliding and flowing (Figure 9.15). Falling is downward from a topographic high place, such as a cliff or mountain, whereas subsiding is downward via collapse of the surface. Sliding occurs where a semi-coherent mass slips down and out on top of an underlying failure surface. Flowing occurs when a moving mass behaves like a viscous fluid flowing down and out over the countryside.

The types of movements will be examined in a series of examples of **falls** and **flows**, **slides** and **subsides**. Although in popular language mass movements are often described using the generic term "landslide," in geotechnical engineering, the term "slide" refers specifically to a mass movement associated with a more or less well-defined failure surface. In slides, there is limited deformation within the moving material, whereas in flows the material is thoroughly deformed during movement. In practice, mass movements often exhibit characteristics from two or more types and are, in that case, classified as complex events.

Falls

Rock masses commonly are fractured into three nearly perpendicular directions (Figure 9.16). Each fracture is a weakness that separates a block of rock. Where vertical fractures are well developed, some blocks of rock might pivot forward about a fixed point near their base—not unlike giant dominoes—a rotational movement called **topple**. Falls occur when elevated rock masses separate along fractures, rock layers, or other weaknesses. When a mass detaches, it mostly falls downward through the air via free-fall and then, after hitting the ground, moves by bouncing and rolling. The most common triggers for falls—heavy rain and frost wedging—are related to the external roles of water. In mountainous regions, their actions combine to detach boulders from rock faces. Large chunks of rock fall at the base of the cliffs where they accumulate to form **talus slopes** (Figure 9.17).

Figure 9.15
Classification of mass movements.

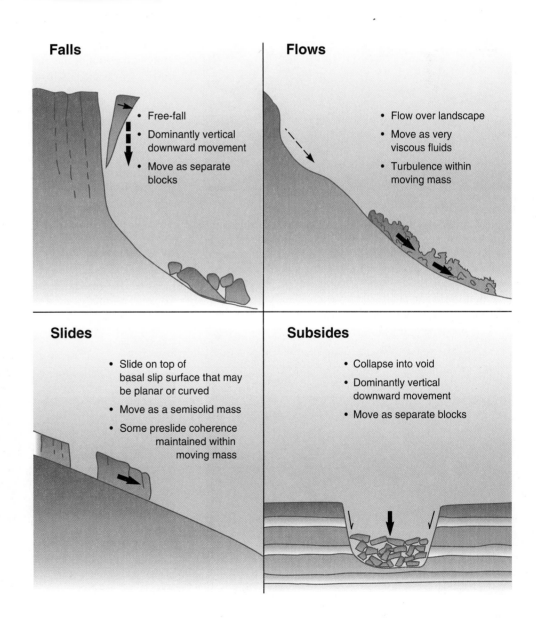

Falls
- Free-fall
- Dominantly vertical downward movement
- Move as separate blocks

Flows
- Flow over landscape
- Move as very viscous fluids
- Turbulence within moving mass

Slides
- Slide on top of basal slip surface that may be planar or curved
- Move as a semisolid mass
- Some preslide coherence maintained within moving mass

Subsides
- Collapse into void
- Dominantly vertical downward movement
- Move as separate blocks

Figure 9.16
A block of sea-cliff sandstone gets ready to fall on Moonlight State Beach in Encinitas, California. Do you see the three mutually perpendicular fractures that allow this block to separate from the cliff?
Photo: © Pat Abbott.

1841 AND 1889 ROCKFALLS, QUEBEC CITY

Quebec City, founded in 1608, occupies a majestic location on top of a steep cliff, overlooking the St. Lawrence River where it narrows to a width of just over 1 km (Figure 9.18). In fact, the name "Quebec" comes from the Algonquin word meaning "narrow strait." The early French explorers saw sparkling quartz crystals in the rocks and, in their enthusiasm, optimistically named the cliff "Cap-aux-Diamants" (Cape Diamond). Quebec City first developed along a narrow ribbon of land on the shore of the St. Lawrence River where houses were built literally with their backs on the cliff.

The Cap-aux-Diamants is the result of the large-scale collision between the Precambrian Canadian Shield and the Appalachians. Sedimentary rock layers have been deformed so extremely by tectonic forces that they now stand vertically to form a cliff ranging between 60 and 100 m in elevation. This precarious geometry has resulted in 53 slope failures since 1775, causing 88 fatalities, 70 serious injuries, and the destruction of 20 houses (Figure 9.19). The 1.5 km–long stretch of land immediately at the foot of the cliff is the deadliest natural hazard corridor in Canada's history. The orientation of the rock layers relative to the topography changes progressively along the escarpment: the southern portion is prone to rock slides (Figure 9.20), whereas the northern and central portions experience rockfalls.

A major rockfall occurred on 17 May 1841 in the central portion of the Cap-aux-Diamants, following two days of heavy rain. The excess water had filled vertical crevices, causing an enormous rock mass to detach from the cliff and to crash in the narrow Champlain Street below. The horror of the event is conveyed in a painting by Joseph Légaré where sinister clouds overlook a scene

Figure 9.17
Steep, unstable talus slopes in Banff National Park.
Photo: © Claire Samson.

Figure 9.18
Panoramic view of Quebec City from Levis on the south shore of the St. Lawrence River.
Photo: © Claire Samson.

Figure 9.19
Satellite view of the Cap-aux-Diamants and Old Quebec City (compare this map view with the photograph presented in Figure 9.18) with the locations of most destructive mass movements. The large diamond-shape structure is the Citadel, built by the British from 1823 to 1832 to protect the city.
Courtesy of Jacques Locat, Laval University.

Figure 9.20
The south portion of the Cap-aux-Diamants is characterized by subvertical slivers of rock sliding down along well-defined planar surfaces.
Photo: © Claire Samson.

of destruction as rescuers extract victims trapped in the rubble (Figure 9.21). The local newspaper *Québec Daily Mercury* ran as headlines:

A DREADFUL CATASTROPHE!
Fall of Rock Last Evening in Champlain Street.
30 FAMILIES BURIED BENEATH!
Seventeen Dwellings Crushed—Result of Late Heavy Rainfalls.
FORTY PEOPLE KILLED OR MISSING

The newspaper also published the account of survivor George Hayden: "Mr. George Hayden was standing near Mr. Berrigan's door for some time before the fatal rock descended. 'It is useless for us to deny,' said he last night, 'that we had not ample warning given us of a disaster. I was standing talking with poor Nolan and Farrell, who are now dead, and with Perry, when portions of the rock fell at intervals of about five minutes, first in small quantities, then more profusely. After the second slide occurred, I said it was time for us to move, and managed to get away. Nolan might have done the same, but ran into his house to call his wife."

After the tragedy, the federal government bought and demolished several houses standing in particularly vulnerable locations, immediately below the Dufferin Terrace. A retaining wall was built to hold back the rocks. Several crevices were filled with cement to prevent the infiltration of water. These measures proved insufficient.

On 19 September, 1889, after 12 hours of torrential rain, a major rockfall occurred only a few tens of metres away from the site of the 1841 failure, at the south end of the Dufferin Terrace (Figure 9.22). Several vertical crevices burst open as water exerted excess pressure on their walls. Tonnes of rock fell in Champlain Street, filling it

Figure 9.21
View of Champlain Street after the 1841 rockfall. Painting by Joseph Légaré (1795–1855). The structure on top of the Cap-aux-Diamants is the Dufferin Terrace, a walkway overlooking the St. Lawrence River.

Source: Musée de la civilisation, collection du Séminaire de Québec. Éboulis du cap Diamant. Joseph Légaré. Vers 1841. Pierre Soulard, photographe. N° 1991.33

Figure 9.22
The site of the 1889 rockfall (area circled in blue) is prominently displayed on this stamp "View of the Citadel at Quebec," issued in 1930. The stamp had probably been designed based on earlier photographs of the event.

Source: © Canada Post Corporation (1930). Reproduced with permission.

with 10 m of rubble and flattening seven houses (Figure 9.23). The problem might have been exacerbated by the presence of a defective drain, which channelled water on a vulnerable point along the escarpment.

The engineer of the City of Quebec at the time, M.C. Baillargé, had extensively studied the Cap-aux-Diamants. His geological cross-section, published in 1893, clearly shows the vertical crevices—some of them 35 m deep and 1 m wide at the surface—causing instability along the escarpment and is still the reference today (Figure 9.24). Following the 1841 rockfall, Baillargé had recommended that an extensive series of buttresses be built at the base of the cliff, a recommendation rejected in favour of less-costly measures. Baillargé had also identified a

particularly unstable zone along the Cap-aux-Diamants, precisely the area that failed in 1889. Today, it is the responsibility of each landowner to ensure that proper mitigation measures are taken (Figure 9.25). The City of Quebec grants as much as $80,000 to owners undertaking stabilization work.

Slides

Slides are movements above one or more failure surfaces (Figure 9.15). Basal failure surfaces typically are either (1) curved in a concave-upward sense in **rotational slides** or **slumps** or (2) nearly planar in **translational slides**. The slide mass maintains some degree of coherence as it slides down the underlying slip surface.

ROTATIONAL SLIDES

Rotational slides move downward and outward on top of curved slip surfaces (Figure 9.4). Movement is more or less rotational about an axis parallel to the slope. The centre of rotation can be approximated by piercing a cross-section with the point of a compass and then swinging the compass in an arc to draw a basal failure surface (Figure 9.26a). This is the Swedish circle analysis of slope stability used to calculate driving versus resisting forces, giving a quantitative understanding of how close a slope is to failing. Material above the failure surface can be divided into a driving mass resting on a base inclined out of the hill and a resisting mass sitting on a base inclined back into the hill. In effect, the slope is an equilibrium situation in which a driving mass seeks to break free and move downward and outward, but it is blocked by a resisting mass that acts as a wedge holding the driving mass and slope in place.

(a)

(b)

Figure 9.23
Site of the 1889 Quebec City rockfall. (a) Historical photograph by Louis-Prudent Vallée. (b) Current site stabilized using steel mesh.

Photos: (a) Musée de la civilisation, fonds d'archives du Séminaire de Québec. Éboulis du Cap Diamant. Louis-Prudent Vallée, photographe. 1889. N° Ph1986-0014 (b) © Claire Samson.

Figure 9.24
Structural cross-section of the 1889 rockfall site high-lighting numerous vertical crevices.

Source: Used with permission of Canadian Society of Civil Engineering.

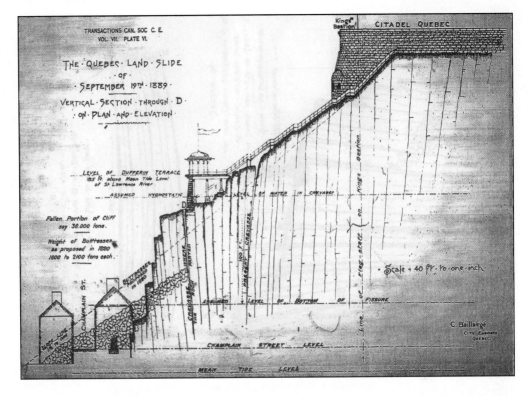

Figure 9.25
This combined car shelter and buttress on Sault-au-Matelot Street at the base of the escarpment provides extra support while respecting the style of Old Quebec City, a UNESCO World Heritage Site.
Photo by J. Locat.

When a rotational slide occurs, its head moves downward and typically rotates backward (Figure 9.26b). Water falling or flowing onto the head of the slide mass ponds in the basin formed by the backward tilt. The trapped water sinks down into the slump mass, causing more instability and movement. Because the scarp at the head of a slump is nearly vertical, it is unstable, thus setting the stage for further mass movement. The toe of a slump moves upward, riding out on top of the landscape (Figure 9.26b). Rotational slides move only short distances; their arcuate movements tend to restore equilibrium soon because the driving mass decreases and the resisting mass increases.

TRANSLATIONAL SLIDES

In translational slides, masses move down and out by sliding on surfaces of weakness, such as fractures, a clay-rich layer, soft rocks slipping off hard rocks, and hard rocks being spread apart by movements within underlying soft rocks. A translational slide may move as long as it sits on the downward-inclined surface and its driving mass still exists.

Translational slide masses behave in different fashions: (1) They may remain basically coherent as block slides. (2) The sliding mass may deform and disintegrate to form a debris slide. (3) Lateral spreading may occur where the underlying material fails and flows, thus causing the overlying coherent material to break apart and move.

1929–1930 Block Slide, Point Fermin, California
An excellent example of a block slide lies in Point Fermin, near Los Angeles, California. Just east of Point Fermin, the rocks include layers of sandstone and clay-rich mudstone inclined 10° to 22° seaward (Figure 9.27). Beginning in January 1929, a 800-metre long block slide, with 2 hectares of its mass on land, began sliding slowly seaward down the inclined bedding on top of a particularly slippery clay layer. From January 1929 to June 1930, the slide block shifted from 2 to 2.5 m seaward, basically remaining whole during movement. No one was killed by this slow movement, but homes sitting atop 30 m high sea cliffs were slowly twisted out of shape and had to be removed (Figure 9.28). Movement apparently was triggered by

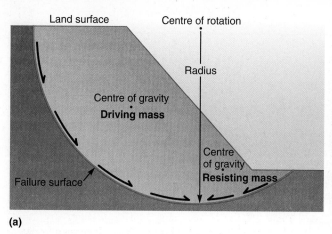

(a)

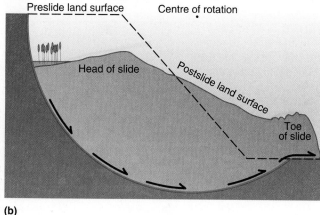

(b)

Figure 9.26
(a) Swedish circle analysis of slope stability. A compass is set at the centre of rotation, and then an arc is swung, approximating the basal failure surface. Computations of driving and resisting forces help determine the stability of the slope. (b) A rotational slide with movement around a centre of rotation. Notice the backward-tilted head and bulged toe.

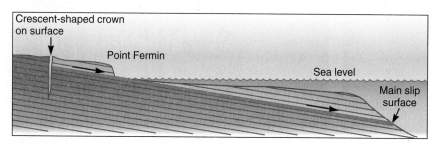

Figure 9.27
Cross-section through Point Fermin, California, showing a block slide on top of an inclined slippery clay layer. Movement is toward the unsupported slope lying offshore.
Source: © W. J. Miller.

Figure 9.28
View of the head of the Point Fermin translational slide. Note the foundation slabs of destroyed homes.
Photo: © by John S. Shelton.

excess water from yard irrigation seeping down to layers of weak clays, which expanded and lost strength.

1971 Lateral Spread, St-Jean-Vianney, Quebec

In eastern Canada, 1971 was a bad year for lateral spreads, with two major liquefaction events occurring almost simultaneously in Quebec and Ontario. The winter of 1970–71 brought a record snowfall to the St. Lawrence River Valley, and spring melting had occurred rather slowly, contributing to the overall soil saturation.

St-Jean-Vianney was a suburban community of 1,300 people living in modern bungalows, neatly aligned on a grid plan in the Saguenay region of Quebec. On Tuesday 4 May 1971 late in the evening, hockey fans were in front of their television sets watching the playoff game between Montreal and Chicago when the ground opened beneath their feet.

It had rained hard in April, and water had infiltrated the ground to saturate a layer of sensitive clay. At 10:45 p.m., in a matter of minutes, the clay liquefied, losing all strength. The lateral spread started on the bank of a small creek, and progressed rapidly inland, in classical **retrogressive sliding** behaviour. The liquefied material dropped 30 m to form a canyon approximately 1,500 m long by 400 m wide. Large rafts of earth material slid down into the depression remaining coherent enough to carry several homes relatively intact (Figure 9.29). Thirty-one lives were lost in the event, all of them during the initial, rapid retrogressive phase of the slide. A man running for his life reported having to run on what seemed moving stairs, which corresponds to a rate of movement of 5 m/s.

The exact trigger of the St-Jean-Vianney lateral spread remains unclear, although some indications point to engineering work taking place to channel a small

Figure 9.29
During the St-Jean-Vianney lateral spread, several homes (circles) slid on a semi-liquid mix of clay, snow, and water into a broad depression. Amazingly, a few of them remained structurally intact, having been carried on "rafts" of coherent material.

Photo: Reproduced with the permission of Natural Resources Canada 2008, courtesy of the Atlas of Canada. http://atlas.nrcan.gc.ca/site/english/maps/environment /naturalhazards/landslides/fig_21_land_vianney.jpg/image_view.

underground creek in the area. One thing is sure: aerial photographs show that the 1971 lateral spread, which displaced 7.6 million m³ of material, occurred within the scar of an earlier, much larger slide that moved 200 million m³ of material (Figure 9.30). The former lateral spread had probably been triggered by the 1663

Figure 9.30
Aerial photos of St-Jean-Vianney, Quebec, dating from 1972. Compare the extents of the 1971 (blue) and 1663 (red) lateral spreads.

Photo: National Air Photo Library, Centre for Topographic Information, Natural Resources Canada, Image A23076.

Charlevoix earthquake (see Chapter 5). This crucial point had been overlooked by urban planners. St-Jean-Vianney is now abandoned. The federal government declared the site unfit for habitation, and all residents were relocated.

1971 and 1993 Lateral Spreads, Lemieux, Ontario

Only one week after the St-Jean-Vianney tragedy, a lateral spread in sensitive Leda clay occurred just outside the village of Lemieux in eastern Ontario (Figure 9.9). The lateral spread exhibited retrogressive behaviour, starting on the banks of the South Nation River and moving inland almost half a kilometre (Figure 9.31a). It moved approximately 7 million m³ of agricultural land but, fortunately, did not affect inhabited areas. The potential for a disaster, however, was recognized, and the Geological Survey of Canada was mandated to evaluate risk. The study concluded that Lemieux was located in an area particularly susceptible to large rapid lateral spreads. As a precautionary measure, the village was expropriated and dismantled in 1991 (Figure 9.32). Residents were relocated at the expense of the Ontario government. When a major lateral spread occurred two years later in the vicinity of the former town site, it caused disruption but no lives were lost (Figure 9.31b). The 1993 lateral spread, like its precursor in 1971, was initiated on the banks of the South Nation River. It retrogressed some 700 m inland, mostly in the first 15 minutes of the event. Some 3.5 million m³ of material was displaced, damming the river for four days and causing floods for 25 km upstream. The 1971 and 1993 lateral spreads drew attention to the weakness of the banks of the South Nation River. To prevent the banks from acting as points of initial failure, a protective rock berm has been built in several places (Figure 9.33). The berm serves the double purpose of preventing erosion and providing extra support on the toe of the slope.

Flows

Flows are mass movements that behave like fluids. The materials within flows range from massive boulders to sand to clay to mixtures of them all. Water content varies from dry to sloppy wet. The velocities of flows range from barely moving creep and gelifluction to observed speeds of 75 m/s. Within the moving masses, internal movements dominate, and failure surfaces are absent to short-lived. Many names have been used to describe flows, on the basis of the type of material moving downslope (for example, loess flow, mudflow) or according to particle size (for example, earthflow for fine soils; **debris flow** for coarse soils (Figure 9.61)). All of them, however, are characterized by fluid-like behaviour. Their classical morphology includes a starting zone where the initial failure occurs, a narrow track, and a widening runout zone where the moving material finally stops and accumulates, often in lobes (Figure 9.34).

(a)

(b)

Figure 9.31

The Lemieux lateral spreads of (a) 1971 and (b) 1993 Photos

(a) Reproduced with the permission of Natural Resources Canada 2008, courtesy of the Atlas of Canada. http://atlas.nrcan.gc.ca/site/english/maps/environment/naturalhazards/landslides/fig_21_land_vianney.jpg/image_view (b) Reproduced with the permission of Natural Resources Canada 2008, courtesy of the Geological Survey of Canada (Photo 1993-296 by S.G Evans). http://geoscape.nrcan.gc.ca/ottawa/landslides_e.php.

CREEP

Gravity induces materials to move in many ways, including creep, the slowest but most widespread form of slope failure. Creep is an almost imperceptible downhill flow of the **soil** and uppermost **bedrock** zones. Creep is most commonly seen by its effects on objects, such as telephone poles and fences that lean downslope or trees whose trunks have deformed due to growing upward while rooted in material that is slipping downhill (Figure 9.35a). The soil zone slips in ultraslow movements as individual particles shift and move in response to gravity; the upper bedrock zone yields to the pull by curving downslope (Figure 9.35b).

By what mechanisms do soil and rock actually move? The volume of soil does not stay constant but instead expands and contracts. Several processes cause expansion. (1) Soil has a high percentage of void space or **porosity**. When water filling these pores freezes, it

Figure 9.32

The parish church had to be demolished when the village of Lemieux was abandoned as a preventive measure.

Photo: Reproduced with the permission of Natural Resources Canada 2008 (photo 2008-161).

Figure 9.33

A rock berm stabilizes the banks of the South Nation River in the Lemieux area.

Photo: Reproduced with the permission of Natural Resources Canada 2008 (photo 2008–162).

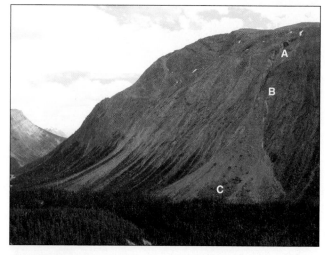

Figure 9.34

Rockslide-rock flow draping a mountain flank in Banff National Park. The failure was initiated as a slide (area A) and continued as a flow (areas B and C). A: Starting zone; B: Track; C: Runout zone.

Photo: © Claire Samson.

(a)

(b)

Figure 9.35

(a) Block diagram of a slope showing the effects of creep. Soil moves slowly, and bedrock deforms downhill. (b) Creep has deformed rock layers near Marathon, Texas.

Photo by NOAA.

expands in volume by 9%, swelling the soil volume and lifting the ground surface upward. (2) When soil rich in expandable materials, such as some types of **clay minerals**, is wetted, it absorbs water and expands. (3) Heating by the Sun causes an increase in volume. Soil expands perpendicular to the ground surface. Several processes contract masses of soil, rock, and water, causing the ground surface to lower. Shrinkage occurs when soil (1) thaws, (2) dries, or (3) cools. Lowering of the surface is influenced by the vertical downward pull of gravity, causing a net downslope movement of particles in the soil zone (Figure 9.36).

In periglacial environments like Arctic Canada, a particular type of soil creep, gelifluction, develops in **permafrost**. During the short summer, the first few centimetres of permafrost melt. Unable to infiltrate the permanently frozen ground beneath, the excess water saturates surface sediments. These waterlogged sediments show little strength or cohesion. They tend to flow down even along barely perceptible slopes (Figure 9.37). Gelifluction is a slow process with typical rates of movement on the order of a few centimetres per year, and is unlikely to cause direct harm. Permafrost behaviour is nevertheless an important issue when designing infrastructure in northern regions.

1995 AND 2005 SLUMP AND FLOWS, LA CONCHITA, CALIFORNIA

The southern California coastline features small communities nestled between steep hills and some world-famous surfing locations. La Conchita is one of these communities in this seemingly charmed region. Unfortunately, the stretch of 180 m high cliffs along this coastline has been shedding mass movements since historical records began in 1865. In March 1995, two events brought misery. A

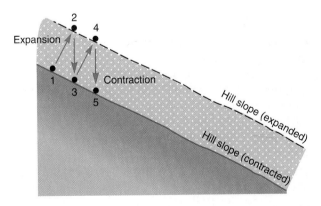

Figure 9.36

How creep works. Surface materials expand perpendicular to the hill slope (e.g., from point 1 to point 2) upon freezing of pore water, swelling when wetted, and heating by the Sun. Surface materials contract (e.g., from point 2 to point 3) upon thawing, drying, and cooling. Contraction occurs under the pull of gravity and is toward the centre of the Earth. The result is a net downslope movement of materials.

Figure 9.37
A dark band of water-saturated sediment slowly moves down-hill by gelifluction toward a small lake (Lac de Gras, Northwest Territories).
Photo: © Claire Samson.

deep-seated, coherent slump that evolved into an earth-flow moved slowly enough for people to get out of its path, but it destroyed nine houses (Figure 9.38). A few days later, a debris flow damaged five more houses. Months of extraordinarily high rainfalls had raised the water table, triggering a failure at depth. The upper parts of the moving masses were dry and gave off clouds of dust.

Despite these destructive events, the lure of the physical setting keeps the community fully populated. Almost 10 years later, on 10 January 2005, about 15% of the 1995 slide mass remobilized into a highly fluid debris flow. The flow overran a retaining wall built to stop landslides, then flowed into La Conchita, moving about 5 m/s, destroying 15 houses, seriously damaging 23 others, and killing 10 people (Figure 9.39). This event followed a 15-day period of near-record rainfalls.

Will destructive slumps and deadly flows continue to penetrate into La Conchita? Yes.

Complex Events

Many mass movements involve combinations of topple, fall, slide, and flow at different times and places along their travel route, and are referred to as "complex events." Common examples include slumps that change into earthflows and topples degenerating into rockfalls and debris flows.

1962 AND 1970 NEVADOS HUASCARAN EVENTS, PERU

Nevados Huascarán is the highest peak in the Peruvian Andes. The west face of the north peak is granitic rock cut by nearly vertical fractures roughly parallel to the face. At 6:13 p.m. on 10 January 1962, with no perceptible triggering event, a huge mass of rock and glacial ice fell, initiating a debris flow. The debris flowed down river valleys

Figure 9.38
This earthflow broke loose from an ancient slump and destroyed several homes in La Conchita, California, in March 1995.
Photo: © US Geological Survey.

like bobsleds, rising higher on the outsides of valley bends and lower on the inside bends. Some debris flowed up and out of the valley at bends, but most stayed between the valley walls and issued forth as a 10 to 15 m high mass, spreading out as a lobe covering 3.5 km², including part of the town of Ranrahirca (meaning "hill of many stones"); 4,000 people died. The debris flow had a volume of 13 million m³ and travelled at speeds of 170 km/h. The slide left a scar on Nevados Huascarán, including a 1 km high overhanging cliff. A final report on the tragedy stated:

> The people are adjusting to this huge scar that lies across their land and their lives . . . But they say that Huascarán is a villain who may yet have more to say.

Eight years later, on 31 May 1970, a subduction-zone earthquake of magnitude 7.7 occurred beneath the Pacific Ocean 135 km away, with a hypocentre at 54 km depth. Shaking lasted 45 seconds, but before that time was up,

Figure 9.39
Following many days of heavy rain, this debris flow broke loose from the 1995 earthflow mass, destroying 15 homes and killing 10 people on 10 January 2005.
Photo: © US Geological Survey.

Figure 9.40
Aerial view of Nevados Huascarán and the 1970 debris avalanche that buried 18,000 people. Vertical drop from summit to Rio Santa is 4,144 m, and horizontal distance is 16 km.
Photo: © US Geological Survey.

a gigantic portion of the same west-facing slope of the north peak of Nevados Huascarán failed with a sound like a dynamite blast or sonic boom, and a cloud of dark dust obscured the mountain from view. The side of the mountain between 5,500 to 6,400 m elevation fell away, including a 30-m thick glacier. The mass was nearly 100 million m^3 of granitic rock, ice blocks, glacial sediments, and water. It moved at speeds of 280 to 335 km/h, devastating an area of 22.5 km^2 and killing 18,000 people (Figure 9.40).

The event began as a fall, transformed into a debris avalanche with an airborne segment, and then moved down the Rio Santa as a debris flow for over 50 km. The sequence was

1. A vertical fall for 400 to 900 m.
2. The fallen mass landed on a glacier and slid along its surface, scooping up snow.
3. The debris avalanche raced up the side of a glacial-sediment hill, launching much debris into the air.
4. For the next 4 km downslope, boulders with weights up to several tonnes each rained from the sky, pulverizing houses, people, and animals. The deadly rain of mega-boulders left the ground pockmarked with craters like a heavily bombed battlefield.
5. The mass recombined as a flow, reaching the 230 m high Cerro de Aira (*cerro* is Spanish for hill), which had protected the city of Yungay during the 1962 event. No such luck this time. A lobe of debris overflowed Cerro de Aira, burying Yungay and 18,000 people beneath more than 30 m of debris. It

was especially bad timing because this was a Sunday afternoon and the population was swollen with visitors from the surrounding region. The scene was well described by survivors who witnessed the event from Yungay's highest point and the safest place in town, the cemetery.

6. Meanwhile, the main mass of material continued racing toward the Rio Santa, preceded by a strong wind pushed in front of it. The main lobe of debris swept across the Rio Santa and ran 83 m up the far slope, killing 60 people in the town of Matacoto, before it fell back like an ocean wave from the shore. Today, the glacier above the 1962 and 1970 breakaway sites has large fissures, suggesting the mountainside beneath is still fractured and unstable. The odds are high that the repopulated areas downslope will again experience another killer debris flow.

STURZSTROMS

Rockfalls and small-volume rock avalanches tend to flow horizontally for distances less than twice their vertical distance of fall; these short distances of transport are due to the slowing effects of internal and external friction. However, very large rockfalls, with volumes in excess of 1 million m^3, commonly travel long distances; some travel up to 25 times farther than their vertical fall. These long-runout flows, called **sturzstroms** (in German, *sturz* means "fall" and *strom* means "stream"), imply lower coefficients of internal friction. Sturzstroms have been observed moving at rates up to 280 km/h, even running up and over sizable hills and ridges lying in their paths.

1881 Elm Sturzstrom, Switzerland

With the advent of compulsory education in Europe in the 19th century, there arose a demand for **slate** boards to write on in classrooms. To help satisfy this need, some Swiss farmers near Elm became amateur miners, quarrying slate from the base of a nearby mountain. By 1876, an arcuate fissure formed about 360 m above their quarry, opening about 1.5 m wide. By early September 1881, the quarry had become a V-shaped notch about 180 m long and dug 60 m into the slope. At this time, the upslope fissure had opened to 30 m wide, and falling rocks were frequent and coupled with ominous noises coming from the large overhanging rock mass. These signs caused the miners to halt work. The inhabitants assumed the rock mass would fall down; but they did not think it would also flow up a steep slope and down their mountain valley to bury 115 of them. But it did.

On 11 September 1881, the Elm event unfolded as a drama in three acts: the fall, the jump, and the surges up a slope and down the nearly flat valley floor (Figure 9.41). Act 1, the fall, was described by Mr. Wyss, the Elm village teacher, from the window of his home:

> When the rock began to fall, the forest on the falling block moved like a herd of galloping sheep; the pines swirled in confusion. Then the whole mass suddenly sank.

Apparently, the formerly rigid mass of rock had already begun to disintegrate during its free fall. In act 2, the jump, the fallen mass hit the flat floor of the slate quarry, completely disintegrated, and then rebounded with a big jump forward, also described by teacher Wyss:

> Then I saw the rock mass jump away from the ledge. The lower part of the block was squeezed by the pressure of the rapidly falling upper part, disintegrated, and burst forth into the air . . . The debris mass shot with unbelievable speed northward toward the hamlet of Untertal and over and above the creek, for I could see the alder forest along the creek under the stream of shooting debris.

The bottom surface of the jumping mass was sharply defined. Eyewitnesses could see trees, houses, cattle, and fleeing people under the flying debris. The upper surface was not so sharply defined; it was a cloud of rocks and dust. Residents of Untertal who saw the jumping mass coming toward them ran uphill to save themselves. This turned out to be the wrong choice, as part of the flying debris hit their hill slope, fluidized, and flowed upslope 100 m, overtaking and burying them. At the same time, some dogs and cows instinctively moved sideways, thus avoiding the debris flow.

In act 3, the surges, the disintegrated mass of rock was now fully in contact with the ground and flowed rapidly down the valley floor. Its motion was described by Kaspar Zentner, who barely eluded the flow:

> The debris mass did not jump, did not skip, nor did it fly in the air, but was pushed rapidly along the bottom like a torrential flood. The flow was a little higher at the front than in the rear, having a round and bulgy head, and the mass moved in a wave motion. All the debris within the stream rolled confusedly as if it was boiling, and the whole mass reminded me of boiling corn stew. The smoke and rumble was terrifying. I now ran breathlessly over the bridge and bent around the corner of Rudolf Rhyner's house. Then I turned back and held myself

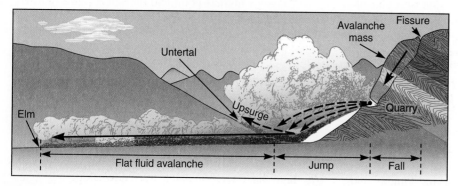

Figure 9.41

Cross-section of the 1881 Elm debris avalanche in Switzerland. A drama in three acts: the fall, the jump, and the surges. The rock debris deposited on the valley floor maintained the same relative positions it had in the bedrock layers of the mountain.

firmly against the house. Just as I went past the corner the whole mass shot right past me at a distance less than 1 metre away. The debris flow must have been at least 4 metres high. A single step had saved me. During the last jump I noticed that small stones were whirling around my legs like leaves in the wind. The house crunched, moved and seemed to be breaking apart. I fled on hands and knees through the garden until I got to the street. I was then safe. I had no pain anywhere and no stones had hit me. I did not feel any particular air pressure.

Although the moving mass at Elm looked and behaved like a "torrential flood" and a "boiling stew," it was not a watery mass but a dry one whose internal fluid was dust and air. Visitors who later viewed the mass of deposited debris remarked how similar its appearance was to a "lava flow." The facts are these: a mass of broken rock with a volume of 10 million m^3 dropped 600 m and then flowed 2.23 km as a dry mass moving at 180 km/h.

Movement of Sturzstroms

How do such large masses of debris move so far and so fast, and behave so much like a fluid? Numerous hypotheses have been proposed. (1) Some rely on water to provide lubrication and fluid-like flow, but some observed flows are masses of dry debris, as at Elm. (2) Other hypotheses invoke the generation of steam to liquefy and fluidize the moving mass, or (3) they call for frictional melting of material within the moving mass; both ideas (2) and (3) fail because some long-runout deposits contain blocks of ice or lichen-encrusted boulders, showing that no great amount of internal heat was generated nor was internal friction ever at a very high level. (4) A popular hypothesis suggests the falling mass traps a volume of air beneath it and then rides partially supported on a carpet of trapped air that enables it to travel far and fast. This idea has never been verified and seems most unlikely. For example, after its early airborne jump, the Elm sturzstrom was described as being in contact with the ground, and in fact, it dug up pipes buried a metre below the surface. Additional problems for the air-cushioned flow hypothesis are deposits with identical flow features on the ocean floor, and on the Moon and Mars, where no or very little atmosphere is available.

So it appears that neither water, heat, nor a trapped cushion of air is necessary for a long-runout debris flow. A remarkable fact helps guide the formulation of another hypothesis. After the Elm mass fell, disintegrated, jumped, and flowed 2.23 km and the rubble had come to rest, the original layering in the bedrock of the mountainside was still recognizable. Even though the debris had flowed according to all eyewitness accounts, the hunks of debris stayed in their same relative position (Figure 9.41). In the words of German geologist Albert Heim, who studied the scene in 1881:

When a large mass, broken into thousands of pieces, falls at the same time along the same course, the debris has to flow as a single stream. The uppermost block, at the very rear of the stream, would attempt to get ahead. It hurries but strikes the block, which is in the way, slightly ahead. The kinetic energy, of which the first block has more than the second, is thus transmitted through impact. In this way the uppermost block cannot overtake the lower block and thus has to stay behind. This process is repeated a thousandfold, resulting eventually in the preservation of the original order in the debris stream. This does not mean that the energy of falling blocks from originally higher positions is lost; rather the energy is transmitted through impact. The whole body of the mass is full of kinetic energy, to which each single stone contributes its part. No stone is free to work in any other way.

Who would guess that the pieces of rubble in a rapidly moving debris stream would keep their relative positions next to their neighbours? How is this relationship to be explained? A provocative hypothesis involving acoustic energy within the moving mass has been proposed by U.S. geophysicist Jay Melosh. Apparently, an immense volume of falling debris produces much vibrational or acoustical energy within its mass. The jostling and bumping back and forth of fragments produces acoustic (sound) energy that propagates as internal waves. The trapped acoustic waves may act to fluidize the rock debris, allowing the rapid fall velocity to continue as rapid flow velocity in a process called **acoustic fluidization**.

DEBRIS AND ROCK AVALANCHES

Debris and rock avalanches form when a massive rockfall explodes apart on contact with a slope. They are a transitional type of mass movement, initiated as rockfalls and evolving into a rapid flow of material.

1903 Frank Slide, Alberta

The town of Frank, Alberta, occupied a beautiful site in the Crowsnest pass, near the Alberta–British Columbia border in the Rockies. The coal mining boom town had opened only in 1901, and had been promoted to investors as "the world's richest coal mine" and a metropolis-to-be. Frank's place in history changed on 29 April 1903 when residents were startled at 4:10 a.m. by the noise coming down from Turtle Mountain (see photo of chapter opener and Figure 9.42). A 90-million-tonne mass of dipping limestone layers slid down their basal surface, dropped 1 km into the river valley, shattered, and then flowed 3 km across the valley and climbed 130 m up and over the terraced valley wall on the opposite side. The whole event lasted only 100 seconds, but it pulverized the southern end of town, killing about 75 people, including several families buried in their sleep. Fortunately, the colossal

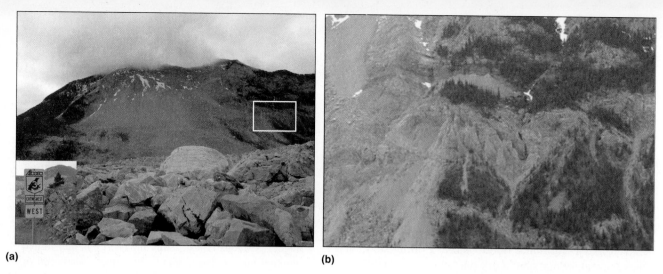

(a) **(b)**

Figure 9.42
View of Turtle Mountain and its boulder field. The enlarged area shows the rock pinnacles of North Peak.
Photos: © Claire Samson.

mass movement missed Frank's downtown area, where most residents lived, by a few hundred metres.

Eyewitnesses included the engineer of a train backing up to the coal mine when he heard the rock breaking high up on Turtle Mountain. He quickly switched to full speed ahead and chugged to safety as he watched miners at the loading dock sprinting for their lives be overrun and killed by the rock flow. The seventeen miners who were working underground during the night shift felt a powerful air blast that knocked them off their feet and blew all the lights out. They soon realized that they were trapped underground in a precarious situation, the entrance of the mine being blocked by rocks and timber, and the lower mine tunnel rapidly filling with water. Their only option was to dig themselves out. Based on their extensive knowledge of the mine, they decided to follow a coal seam that they knew outcropped on the side of the mountain. After digging through coal (6 metres) and limestone (3 metres), all of them reached the surface safely, barely recognizing the landscape around them.

The Frank "slide" (technically, a debris avalanche) has held an enduring fascination with the general public. Several myths surround the event. Is it true that the safe of the local branch of the Union Bank of Canada (containing $500,000 in U.S. silver dollars ready for payday) still lies somewhere beneath the rubble? Did an Indian chief really visit the Mayor of Frank the evening before the slide to warn him of the incoming danger? Historians know the first supposition is a myth: the bank, located downtown, was not damaged in the event. The second myth has some elements of truth: small pieces of rock fell regularly from Turtle Mountain. First Nations people called it "The Mountain That Moves." They would not camp beside it, and had warned residents about the potential danger.

Simple geological cross-sections provide clues to the causes of the tragedy (Figure 9.43). Turtle Mountain is an anticline, a hill formed by deformed layers of rocks folded in the form of an arch. On the side of the mountain facing Frank, layers are oriented parallel to the slope, an adverse geological setting as we saw earlier in this chapter. The debris avalanche was triggered when rocks failed at the contact between layers, and dipping limestone blocks slid down their basal surface. Secondary causes included coal mining inside the mountain and dramatic changes in weather conditions—a quick freeze—that night.

The event created two peaks on either side of the main avalanche scar. North Peak, rising directly above town, was judged menacing enough to warrant relocating of the town a short distance away (Figure 9.42). The debris avalanche site is now an organized tourist attraction with the Frank Slide Interpretive Centre, audiovisual program, and self-guided hiking trails.

Subsidence

In subsidence, the ground moves down (Figure 9.15). The surface either sags gently or drops catastrophically as voids in rocks close. This is not the down-dropping associated with tectonic plates, fault movements, or volcanism but rather is either the slow compaction of loose, water-saturated sediments or the rapid collapse of overlying earth into caves.

SLOW SUBSIDENCE

In many areas of the world, the ground surface is slowly sinking as fluids are removed below the surface (Table 9.3). When water or oil are squeezed out or pumped up to the surface, the removal of fluid volume and the decrease in pore-fluid pressure cause rock grains to be crowded closer together; this results in subsidence of the ground surface.

The fluids within rocks help support the weight of overlying rock layers. The effect is similar to that of

Figure 9.43
Geological cross-sections of Turtle Mountain before, during, and after the 1903 debris avalanche.
Source: Kerr, J.W. 1990. Frank Slide. Barker Pub. Ltd.

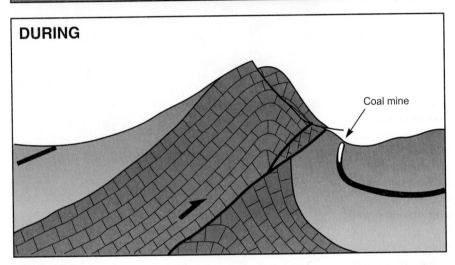

BEFORE

Turtle Mountain Anticline

Blairmore Mine

Frank Coal Mine

Crowsnest River

Coal removed

Hard Limestone

Soft shale, sandstone and coal

DURING

Coal mine

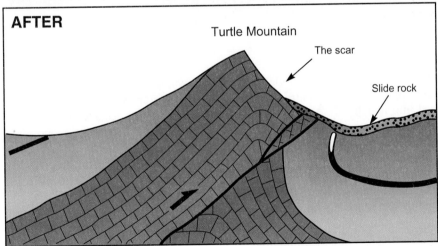

AFTER

Turtle Mountain

The scar

Slide rock

carrying a friend in a swimming pool where the water helps support your friend's body weight. Some examples will help illustrate the subsidence problem.

Groundwater Withdrawal, Mexico City

The Valley of Mexico has been a major population centre for many centuries. People need water so the Aztecs, and later the Spanish, built aqueduct systems to bring water in from the surrounding mountains. In 1846, it became well recognized that a large volume of groundwater lay beneath the city. The convenience of abundant freshwater lying underfoot led to drilling wells to make large withdrawals of underground water. But the water has been withdrawn faster than the natural rate of replenishment. People are using more of the underground water each year than rainfall can resupply, so the land subsides.

City	Maximum Subsidence (metres)	Area Affected (km²)
Table 9.3		
Bangkok, Thailand	1	800
Houston, Texas	2.7	12,000
London, England	0.3	300
Mexico City, Mexico	10	3,000
Nagoya, Japan	2.4	1,300
New Orleans, Louisiana	3	175
Niigata, Japan	2.5	8,300
Shanghai, China	2.7	120
Taipei, Taiwan	1.9	130
Tokyo, Japan	4.5	3,000
Venice, Italy	0.3	150

Figure 9.44
Venice is built on the subsiding ground of a river delta. Notice how the former doorway has been bricked shut to keep out the sea.
Photo: © MedioImages/Getty Images

In the centre of the city the land sank about 10 m between 1846 and 1954. The city centre now lies lower than the level of nearby Lake Texcoco.

How can land subsidence be stopped? Stop pumping out groundwater. Can the land subsidence in Mexico City be reversed? No. Groundwater withdrawal is now banned in the city centre and has been moved to new wells in the north and south of the valley. Land subsidence of 2 to 8 cm a year is now occurring in the new areas of groundwater withdrawal. Supplying the water needs of 20 million people is not easy in an area where the evaporation rate is greater than the precipitation rate.

Long-Term Subsidence, Venice, Italy

Venice is one of the most improbable cities in the world. It began during the collapse of the Roman Empire in the 5th century CE when local people moved into marshes and islands in a malaria-ridden lagoon to gain some protection from invading armies from the north. The city is built on soft sediments that compact and sink under the weight of its buildings at the same time that the global sea level is rising. From about 400 to 1900 CE, Venetians struggled to stay above water as sinking land helped the sea rise about 13 cm per century (Figure 9.44). To stay above water, Venetians built up the islands using boatloads of imported sand and slowed the sinking of buildings by driving wood poles down into the sediment to make more stable foundations. In the 20th century, the rate of rise of the sea doubled to about 25 cm per century due in part to pumping up groundwater from the 1930s to 1970s. Projections for the 21st century suggest the sea will rise about 50 cm. What can Venetians do to save their sinking city? One proposal is to spend billions of dollars to install movable floodgates across the three entrances to the lagoon to stop Adriatic seawater from flooding the lagoon during high tides and storms. However, these same floodgates would harm the economy by disrupting shipping and cause health problems by blocking the outflow of pollutants. Should the floodgates be built? Or should Venetians do as their ancestors did and keep bringing in sediment to raise the ground level? A third proposal is to pump seawater or carbon dioxide into a sand mass lying 600 to 800 m below the city in an attempt to "pump up" the region by about 30 cm in 10 years. There is no easy and permanent solution for this sinking city.

CATASTROPHIC SUBSIDENCE

Most **limestone** formed in warm, shallow seas in the geological past by the accumulation and disintegration of shells and skeletons of organisms that remove calcium

In Greater Depth

How to Create a Cave

Caves usually occur in limestone. The same equation that describes the formation of limestone also describes its dissolution into caves. The basic equilibrium equation is

$$Ca^{++} + 2HCO_3^- \rightleftharpoons CaCO_3 + H_2CO_3$$

where Ca^{++} is calcium ion, HCO_3^- is bicarbonate ion, $CaCO_3$ is limestone, and H_2CO_3 is **carbonic acid.** When the equation runs from left to right, limestone is precipitated. When the equation runs from right to left, limestone is dissolved (Figure 9.45). The primary variable controlling whether limestone is precipitated or dissolved is the amount of carbonic acid present. And the main variable controlling the concentration of carbonic acid is the amount of carbon dioxide (CO_2) in solution:

$$H_2O + CO_2 \rightleftharpoons H_2CO_3$$

If dissolved carbon dioxide content is high, then the water is rich in carbonic acid and limestone is dissolved. This also describes our familiar bottles of carbonated drinks, where flavoured sugar water holds large quantities of CO_2 in solution under pressure. Carbon dioxide contents are highest when water is under pressure and cold; that is, the gas bubbles are held in solution.

Figure 9.45 Dissolution has created a coarse honeycomb texture in the limestone of the Palisser formation at Canmore, Alberta. Rock climbers practise their skills on this rock face where voids are the perfect size (a few centimetres across) for anchoring hands and feet.
Photos Courtesy of Karin Michel.

: (Ca), carbon (C), and oxygen (O) from seawater to make their skeletal material of calcium carbonate ($CaCO_3$). Some organisms build limestone directly as reefs. Other organisms die and their shells, spines, and other mineralized remains are bound together by $CaCO_3$ precipitated as cement filling the void spaces. Today, limestones in several parts of the world have naturally acidic freshwater flowing through them, dissolving them and forming extensive networks of caverns. When the levels of underground water drop during a drought or due to pumping of groundwater, the removal of the water lessens the internal support that helps hold up the roofs of caves. The loss of buoyant support that occurs when groundwater is drained from caves weakens some so much that their roofs collapse suddenly and catastrophically to form **sinkholes.**

Much of the Florida peninsula is underlain by limestone that is covered in most areas by 15 to 30 m of muddy sands. When the underground water body is lowered due to drought reducing the water supply or by humans making excessive withdrawals by overpumping wells, then caverns in limestone may be drained of water. Remove the water and the weakened cavern may collapse. On 8 May 1981, a small depression on the ground in Winter Park, Florida, grew to a 45 m diameter sinkhole within 15 hours. Before a week was up, the sinkhole was 100 m across and 34 m deep (Figure 9.46). The collapsing cavern claimed one house, several Porsches from a repair shop, and the deep end of the municipal swimming pool.

Snow Avalanches

Few things are more central to the Canadian way of life than snow. In fact, in the view of the French 18th-century writer Voltaire, Canada simply reduced to "a few acres of snow. . . ."

Heavy snowfalls on steep slopes yield to the pull of gravity and fail as snow avalanches. They may be understood using the same mass-movement principles for earth and rock. Just like earthen mass movements, snow avalanches creep, fall, slide, and flow. Avalanches begin in the starting zone where slopes are steepest (usually 30° to 45°) and then move down slopes of 20° to 30°, commonly guided by topography along a narrow track, and finally come to a halt in the runout zone (slopes usually less than 20°). (Compare Figures 9.34 and 9.47). Avalanches vary from the size-1 **sluff** (mass of 10 tonnes of snow or less) which is relatively harmless to people to the size-5 monster (mass of 100,000 tonnes of snow) that can destroy a village or flatten a forest of 40 ha. They move at rates ranging from barely advancing to measured speeds of 370 km/h. Their travel distance varies from only a few metres to several kilometres. For example, an avalanche of about 765,000 m³ was unleashed down the slopes of Mount Sanford in Alaska on 12 April 1981; it dropped over 3 km and flowed for 13 km, including running up and over a 900 m high ridge.

Snow layers develop one by one, storm by storm. At any given time, the **snowpack** in a particular area is a heterogeneous column composed of several layers with

Figure 9.46
Aerial view of Winter Park, Florida, in May 1981. Sinkhole is 100 m wide and 34 m deep. Note the failed municipal swimming pool at bottom and the four-lane road on the left.
Photo: © US Geological Survey.

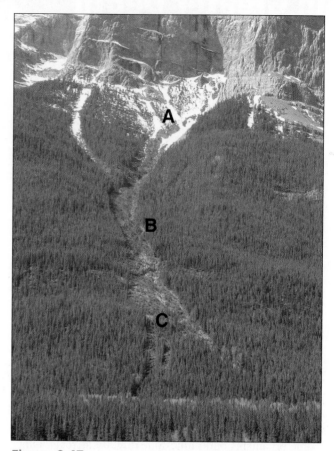

Figure 9.47
A recent avalanche has left its imprint on a mountain flank in Banff National Park. A: Starting zone; B: Track; C: Runout zone.
Photo: © Claire Samson

different characteristics of thickness, strength, hardness, and density (Figure 9.48). Fresh "powder" snow is composed of 95% void space and does not stick together in a ball. On the other hand, wet snow, which is typical of late-season snowfalls, includes liquid water between particles of ice and is much more cohesive. Subtle differences in snow properties have been captured in the 31 words for "snow" used in Inuktitut. For example, *aqilluqqaaq* means "fresh and soggy snow," whereas *katakartanaq* is "crusty snow, broken by steps," and *pukak* refers to "dry snow crystals, like sugar powder."

The properties of the different snow layers can change over time. A snowpack is commonly warmer than the surrounding air, so snowflakes within the column transform. New snow exhibits beautiful six-sided crystals. As the crystals age, their exterior melts and refreezes. They become more rounded, more densely packed, and more cohesive. This process allows the snowpack to build to a greater thickness. In very cold weather, water vapour occasionally transforms directly into ice to form hoar crystals on the surface or at the base of the snowpack (see the diagram of the different states of water in Figure 10.5). Hoar is characterized by relatively large crystals, and decreases the density and therefore the strength of the snowpack (Figure 9.49).

Most avalanches occur naturally during or soon after snow storms, the 24 hours following a heavy snowstorm being the most critical. Avalanches commonly initiate on steep slopes when snowfall builds to 0.5 to 1.5 m thick. But snow thicknesses can reach 2 to 5 m before failing in big avalanches that can be devastating. Why does snow sometimes build into thick masses on steep slopes? It depends on the internal structure of the snowpack. Conditions decreasing stability include the presence of weak layers within the snowpack and the orientation of the slope with respect to the dominant wind direction. On downwind slopes, the wind decelerates and dumps snow, and can contribute to the formation of precariously suspended cornices.

The styles of avalanches vary, depending on snow cohesion. Two main types are *loose-powder avalanches*

Figure 9.48
A heterogeneous snowpack. Weak layers are less dense and more transparent than adjacent layers.
Photo: © Jim Bay.

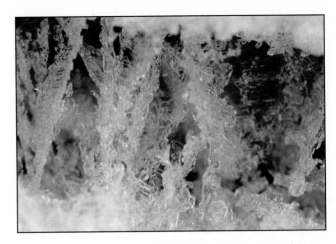

Figure 9.49
Feather-shaped hoar crystals.
Photo: Bruce Jamieson, Civil Engineering Department, University of Calgary.

Figure 9.50
A loose-powder avalanche flows toward three hikers.
Photo: © Royalty-Free/Corbis

(flows) and *slab avalanches* (slides). Loose, powdery snow has a low amount of cohesion. A loose-powder avalanche typically fails at a point source and develops in an inverted "V" shape. It triggers more and more snow into moving during its downhill run and spreads out laterally (Figure 9.50). The speed of loose-powder avalanches is approximately 65–100 km/h.

Slab avalanches involve the breaking free of slabs of cohesive snow from their poorly anchored base. A fracture first develops on the perimeter of the slab, and then spreads to a weak layer at the base (Figure 9.51). The failures are analogous to translational slides, where an upper mass breaks free and slides down and out on top of a layer beneath it. The sliding slabs typically break up and turn into flows during their downslope movement (Figure 9.52). Slab conditions can develop when a layer of hard-wind deposited snow is added on top of light-wind deposited snow, or a layer of heavily cemented snow sits on a layer of loose snow, or a dense layer of snow sits on a low-density layer. Within the pile of snow layers are melt-freeze crusts that form during times of surface

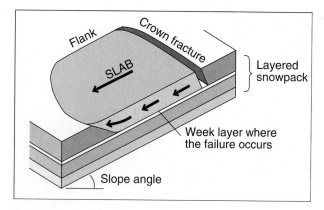

Figure 9.51

Development of a slab avalanche.

Source: Reproduced with the permission of Natural Resources Canada 2008, courtesy of the Geological Survey of Canada (GSC Bulletin 548).

Figure 9.52

A slab avalanche is triggered by a downhill skier. Notice the vertical cracks at the head, the broad area of rupture, and the moving slabs.

Source: US Forest Service/USGS

exposure between snowfalls. The result is a heterogenous pile of separate and distinct layers that contain numerous potential failure surfaces within them. Slab avalanches are the most dangerous avalanches. They move at speeds between 30 and 65 km/h, slower than loose-powder avalanches, but usually carry wet, heavy snow with enough momentum to hit hard.

Although isolated incidents can occur anywhere in Canada where there is a dangerous mix of steep topography and abundant snowfalls (see the case history of Kangiqsualujjuaq in Chapter 1), avalanche risk is highest in the Rockies. In recent years, prominent signage has been installed along the main thoroughfares in the area to keep motorists vigilant (Figure 9.53). No stops are allowed in known avalanche corridors. Established in 2004, the Canadian Avalanche Centre, headquartered in Revelstoke, British Columbia, is Canada's national public avalanche safety organization. The Centre and its partners issue avalanche forecast bulletins for 16 areas in the Rockies and the Haute Gaspésie in Québec. Avalanche forecasting is based on observations of recent avalanches, assessments of snowpack stability, and weather conditions. Bulletins include colour-coded forecasts of avalanche danger, based on the international avalanche danger scale (Figure 9.54), and travel advisories. The best mitigation strategy in the back country remains avoidance. Closer to population centres, in the vicinity of winter sport resorts, for example, active measures might be necessary. Such measures include the use of explosive charges and artillery shells to artificially induce small avalanches and thus prevent the accumulation of threatening masses of snow in unstable areas.

1910 SNOW AVALANCHE, ROGERS PASS, BRITISH COLUMBIA

Rogers Pass is surrounded by the rugged beauty of the Selkirk Mountains in Glacier National Park, British Columbia. The pass is a major transportation corridor through the Rockies, which includes the routes of the Canadian Pacific Railway and Trans-Canada Highway.

From the opening of the pass by Canadian Pacific Railway in 1884, the area had been plagued by numerous snow avalanches. The snow-removal technology at the time included a steam locomotive fitted with a huge rotary plough on the front, backed up by the efforts of a "shovel gang," a team of men equipped with shovels, saws, and picks. On the evening of 4 March 1910, under the light of lanterns, a group of night workers were busy removing the 7 metres of hard-packed snow an avalanche from Cheops Mountain had dumped on the tracks a few hours before. A second avalanche, from the ominously named Avalanche Mountain located on the opposite side of the pass, caught them in action. Of the party of 63 men, only one survived. Historical photographs have captured the violence of the event and the frenzy of the rescue operation (Figures 9.55 and 9.56). By midday the following day, 600 people were digging in the snow and rubble, and 58 bodies had been recovered. The bodies of the four remaining victims were found later in the spring when snow melted.

This tragedy brought to 250 the number of people killed in avalanches in Rogers Pass since the construction of the railway. The avalanche of 4 March 1910 was to be the last major disaster in the area. It prompted the

Figure 9.53
Avalanche warning signs.

Photos: (left) courtesy of Karin Michel and (right) courtesy of Peter Fernburg.

Danger	Description	Travel Suggestions
LOW	Natural avalanches very unlikely. Human triggered avalanches unlikely. Generally stable snow; isolated areas of instability.	Travel is generally safe. Normal caution advised.
MODERATE	Natural avalanches unlikely. Human triggered avalanches possible. Unstable slabs possible on steep terrain.	Use caution in steeper terrain on certain aspects.
CONSIDERABLE	Natural avalanches possible. Human triggered avalanches probable. Unstable slabs probable on steep terrain.	Be more cautious in steeper terrain. Be aware of potentially dangerous areas of unstable snow.
HIGH	Natural and human triggered avalanches likely. Unstable slabs likely on a variety of aspects and slope angles.	Travel in avalanche terrain not recommended. Safest travel on windward ridges or lower angle slopes without steeper terrain above.
EXTREME	Widespread natural or human triggered avalanches certain. Extremely unstable slabs on most aspects and slope angles. Large destructive avalanches possible.	Travel in avalanche terrain should be avoided and travel confined to low angle terrain well away from avalanche path runouts.

Figure 9.54
International avalanche danger scale.

Source: American Avalanche Association.

Figure 9.55
The 1910 Rogers Pass avalanche overturned this 150 tonne locomotive.

Source: Image D-00188 courtesy of Royal BC Museum, BC Archives.

Figure 9.56
Two-step benched road cut in Gatineau, Quebec.

Photo: © Claire Samson.

redesign of the railway route and the construction of the Connaught Tunnel, which opened in 1916.

Mitigation

Mass movements occur in so many places around the world that almost everyone can feel or see their effects. Let us examine the various mitigation strategies deployed for controlling them.

Remove the hazard. You probably see this most often along road cuts. On the slopes above the road, the hazard is lessened by scaling loose rock (Figure 9.62), decreasing the slope angle or benching, a technique in which the slope is remodelled as a series of steps (Figure 9.57).

Reinforce the hazard. What are the strategies for controlling slides of both rotational and translational styles? Actions taken involve unloading the head, reinforcing the body by inserting rock bolts and cylinder piles (Figure 9.58), and supporting the toe (Figure 9.33). Drainage systems are also often added to reduce the pore-water pressure on the potential failure surface or within the driving mass.

Contain the hazard. Unstable material can be held in place on the slope with nets of strong wire mesh (Figure 9.23b), a fence being ready to catch any rocks that do escape and fall before they reach the road (Figure 9.20). Common actions to control flows involve steering the flow into the direction of least harm by building walls and digging channels.

Figure 9.57
Rescue party digging in snow and rubble on 5 March 1910 in Rogers Pass.

Source: Image D-00186 courtesy of Royal BC Museum, BC Archives.

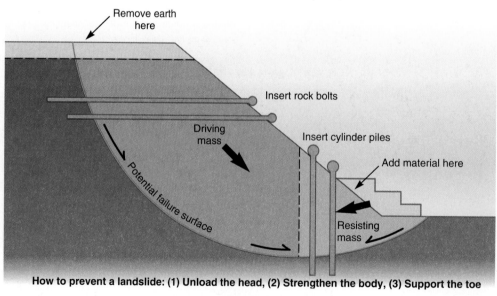

How to prevent a landslide: (1) Unload the head, (2) Strengthen the body, (3) Support the toe

Figure 9.58
A hill slope of homogeneous materials may fail along an arcuate basal surface. The slope is in equilibrium when a driving-mass portion is kept from moving by a resisting-mass portion. Removing from the driving mass, strengthening the body, or adding to the resisting mass can prevent a landslide. Does this situation bring to mind any construction practices in your area?

In Greater Depth

What to Do If You Are Caught in a Snow Avalanche

Before

Before venturing in the back country, consult avalanche forecast bulletins (Figure 9.54) and travel advisories. Stay away from sensitive areas. Be alert to changing weather conditions.

Do not go out alone. Designate a group leader and have a plan in case an accident occurs. Everyone in your group should carry a first aid kit, a collapsible shovel, and a probe. People should wear transceivers, devices capable of both transmitting and receiving radio signals. Mountain enthusiasts are wise in investing in a ski jacket with a built-in beacon. An interesting new device is a flexible breathing tube and mouthpiece attached near the user's face and connected to a small hollow chamber strapped to the chest. The device, which resembles a snorkel, allows a buried victim to breathe snow-free air and, via a system of valves, separates the exhaled from the inhaled air, reducing the risk of asphyxiation. Another recent development is the avalanche air bag system, which is folded in a backpack, like a parachute. It inflates by pulling a ripcord and provides buoyancy. This is an important point since only 5 to 10% of victims survive being buried in more than 1.5 m of snow.

During

As soon as the snow starts to move, try to escape to the side. Attempts to outrun the avalanche will not work. If you are caught, rid yourself of ski, poles, backpack, etc. to make yourself lighter.

Use a swimming motion to stay near the surface of the snow. If you are in over your head, try to maintain an air pocket in front of your face as many avalanche fatalities are caused by suffocation. If you are trapped, remain calm so that your body can better conserve energy.

After

In isolated areas, survival depends on the search organized by group members. Time is critical as survival rates drop rapidly with time: for shallow burials in 1.5 m of snow or less, the survival rate is 50% for a 30-minute burial but only 15% for a 2-hour burial. Initiate the search as soon as the area is safe from avalanche danger. Start from the "last seen position," and heading to the avalanche toe in zigzagging patterns. Stop every 10 m to listen for a signal. Victims wearing transceivers are usually found within 5 to 15 minutes by their companions. Once the source of signal has been located, poke about the snowpack with your probe to locate the victim. Digging in the hard-packed snow will take several minutes. Extract the victim gently as the person might be injured.

With all due respect to St. Bernard dogs, an icon of alpine mountain rescue, there have been no reports of avalanche victims found alive by especially trained dogs in Canada. The dogs simply cannot reach the scene quickly enough.

Support the hazard. Special buttresses are sometimes designed to provide additional support to overhanging blocks, or weak and crumbly rock layers (Figure 9.25).

Protect against the hazard. In extreme circumstances, tunnels and snow sheds are built to provide direct protection for roads and railway tracks against mass movements and snow avalanches (Figure 9.59).

Figure 9.59
A concrete shed (left) and tunnel (right) protect the railway track along a segment particularly vulnerable to earth flows and snow avalanches west of the Kicking Horse Pass near Field, British Columbia.
Photo: © Claire Samson.

In Greater Depth

The Sea-to-Sky Corridor

The Sea-to-Sky transportation corridor links Vancouver, Squamish, and Whistler, following the coast and a picturesque valley through British Columbia's Coast Mountains (Figure 9.60). The corridor includes a BC Rail line and Highway 99 running parallel to each other. The windy highway has claimed several motorists' lives over the years, earning the sad nickname of "sea-to-die" highway . . . To increase safety, a major engineering project is underway to widen and straighten the road, a challenging endeavour as it cuts through one of the most active landslide areas in Canada.

Over the last hundred years, 154 reported landslide events occurred along the corridor, accounting for approximately 18% of Canada's landslide-related deaths (Figure 9.60). A single rock avalanche at Jane Camp in March 1915 took the lives of 56 mine workers, the second-worst Canadian landslide disaster in terms of casualties. The most frequent types of mass movements along the Sea-to-Sky corridor are rockfalls and debris flows, often triggered by weather events. On average, Highway 99 is closed once a year when heavy rain near the mountain summits runs off into torrents carrying a heavy load of detritus and sediment. The mix descends down the valleys at high speed, accumulating as debris fans at the foot of the slopes (Figure 9.61). The most recent incident occurred in 4 February 2007 when tonnes of rock and mud were strewn across the highway, blocking all lanes for more than seven hours. Dynamite had to be used to destroy a boulder that was too big to be moved.

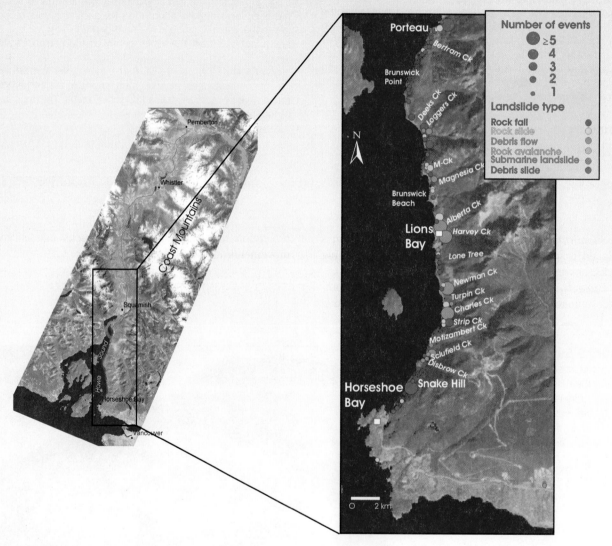

Figure 9.60 (Left) An aerial landscape of the Sea-to-Sky corridor with Highway 99 drawn as a red line. The view has been created by fusing satellite images and computer-generated topography. (Right) The southern section of the corridor is particularly active for mass movements.

Source: Blais-Stevens, A. and D. Septer, 2006, Landslides along the Sea to Sky corridor, Sea to Sky Geotechnique Conference, Canadian Geotechnical Association, Vancouver, Oct. 2006, 448-455.

In Greater Depth

Although there has been an increase in reported mass movements along the Sea-to-Sky transportation corridor in the 1980s and 1990s due to an increase in population and greater awareness, there has been no landslide-related casualty since the early 1990s. This fact can largely be attributed to a vigorous mitigation program. In addition to classic mitigation measures like rock scaling (Figure 9.62), culverts, and retaining walls, several innovative solutions have been put in place. In particular, several concrete flumes have been built to channel excess water, mud, and debris during major flooding events. Charles Creek, a particularly sensitive area, which has experienced seven historical debris flows, is now protected by a large concrete catchment basin designed to collect debris upstream from Highway 99, the railway, and the community built on its alluvial fan (Figure 9.63). The basin can be cleared out after a major debris flow.

The current Highway 99 improvement project is progressing well. It will be completed in 2009, in time for the spectators of the 2010 Winter Olympics to travel safely to Whistler to enjoy the skiing and sliding events.

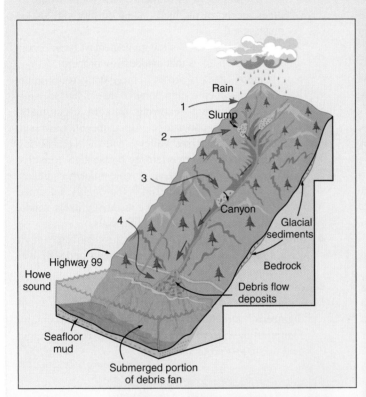

Figure 9.61 Typical debris flow in the Sea-to-Sky corridor. (1) Torrential rainfall swells streams along the mountain crest. (2) Sediment slumps into a raging stream, forming a debris flow that surges down the channel. (3) The debris flow swells in volume as it picks up additional sediment and trees from the channel and canyon walls. (4) The debris flow emerges from the canyon onto a fan where it damages houses, roads, bridges, and a rail line.

Source: Natural Resources Canada.

Figure 9.63 The Charles Creek catchment basin stops debris flow deposits before they reach the road, the railway track, and the homes built on the debris fan.

Photo: © O. Hungr

Figure 9.62 Rock scaling removes loose rock from unstable slopes.

Summary

- Gravity tugs incessantly at all landforms on Earth, commonly causing failures called mass movements.
  - Slopes approach failure due to external factors, such as steepening of the slope, adding mass upslope, or removing mass low on a slope.
  - Internal factors that make a slope weak include inherently weak materials such as clay minerals, decreasing cohesion through solution or internal erosion, weight of pore water and elevated pore-water pressure, and adverse geological structures, such as inclined bedding and fault surfaces.
- Movement usually is initiated by a triggering event, such as heavy rains, an earthquake, or human activities. In Canada, most mass movements occur in the spring and the fall in conjunction with meteorological events. They are prevalent in the Rockies because of the steep topography.
- Mass movements range from the barely perceptible surface creep of hill slopes and gelifluction of periglacial soils to events involving material moving in excess of 325 km/h.
- Major types of mass movement are downward, as in falling or subsiding, or downward and outward, as in sliding and flowing.
  - Falls are rock masses dislodged from elevated slopes. Slides are mass movements on top of failure surfaces.
  - Flows are mass movements that behave like fluids, even when they are dry.
  - Complex events include characteristics of several types of mass movements in a single event.
  - Subsidence occurs when the surface drops down either slowly in response to removal of subsurface fluids or catastrophically.

- In slides, the displaced material retains some coherence during movement.
  - Concave-upward, curved failure surfaces produce rotational slides. The slide head tilts backward, the toe bulges upward, and little distance is travelled. Rotational slides are a common destroyer of property, but their slow movements rarely kill anyone.
  - Slides on top of inclined, planar surfaces are called translational.
    - Block slides are a slow movement of large coherent rock masses that can destroy property.
    - Lateral spreads are extremely dangerous events during which a clay layer in the subsurface suddenly liquefies, carrying rafts of earth material rapidly downslope. Along the St. Lawrence and Ottawa River Valleys, and in neighbouring regions, areas underlain by post-glacial sensitive clay are particularly vulnerable to lateral spreads.
- In flows, the displaced material is thoroughly deformed during movement. Flows may be made of gravels, sands, muds, snow, ice, or mixtures of materials.
- Snow avalanches are similar to mass movements of earth. Loose-powder avalanches are flows and slab avalanches are slides.
- People are not defenceless against mass movements. Mitigation is achieved through an amazing variety of engineering structures that remove, reinforce, contain, or support the hazard, such as buttresses, rock bolts and steel mesh, and protective sheds.

Terms to Remember

acoustic fluidization 251
bedrock 246
carbonic acid 256
chemical weathering 232
clay minerals 247
creep 230
debris flow 245
fall 239
flow 239
groundwater 236
lateral spread 233

limestone 254
permafrost 247
piping 235
pore-water pressure 235
porosity 246
retrogressive sliding 244
rotational slide 242
sensitive clay 233
sinkhole 255
slate 250
slide 239

sluff 255
slump 242
snowpack 255
soil 246
sturzstrom 250
subside 239
talus slope 239
topple 239
translational slide 242
water table 236

Questions for Review

1. Which natural disasters can cause mass movements?
2. Which natural disasters can be triggered by mass movements?
3. Draw a cross-section through a slope and explain external actions that are likely to cause mass movements.
4. Draw a cross-section through a clay mineral. Explain the physical properties that promote swelling and shrinking.
5. Draw a water molecule and explain how it links up so readily with some clay minerals.
6. How do pore waters become pressurized? What is their role in mass movements?
7. Why are mass movements more frequent in Canada in the spring?
8. List some adverse geological structures inside hills that facilitate mass movements.
9. What triggering events set off rapid mass movements?
10. Why do large cavern systems form in limestone? Why do they sometimes collapse and form sinkholes?
11. What type of economic activities are most adversely affected by mass movements?
12. Compare snow avalanches to mass movements of soil and rock.
13. What mitigation strategies can be used against both mass movements and snow avalanches?

Questions for Further Thought

1. Roadways are commonly cut into the base of slopes. When mass movements block the road, they are quickly removed. What is wrong with this whole process?
2. Does deforestation increase the risk of mass movements?
3. In your home area, how many engineering structures can you visualize that were built to stop or control mass movements? Look for them as you travel about.
4. Why are areas affected by regional subsidence more susceptible to flood and hurricane damage?
5. What circumstances warrant a preventive evacuation of people from their homes to protect them from a potential landslide?
6. Should all Canadian territory be mapped for landslide hazards?
7. Should access to the back country be forbidden to recreationists when the avalanche danger is moderate, considerable, high, or extreme?

CHAPTER

10

Atmosphere, Oceans, and Climate

"The farther backward you can look, the farther forward you are likely to see."

Winston Churchill

Outline

- Weather versus Climate
- Solar Radiation Received by Earth
- Water and Heat
- Vertical Movement of Air
- Layering of the Lower Atmosphere
- General Circulation of the Atmosphere
- General Circulation of the Oceans
- The Greenhouse Effect—A Tale of Three Planets
- Climate History of the Earth: Timescale in Millions of Years
- Glacial Advance and Retreat: Timescale in Thousands of Years
- Climate Variations Since the Last Glaciation
- Summary

Photo: © G Marc Lane Photography

THE MAYAN CIVILIZATION AND CLIMATE CHANGE

Weather is associated with short-term local or regional events that can be either beneficial or cause death and destruction, whereas climate change can be linked to regional or global events at the decadal to millennial-scale that, depending on the circumstances, might facilitate either the rise or collapse of entire civilizations. For example, the Mayan civilization of Mesoamerica made great accomplishments in agriculture, irrigation, social organization, mathematics, and astronomy during a thousand-year period characterized by a relatively benign climate. However, a century-long pattern of decreased rainfall caused problems that intensified during multi-year droughts centred on the years 810, 860, and 910 CE. The droughts seem to have set off a chain of events that led the Maya to a cessation of monumental inscriptions and large-scale architectural construction, permanent abandonment of many urban areas in the southern and central lowlands (Figure 10.1), and the breakdown of social and political order leading to wars. Population density in some cities declined by 90%, and society became increasingly decentralized, forcing most people to return to a life of rural subsistence.

Climate change is not something that affected only ancient civilizations. Climate changes continually, and as the only constant about climate is change, either gradual or sudden, it is prudent that scholars in our modern civilization study the impact that previous climate change has had on civilizations like that of the Maya. With a global human population projected to reach 11 billion in the 21st century, the fate of our own civilization may be linked either negatively or positively to climate change.

Weather versus Climate

This chapter begins a major shift in energy sources as we move in the next few chapters to those processes and disasters fuelled by the Sun. The news media bring us tales of tornadoes, killer heat waves, hurricanes, and floods; these processes all fall into the realm of weather but not into the area of climate. **Weather** covers short-term processes, whereas climate refers to long-term conditions. **Climate** involves phenomena such as Ice Ages, multi-year droughts, changes in greenhouse gas content in the atmosphere, and shifting circulation patterns in the ocean. Or as Mark Twain wrote in his short story, *English as She is Taught*, "Climate lasts all the time and weather only a few days."

The Sun's energy heats the Earth unequally. The equatorial area faces the Sun more directly than do the polar regions. During the course of a year, the equatorial area receives about 2.4 times as much solar energy as the polar regions. The Earth's spin helps set the heat-carrying oceans and atmosphere in motion. Gravity then works to even out the unequal distribution of heat by pulling more forcefully on the colder, denser air and water masses. Circulation of the relatively rapidly moving atmosphere and slowly flowing oceans is a major determinant of climate and weather all around the Earth. The province of weather and climate is a province of continual change. We experience the hour-to-hour, day-to-day, and season-to-season changes in atmospheric conditions known as weather. When weather is viewed over the longer time spans of decades, centuries, and on up to intervals of millions of years, it is called climate. The understanding of both weather and climate involves many of the same scientific principles, and this chapter begins with some of those principles.

Figure 10.1
The Mayan ruins at Uxmal in Yucatan, Mexico, are a favourite destination for tourists.
Photo: © Pat Abbott.

Climate affects all life on Earth and, as climate changes, all life must adapt to the new conditions. Some species thrive during and after a given change. They are joined by new species well adapted to the climate of the time. Meanwhile, other species cannot survive the changes and either migrate to more hospitable areas or become extinct. The record of **extinctions** is covered in Chapter 15.

Solar Radiation Received by Earth

In Chapter 2, the Sun is discussed as an external source of energy for the Earth. Incoming solar radiation is received at short wavelengths. Outgoing terrestrial radiation is emitted in long wavelengths. A global energy budget is shown in Figure 2.27.

Solar radiation is absorbed in massive amounts in the equatorial belt between about 32°N and 34°S latitudes (Figure 10.2). The equatorial zone faces the Sun directly, thus incoming sunlight strikes the surface at steep angles, allowing a high percentage of the energy

to be absorbed, especially in seawater. Polar latitudes receive far less of the Sun's energy because the incoming solar radiation arrives at a low angle, causing much to be reflected. In fact, the high latitudes show a net cooling because the heat reradiated back to space is greater than the amount locally gained from the Sun. Some of the excess heat of the low-latitude equatorial zone is transported to the high-latitude polar regions (Figure 10.2). The mid-latitudes are zones of energy transfer. Cold air flows equatorward and hot winds move poleward, transferring much heat, especially carried in water vapour. This energy transported in moving air masses is often released in severe storms.

There is an interesting climatic feedback cycle in the polar zones. They receive less solar energy and are colder, thus helping snow and ice to form (Figure 10.3). But then the presence of snow and ice raises albedos from the 5 to 35% reflectance range off water, soil, and vegetation up to the 60 to 90% reflectance off fresh snow and ice. Increasing the albedo makes the cold polar climate even colder. The reverse is true during a warming cycle.

Higher albedo can help lower Earth's surface temperature, but the greenhouse effect can help raise it. Solar radiation reaches Earth in short wavelengths, where it is

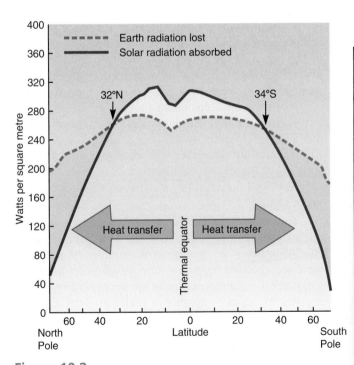

Figure 10.2
Energy radiated from the Earth's surface and energy absorbed from solar radiation are plotted against latitude. Poleward from latitudes 32°N and 34°S, the energy deficit increases. Heat is transported poleward from tropics via ocean and atmosphere, tending toward energy equilibrium.

Source: NOAA Meteorological Satellite Laboratory, Washington, DC.

Figure 10.3
Prince of Wales Icecap, Ellesmere Island, Nunavut.

Source: Image courtesy of MODIS Rapid Response Project at NASA/GSFC.

absorbed and thus raises the temperatures of land, water, and vegetation (Figure 2.27). Any body with a temperature above absolute zero (-273°C, or 0 K) radiates some heat toward cooler areas. When excess heat is reradiated, it is at long wavelengths that can be absorbed by greenhouse gases in the atmosphere such as water vapour, carbon dioxide, and **methane**. Following this absorption, most of the energy is radiated back down to Earth's surface; this is the greenhouse effect and it warms the climate of the Earth (Figure 2.27). About 95% of long-wavelength reradiated heat is trapped and held within Earth's atmosphere, where it raises Earth's average surface temperature to about 16°C. Without the greenhouse effect, the Earth would be uninhabitable with an average surface temperature of −16°C. The greenhouse effect on Earth will be examined twice: (1) the intense greenhouse in Earth's early history and (2) the human-increased greenhouse of the 20th and 21st centuries.

Water and Heat

Water has a remarkable ability to absorb heat (see In Greater Depth box: Water—The Most Peculiar Substance on Earth in Chapter 2). It has the highest heat capacity of all solids and liquids (Table 10.1), except liquid ammonia (NH_3). The amount of heat required to raise the temperature of water, its **specific heat**, is high. Sand and rock have smaller specific heats and heat capacities than water. Even though land heats to higher temperatures, it does so only to shallow depths because sand and rock are opaque to the Sun's rays; the resultant heat held is small compared to that absorbed by the same volume of water. Not only can water absorb more heat per unit volume, but also solar radiation penetrates to depths of several hundred metres, where it is absorbed and carried away by moving water masses.

As an everyday illustration of the differences in heat capacity and transfer, remember how unbearably hot beach sand can be on your bare feet at the same time that ocean or lake water is much cooler. At night, the situation reverses as the sand, with its low heat capacity, releases its heat and becomes uncomfortably cool to bare feet, while the water temperature has changed little.

Water vapour in the atmosphere ranges from near 0 to 4% by volume, but its importance in determining weather is great. The amount of water vapour in the air is measured as **humidity**. Relative humidity is the ratio of absolute humidity to saturation humidity. Saturation humidity is the maximum amount of water an air mass can hold, and it increases with increasing temperature. If the temperature of an air mass is lowered without changing its absolute humidity, it will reach a relative humidity of 100% simply because at each lower temperature, a lower saturation humidity will apply. When relative humidity reaches 100%, then excess water vapour condenses and forms liquid water; this temperature is the **dew-point temperature** of the air mass.

Temperature and humidity combine to make us feel a perceived temperature. As humidity increases, we perceive that temperature is rising. In 1965, Canadian meteorologists devised an index, a *humidex*, which combines temperature and relative humidity into a perceived temperature that more accurately describes what we feel on hot, humid days (Figure 10.4).

Water absorbs, stores, and releases tremendous amounts of solar energy (see Chapter 2) when it changes phases between solid, liquid, and gas (Figure 10.5). Ice melts to water when supplied with about 334,000 joules of heat per kilogram; this energy is stored as latent heat in the water. Water evaporates to water vapour when it absorbs about 2,260,000 joules per kilogram of water; this energy is stored in water vapour as the latent heat of vaporization. Ice can change to vapour directly without passing through a liquid state, but it requires both the 334,000 J/kg for melting and the 2,260,000 J/kg for evaporation. The process of changing directly from solid to gas is called **sublimation**. You probably have seen sublimation when dry ice (frozen CO_2) changes to vapour.

The latent heat carried in water vapour is released upon condensation to liquid water. The **latent heat of condensation** gives up the same number of joules as were absorbed during evaporation. When water freezes to ice, it releases stored energy as the latent heat of fusion; it gives up the same number of joules as were absorbed during melting. Water vapour can change directly to ice in deposition; it gives up both the latent heats of melting and evaporation. You may have seen deposition of water vapour to ice in the build-up of "frost" in the freezer compartment of some refrigerators.

Water and water vapour are important for absorbing solar radiation, transporting heat about our planet, and releasing that heat. All of this heat transport helps prevent extreme ranges in temperature on Earth.

Table 10.1

Thermal Properties of Selected Materials

	Density kg/m³ ×	Specific Heat J/kg/K =	Heat Capacity J/m³/K
Air	1.3	1,004.8	1,306
Quartz sand	1,650	795.5	1,312,575
Granite	2,700	795.5	2,147,850
Water	1,000	4,186.8	4,186,800

Relative Humidity (%)

Air Temperature (°C)	100	95	90	85	80	75	70	65	60	55	50	45	40	35	30	25	20
21	29	29	28	27	27	26	26	24	24	23	23	22					
22	31	29	29	28	28	27	26	26	24	24	23	23					
23	33	32	32	31	30	29	28	27	27	26	25	24	23				
24	35	34	33	33	32	31	30	29	28	28	27	26	26	25			
25	37	36	35	34	33	33	32	31	30	29	28	27	27	26			
26	39	38	37	36	35	34	33	32	31	31	29	28	28	27			
27	41	40	39	38	37	36	35	34	33	32	31	30	29	28	28		
28	43	42	41	41	39	38	37	36	35	34	33	32	31	29	28		
29	46	45	44	43	42	41	39	38	37	36	34	33	32	31	30		
30	48	47	46	44	43	42	41	40	38	37	36	35	34	33	31	31	
31	50	49	48	46	45	44	43	41	40	39	38	36	35	34	33	31	
32	52	51	50	49	47	46	45	43	42	41	39	38	37	36	34	33	
33	55	54	52	51	50	48	47	46	44	43	42	40	38	37	36	34	
34	58	57	55	53	52	51	49	48	47	45	43	42	41	39	37	36	
35		58	57	56	54	52	51	49	48	47	45	43	42	41	38	37	
36			58	57	56	54	53	51	50	48	47	45	43	42	40	38	
37				58	57	55	53	51	50	49	47	45	43	42	40		
38							57	56	54	52	51	49	47	46	43	42	40
39									56	54	53	51	49	47	45	43	41
40										57	54	52	51	49	47	44	43
41											56	54	52	50	48	46	44
42												56	54	52	50	48	46
43													56	54	51	49	47

Humidex (°C)	Degree of comfort
20–29	No discomfort
30–39	Some discomfort
40–45	Great discomfort; avoid exertion
46 and over	Dangerous; probable heat stroke

Figure 10.4
A humidex, a table combining temperature and relative humidity to yield the temperatures perceived by humans.
Source: © Meteorological Service of Canada.

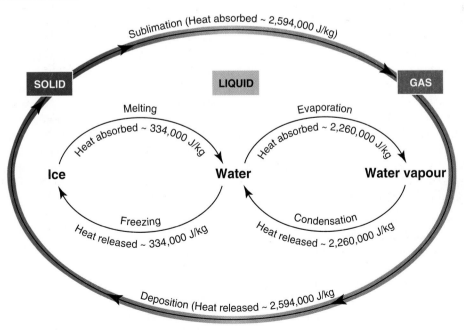

Figure 10.5
Water changing state from solid to liquid to gas absorbs heat. Water changing state from gas to liquid to solid releases heat.

Vertical Movement of Air

Air is easily compressed. Gravity pulls on the atmosphere, causing each layer of air to press down ever more heavily on the air layer below it. Nearing the Earth's surface, air is increasingly compressed and becomes progressively denser. About 75% of the atmosphere lies within its bottom 10 km.

Just as with water and magma, air wants to flow from higher toward lower pressure, from the higher pressures at the Earth's surface up through the progressively lower pressures high in the atmosphere. This tendency to flow upward from high to low pressure must overcome the opposing pull of gravity.

How can air near the surface overcome the pull of gravity and rise? The most common way is by adding heat to the air. As heated air rises, it encounters progressively lower pressures, causing the air to expand and become less dense. The process of expanding causes cooling, an **adiabatic process** in which temperature changes without loss of heat. When cool air from aloft sinks, it compresses and becomes denser but warmer. This is an adiabatic process in which temperature changes without gaining heat. The amount of heat in the sinking air mass does not change, but because it compresses into a smaller volume, the temperature rises.

Adiabatic temperature changes produce cooling when air rises and expands in volume, and warming when air descends and compresses into a smaller volume.

As rising air moves upward through ever-decreasing pressure, it expands and cools adiabatically about 10°C per km of rise. As the air cools, it has less ability to hold water vapour; thus, its relative humidity increases. When the rising air reaches 100% humidity, excess water vapour will condense and form clouds. The altitude where 100% humidity is reached is known as the **lifting condensation level**. When water vapour condenses, it releases the latent heat it absorbed when evaporated. The released latent heat slows the rate of upward cooling to about 5°C per km of rise.

DIFFERENTIAL HEATING OF LAND AND WATER

Land heats up quickly, but the low heat capacity of rock causes the land to lose heat readily and cool down quickly. Water warms up more slowly, but its high heat capacity allows it to retain heat and cool slowly.

As temperatures drop in the winter, the land cools quickly but the ocean retains its warmth, causing warm, moist air to rise (Figure 10.6a). Cool air over the land sinks toward the surface, forming a region of high-pressure air over the land. This cold, dry air flows out over the ocean.

As temperature rises in the summer, the land heats up quickly while the ocean warms up much more slowly. Hot, dry air forms over the land and rises, producing low-pressure air over the land (Figure 10.6b). Cooler moist air above the ocean is drawn in to replace the warm air rising above the low-pressure zone on land. The moist air from above the oceans warms as it moves over the hot land, and then it rises and reaches colder levels of the atmosphere, where its water vapour condenses and falls as rain. This process creates the summer **monsoon** rains that are especially important in India and Bangladesh and to a much smaller degree in southwestern North America. The monsoonal air helps bring hurricanes ashore (see Chapter 12).

The atmosphere responds readily to the Sun's radiation; warm air rises and cool air sinks. But the vertical movement of air is small compared to its horizontal motion (i.e., wind). Air masses flow horizontally from high pressure toward low pressure, seeking an equilibrium condition.

Layering of the Lower Atmosphere

The atmosphere of the Earth is separated into layers of different density. Most of the moisture and "weather" occurs in the lowest layer of the atmosphere, the **troposphere** (Figure 10.7). The troposphere ranges from about 8 km thick at the poles to 18 km at the equator. The troposphere is warmer at its base and colder above, thus creating a basic instability as lower-level warm air rises and upper-level cold and dense air sinks. The density contrasts set off a constant mixing of tropospheric air that is part of our changing weather pattern.

The top of the troposphere, the **tropopause**, is a significant boundary where the cooling-upward trend reverses and the air begins to warm upward through the **stratosphere** (Figure 10.7). The temperature inversion acts as a barrier or lid that confines weather to the troposphere below. The stratosphere, which draws its name from its stratified condition where warmer air sits on top of cooler air, is a stable configuration. The stratosphere is home to cold, dry, and ever sunny conditions.

General Circulation of the Atmosphere

Circulation of Earth's atmosphere is necessary because solar heat is received in different amounts at different latitudes (Figure 10.2). The general circulation of Earth's

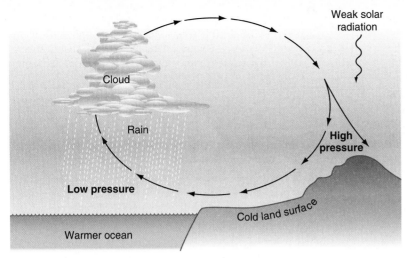

(a) Winter

Figure 10.6

(a) Winter. Rapid cooling of the land causes cool air that flows offshore to replace the air rising above the warmer ocean; this airflow produces rain on the ocean. (b) Summer. Rapid heating of the land causes warm air that rises and is replaced by moist air drawn in from above the cooler ocean; this airflow brings rain to the land.

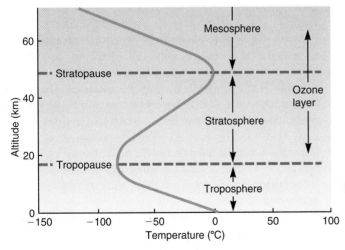

(b) Summer

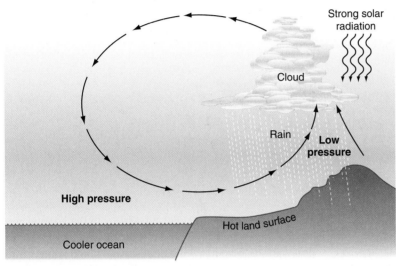

Figure 10.7

Cross-section through Earth's lower atmosphere. Ozone captures solar energy. The temperature inversion at the tropopause acts as a lid holding moisture and "weather" in the troposphere.

atmosphere transports heat from the low latitudes around the equator to the high latitudes of the poles. In simplest form, this redistribution of energy could be accomplished by one large convection cell flowing between the equator and pole in each hemisphere. Heated equatorial air would rise and flow toward the poles at upper levels, becoming progressively cooler until reaching the poles, where it would sink and flow as cold air over the surface, becoming progressively warmer on its return to the equator. But the rapid rotation of the Earth complicates the process; it reduces the size of the convection cells and increases their number to three in each hemisphere: Hadley, Ferrel, and polar cells (Figures 10.8 and 10.9).

LOW LATITUDES

The intense sunshine received in the equatorial belt powers huge air circulation patterns known as **Hadley cells** (Figure 10.9). Warm, moist equatorial air rises in giant columns to high altitudes, where it cools and drops its

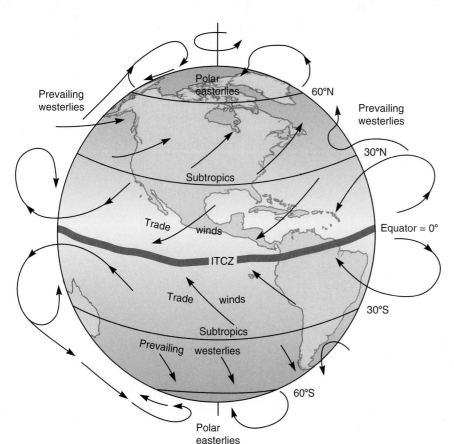

Figure 10.8
General circulation of the atmosphere. Warm air rises at the equator at the intertropical convergence zone (ITCZ) and sinks in the subtropics. Cold air at the poles sinks and flows toward the equator. The middle latitudes are transfer zones where warm air moves poleward and cold air flows equatorward.

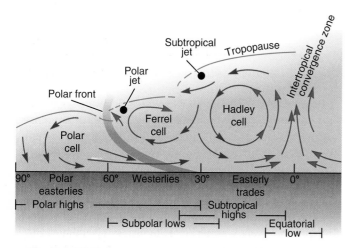

Figure 10.9
Cross-section of the average air circulation between the equator and a pole.

adiabatically as it descends and returns to the surface as a warm and dry air mass. Some of the descending air flows poleward as westerly winds (westerlies), and some flows equatorward as the trade winds (Figure 10.8).

The warm air descending in the Subtropical High Pressure Zone has low moisture content; thus, precipitation is scarce. The warm, dry winds of the subtropical belts are responsible for many of the world's great deserts, such as the Sahara and Kalahari of Africa, the Sonora of North America, and the Great Australian Desert.

The Hadley cell circulation is completed where the trade winds from the northern and southern hemispheres meet in the tropics at the **intertropical convergence zone** (ITCZ) (Figure 10.8). Water vapour picked up by the trade winds as they flow over land and sea is carried upward at the ITCZ in the rising limb of a Hadley cell, where the water vapour condenses and contributes to the heavy rainfalls.

Solar radiation is the energy source that powers Hadley cell circulation. Because the amount of solar energy received in the northern and southern hemispheres varies with the seasons, the location of the ITCZ moves also; it shifts northward during the northern hemisphere summer (June to September) and southward during the southern hemisphere summer (December to March).

condensed moisture as abundant rain on the tropics. The rising limb of a Hadley cell carries an enormous amount of heat from low to high altitudes.

After dropping rain on the tropics, the upper-elevation air is then cooler and drier; it spreads both north and south. Around 30°N and S latitudes, the now-denser air sinks at the Subtropical High Pressure Zone, warming

MIDDLE AND HIGH LATITUDES

The Hadley cell air that sinks to the Earth's surface in the subtropics in both hemispheres creates a global band of high-pressure air around 30° N and S latitude (Figure 10.9). Air flows away from the subtropical high-pressure zones in all directions.

Cold air flows over the land from both poles. Around 60°N and S latitudes, these cold air masses collide with the westerly wind masses of the mid-latitudes at the *polar front* (Figure 10.9). The rising air around 60°N and S latitudes creates the subpolar low-pressure zone.

The Hadley, Ferrel, and polar air-circulation cells create major convergent zones at the ITCZ and the polar front. At the ITCZ in the equatorial belt, two similar air masses meet as the trade winds converge and rise upward in a great vertical wall of cooling air that drops massive amounts of rain. At the polar front around 60° latitude, two dissimilar air masses converge, although there is no great vertical wall of rising air analogous to that at the ITCZ. Instead, the cold and dense polar air collides with and flows under the warmer air of the mid-latitudes. This collision zone forms a complex pattern of sloping fronts between regional air masses.

This global wind pattern is modified by the interference of continental masses, including mountain ranges; by seasonal warming and cooling affecting both the northern and southern Hemispheres; and by the Coriolis effect (see In Greater Depth box: Coriolis Effect). The equatorial region Hadley cells and the polar cells operate as described. However, the mid-latitudes are a much more turbulent zone where competing polar and tropical air masses transfer their energies back and forth as the seasons and location of the polar jet stream vary, commonly creating severe weather conditions.

Air Masses

The air masses that move across North America come mainly from several large source areas (Figure 10.10). The polar air masses are cool to cold, while the tropical air bodies are warm to hot. Air masses that gather over land are dry, whereas those that form over water are moist. The dominant direction of air-body movement is from west to east under the influence of the Earth's rotation. Thus, air masses that build over the northern Pacific Ocean have a much greater chance of affecting North America than those that form over the North Atlantic Ocean.

Fronts

The boundaries between different air masses are called **fronts**. (The term *front* came out of World War I, from the battlefronts where armies clashed.) Many of the clouds and much precipitation are associated with fronts. A front is a sloping surface separating air masses that differ in temperature and moisture content (Figure 10.11).

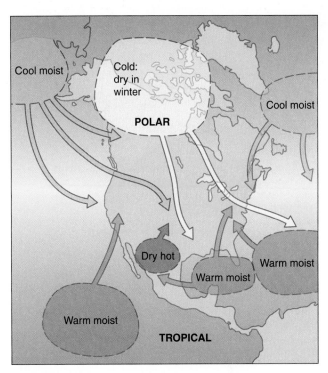

Figure 10.10

Map showing areas where large air masses acquire their temperature and moisture characteristics before moving about North America.

Source: Adapted from J. Eagleman, *Severe and Unusual Weather,* 1983; Van Nostrand Reinhold, New York.

Weather fronts can sometimes trigger severe weather and violent storms. The largest frontal system in the northern hemisphere separates cold polar air from warm tropical air along the polar front (Figure 10.9).

The advance of a cold front acts like a wedge, lifting warm air up to higher altitudes (Figure 10.11a). When rising warm air is moist and unstable, it often forms tall clouds that may grow into thunderstorms. Figure 10.12 shows the clouds and rain along a cold front.

You can create and observe your own weather front at home. Open the door to the freezer compartment of your refrigerator and watch the cold air mass flow out. The cold air body moves into the warmer, moister air of the room, causing clouds and small-scale precipitation.

A warm front leads the advance of a warm air mass in a flatter wedge. The lighter-weight warm air flows up and over a cooler air mass along a gentle slope. The warm air cools as it rises along the broad and gentle front, commonly producing widespread clouds and drizzle (Figures 10.11b and c).

Jet Streams

Jet streams are relatively narrow bands of high-velocity winds that flow from west to east at high altitudes. There are two main jet streams in the northern

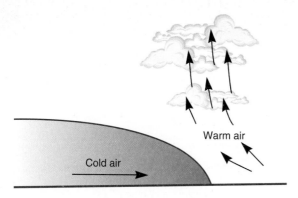

(a) Cold front

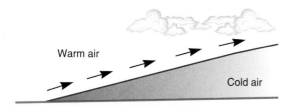

(b) Warm front

(c)

Figure 10.11
Schematic cross-sections of fronts and air masses. (a) A cold front wedges under warm air, forcing it upward. (b) A warm front runs up and on top of a cold air mass. (c) A warm front moving north (to the right) runs up a shallow, sloping cold air mass, producing clouds over the north shore of Lake Erie, Ontario.
Photo: © John S. Shelton.

Figure 10.12
A cold front moving near Drumheller, Alberta, causes thunderstorm clouds and heavy rain showers over this beautiful canola field.
Photo: © Rolf Hicker Photography.

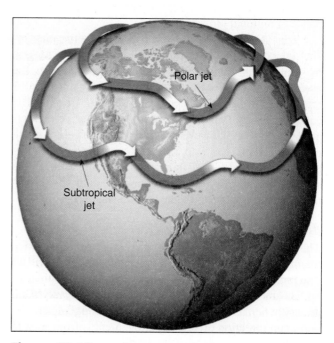

Figure 10.13
The subtropical and polar jet streams flow in a meandering path from west to east. They exist where the expanded volume of warm air slopes down toward the compressed volume of cold air.

and southern hemispheres, a polar jet and a subtropical jet (Figure 10.13). They occur high in the atmosphere where the major air circulation systems meet (Figure 10.9).

The subtropical jet stream runs north of the tropics, at about 25° latitude and 13 km above the ground (Figure 10.15). The tropical atmosphere absorbs heat; the air expands, becomes less dense, and rises to begin

circulating in a Hadley cell (Figure 10.9). Travelling up through a column of warm air, there is a slower rate of pressure decrease than moving upward through a column of cold air. The result aloft is that higher-pressure

In Greater Depth

Coriolis Effect

Circulation of the atmosphere and oceans is inevitable because solar heat is received unevenly around the Earth. The Earth rotates rapidly and sets cold and warm air and ocean masses into motions that are altered by topography. The velocity of rotation on Earth's surface varies by latitude from 465 km/s at the equator to 0 km/s at the poles (Figure 10.14). Because there are different velocities at different latitudes, bodies moving across latitudes will follow curved paths. This is the **Coriolis effect,** named for French mathematician Gaspar Coriolis, who described it in 1835.

In the northern hemisphere, all moving masses will sidle off to their right-hand side when viewed down the direction of movement; in the southern hemisphere, moving bodies will veer toward the left (Figure 10.14). The magnitude of the Coriolis effect increases with horizontal speed of the moving body and with latitude; it is zero at the equator. The Coriolis effect is important in determining the paths of ocean currents, large wind systems, and hurricanes; possibly important for a large thunderstorm; probably not important for individual tornadoes; and negligible for water draining down kitchen sinks or toilets.

The Coriolis effect causes winds to veer into arcuate paths. For example, watch the course hurricanes travel and see how prominently their paths curve (Figures 12.10, 12.15, and 12.22).

The Merry-Go-Round Analogy

A good way to visualize the Coriolis effect is to go with friends to a local playground that has a merry-go-round, a large circular wheel that rotates horizontally around a pole. When the merry-go-round is spinning counter-clockwise, visualize being above it and looking down for an analogy of the northern hemisphere. As the merry-go-round whirls rapidly, which person is moving faster, the one in the centre (North Pole) or the one on the outside (equator)? The outside (equator) rotates much faster (compare to Figure 10.14). If the person riding in the centre tosses a ball directly at the rider on the outer rim, will the ball reach the targeted person? Probably not; the person will have rotated

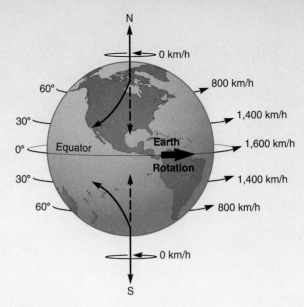

Figure 10.14 The Coriolis effect describes how air and ocean masses tend to follow curving paths because of the rotating Earth. Looking down the direction of movement (dashed lines), paths veer toward the right (solid line) in the northern hemisphere and toward the left (solid line) in the southern hemisphere.

away. If you were standing on the ground and watching only the flight of the ball, it obviously moves in a straight line. But if you change your frame of reference and plot the path of the ball on top of the moving merry-go-round, the path appears to curve to the right.

Now spin the merry-go-round in the opposite direction, in a clockwise pattern analogous to the southern hemisphere viewed from above the South Pole. All other factors are the same, but the ball tossed from the centre to the outside now appears to curve to the left (compare to Figure 10.14).

tropical air flows toward the lower-pressure polar air in the upper atmosphere, creating strong poleward flows of air. But these poleward airflows occur on a rapidly spinning Earth, which turns them into belts of high-speed jet-stream winds from the west.

The most powerful and variable jet stream is the polar jet, which races from west to east at average latitudes of about 55° at elevations of about 10 to 14 km. A polar jet is a belt of winds about 1,000 km wide and a few kilometres thick, flowing as fast as 600 km/h in its central "core." A polar jet stream's path is ever-changing, like that of a meandering river. Meanders in the flow can bend so much that, locally, jet-stream flow directions may be to the north, south, or west. As the flow path twists and turns, it may cut off and abandon some flow loops, temporarily achieving a straighter west-to-east flow.

A polar jet stream also changes position with the seasons. In the northern hemisphere, it flows over Canada during the summer, when the warm air volume is greatest; during the winter, it migrates southward over the United States as the volume of northern hemisphere cold air increases to its maximum. During each hemisphere's winter, the atmospheric temperature contrasts between pole and equator are greatest, and each polar jet races its fastest. When polar jets reach speeds around 200 km/h, they have significant effects in moving heat and air masses, as well as in provoking storms.

The polar jet stream results from temperature differences, but its existence in turn influences the movement and behaviour of warm and cold air masses. The polar jet stream flows from west to east, under the influence of the Earth's rotation, in both the northern and southern hemispheres.

Rotating Air Bodies

Rising warm air in the northern hemisphere creates a low-pressure zone that is fed a surface inflow of air that moves counter-clockwise (Figures 10.16 and 10.17). Descending air in a northern hemisphere high-pressure zone flows out over the ground surface as clockwise-blowing winds.

The meanders in the polar jet stream can help create rotating air bodies. In the northern hemisphere, the bends in the west-to-east flow of the polar jet create areas of diverging air east of *troughs* of lower pressure, and regions of converging air west of *ridges* of higher pressure (Figure 10.18). A trough in the jet stream in the northern hemisphere refers to a bend that is concave northward, whereas a ridge is a bend that is convex northward.

The lower-pressure zone at a trough forms the core of a cyclonic circulation, a counter-clockwise flow. In a **cyclone**, the winds include a surface inflow of winds toward the low-pressure core, feeding a large updraft of vertically rising air that cools, forming clouds and rainy weather, as well as producing an upper-level outflow of air.

Figure 10.16
Space shuttle photo in the northern hemisphere of a giant, low-pressure system with air rotating counter-clockwise around it.
Photo: © NASA.

The above process is reversed at a ridge in the jet stream. Here, the upper-level air flow imparts a clockwise rotation about a high-pressure zone; this is an **anticyclone**, moving clockwise. At an anticyclone, air converges in

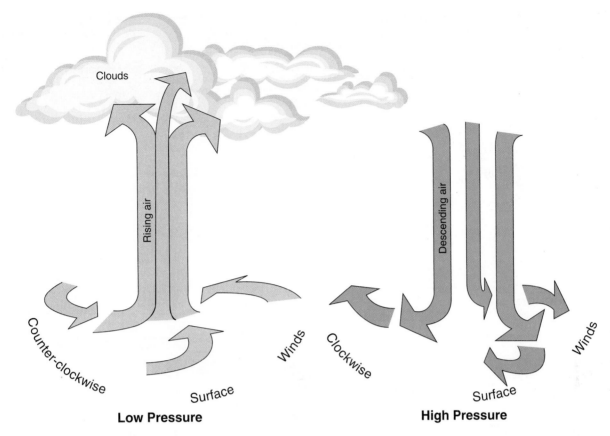

Figure 10.17
Air rises at a low-pressure zone in the northern hemisphere; it is fed by counter-clockwise surface winds. Descending air at a high-pressure zone flows over the ground surface as clockwise winds.

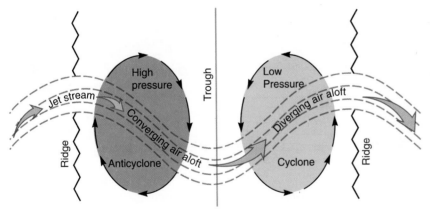

Figure 10.18
Influence of the polar jet stream aloft in creating counter-clockwise cyclonic winds around a low-pressure zone and clockwise anticyclonic winds around a high-pressure zone at the surface.

the upper atmosphere and descends, adding to the high-pressure centre, and then flows outward over the Earth's surface. The descending air warms and usually creates dry and calm conditions on the ground.

OBSERVED CIRCULATION OF THE ATMOSPHERE

Air pressure and wind patterns on Earth show some consistency but also have significant variations by hemisphere

and season (Figure 10.19). Both hemispheres have subtropical high-pressure zones around 30° latitude, where air descends to the surface via Hadley cells (Figure 10.9). Subpolar lows form around 60° latitude, where polar air (polar cell) meets mid-latitude air (Ferrel cell) and rises.

The southern hemisphere is dominated by water with its great capacity for heat storage, so seasonal changes are not as great. The northern hemisphere is dominated by land, with its smaller heat capacity leading to significant

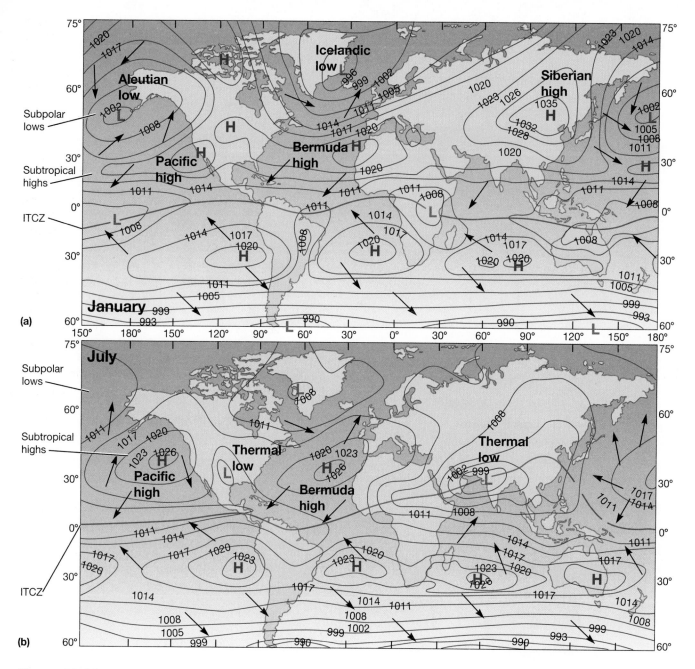

Figure 10.19
Average surface pressure (in hectopascals) and global wind patterns for January (top) and July (bottom).

variations in wind patterns. As the seasons change, the directions of winds and heat flows change.

In January, in the northern hemisphere winter, there is a strong high-pressure air mass of cold air known as the *Siberian high* that influences Eurasian weather; there is an analogous but smaller high-pressure system over wintry North America (Figure 10.19a). Cold air flows off the continents as increasing volumes of air rise in subpolar low-pressure zones known as the *Aleutian* and *Icelandic lows*.

In July, in the northern hemisphere summer, the Eurasian and North American continents have warmed and hot air rises in thermal lows (Figure 10.19b). This aids the strength of the high-pressure systems over the oceans known as the *Pacific* and *Bermuda highs*. The onshore flow of moist air brings monsoonal rains and hurricanes onto the land, especially in South Asia.

The seasonal shifts of the Pacific and Bermuda highs and the Aleutian and Icelandic lows are major determinants of the paths of jet streams and hurricanes.

General Circulation of the Oceans

The surface and near-surface waters of the oceans absorb and store huge quantities of solar energy, especially in the low latitudes. Some of this heat penetrates downward into deeper water in low latitudes when denser, salty warm water undergoes turbulent mixing by tides and winds. Circulation of surface and deep-ocean waters distributes heat throughout the oceans and affects climate around the world.

SURFACE CIRCULATION

The surface circulation of water through the ocean basins is mostly driven by winds (Figure 10.20). Blowing winds drag on the sea surface and push against swells to move water. When the top layer of water moves, it drags on the underlying water layer, causing it to move, and so forth; this process moves water down to a depth of about 100 m. The flow directions of surface water are modified by the Coriolis effect and by deflection off continents.

Surface circulation carries heat from the warm low-latitude waters toward the poles. For example, look at the North Atlantic Ocean in Figure 10.20. Warm surface water is blown westward from Africa into the Caribbean Sea and Gulf of Mexico, where its westward path is blocked by land, forcing the seawater to escape northward along the eastern side of North America and over to Europe. The heat in this seawater adds significant warmth to the winter climate of Atlantic Canada and northwestern Europe.

DEEP-OCEAN CIRCULATION

The oceans are layered bodies of water with less-dense water layers floating on top of progressively denser water layers. The density of water is increased by (1) lowering its temperature or (2) increasing its content of dissolved salts. The deep-ocean waters flow in an overturning circulation called **thermohaline flow** (Figure 2.29). The word *thermohaline* uses *thermo* for heat and *haline* from halite, the name for rock salt. Seawater density is increased (1) at high latitudes, where water temperature is lowered, (2) in the Arctic and Antarctic, where remaining seawater is made saltier by rejected salts excluded from seawater frozen to sea ice, and (3) in warm climates, where evaporation removes fresh water, leaving the remaining

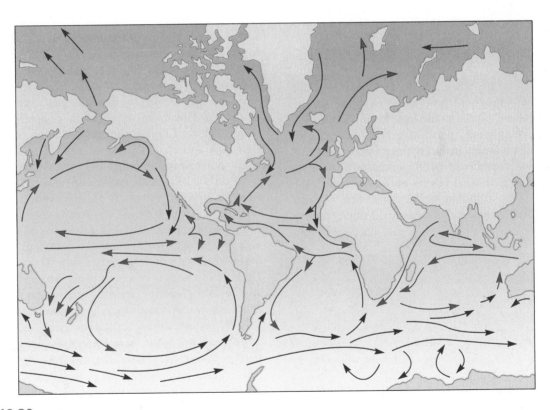

Figure 10.20
Circulation of the wind-blown surface waters of the oceans. Notice how the equatorial waters are deflected both northward and southward by the continents, thus sending warmer waters toward the poles. Also note that the only latitude not blocked by continents (60°S) has a latitudinal flow; this is the Southern Ocean and it encircles Antarctica. Red arrows indicate warm water; blue arrows are cold water.

seawater even saltier. Most of the deepest and densest ocean water today forms in the high-latitude North Atlantic Ocean and in the Southern Ocean.

We now turn to Earth's long-term climate, beginning with the oldest and longest-lasting climates.

The Greenhouse Effect—A Tale of Three Planets

The climatic regime of the early Earth, the third planet from the Sun, can be appreciated by looking at the atmospheric compositions of the inner planets (Table 10.2). The first atmospheres of Venus, Earth and Mars, which existed shortly after they formed some 4.6 billion years ago, were primarily composed of H_2 and He. These relatively light gases were lost to space early on due to the gravitational pull of these worlds not being strong enough. These gases are still important components of gas giants like Jupiter and Saturn, which have very strong gravitational fields.

As these early atmospheres bled off to space, new atmospheres formed on all three planets to replace them. The interiors of Venus, Earth and Mars became heated due to radioactivity resulting in numerous volcanoes and fumaroles, which released enormous quantities of gases, most notably H_2O vapour and CO_2 into the atmosphere.

During this time, when no life was present on the Earth and the atmosphere was full of CO_2, the surface temperature of our planet would have been about 290°C (Table 10.2). Why would Earth have been so hot? This global warming was due in part to the greenhouse effect. A glass-walled greenhouse is often used to provide an incorrect analogy of what occurs on a planetary scale. The glass admits incoming visible light, that is, solar radiation with short wavelengths (about 0.5 micrometres).

The Sun's short-wave radiation warms objects inside the greenhouse. When the light strikes something in the greenhouse the object heats up and infrared radiation of longer wavelengths (about 10 micrometres) is given off. Since glass is opaque to the long-wavelength radiation, heat begins to build up by suppressing convection and turbulent mixing within an enclosed space. This can be demonstrated by opening a small window near the roof of a greenhouse, which results in an almost immediate sharp drop in temperature. In contrast, the Earth is surrounded by a dynamic and highly interactive atmosphere where clouds and the concentration of greenhouse gases such as H_2O vapour and CO_2 strongly influence climate by reducing radiation loss, not convection.

Venus is the second planet from the Sun and thus receives intense solar radiation. Much of that solar energy is trapped by its dense, CO_2–rich atmosphere, little changed in 4 billion years, which helps create surface temperatures of about 477°C. Life on Venus is difficult to visualize when temperatures are so high that surface rocks glow red like those in a campfire ring.

Why did the Earth and Venus end up being so different? The major difference in the evolution of these planets was the presence of major oceans on Earth, which never developed on Venus due to its closer proximity to the Sun. On Earth, outgassed H_2O vapour precipitated to form oceans, where atmospheric CO_2 dissolved rapidly to form weak carbonic acid (H_2CO_3). The H_2CO_3 reacted with the rocky ocean floor to form limestone (Table 10.3). (The process by which carbon [C] is precipitated from seawater is described by the equations in the In Greater Depth box: How to Create a Cave in Chapter 9.) A second major sink for CO_2 developed after organisms with hard parts first appeared 543 million years ago. Most of these shelly organisms began forming their skeletons from calcium carbonate ($CaCO_3$) and as this skeletal debris began to accumulate on the ocean floor it eventually turned to limestone. About 80% of CO_2 is now chemically tied up in such biologically produced limestone. Most of Earth's vast amount of CO_2 thus became sequestered in the oceans and seabed, and did not accumulate in the atmosphere. On Venus there was no ocean to absorb atmospheric CO_2 so it just kept building up in the atmosphere. As the Earth is a water world, the runaway greenhouse conditions that exist on Venus could never develop here.

Mars is the fourth planet from the Sun. In sharp contrast to Venus, its greater distance from the Sun causes it to receive much less solar energy. Mars is drier than the Sahara and colder than Antarctica with less than 1% of Earth's atmospheric pressure. Approximately 95% of its atmosphere is CO_2, which helps hold the heat it does receive and maximizes its average surface temperature to a still very cold −53°C. It is so cold that during the Martian winter more than 25% of the atmosphere itself precipitates out to form a frost on the surface. Mars is much

Table 10.2

Atmospheres of the Inner Planets

	Venus	Early Earth	Mars	Earth Today
CO_2	96.5%	98%	95.3%	0.038%
N_2	3.4%	1.9%	2.7%	78%
O_2	trace	trace	0.13%	21%
Ar	0.01%	0.1%	1.6%	0.93%
Temperature (°C)	477	290	−53	16
Pressure (kilopascals)	9,200	6,000	0.6	100

smaller than Earth and considerably less tectonically active. Over time, because of a lower gravity, it has lost 70–90% of its available water to space. CO_2 has become less depleted during that interval due to its higher molecular weight. With any oceans that may have existed on Mars gone eons ago, so went any opportunity to sequester CO_2 as limestone. This explains the high concentration of CO_2 in the Martian atmosphere.

Today, greenhouse gases, including the most abundant greenhouse gas by far, water vapour, make up only 0.25% of the Earth's atmosphere, but they help create the weakened greenhouse effect that keeps Earth's average temperature at 16°C; this is 34°C higher than it would be if water vapour, CO_2, and other greenhouse gases were absent. If these gases were not present in the atmosphere, the average temperature at the Earth's surface would be about −18°C, and life would be very different from what we know.

Earth's atmosphere has changed considerably over time. Life processes have played an influential role in the level of various atmospheric gases present. For example, plants remove CO_2 from the atmosphere via photosynthesis and respire O_2 as a by-product, which has built up over time in the atmosphere. Factors such as celestial-solar variation, plate tectonics, ocean circulation, mountain building and glaciations have also been important controls over climate and the makeup of the atmosphere, which explains why the proportion of atmospheric gases, including greenhouse gases like water vapour and CO_2, has varied so considerably throughout the last half billion years (Figure 10.21).

The Earth has always been influenced by a greenhouse effect, and life has always been in dynamic equilibrium with it. Since the late 1940s humans have been changing the CO_2 concentration in the atmosphere by burning tremendous volumes of plants, both living (trees and shrubs) and dead (coal, oil, and natural gas). Combining the C in plants with O_2 via fire returns large amounts of CO_2 to the atmosphere (Figure 10.22). About 6 gigatonnes (1 gigatonne equals 10^9 tonnes) are returned to the atmosphere each year by burning fossil fuels. The human contribution is small compared to the natural fluxes between the atmosphere and ocean, and between the atmosphere and continents, each of which exchanges in excess of 300 gigatonnes annually. Although human changes in CO_2 and other gases are relatively small, they may be enough to trigger climate shifts that cause major problems. We will examine the increasing greenhouse effect and the role of humans in Chapter 11.

Climate History of the Earth: Timescale in Millions of Years

Many sedimentary rocks contain information about the climate at the time they formed. Warm climates are indicated by (1) fossil reefs and most limestones; (2) aluminum ores, which form only in tropical soils; and

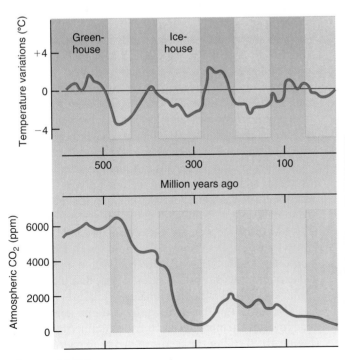

Figure 10.21
Five hundred million years of climate change and atmospheric CO_2 concentrations. The Earth's climate alternates between greenhouse and icehouse conditions that are controlled by a variety of factors.
Source: Veizer, 2005. Geoscience Canada, v. 13, p. 13–28.

Table 10.3	
Carbon on Earth (gigatonnes)	
Atmosphere	720
Oceans	
Total organic matter	1,000
Seawater layers	
Surface water	670
Deep water	36,730
Continents	
Living biological mass	~800
Dead biological mass	1,200
Fossil fuels (oil, coal, gas)	4,130
Organic matter in mudstone	15,000,000
Limestone	>60,000,000

Source: P. Falkowski and others, The Global Carbon Cycle. *Science*, 290 (2000): 291–96.

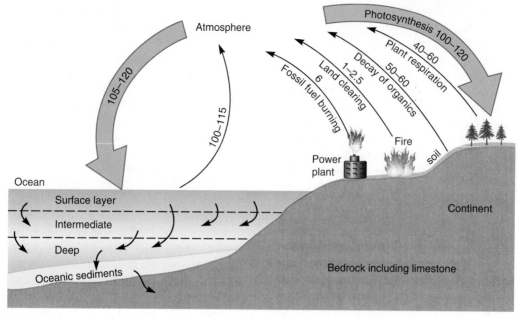

Figure 10.22

Annual cycle of carbon exchange measured in gigatonnes. Plants take in CO_2 from the atmosphere during photosynthesis. CO_2 is returned during plant respiration, during decay after death, and by burning of forests and fossil fuels. Near equilibrium exists between CO_2 in ocean surface water and the atmosphere. The ocean "pumps" some CO_2 into deep-water storage. Organisms remove dissolved CO_2 to build shells, which end up in sediments.

(3) beds of salts that crystallize when water bodies evaporate under high-temperature, arid climates.

Cold climates may be marked by the powerful erosion of glaciers that sculpt the landscape, leaving polished and grooved surfaces beneath them (Figure 10.23) and dumping massive piles of debris. The distribution of fossil

Figure 10.23

Glacial grooves carved in rock by a former glacier. This rock is exposed near Yellowknife, Northwest Territories.

Source: Tyhee Development Corp.

organisms tells much about ancient climates. For example, when fossil shells of organisms that live only in polar seas also are found in abundance in rocks formed in mid-latitudes, it suggests that the world climate must have been colder at that time.

Rocks and fossils tell of extreme variations and changes in world temperature and precipitation throughout geological time. Warm and cold intervals come and go, but they do not necessarily correlate with wet and dry periods, nor is there a pattern to the arrivals and departures of various climates.

Earth's climate depends on the balance between incoming and outgoing heat. At any given time, the atmosphere-ocean-continent system may be gaining or losing in its overall heat budget. Global heat supply has a profound effect on water, which exists on Earth's surface at the transition between its three phases of ice (solid), liquid, and vapour (gas). Water has such a tremendous capacity to either absorb or release heat that it acts as a powerful control on global climate.

The surface of the Earth is divided into temperature zones of frigid, temperate, and torrid as defined by latitude (Figure 10.24). Climate seems to swing like an irregular pendulum from ages where cold temperatures of the frigid zone dominate the Earth to other times when warmth covers most of the world. During a frigid period, an Ice Age, the colder climates of the high latitudes expand in area while the area of warmer climate in the low latitudes

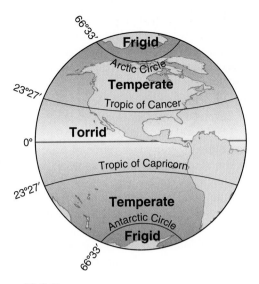

Figure 10.24
Five great divisions of the Earth's surface today with respect to temperature and latitude.

shrinks but does not disappear. Conversely, in an era of warmth, a Torrid Age, the globe is marked by expansion of the subtropical climatic zones, while the cold-climate belts shrink back toward the poles. Let's review examples of extreme climates.

LATE PALEOZOIC ICE AGE

One of the major Ice Ages in Earth history began around 360 million years ago and lasted until 260 million years ago. For a glacial interval to last so long, broad-scale and long-lasting conditions are required. The major factors appear to be changes in the shapes, sizes, and orientations of the continents and oceans.

1. An initial, absolute requirement for an Ice Age is having one or more large continental masses near the poles. A polar landmass is necessary to collect the snowfall that allows the build-up of immense, 3 km thick ice sheets that bury continents. Massive glaciers cannot be built on top of ocean water. In Late Paleozoic time, the continents were largely united as the single landmass Pangaea. The southern portion of the Pangaea super-continent is Gondwanaland; it moved across the south-polar region and was progressively covered by major ice sheets. South America–Africa probably first supported the great ice sheet, then Antarctica, and finally Australia (Figure 10.25).

2. Another important consideration is ocean-water circulation. No matter how much the Sun's brightness varies, equatorial waters will receive more solar energy than polar waters. Without continents present to block ocean-water flow, the warm equatorial waters simply circulate latitudinally (east–west) due to the spin of the Earth.

What does warm water have to do with building massive ice sheets? In the hydrologic cycle, water must first be evaporated from the ocean before clouds can form and move over cold landmasses to drop snow. Cold water is extremely difficult to evaporate; warmer water is a great help in promoting evaporation. The geological record shows that Ice Ages are favoured when oceanic circulation is more longitudinal (north–south) than latitudinal (east–west). When the continents are aligned in a north–south direction, they act to block latitudinal circulation of ocean water, thus sending warmer equatorial waters toward the poles, where evaporation can form the clouds that yield the snowfall that builds up on polar landmasses as glaciers. The continents had a north–south alignment

Figure 10.25
Late Paleozoic ice masses on Gondwanaland. Not all of these continental glaciers existed at the same time. Arrows approximate path of drifting Gondwanaland over the fixed position of the South Pole. Numbers mark positions of the South Pole in millions of years ago.

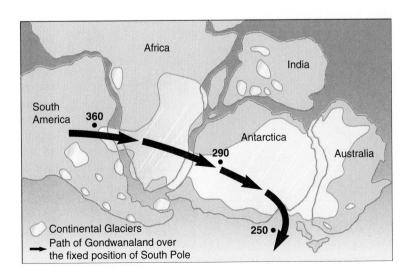

during Late Paleozoic time, as they do today in the current Ice Age (Figure 10.20).

Why did the Late Paleozoic Ice Age end? Possibly because Gondwanaland began to break up and disperse. As the continents moved apart, ocean circulation patterns around the world were changed. Warm waters stayed near the equator, and cold waters encircled the poles, thus drastically reducing the moisture supplied to polar landmasses. Additionally, when continents move away from the poles, no platform exists for the accumulation of snow and the building of glaciers.

LATE PALEOCENE TORRID AGE

The world was warming during Paleocene time (65 to 55 million years ago). There was more heat in the Paleocene oceans and atmosphere than at any time since. The equatorial zones had tropical temperatures and rainfalls higher than, but similar to, what they enjoy today; however, more poleward latitudes were markedly warmer. Sea-surface temperatures in the Southern Ocean around Antarctica were 10° to 15°C warmer than today based on measurements of oxygen isotopes (Figure 10.26).

What was the world like during the Late Paleocene Torrid Age? There was less difference in temperature between tropical and polar waters; an absence of cold, dense, sinking water at the poles; and less difference in temperature between surface and deep-ocean waters. This means that the pull of gravity would have been less effective and ocean circulation would have been more sluggish.

Temperature differences in the atmosphere also would have decreased, resulting in more peaceful weather worldwide. There was an absence of strong seasons, weather was more constant, and rainfall was more evenly distributed throughout the year. Most of the world was wetter and warmer. Continental ice sheets apparently did not exist anywhere. Evergreen (coniferous) and warm deciduous forests covered much of the land. Hot deserts and

arctic tundra covered smaller percentages of the ground. Most of Canada was covered by either tropical or subtropical climates. Along the coastal zones, subtropical conditions existed above the Arctic Circle, as is shown by fossil crocodiles and palm trees.

How did Earth's climate become so dominated by warmth? Several factors apparently combined to turn up the heat. (1) The equatorial zones were largely covered by oceans, allowing more absorption of solar heat. (2) As oceans warmed, areas covered by snow and ice decreased, thus exposing more land. Snow and ice reflect the Sun's rays; land absorbs heat. (3) Enormous outpourings of lavas from the opening North Atlantic Ocean are likely to have released large volumes of gases to the atmosphere, which may have increased global warming via the greenhouse effect. (4) The oceans changed their style of density differentiation. At present, cold Antarctic and Arctic waters are the densest of all waters; they sink and flow along the ocean deeps. By Paleocene time, the polar water became so much warmer that the heaviest waters might have been tropical waters that had become saltier due to evaporation. Warm, oxygen-deficient, salty waters apparently sank, flowing through the ocean deeps and warming up the oceans from surface to bottom. Warm, salty water masses moving along the ocean bottoms would have affected deep-ocean life. Organisms used to living in cold, oxygen-rich bottom waters had the shock of their environment becoming warm and oxygen-poor. At about 55 million years ago, the massive change in deep-sea water temperature reached a peak, causing up to 50% of unicellular deep-sea animal species to become extinct—a natural disaster.

What was responsible for the final increase in warmth? The warming of ocean bottom waters about 8°C caused melting of icy **methane hydrates** on the seafloor, thus releasing methane gas to the atmosphere. What are methane hydrates? Bacteria living on the deep ocean floor release methane (CH_4) as part of their life process, but the overlying water is so cold and the pressure from the weight of the overlying water is so great that the methane is locked up inside linked, near-freezing water molecules to form an icelike deposit (Figure 10.27). Methane hydrate holds more energy than all of Earth's oil, coal, and natural gas combined. It becomes unstable if temperature rises a few degrees above freezing or if pressure is less than that of 500 m of overlying ocean. Today, about 15 trillion tonnes exist on the seafloor; melt it and the world would see a sharp greenhouse increase in temperature. Recent analyses of carbon isotopes in Late Paleocene sedimentary rocks suggest that a major release of methane occurred about 55 million years ago. The methane release occurred during a 10,000-year-long interval. This is a very short time for the atmosphere to receive such a large volume of a powerful greenhouse gas (methane has a 21-times-stronger capacity to trap heat than

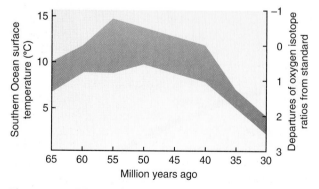

Figure 10.26
Surface temperature of the Southern Ocean over time, based on oxygen isotope measurements.

Oxygen Isotopes and Temperature

Ancient temperatures can be determined from the ratio of stable isotopes of oxygen in the $CaCO_3$ shells (fossils) of single-celled sea life. An atom of oxygen may have either 16, 17, or 18 protons and neutrons in its nucleus. Water evaporated from oceans removes more of the lighter common oxygen (^{16}O) and less of the heavier ^{18}O. This ^{16}O-enriched water is locked up on land as ice and snow, leaving the ocean with ^{18}O-enriched water. Shells constructed from seawater incorporate the $^{18}O/^{16}O$ ratio of the seawater during their lifetime within their $CaCO_3$ shell walls. Thus, measurement of the $^{18}O/^{16}O$ ratio in shells acts as a paleothermometer, which is used to estimate the temperatures of ancient seas. Heavier seawater (^{18}O-enriched) corresponds to cooler climates and lighter seawater (^{18}O-depleted) corresponds to warmer climates.

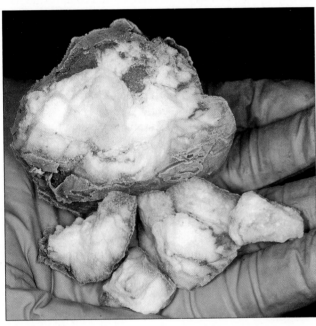

Figure 10.27
Methane hydrate is an icelike deposit of methane trapped within near-freezing water on and under the ocean floor. This sample is from offshore Oregon.

carbon dioxide). During about 250,000 years of excess methane in the atmosphere, the Earth experienced its warmest climate of the last 65 million years. Over time, the methane oxidized to CO_2, which was withdrawn and used by life, and then finally global temperatures began to decrease.

The world changed from a Late Paleozoic icehouse to a Late Paleocene hothouse. But climatic change is the way of the world.

LATE CENOZOIC ICE AGE

Beginning from the temperature peak at 55 million years ago, the Earth began the long-term cooling trend that has carried us into our current Ice Age (Figure 10.26). The sequence of events included

- After 55 million years ago, the torrid climate began cooling as methane was reduced in the atmosphere.

- At 40 million years ago, Antarctica was surrounded by cold water.
- At 34 million years ago, glaciers were widespread in Antarctica.
- At 14 million years ago, a continental ice sheet existed on Antarctica and mountain glaciers were in the northern hemisphere.
- At 5 million years ago, the Antarctic ice sheet had expanded.
- At 2.5 million years ago, continental ice sheets existed in the northern hemisphere.

Why have these changes occurred? There is no single answer. Several variables have interacted in a complex fashion to bring about the climatic cooling of the last 55 million years. The relative importance of these variables is the focus of current study for many scientists around the world. The main factors appear to be related to plate-tectonic changes, that is, the changing positions of continents and oceans. (1) The climatic change is associated with the ongoing breakup of Pangaea into separate continents (Figures 3.18 and 3.19). (2) As continents drifted, seaways opened and closed, thus altering the circulation patterns within the oceans and the distribution of heat about the globe. (3) Continental masses have moved into polar latitudes, with Antarctica centring on and rotating about the South Pole, while North America and Eurasia have moved to encircle the North Pole region. (4) As snow and ice began accumulating on polar landmasses, they reflected more sunlight (increased albedo), and thus heat, back to space. (5) Circulation of the ocean water around the equator was restricted at about 23 million years ago with the closure of the eastern Mediterranean Sea and ended at 3 million years ago when volcanism completed building the Isthmus of Panama as a north-south barrier that blocked east-west ocean-water flow. (6) The area of shallow oceans has been reduced, so less water surface is available to absorb sunlight. (7) The uplifts of the Tibetan Plateau and Himalaya Mountains in Asia and the Colorado Plateau in the western United States have deflected west-to-east atmospheric circulation in the mid-latitudes with resultant airflows to the north and return flows to the south.

The Last Three Million Years

The ice sheet on Antarctica is older and more stable than ice in the Arctic. The cold ocean water circulating around Antarctica (Figure 10.20) helps isolate the continent from major changes. The ice sheets on North America and Eurasia have a greater effect on global climate change because they expand and shrink in more dynamic fashion. Their initial growth as continental glaciers occurred between 3.0 and 2.7 million years ago, and coincided with the formation of the Isthmus of Panama. What is the cause and effect here? Once Central America formed a continuous link between North and South America, it blocked westward-flowing ocean water and began diverting the warm water of the Caribbean Sea and Gulf of Mexico and forcing it to flow northward along the western Atlantic Ocean. The warm water delivered to Canada and Europe caused greater evaporation and formation of water vapour, which resulted in greater snowfall, which accumulated to build glaciers.

Once continental ice sheets existed in the northern hemisphere, they underwent complex cycles of glacial advance and retreat, with 33 cycles recorded. The cycles appear to have been present during earlier Ice Ages and are linked strongly to regular variations in the Earth's orbit and rotation called Milankovitch Cycles as described in detail in the next section.

Glacial Advance and Retreat: Timescale in Thousands of Years

During the last one million years, Earth has hosted about ten Ice Age glacial advances. As an Ice Age begins, ocean surface water evaporates, and some precipitates on the continents as snow. Snow accumulates and burial pressure converts it into ice. Continental glaciers reach thicknesses of about 3 km, deeply burying the land. The immense volumes of ice deform internally under their own weight and slowly flow out over the countryside like mega-bulldozers, scarring and reshaping the land (Figure 10.28). The record of glacially deposited sediments tells of numerous glacial advances and retreats. Starting in the 1970s, our knowledge of the advance-retreat history has been leaping ahead, thanks to cores of sediments taken from the ocean floor and cores of ice removed from the Greenland continental glacier. Each core holds the cumulative record of the annual deposits of sediment or snow (ice) that may be read like the pages of a history book using techniques such as the ratios of oxygen isotopes.

The emerging story for the last one million years is of worldwide glacial advances that last about 100,000 years followed by retreats that take place more rapidly— withdrawing over periods of a few thousand years termed *interglacials* (Figure 10.29). What causes the cycles of

Figure 10.28
Southern limit of the last glacial advance is shown by the dumped glacial debris (irregular, hilly land on left) on the Waterville Plateau, Washington State.

Photo: © John S. Shelton.

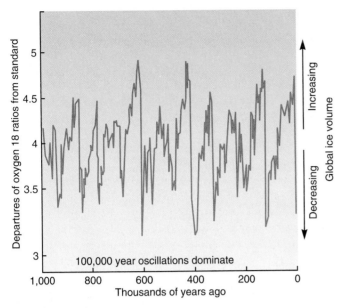

Figure 10.29

World ice-mass volumes of the last one million years based on oxygen isotope measurements.

Source: Data from J. W. C. White, 2004.

Eccentricity:

Changes in shape of orbit: 100,000-year cycle

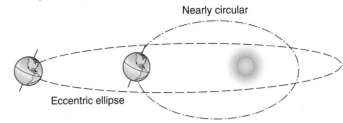

Tilt:

Changes in inclination of Earth's spin axis: 41,000-year cycle

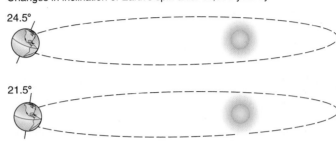

Wobble:

Precession of the equinoxes: 19–23,000-year cycle
Changes in direction of spin axis (same tilt)

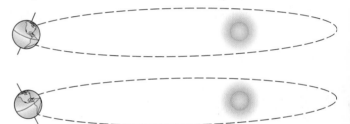

Figure 10.30

Astronomical peculiarities that affect the amount of solar energy received by the Earth. The ellipticity of orbit is exaggerated.

Source: Adapted from *Planet Earth* by V. A. Schmit.

slow buildup and advance of glaciers followed by rapid shrinkage and retreat? The answer lies in the cyclic peculiarities of the Earth's spin and its orbit around the Sun, each of which affects the amount of solar energy received by Earth. Verification of the importance of orbit and rotation cycles came in the 1980s, when computer analyses of data from sediment and ice cores were shown to match the theoretical astronomical framework erected by Serbian astronomer Milutin Milankovitch in the 1920s and 1930s. Milankovitch defined astronomical changes in Earth's orbit, tilt, and wobble, and how they affect the amount of solar radiation received by Earth. An important factor in continental glacier formation is the amount of solar radiation received at high latitudes on Earth each summer. During a warm summer, all the snowfall from the previous winter can melt. But if the winter snowfall of one year can persist until the next winter snowfall begins, then glaciers can start to form. And when glaciers can grow for thousands of years, then continents can become buried by ice.

Milankovitch theory explains that glaciers advance and retreat due to variations in solar radiation received at high latitudes during summer and that these variations are due to changes in Earth's orbit, tilt, and wobble (Figure 10.30).

1. Eccentricity of the Earth's orbit around the Sun. The more elliptical the orbit, the less solar radiation is received and the less snow melts. The shape of the orbit varies every 100,000 years from nearly circular to an eccentric ellipse. The eccentricity time cycle has been similar to the broad-scale, primary length of time for each glacial advance and retreat pairing through the last million years, suggesting that at least for the last million years eccentricity has set the fundamental frequency of the cycles.

2. Tilt of the Earth's axis. The spin axis of the Earth tilts away from the orbital plane in a 41,000-year cycle where tilt varies from 21.5° to 24.5°. Greater tilt angles cause more increased seasonal extremes including more snowmelt. At present, the tilt is about 23.5°. The tilt of the Earth's axis seems to have more strongly influenced glacial advances and retreats prior to one million years ago based on the observed 41,000-year glacial-interglacial cycles during this interval.

3. Precession of the equinoxes where the direction of the tilt changes even though the angle stays the same. The effect is a wobble roughly analogous to what you see in the spin of a toy top. The wobble has a double cycle with periodicities of 23,000 and 19,000 years.

Currently, the wobble places the Earth closest to the Sun during the northern hemisphere winter, giving it milder winters and summers than the southern hemisphere. The changes over time of the eccentricity, tilt, and wobble cycles have been calculated for the past and into the future (Figure 10.31). At present, the eccentricity and tilt each contribute to cooling while the wobble works to warm the climate.

The sediment- and ice-core records seem to show that glacial advances and retreats are synchronous in both the northern and southern hemispheres. How are ice masses around the opposing poles affected simultaneously by astronomical tilts and wobbles? Probably by heat transfer within the world ocean and atmosphere. Any increased heat received in one hemisphere is shared with the other. For example, the Greenland ice-core record shows significant changes. About 14,700 years ago, the Earth began to warm according to changes in the annual ice layers—the ^{18}O, CO_2, and methane contents increased. The increase in ^{18}O means more heat was available to evaporate the heavier oxygen isotope; the increase in CO_2 added to global warming via the greenhouse effect; and the increase in methane is due to an increase in swamps. These measures are symptomatic of the global warming of our current interglacial interval, where ice masses have retreated rapidly.

What was the Earth like around 20,000 years ago when glacial ice masses were at peak extent? The continental

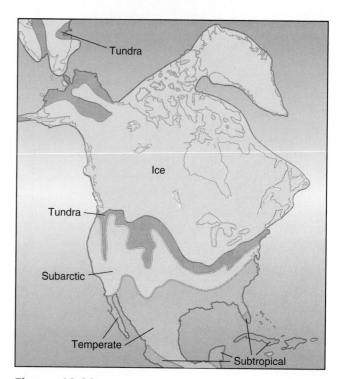

Figure 10.32
Some 20,000 years ago, the extent of glacial ice of the current Ice Age was at its maximum.

ice sheets contained about 70 million km^3 of ice, and the ice masses had spread out to cover about 27% of today's land, including all of Canada and part of the northeastern United States (Figure 10.32). Each ice sheet had its own cell of atmospheric high pressure that displaced mid-latitude storm systems to the south. The displacement of storm systems increased mid-latitude rain, turned the desert basins of the southwestern United States into a series of lakes, and produced much heavier rainfall over the Mediterranean region. The high pressure over Asia kept away its monsoonal rains, thus increasing the aridity of the Indian subcontinent.

The amount of seawater required to build the glaciers resulted in sea level ~ 130 m lower than today (Figure 10.33). But extensive ice masses carry some of the seeds of their own destruction: shrinking ocean surface area plus colder ocean water mean less water evaporation with less snowfall. Cutting down on evaporation reduces the supply of snow necessary to maintain glaciers, thus they shrink.

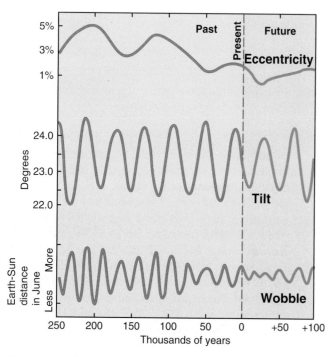

Figure 10.31
Patterns of eccentricity, tilt, and wobble for the past, present, and future.
Source: Data from A. Berger.

Climate Variations Since the Last Glaciation

The air temperature over the Greenland ice cap has significant warm stages followed by colder intervals, as recorded by oxygen-isotope ratios in ice layers

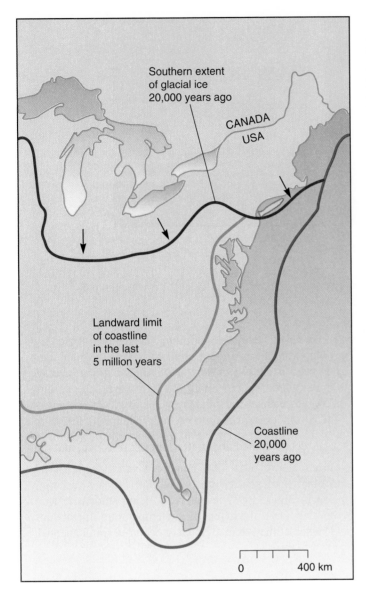

Figure 10.33
Some past positions of coastlines.
Source: S. J. Williams, et al. "Coasts in Crisis," US Geological Survey Circular 1075, 1990.

(Figure 10.34). Even during the heart of the latest Ice Age glacial advance, from 20,000 years ago and earlier, there were spikes of warmer temperatures. Look at the temperature conditions in Figure 10.35 following 20,000 years ago: (1) conditions began to warm; (2) the warming was interrupted by the Older Dryas cold stage; (3) the cold interval was suddenly replaced by the elevated temperatures of the Bølling period; (4) the higher temperatures deteriorated through the Allerød interval; (5) then temperatures plunged back into the depths of the Ice Age during the Younger Dryas stage from 12,900 to 11,600 years ago; and (6) last came the current interglacial period.

Look again at Figure 10.35 and note the sharp rises and falls in average annual temperature. How much did temperature rise or fall in a brief time? Temperature changes of 3° to 5°C occurred in just a few hundred years. Rates of temperature change used to be viewed as occurring gradually, analogous to using a dimmer switch to lower the lights. However, the rapid temperature changes recorded in Greenland ice show us that the best analogy may not be the dimmer switch but the on–off switch. If one of these rapid temperature changes occurred today, life as we know it would change markedly. Rainfall patterns would change as some wet areas become dry and some dry areas become wet. Crop-growing lands of the world would change with some countries gaining and some losing.

Why the sudden jumps or drops in temperature? One suggested cause relies on changes in the North Atlantic Ocean. As the massive ice sheets on the continents were melting, enormous lakes of pure, cold water held back by ice dams formed. The shape of the land surface and the sediment record tell of enormous floods produced by the failure of the ice dams (see Chapter 13). Floods of cold, glacial meltwater would flow from the Mississippi, St. Lawrence, Columbia, and other rivers out on top of seawater, creating a surface layer of cold, nonsaline water. In the North Atlantic Ocean, this cold surface-water layer would alter the ocean-circulation pattern shown in Figure 2.29 by stopping Arctic seawater from sinking and by blocking the northward inflow of Gulf Stream warm water.

As long as North Atlantic cold, salty seawater sinks and flows away as deep-ocean currents, it is replaced by warm surface water flowing up from the Gulf of Mexico and Caribbean Sea. With warm water in northern latitudes, the winds pick up tremendous amounts of heat and warm the adjacent lands of Greenland and Europe. But when Arctic surface water is fresh and cold, then its low density prevents sinking and its cold temperature results in colder air temperatures. Some researchers suggest that this is what happened during the Younger Dryas (Figure 10.34). Glacial meltwater floods from 12,900 to 12,700 years ago would have put cold freshwater on top of the North Atlantic Ocean, shutting down the circulation system of Figure 2.29. Under this hypothesis, it took another 1,100 years for solar energy to return the ocean surface to its warmer, saltier condition and the present circulation system. However, other researchers dispute this proposal and have presented convincing counter evidence that there was insufficient freshwater available to disrupt the North Atlantic heat pump.

Remember that sea level was 130 m lower at the peak of continental glaciation and that the removed water was stored on land as glacial ice. When the glaciers retreated, sea level rose by the inflow of cold freshwater freed by the melting of glacial ice. The return of this massive

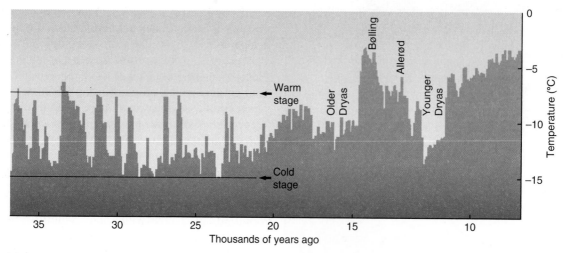

Figure 10.34
Air temperature over the Greenland continental glacier as recorded by oxygen-isotope ratios of ice at the glacier summit.

volume of meltwater affected the oceanic distribution of heat; this is a climate-modifying process. The last melting of the ice sheets is recorded by the sea-level rise curve (Figure 10.35).

At about 7,000 years ago, average global temperatures were warmer and rainfall totals had risen. At this time, known as the "climatic optimum," even North Africa had enough rainfall to support civilizations. Since then, there has been a 7,000-year-long lowering of global average temperature totalling about 2°C. However, the cooling trend has had several smaller cycles of glacial expansion and contraction superimposed on it (Figure 10.36).

The combined effects of Earth's orbital patterns of eccentricity, tilt, and wobble caused this cooling trend, but climate records show numerous variations testifying to other processes also at work. The climate variations seen in Figure 10.37 are actively being studied to learn more about (1) the extent of the temperature fluctuations, (2) whether they were regional or occurred simultaneously

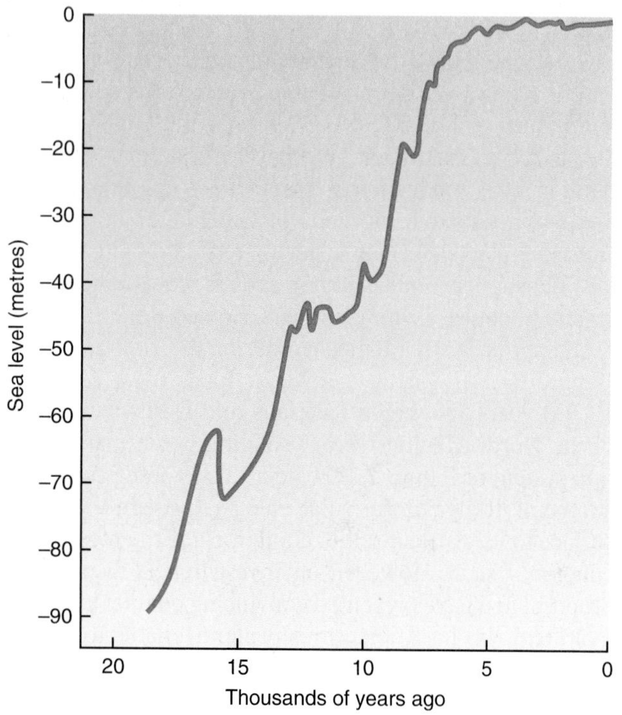

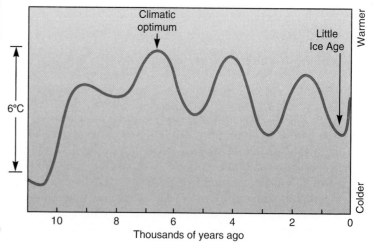

Figure 10.35
Rise in sea level in northwest Europe during the last 18,000 years.
Source: After Morner, 1971.

Figure 10.36
Generalized trends in global temperature for the last 11,000 years.
Source: Data from J. Imbrie and K. P. Imbrie.

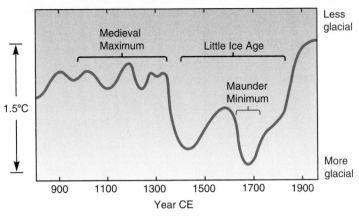

Figure 10.37

Climate of the last 1,000 years, based on European winters.

Source: Data from J. Imbrie, and K. P. Imbrie, *Ice Ages,* 1979; Harvard University Press, Cambridge.

around the world, and (3) the causes of the changes. This information is being sought using scientific data such as oxygen isotopes in glacial ice layers and in the annual growth rings of corals, and in tree-ring widths and densities. The last thousand years find us in the realm of human history with ever-improving observational records. Historical records studied to learn about past climates include (1) tax records of grain and grape crops; (2) advances and retreats of mountain glaciers; (3) paintings of winter scenes showing frozen lakes, rivers, and ports; and (4) numbers of weeks per year of sea ice around Iceland.

Looking at Figure 10.37 reveals a warm period from about 1000 to 1300 CE referred to as the **Medieval Maximum**. During this time, northern Europeans emigrated to Iceland, where the almost ice-free coast helped fishers build thriving industries. The coastal plains of Greenland also were settled by Europeans who farmed the land. In England, wine grapes were grown and harvested. But this did not last.

The **Little Ice Age** affected Europe from about 1400 to 1900 CE. It was originally defined by Francois Matthes in 1939 as an "epoch of renewed but moderate glaciation." Late in the Little Ice Age, part of northeastern Canada had accumulated permanent snowfields and the beginning of an ice sheet. Cold winters in Europe led to shorter growing seasons, with reduced crop yields leading to local famine. Mountain glaciers advanced throughout Europe. The fishing industry in Iceland was slowed by many weeks of sea ice each year.

Climatic conditions during the Little Ice Age were far from constant as smaller-scale warmings and coolings occurred (Figure 10.37). One colder interval between 1645 and 1715 CE is known as the **Maunder Minimum**. During this time, minimal sunspot activity was noted by astronomers and it is estimated that the Sun may have been 0.25% weaker.

What processes were involved in the climate changes of the last thousand years? (1) Changes in Earth's orbital patterns caused cooling. (2) A lessening of solar-energy production caused cooling. (3) Volcanism caused changes. (4) There probably were interactions between the ocean, the atmosphere, and the ice sheets that are yet to be understood.

Our current Ice Age is not over. We live during one of the coldest intervals in Earth history, despite the current glacial retreat. About 10% of the continents today remain buried beneath about 25 million km³ of ice, primarily on Antarctica and Greenland. Global temperatures will continue to ratchet down by fits and starts until the next major continental glaciation begins. Based on the previous records of glacial cycles our "warm" interglacial will come to an end within the next few millennia at most. Canada as we know it will cease to exist as it becomes buried under kilometres of ice, spanning thousands of square kilometres. It seems that climatic cycles can be found at any timescale we choose to use.

In Greater Depth

Stradivari Violins

The most famous violins probably are those made by the Italian Antonio Stradivari (1644–1737). He learned his craft as a pupil of Nicolas Amati (1596–1684). In 1684, Stradivari made changes in his violins such as increasing the size of the instrument and using a secret varnish. The reasons for the superior tones of these old violins are still debated. Now it is suggested that Stradivari, Amati, and their contemporaries benefited from the Maunder Minimum that occurred from 1645 to 1715, beginning one year after the birth of Stradivari. During this 70-year-long interval of reduced sunspots and lesser output of solar energy, Earth was in a cold spell with longer winters, cooler summers, and slow, even tree growth. The unique climatic conditions produced dense wood with narrow tree rings. This wood may be the cause of the superior acoustical properties of violins made during the late 1600s to early 1700s.

Summary

- Long-term changes in atmospheric conditions are known as climate, while short-term changes are referred to as weather.
- The amount of solar energy received by the Earth varies over time and with latitude. The cold water and air of the polar areas and the warm water and air of the equatorial belt are in motion due to the Earth's spin and the pull of gravity.
  - In the northern hemisphere, moving masses are pushed to the right of their initial movement by the Coriolis effect.
  - In the southern hemisphere, moving objects are pushed to their left.
- Air masses vary in their temperature and water-vapour content. The atmosphere circulates mainly between low and high latitudes pushed by winds, and to a lesser extent vertically due to density differences.
  - Cold polar air is dense and flows equatorward close to the Earth's surface.
  - Warm equatorial air rises and flows toward the poles at upper levels.
  - Different air masses do not readily mix. They are separated along boundaries called fronts, where most severe weather occurs.
- Energy is absorbed in water vapour during evaporation and released during condensation. Energy is absorbed in liquid water during melting and released during freezing. The circulation of deep-ocean currents is the most important process in the global redistribution of solar energy on Earth.

- The presence of atmospheric gases, such as water vapour, CO_2, and methane, creates a greenhouse effect where incoming, short-wavelength solar radiation passes through the atmosphere, but heat reradiated by the Earth is in longer wavelengths, which are unable to pass back through the atmosphere.
- Many processes have affected climate throughout Earth's history, each with its own operating principles and time scale.
  - Torrid Ages are times when tropical and subtropical conditions cover much of the Earth. They commonly involve buildup of greenhouse gases and extensive shallow seas that absorb solar energy. Warm climates of the past are deduced from evidence such as fossil reefs, tropical soils, evaporite mineral bodies, and widespread fossils of tropical and subtropical organisms.
  - Ice Ages require large continents at the poles to support thick glaciers and continents aligned to deflect warm ocean water toward the poles, where it can evaporate and then fall as snow on land to build glaciers. Ancient cold climates are interpreted from features such as glacially deposited debris, ice-polished and grooved rock surfaces, and wide distribution of fossils of cold-water organisms.
  - Advances and retreats of glaciers during an Ice Age occur on a timescale of thousands of years. These changes are largely due to variations in the orbit and rotation of Earth, affecting the amount of solar energy received.

Terms to Remember

adiabatic process 274
anticyclone 280
climate 270
Coriolis effect 279
cyclone 280
dew point temperature 272
extinction 271

front 277
Hadley cells 275
humidity 272
intertropical convergence zone (ITCZ) 276
jet stream 277
latent heat of condensation 272

lifting condensation level 274
Little Ice Age 295
Maunder Minimum 295
Medieval Maximum 295
methane 272
methane hydrate 288
Milankovitch theory 291

Questions for Review

1. What are the differences between climate and weather?
2. What is latent heat? Is it absorbed or released during (a) melting, (b) freezing, (c) evaporation, (d) condensation?
3. Draw a cross-section through the atmosphere that defines troposphere, tropopause, and stratosphere.
4. What are the relationships between high and low-pressure zones and between cyclones and anticyclones?
5. Explain the cause of the polar jet stream. Why does its position vary across Canada and the United States during a year?
6. Why is the Coriolis effect always to the right in the northern hemisphere and to the left in the southern hemisphere?
7. Explain the greenhouse effect in detail.
8. The earliest Earth had an atmosphere loaded with CO_2 in an intense greenhouse climate. Explain where that atmospheric CO_2 has gone.
9. What information about ancient climates is suggested by (a) fossil reefs? (b) aluminum ore? (c) bodies of sea salt? (d) the area covered by a fossil species? (e) polished and grooved surfaces in rocks?
10. Climate is related to amount of solar radiation received on Earth. How is incoming solar radiation affected by continental ice sheets? Elevated levels of atmospheric CO_2?
11. How can oxygen-isotope ratios be used as an ancient thermometer?
12. What causes glacial advances and retreats during an Ice Age?
13. How much can sea level drop during an Ice Age? What effect does this have on ocean-water temperature and evaporation rates?
14. When massive continental ice sheets melt, what happens to (a) sea level? (b) deep-ocean-water circulation? (c) salinity of sea-surface water? (d) organisms living near the sea surface?

Questions for Further Thought

1. What is the relationship between continental drift and the existence of an Ice Age?
2. What would be the global effect of melting the West Antarctic ice sheet? What would happen to low-lying coastal cities?
3. Considering the climatic history of the Earth, are you alive at a typical time?

Severe Weather

"But It's a Dry Cold!"

— Title of a 1998 book on the Canadian Prairies weather by
E. Wheaton

Outline

The terror of a tornado.
Source: Weatherstock, Inc

lobal warming. Stronger hurricanes. Retreating glaciers. Rising sea level. More wildfires. Every day we can read and hear stories about the warming climate and increasing bad weather. However, to evaluate changes, a long baseline is needed for comparison.

The 20th and 21st Centuries

In the previous chapter, Figure 10.38 showed temperature rising at the close of the 19th century to begin the 20th century at as high a temperature as existed in the preceding 1,000 years. Human activities added to the 20th-century warming combined to produce a century of warmth that was unprecedented in both amount and rate in the last 1,100 years (Figures 11.1 and 11.2). Average global surface temperature rose 0.7°C (+/−0.2°C).

Could a person feel the climate warming of the 20th century? No, because the climate warming is small compared to the day-to-day temperature fluctuations of weather. Although the human body cannot feel the warming, the human eye and brain can record many examples of climate warming (Table 11.1).

Did it warm continuously throughout the 20th century? No. Most of the warming occurred in two time intervals: 1910 to 1944 and since 1977 (Figure 11.1). It appears that the early warming was largely due to a hotter Sun and a lack of global volcanism. According to the World Meteorological Organization in Geneva, the global average temperature has risen about three times faster since 1977 compared to that for the past 100 years. Now into the 21st century, global temperatures are more than 0.7°C above those at the beginning of the 20th century with most of that warming due to increases in atmospheric greenhouse gases.

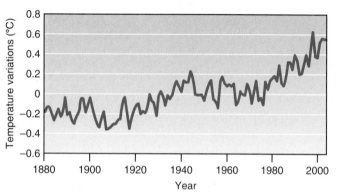

Figure 11.1
Observed changes of average global surface temperatures since 1880.
Source: NOAA.

THE GREENHOUSE EFFECT TODAY

The greenhouse effect is not something new. Earth has always had an atmosphere and always had its surface climate warmed by the greenhouse effect, but the strength of the greenhouse has varied. Remember that early Earth surface temperatures were about 290°C (Table 10.2). Our present surface temperatures are radically lower and have varied little during the past few centuries, when the human race made great advances in many areas of life. Many people question whether it is wise for us to release huge volumes of greenhouse gases and change a climate system we have thrived under, but we are changing it anyway.

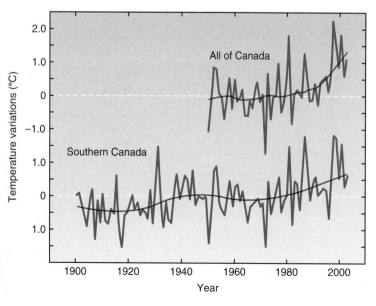

Figure 11.2
Observed trends in temperatures across southern Canada since 1900 and all of Canada since 1948.
Source: X. Zhang, L.A. Vincent, W. D. Hogg, and A. Niitsoo. Temperature and Precipitation Trends in Canada during the 20th Century. Atmosphere- Ocean, Vol. 38(3): 395-429. 2000,.

In Greater Depth

When Did Humans Begin Adding to Greenhouse Warming?

During recent decades the greenhouse warming caused by humans has become well known. For example, we release large quantities of CO_2 to the atmosphere by burning oil, natural gas, coal, and wood. But when did human activities begin producing the greenhouse gases that warmed the climate? According to William Ruddiman of the University of Virginia, humans began warming the climate about 8,000 years ago by widespread cutting and burning of forests to clear land for agriculture; the forest destruction added CO_2 to the atmosphere. Then about 5,000 years ago, rice became extensively grown with techniques that formed artificial wetlands, which gave off methane. Ruddiman calculates that these land uses caused the climate to warm about 0.8°C. If this estimate is correct, then the amount of human warming of climate is about tripled; about 0.8°C by our ancestors over thousands of years and 0.4°C by us in tens of years.

If our prehistoric ancestors did warm the climate over thousands of years, then they probably prevented some little ice ages and helped keep global climate warmer and more stable. Even if we owe them thanks for a warmer climate, remember that their changes took place slowly over thousands of years. Today we are increasing the amount of greenhouse gases in the atmosphere at rates many times faster than our ancestors and we may inadvertently push the climate across some threshold, thus causing an abrupt climate change that presents major problems.

How much of the 20th-century warming was due to natural processes and how much was due to human activities? Natural processes appear to have caused a net increase in temperature of about 0.2°C: changes in Earth's orbital patterns caused a slight cooling of –0.02°C that was offset by a hotter Sun contributing approximately +0.22°C. Human activities were responsible for the remaining 0.2°C increase in global temperature.

How do humans cause the global climate to warm? We add large volumes of greenhouse gases to the atmosphere each year, and the amounts we add increase each year. In Chapter 10, we looked at the early Earth greenhouse, but now we need to revisit the greenhouse effect in its modern condition and see what we are doing to increase it.

Table 11.1

Observed and Measured Effects of Global Warming in Recent Decades

Top 3 kilometres of ocean water absorbed ~90% of added greenhouse warmth; other 10% melted ice and is held in atmosphere.

Satellites show 20% decrease in ice cover since 1970s.

Freeze-free periods are lengthening in mid- and high latitudes.

Asymmetrical warming in many regions. Daily low temperatures are increasing at twice the rate of daily high temperatures.

Longer growing seasons.

Earlier arrival of spring in Europe and North America.

1. Earlier breeding of birds.
2. Earlier arrival of migrant birds.
3. Earlier appearance of butterflies.
4. Earlier spawning of amphibians.
5. Earlier flowering of plants.

Population shifts in latitude and altitude.

1. Europe and New Zealand: treeline climbing to higher altitudes.
2. Alaska: expansion of shrub-covered area.
3. North Atlantic Ocean and offshore California: increasing abundance of warm-water species.
4. Europe and North America: 39 butterfly species extend their ranges northward up to 200 km.
5. Costa Rica: lowland birds extend their ranges to higher elevations.
6. Britain: 12 bird species extend their ranges northward an average of 19 km.
7. Canada: red foxes extend their range northward while Arctic fox range retreats.

Table 11.2

Greenhouse Gases

Gas	Relative Percent Responsible for Greenhouse Warming	Ability to Trap Heat (compared to $CO_2 = 1$)
Carbon dioxide (CO_2)	60	1
Methane (CH_4)	16	21
Nitrous oxide (N_2O)	5	310
Ozone (O_3)	8	2,000
Chlorofluorocarbons (CFCs)	11	~12,000

What greenhouse gases are we adding to the atmosphere now? Carbon dioxide, methane, nitrous oxide, ozone, and several industrially produced gases including the chlorine- and fluorine-bearing chlorofluorocarbons. Table 11.2 lists these greenhouse gases, states how responsible each has been for global warming, and assesses the relative ability of each gas to trap heat via the gas's **global warming potential (GWP)** compared to carbon dioxide.

Remember what these gases do. Chapter 2 describes the solar energy reaching Earth as having short wavelengths in or near the visible spectrum. Earth's atmosphere reflects back about 30% of incoming solar radiation, but 23% passes through to power the hydrologic cycle, while the remaining 47% is absorbed by air, sea, and land (Figure 2.25). As absorbed heat builds up, some is reradiated outward in the longer, infrared wavelengths, but the greenhouse gases prevent their escape from Earth. The greater the volume of greenhouse gases in the atmosphere, the greater the amount of reradiated heat that is absorbed and prevented from escaping into space (Figure 2.27). The trapped heat is held in Earth's climate system. Global warming is so important that we need to know something about each of these gases.

Carbon Dioxide (CO_2)

About 60% of the greenhouse warming caused by humans comes from releasing CO_2 into the atmosphere (Table 11.2). How does carbon cycle through Earth's surface environments? The element carbon is a major building block of life on Earth. CO_2 is removed from the atmosphere by plants during photosynthesis to build their tissue. Upon death, much of the organic tissue is oxi-

dized, and CO_2 both returns to the atmosphere and dissolves in water. Humans have disturbed the carbon cycle by decomposing plants at ever-increasing rates and thus causing CO_2 to increase in the atmosphere and water. In 1800, the CO_2 concentration in the atmosphere was about 280 parts per million (ppm), but it had increased to about 382 ppm in 2006 (Figure 11.3). The increase is greater than 35%, and about 70% of that increase has occurred since 1950.

How do we decompose plants to release CO_2? In two main ways: burning wood and burning fossil fuels. About 20% of the increased atmospheric CO_2 is due to humans burning wood to clear land for agriculture, to heat homes, and to make charcoal for furnaces. Fossil fuels are coal, oil, and natural gas. They form during transformation of dead plant material and plankton in swamps, river deltas, and other organic-rich environments after burial beneath sediments. Over 80% of the energy that powers our global societies is generated by burning fossil fuels, and these energy-producing processes have added about 80% of the excess CO_2 now in the atmosphere.

How is CO_2 removed from the atmosphere? The scorecard for the latter part of the 20th century shows about 20% is removed by plants during photosynthesis, about 25% dissolves in ocean water, and the remaining 55% stays in the atmosphere and traps reradiated heat.

Methane (CH_4)

About 16% of modern greenhouse warming has come from adding methane to the atmosphere. Notice in

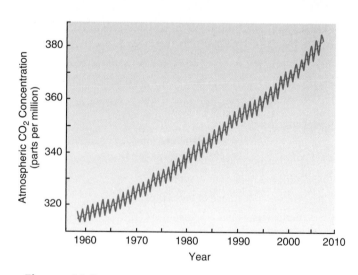

Figure 11.3

Atmospheric carbon-dioxide concentrations measured at Mauna Loa, Hawaii, 1958–2006. Compare these CO_2 increases with the temperature variations in Figure 11.1.

Source: C. D. Keeling, Scripps Institution of Oceanography, and NOAA.

Table 11.2 that the global warming potential or heat-trapping ability of methane is 21 times greater than that of carbon dioxide. Imagine what global warming would be like if methane were released each day in the same volume as carbon dioxide.

Air trapped in ice tells us that methane concentrations in the year 1750 were about 700 parts per billion (ppb), but they have risen more than 150% since then. The increase in atmospheric methane was slow in the 19th century and rapid in the 20th century. How is methane released to the atmosphere? It is released during decomposition of vegetation in oxygen-poor environments such as swamps, rice paddies, and cattle digestive systems. Bacteria remove carbon (C) from dead vegetation, and if oxygen is absent, the carbon combines with hydrogen (H) to make methane (CH_4).

About 30% of methane release occurs by natural decomposition, mostly in wetlands and secondarily via termites. Another significant source of methane release is through "mud volcanoes"; they are cone-shaped piles of mud and rock built by escaping methane. More than 900 mud volcanoes have been located in 26 countries. Azerbaijan has the most and the largest mud volcanoes, with one standing 700 m tall. About 70% of methane is given off by human activities, listed in order of decreasing importance: burning fossil fuels, growing rice, and maintaining livestock. Lesser amounts originate from landfills, burning wood, and rotting of animal waste and human sewage.

Remember that the hottest climate in the last 65 million years occurred when deep-ocean water warmed enough to melt icy methane hydrates on the seafloor, thus releasing a huge volume of methane gas into the atmosphere. If the warming of the deep oceans occurring today continues for enough decades to melt methane hydrates, then a warm climate could become a torrid climate.

Nitrous Oxide (N_2O)

Nitrous oxide is another contributor to the greenhouse effect (Table 11.2). N_2O is produced naturally by bacteria removing nitrogen from organic matter, especially within soils. Humans cause the release of nitrous oxide via agricultural activities, including use of chemical fertilizers. The second important way humans release N_2O is by combustion of fuels in car and truck engines.

Ozone (O_3)

Ozone is a greenhouse gas in both the stratosphere and the troposphere (Table 11.2). It is a gaseous molecule composed of three atoms of oxygen rather than the usual two-atom molecule (O_2). Ozone in the stratosphere acts as a greenhouse gas, helping warm the stratosphere. It is this heat that places the "lid" on the troposphere (Figure 10.7). Ozone is effective at absorbing ultraviolet (UV) radiation emitted by the Sun, thus shielding life from dangerous rays. The UV rays that do pass through the atmosphere and make it to the ground surface cause sunburn and skin cancer.

Ozone is also a principal component of the smog that chokes urban atmospheres. Our automobiles and industries emit gases, some of which react with sunlight to produce the ozone that makes our eyes water and lungs ache. The ozone story is well described by the saying that pollutants are merely resources that are in the wrong place. Ozone in the stratosphere shields us from killing UV rays, but ozone in the air we breathe weakens us and shortens our lives.

Chlorofluorocarbons (CFCs)

Chlorofluorocarbons do not occur naturally. They are examples of gases produced solely by humans. CFCs are used as coolants in refrigerators and air conditioners, foam insulation in buildings, solvents, and other applications. Chlorofluorocarbons are not only greenhouse gases (Table 11.2), but also aid in the destruction of the ozone in the stratosphere, which helps shield life from damaging UV rays. CFCs may remain in the atmosphere for a century, causing so many problems that international treaties have been signed restricting their use.

20th-Century Greenhouse Gas Increases

Why did we release such great volumes of greenhouse gases in the 20th century? The gases were a by-product of many praiseworthy activities such as providing energy for industries, homes, and personal automobiles, and from growing rice and raising livestock for human consumption. It took a long time to recognize how much the climate could be changed by these activities that raised the standard of human existence.

Another significant factor in the increase of greenhouse gases was the 20th-century growth of the human population. In 1900, the world population of humans was about 1.5 billion, but the population had exploded to 6 billion in 1999. Think about that: the human population doubled twice in the 20th century, from 1.5 billion in 1900 to 3 billion in 1960, and then to 6 billion in 1999. Even conservative estimates for 21st-century population growth forecast another doubling to 12 billion people. Most people desire the affluent lifestyle of the industrialized world; this means the billions alive today who don't have that lifestyle plus the billions of people yet to be born. All will be seeking a higher standard of living. The greenhouse gas–caused global warming will be a growing political issue throughout your lifetime.

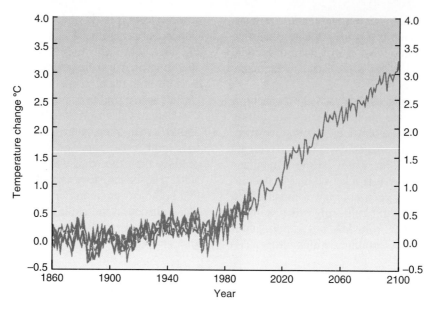

Figure 11.4

Projected change in average global temperature at Earth's surface relative to 1881–1920.

Source: Stott et al., 2000.

THE 21ST CENTURY

How will global climate change in the 21st century? This is a complex question because its answer involves predicting many variables, such as greenhouse gas content of the atmosphere, temperatures around the planet, ocean warmth and circulation patterns, and wind strengths and positions. The question is addressed by constructing **global climate models (GCMs)** involving complex computer simulations. One GCM covering the 21st century forecasts a surface temperature increase of 2.5°C from today (Figure 11.4). GCMs emphasizing CO_2 increases in the atmosphere forecast temperature increases of 1.5° to 4.5°C in the next 50 to 100 years due to doubling CO_2 from its pre-industrial value of 280 parts per million (ppm) to 560 ppm.

Likely global climate changes in the 21st century include significant melting of (1) mountain glaciers, (2) the Greenland ice sheet, and (3) the West Antarctic ice sheet. In the Arctic, significant melting of sea ice and permafrost will occur, and forests will advance north inside the Arctic Circle. As ice melts and seawater warms and expands, global sea level will rise from 30 cm to 1 m. Some regions on Earth will become hotter and drier, and others will become cooler and wetter. Agricultural productivity will increase in some areas and decrease in others. For example, recurrent, severe summer droughts are expected in the grain-growing region of North America (Figure 11.5).

A major climatic shift will occur if the present deep-ocean circulation system is altered (Figure 2.29). At present, in the North Atlantic Ocean, the clockwise circulation of surface water carries warm tropical water to the north, where it releases heat to the atmosphere. As it travels north, the seawater becomes denser, sinks, and then flows south at intermediate depths almost to Antarctica (Figure 11.6). This deep-water circulation is driven by density contrasts in seawater. As the oceans warm, the density contrasts become less. Some studies suggest that over 80% of the human-produced heating since the 1950s is stored in the oceans. If this deep-water circulation system slows, average temperatures over Europe could drop 4°C.

We know that releasing greenhouse gases into the atmosphere causes climate warming, but we do not know what natural changes may occur. Will the Sun emit less (or more) energy in the 21st century? Will global volcanism increase and add a cooling effect, or will it be virtually

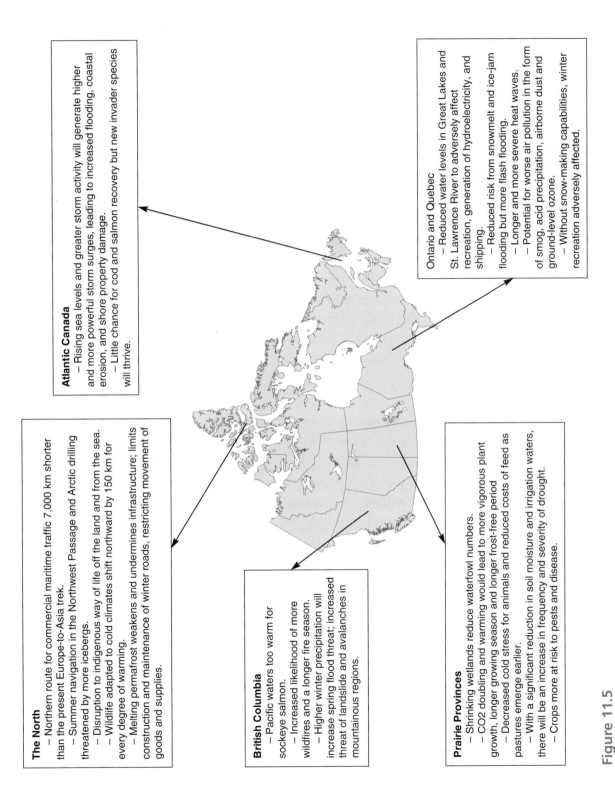

The North
— Northern route for commercial maritime traffic 7,000 km shorter than the present Europe-to-Asia trek.
— Summer navigation in the Northwest Passage and Arctic drilling threatened by more icebergs.
— Disruption to indigenous way of life on the land and from the sea.
— Wildlife adapted to cold climates shift northward by 150 km for every degree of warming.
— Melting permafrost weakens and undermines infrastructure; limits construction and maintenance of winter roads, restricting movement of goods and supplies.

Atlantic Canada
— Rising sea levels and greater storm activity will generate higher and more powerful storm surges, leading to increased flooding, coastal erosion, and shore property damage.
— Little chance for cod and salmon recovery but new invader species will thrive.

British Columbia
— Pacific waters too warm for sockeye salmon.
— Increased likelihood of more wildfires and a longer fire season.
— Higher winter precipitation will increase spring flood threat; increased threat of landslide and avalanches in mountainous regions.

Prairie Provinces
— Shrinking wetlands reduce waterfowl numbers.
— CO_2 doubling and warming would lead to more vigorous plant growth, longer growing season and longer frost-free period
— Decreased cold stress for animals and reduced costs of feed as pastures emerge earlier.
— With a significant reduction in soil moisture and irrigation waters, there will be an increase in frequency and severity of drought.
— Crops more at risk to pests and disease.

Ontario and Quebec
— Reduced water levels in Great Lakes and St. Lawrence River to adversely affect recreation, generation of hydroelectricity, and shipping.
— Reduced risk from snowmelt and ice-jam flooding but more flash flooding.
— Longer and more severe heat waves.
— Potential for worse air pollution in the form of smog, acid precipitation, airborne dust and ground-level ozone.
— Without snow-making capabilities, winter recreation adversely affected.

Figure 11.5
Impacts on Canada from a warmer world

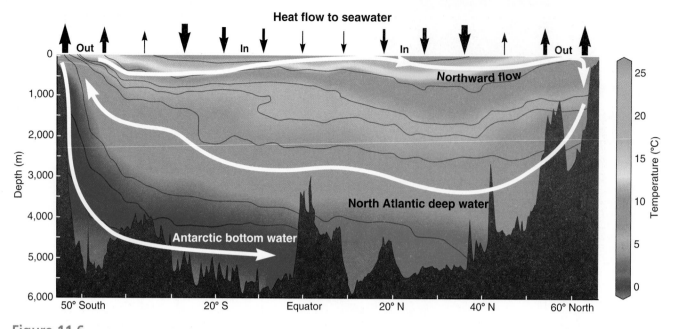

Figure 11.6

Water flow in Atlantic Ocean. Warm equatorial surface water flows north to the Arctic and releases heat to the atmosphere. As water density increases northward, it sinks and flows at depth to Antarctica.

Source: Adapted from G. Hegerl and N. Bindoff, *Science*.

absent? The future is difficult to predict. But look how life has changed. For thousands of years humans lived at the mercy of climate changes, but now *we* change the climate, for better or worse.

Tipping Points

Change is commonly viewed as a gradual process, but sometimes it is not that way. The concept of a **tipping point** recognizes there are points at which small changes suddenly produce large effects. Although changes through the years may be slow and gradual, the response to these changes, at some point, may be abrupt and disproportionate. One of the concerns with rising temperatures due to increasing greenhouse gases in the atmosphere or the increasing rate of glacial melting is that their history of change may not predict the future. Thresholds may be crossed that lead to dramatic changes.

Arctic sea ice melts back each summer, and reaches its smallest geographical extent in August–September each year. Following most summers, the ice cover grows back, reaching its highest extent and thickness usually in March. For 30 years up to about 2002, the average sea ice extent in late summer was 7.7 million square kilometres, declining about 7% per decade. Since then, the rate of ice decay has accelerated dramatically. In 2007, Arctic sea ice reached its lowest extent on record since aircraft reconnaissance of ice cover in the 1950s and the start of satellite measurements in 1979, with a mere 5.32 million square kilometres (Figure 11.7).

Changes in wind and ocean circulation patterns can reduce the ice extent but climatologists believe the main forcing is climate change. With more open water and added heat going into the ocean, it is becoming more difficult for the ice to grow back. Scientists suggest that the summer ice cover has reached a "tipping point" beyond which there is no return and will likely continue to decrease until the ice disappears sometime in the 21st century, marking the first time in a million years the Arctic Ocean is ice-free.

Changing Climate and Weather: Timescale in Multiple Years

The one certainty about climate change is that the climate is changing. Sometimes the change is abrupt or slow; other times the climate appears stable with little apparent change. Few question that the contemporary climate is changing faster and greater now than it has in a very long time. Nowhere have changes been greater than in Canada—warming at twice the global amount in half the time. Because weather and climate are connected, climate cannot change without changing the weather.

Humans and ecosystems are much more vulnerable to the vagaries of weather such as floods, tropical storms, hot spells, blizzards, and local storms than to gradual shifts in climate. Climate change is slow compared to

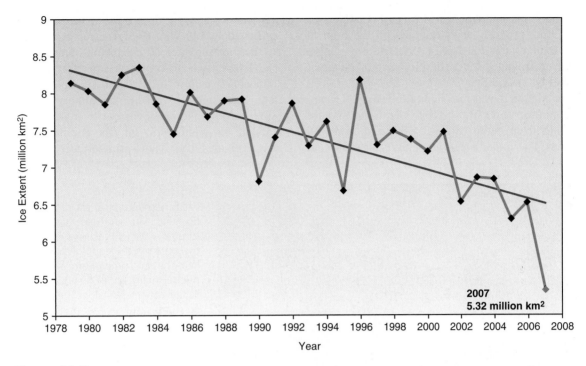

Figure 11.7
Arctic sea ice extent, measured in August of each year between 1979 and 2007 by satellite imagery.
Source: National Snow and Ice Data Center.

day-to-day weather changes. Therefore, understanding the effects of global warming on the incidence of severe weather is crucial to our understanding of the impact of climate change and our response to it.

Are we seeing more weather extremes because there are more to see or are we just getting better at seeing them? Observational evidence of severe weather trends is sketchy—suggestive, but not conclusive. Scientists can't say with full certainty that extremes of weather are on the rise, or that severe weather is more intense or is lasting longer than in the past. (If that were the case it would be consistent with our expectations of climate change). Similarly, you cannot blame a single storm, a dump of snow, or a week's heavy rain on climate change or something that human beings have done. Wild weather is generally rare, localized, and short lived, which makes it difficult for scientists to detect meaningful trends. We are very good at measuring changes in temperature and precipitation; not quite so good at counting thunderstorms or high-wind events.

Several processes change climate on timescales of 1 to 20 or 30 years. Climate change at the scale of years to decades grades into weather, which is highly variable from year to year, making recognition of trends or cycles difficult. For this reason the World Meteorological Organization has determined that it takes 30 years of weather observations to define a climate. When you hear the meteorologist on television give the average temperature for a

particular date, he or she is quoting the 30-year average. This 30-year running average shifts over time though, resulting in a change in climate. There are some recurrent phenomena within the present climate that can cause significant perturbations. Let's look at examples.

EL NIÑO

The high heat capacity of water gives it the ability to absorb and store tremendous volumes of heat upon warming and to release copious quantities of heat upon cooling. The heat supply in the world ocean has a major effect on the atmosphere and on world climate. An example of ocean–atmosphere coupling is the phenomenon commonly marked in South America by the arrival of warm ocean water to Peru and Ecuador near Christmastime, where it is known as **El Niño** (Spanish for "the child"). As we will learn below the term "El Niño" is now reserved for an enhanced version of this phenomenon that occurs every few years.

Typical conditions in the central Pacific Ocean find high atmospheric pressure in the east, resulting in trade winds that blow toward the equator from the northeast and southeast. The trade winds push Pacific Ocean surface waters to the west within the equatorial zone, where they absorb solar energy (Figure 11.8a). The winds push so hard that sea level is not flat; it is about 50 cm higher on the western side of the ocean. The warm water piled up on the west side forms a pool of heated water that evaporates readily, helping produce heavy rainfalls for the tropical jungles of Indonesia and Southeast Asia, and providing a favourable environment for the development of the Great Barrier Reef of Australia.

Meanwhile, on the eastern side of the Pacific Ocean, the warm surface water blown west is replaced by cold waters rising from depth (Figure 11.8b) and from the polar regions. The colder waters along the coast evaporate less readily, and thus deserts are common along the coasts of Ecuador, Peru, Baja California, and California because of the shortage of cloud-producing water vapour.

Every two to seven years, the typical ocean–atmosphere pattern breaks down for about 6 to 18 months. The trade winds weaken, the atmospheric low pressure over Indonesia moves out over the central Pacific Ocean, and winds blow into the Pacific basin from the west (Figure 11.9). The warm surface waters then flow

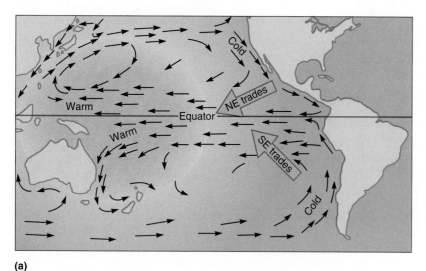

(a)

Figure 11.8
Pacific Ocean typical circulation. (a) Map. The northeast and southeast trade winds combine to push warm surface water westward across the ocean in the equatorial belt. After circling near the poles, the return water flowing along the North and South America coasts is cold. (b) Schematic cross-section. The trade winds stack up warm surface water on the western side of the Pacific Ocean.

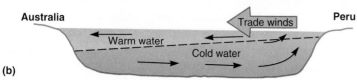

(b)

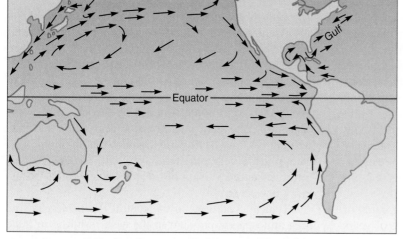

(a)

Figure 11.9
Pacific Ocean circulation during El Niño. (a) Map. Equatorial winds blow toward the centre of the ocean from both sides. (b) Schematic cross-section. Weakened trade winds plus winds from the west cause warm water to accumulate along the equatorial Americas.

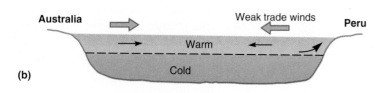

(b)

"downhill" toward South and Central America. Some surface currents are reversed as some winds from the west blow surface water to the east. The reversal places a huge mass of warm water against the Americas (Figure 11.10 (left)), which evaporates more readily and produces more clouds. The warm moist air flowing eastward off the ocean into the Americas commonly leads to heavier rains than the coastal deserts can handle. This phenomenon is what we now term El Niño.

The El Niño of 1997–98 was the strongest weather event of the 20th century. As such, it surpassed the previous holder of the title, the destructive El Niño of 1982–83. Although the 1997–98 event was much larger than the 1982–83 event it was much less destructive, primarily due to greater predictive capability than existed previously.

Early effects of the 1997–98 El Niño included drought and high temperatures, which triggered fires in Australia in the fall of 1997. During December 1997, drought and high temperatures in Alberta triggered massive wildfires

that destroyed livestock and homes. Cyclones also pounded the Mexican Pacific coast through this interval. In the southern United States, extensive flooding paralyzed communities in North Carolina and Tennessee. Further north, the stream of warm air from the Gulf of Mexico fooled cherry trees into blooming in Washington D.C. On the positive side, the El Niño may have been responsible for an unusually thick blanket of snow, which saved the lives of all 42 passengers on Air Canada Flight 646 that crashed when landing in poor visibility in Fredericton, New Brunswick, on 16 December.

The high-level atmospheric winds also are affected by reversal of flow direction during an El Niño. The change brings negative and positive results. For example, in the United States during the 1997–98 El Niño, winds flowing eastward caused heavy rains and floods in California and brought higher rainfall with some tornadoes to the southeastern states, but helped break apart Atlantic and Caribbean storms, resulting in fewer hurricanes along the Atlantic coast. Meanwhile, the midwestern and northern

Figure 11.10
Pacific Ocean water temperatures during an El Niño in January 1998 (left) and during a La Niña in February 1999 (right). Warmer water is white or red; colder water is purple or blue.
Source: © JPL/NASA.

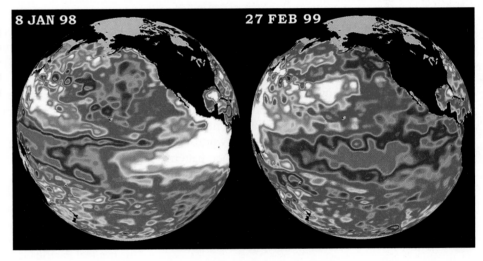

states had a warmer winter with reduced damages to crops, increased economic productivity, and a below-average number of deaths. The 1997–98 El Niño brought more economic gains than losses as well as fewer fatalities than would occur normally to the United States as a whole (Table 11.3).

The El Niño effects in the Pacific Ocean basin are impressive, but the ocean–atmosphere system is linked on a larger scale (Figure 11.11). In the South Pacific Ocean, the shifting of weather patterns is known as the Southern Oscillation; it occurs when the usual low-pressure atmosphere is replaced by high-pressure air, as measured at Darwin on the north coast of Australia. For example,

Table 11.3

Estimated Impacts on the United States of the 1997–98 El Niño

Losses
Human lives lost: 189
Economic losses: US$4.5 billion

Benefits
Human lives *NOT* lost: 850
Economic gains: US$19.5 billion

Source: *American Meteorological Society Bulletin.*

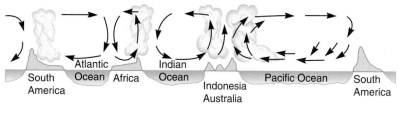

(a) Normal Circulation

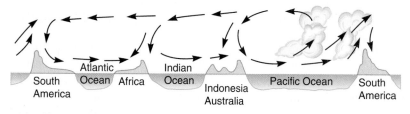

(b) El Niño Condition

Figure 11.11
Cross-sections of southern hemisphere atmospheric circulation. (a) With "normal circulation," moist air rises over the landmasses, condenses, and falls as rain on eastern South America, eastern Africa, and Indonesia-Australia. (b) With El Niño conditions, eastern Africa and Indonesia-Australia do not get their customary rain, while western South America receives heavy rainfall.

in late 1996, strong weather systems in the Indian Ocean migrated into the western Pacific Ocean before the strong El Niño of 1997–98. The combined system is called the El Niño/Southern Oscillation (ENSO).

It is increasingly evident that unusually high rains in one area and drought in another are not isolated events; rather they are parts of a globally connected weather system. Such changes, which occur in one area, and trigger other changes around the world, somewhat like a falling line of dominoes—knock over one and it starts the process whereby they all fall down— are known as "**teleconnections.**" Every several years the tropical atmosphere goes through changes that link up around the world. The tropical Indian Ocean warms and its weather pattern may blow into the western Pacific Ocean, setting off an El Niño. After the El Niño wind shifts cross the Pacific Ocean and South America, the tropical Atlantic Ocean may begin to warm. This global circuit takes about four years to move around the Earth.

LA NIÑA

The surface waters of the ocean are a mosaic of warmer, intermediate, and cooler water masses that exert strong controls on regional weather. The Pacific Ocean sea-temperature is monitored by the Topex-Poseidon satellite. When warmer than normal surface waters extend along the west coast of the Americas during an El Niño, they usually bring high rainfalls and accompanying floods. But El Niño has a sister called **La Niña** ("the girl") and she has a different personality. La Niña occurs when cooler water moves into the equatorial Pacific Ocean (Figure 11.10 (right)).

During a La Niña, trade winds are stronger and other wind systems change their paths, bringing different weather patterns across North America. A typical La Niña winter brings cold air with high rainfall precipitation to the northwestern United States and western Canada but causes below-average rainfall precipitation elsewhere in North America. The winter of 1999–2000 was typical with heavy rainfalls in the Pacific northwest and below-average rainfalls in other regions, accompanied by numerous wildfires in the southwestern United States.

La Niña allows the growth of hurricanes in the Atlantic Ocean, spelling trouble for the coastal areas of eastern North America and the Gulf of Mexico. There are also hazards associated with the La Niña cooling in the Pacific Ocean. La Niña leads to decreased rainfall in the American Southwest, helping dry out the El Niño–fed vegetation, leading to wildfires as in the summers of 2000 and 2002.

El Niño and La Niña are the extreme conditions in which warm or cold water masses strongly influence the distribution of rainfall. Extreme ocean conditions make weather prediction easier. However, there are times when the tropical Pacific Ocean is neither excessively warm nor markedly cool but instead is neutral. The weaker signal from the ocean makes weather more difficult to predict. NASA oceanographer William Patzert has suggested the term "**La Nada**" for this neutral condition.

One of the most difficult, and most common, questions meteorologists receive is "was that storm caused by El Niño/La Niña?" To identify the impact of these phenomena, researchers perform modelling experiments aimed at identifying how El Niño/La Niña affects forecasts of weather events. This is done by running an ensemble of model forecasts, with and without boundary conditions containing the anomalous sea surface temperatures associated with El Niño/La Niña. The difference between the two forecasts provides an indication of how a particular weather event may have been influenced by the anomalous sea temperatures. Using this approach, researchers

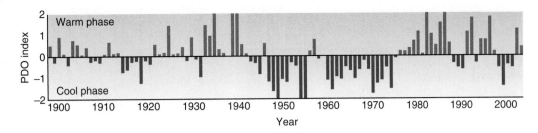

Figure 11.12
The monthly Pacific Decadal Oscillation (PDO) index from 1900 to 2004. Warm phases have more storms and rains, whereas cool phases bring the opposite.

have found evidence that the great St. Lawrence River Valley ice storm of 1998 (see Chapter 1), the second most costly natural disaster in Canadian history, was a direct result of the El Niño.

PACIFIC DECADAL OSCILLATION

In recent years, another weather-influencing cycle, the Pacific Decadal Oscillation, has been recognized by studying sea-surface temperatures in the Pacific Ocean. These cycles persist at two periodicities, one from 15 to 25 years and the other from 50 to 70 years (Figure 11.12). They occur as mid-latitude conditions of the Pacific Ocean that have secondary effects on the tropics. Compare this to El Niño, which lasts 6 to 18 months as low-latitude (tropical) conditions of the Pacific Ocean with secondary effects on the mid-latitudes.

The Pacific Decadal Oscillation has a warm phase accompanied by decreased storminess and rainfall to British Columbia and the adjacent regions. Warm phases occurred from 1925 to 1946 and 1977 to 1999. Cool phases with increased numbers of storms impacting western Canada were in effect from 1890 to 1924, 1947 to 1976, and 1999 to present.

The Rising Cost of Severe Weather

Weather kills. People drown in floods, are struck down by random bolts of lightning, are battered in hurricanes, are chased and tossed by tornadoes, and die during heat or cold waves.

Based on an analysis of the worldwide frequency and distribution of natural disasters from 1988 to 1997, the Munich Reinsurance Company concluded that almost two-thirds of the 6,000 events recorded were storm- or flood-related. A similar analysis from the World Meteorological Organization in Geneva for the decade 1991–2000 also revealed that the number of people affected by weather-related disasters averaged 211 million per year,

seven times those affected by conflict, with 98% of the people affected from developing countries.

Severe weather is expensive and getting costlier. And that trend is accelerating (Figure 11.13). According to insurers, 2005 was the costliest year ever, with record losses from weather-related disasters around the world totalling $200 billion—about double the losses of 2003, quadruple those of 2002, and eight times those of 2001.

In Canada, weather-related natural disasters increased from 2 to 4 per year in Canada in the first half of the 20th century to about 12 per year in the 1990s (Figure 1.6). Further, insured costs have jumped logarithmically (Table 11.4).

Climate simulations can offer so far only preliminary indications on the frequency, intensity, and duration of extreme weather events in the future. Experts have considerable confidence in how temperature extremes will evolve, less so with precipitation, and much less so with major storms such as hurricanes, tornadoes, and blizzards.

Before studying the different types of severe weather, please read and understand the basic principles of meteorology described at the beginning of Chapter 10.

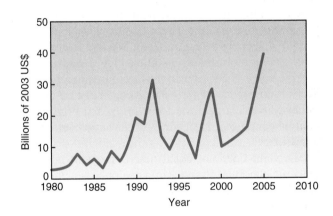

Figure 11.13
Insured losses from weather-related disasters, 1980–2004. The 1992 and 1999 peaks correspond to hurricane Andrew in the United States and to blizzards Lothar and Martin in western Europe, respectively.

Source: Munich Reinsurance Company.

Table 11.4

Costs of Natural Disasters to the Canadian Insurance Industry in Excess of $100 million.

Total insured cost (Millions of 2003 Cdn$)	Fatalities	Date	Event	Location
1818	28	1998	St. Lawrence River Valley Ice Storm	Ontario to New Brunswick
500	0	2005	Flood	Toronto, ON
412	0	1991	Hailstorm	Calgary, AB
386	0	1999	Hailstorm	Calgary, AB
300	0	2005	Flood	Calgary, AB
250	Unknown	2003	Forest fires	Alberta and British Columbia
218	10	1996	Flood	Saguenay, QC
215	27	1987	Tornado	Edmonton, AB
215	0	1993	Flood	Winnipeg, MB
180	0	2004	Flood/Hailstorm	Edmonton, AB
164	0	1996	Flood/Hailstorm	Winnipeg, MB
133	12	1985	Tornado	Hopeville to Barrie, ON
133	0	1996	Hailstorm	Calgary, AB
130	11	1999	Blizzard	Southern Ontario
107	0	2000	Storm	Southern Ontario
100	2	2006	Storm	Vancouver, BC
100	8	2003	Hurricane Juan	Nova Scotia and PEI
100	0	2004	Flood	Peterborough, ON
100	0	2006	Storm	Southern Ontario

Source: Used with permission of Institute for Catastrophic Loss Reduction.

Drought and Famine

Dry weather may occur on long or short timescales. As continents drift and ocean basins open and close, large regions may be cut off from moisture supplies and kept in long-term desert conditions. On a shorter timescale, changes in the position of jet streams or atmospheric convergence zones may keep moisture-bearing air away from large areas for many years, bringing on drought conditions. Heat waves occur on an even shorter timescale.

Drought does not equal desert. Drought describes times of abnormal dryness in a region when the usual rains do not appear and all life must adjust to the unexpected shortage of water. The lack, or reduction, of moisture can cause agricultural collapse or shortfalls, bringing famine, disease, and death, and causing mass migrations to wetter areas. Famine is the slowest moving of all disasters. Earthquakes, volcanic eruptions, tornadoes, and the like all hit suddenly and with great force and then quickly

are gone. But famine is slow. First, the expected rains do not arrive, and then vegetation begins to wither, food supplies shrink, and, finally, famine sets in.

Unlike other natural disasters, drought tends to drive people apart rather than bring them closer together. The shortages of food and water lead to conflict as people, communities, and governments battle each other for the means to survive. After an earthquake or flood, people are commonly at their best as they aid their neighbours and strangers in need; during a drought, people are typically at their worst as they fight for survival.

In the *early stage* of a famine, food is still available, but there is not enough. Healthy people can lose up to 10% of their body weight and still remain mentally alert and physically vigorous. In the *advanced stage,* body weight decreases by around 20%, and the body reacts to preserve life itself. Body cells lower their activity levels, reducing the energy needed to keep vital functions going. People sink into apathy. In the *near-death stage,* when 30% or more of body weight has been lost, people become indifferent to their surroundings and to the sufferings of others, and death approaches.

THE 1930S DUST BOWL

One of the greatest weather disasters in North American history occurred during the 1930s, when several years of drought turned grain-growing areas in the Great Plains into the "Dust Bowl." Failed crops and malnutrition caused abandonment of thousands of farms and the broad-scale migration of people. This human drama was captured in many articles and books, including *The Grapes of Wrath* by John Steinbeck:

> Now the wind grew strong and hard,
> it worked at the rain crust
> in the corn fields.
> Little by little the sky
> was darkened by the mixing dust,
> and the wind felt over the earth,
> loosened the dust and carried it away.

What happened to cause the drought? Recurrent large-scale meanders in the upper-air flow created ridges of high pressure with clockwise flows resulting in descending air (Figure 11.14). The upper-level high-pressure air was already dry, but as it sank, it became warmer, thus reaching the ground hot, dry, and thirsty. As the winds blew across the ground surface, they sucked up moisture, killing plants and exposing bare soil to erosion. Some of the blame for the Dust Bowl was heaped onto the farmers for ploughing deeply through drought-tolerant native grasses and exposing bare soil to the winds. The ploughed lands were sowed with seeds of plants that could not handle drought and thus died, exposing more soil. The farming practices were not the best, but they did not cause the drought; they just accentuated its effects.

Dust clouds resembling ominous thunderclouds rolled along the ground, and smothered everything in their path (Figure 11.15). The clouds of dust and topsoil, also known as black rollers or blizzards, blotted out the Sun and blew the dirt thousands of kilometres away. Residents stayed indoors and sealed the cracks of doors and windows to stop the dust and dirt getting in. They tied handkerchiefs over their noses and mouths to protect their eyes from the stinging dust particles.

The drought began in 1930, a particularly bad time. Only months before, in October 1929, the American stock market crashed, and the world economy began sinking into the Great Depression.

Drought is Canada's most expensive natural disaster in a cumulative sense. It accounts for six of the ten most costly natural disasters in Canada over the past century (Table 1.5). The effects of drought in Canada are felt mostly in the Prairies, especially in the arid portion of southern

Figure 11.14
Dry conditions in Canada and the central United States are commonly caused by a long-lasting, high-pressure ridge in the upper troposphere. The ridge causes anticyclones (clockwise rotations) where warm air aloft descends, warming further and lowering its humidity, and then sucking up moisture from the land below. The mid-continent high-pressure ridge also blocks the northward flow of moist Gulf of Mexico air.

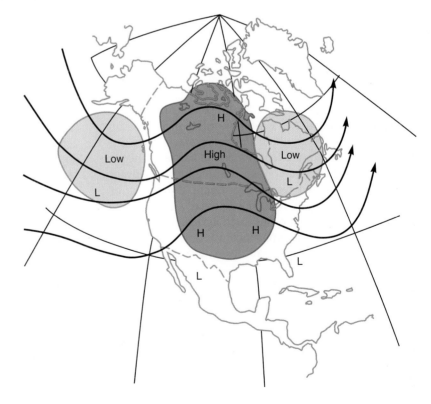

Figure 11.15
A dust storm rolls into Stratford, Texas, in 1935.
Photo: © NOAA.

Saskatchewan and Alberta known as Palliser's Triangle. During the "Dirty Thirties" a quarter of million people abandoned the West, which led to major policy changes in agriculture and land management. Between 1933 and 1937, the Prairies received about 40% less rainfall than normal for that area. Thousands of head of livestock were lost or killed by ranchers with no water to offer them. Crops were withered and stunted.

Since the 1930s, other serious droughts have plagued North America (Figure 11.16). The hottest summers are generally drought years, so when the rains fail, crops wither rapidly in the torrid heat. On the Prairies, nine of the 10 driest years since 1948 were also warmer than normal, including 1961, which featured both the driest (−49%) and the hottest (+2.6°C) summer in 60 years of record (1948 to 2007).

Rivalling the 1930s in terms of drought frequency, intensity and duration were the 1980s. In many areas, 1988 was the hottest summer on record. Growing season rainfalls across the southern Prairies averaged between 50% and 80% of normal. The dry period had really began in September 1987 and continued through the relatively snow-free winter and record dry spring. The effects of the 1988 drought were disastrous for nearly all segments of the Canadian economy, although agriculture was particularly hard hit. Grain production was down by an average 31% from 1987, and export losses were estimated at $4 billion. Ranchers were forced to thin their herds or move their cattle long distances to find adequate grazing land. As a result of their economic difficulties, about 10% of farmers and farm workers left agriculture in 1988.

Recent droughts on the Prairies have been quite severe. For some areas, the years between 2001 and 2002 were drier than the driest years of the 1930s. No three-year period in the 1930s or 1980s or any other decade could compare to the moisture shortfalls as large as those between 2001 and 2003—just too many dry and warm seasons back to back to back. While past growing seasons were drier, recent winters have been a third drier than winters 70 years ago. Recent droughts are year-round.

Drought is one of the hazards likely to worsen as a result of climate change. Researchers at the University of Regina used tree-rings and mud from Prairie lake bottoms to conclude that 20th-century droughts were characterized by moderate severity and single drought years or at worse back-to-back drought years. Prior to the 20th century, prolonged droughts of more than a decade in duration had been common. If anything, the past 100 years have been relatively benign—wet and humid. The absolute worst-case scenario occurred 1,500 years ago, when a 70-year drought prevailed in central Saskatchewan. In the modern era, one of the worst periods of drought was immediately before the Prairies were settled by Europeans, from the 1850s until about 1890. Droughts also occur in eastern Canada, although there they are usually short-lived, localized, and less frequent and less severe than in the Prairies.

Heat Wave

The days of high temperatures during a heat wave may be one of the least appreciated of the weather-related disasters. The heat wave is an invisible, silent danger and it can kill in large numbers. Hurricanes, tornadoes, and floods grab the headlines, but heat waves kill more people worldwide.

Heat does not kill many Canadians, but that is not to say it hasn't in the past or that it won't in the future. Seventy years ago an average of 50 Canadians died each year from extreme heat or too much sun. Heat mortality figures dropped to seven a year in the 1970s. Today, a single death from heat stroke usually makes the national news.

Somewhat surprising for Canada, being the second-coldest country in the world, is that the greatest cause of death from a natural disaster in the last 100 years was not cold or snow but a lengthy hot spell in 1936 (Table 1.4; Figure 1.8). In late June and July that year, hot air from the American southwest desert drifted across the United States and northward into Canada. It was a huge continental-size heat wave. Shade temperatures reached almost 50°C in Kansas and the Dakotas, 44°C in Manitoba, and 42°C in Ontario—temperature records that still stand. As with most heat waves, it was the high night-time minima that took the greatest toll because they were too elevated to offer any respite to people already stressed by heat exposure during the day. The daily minimum temperature in Toronto on 11 July was 26.6°C; and for four nights the temperature didn't dip below 25°C. Only twice before in 100 years had the night-time minima stayed above 25°C, in 1911 and 1917; and only seven times since 1936. The extreme heat buckled highways, warped

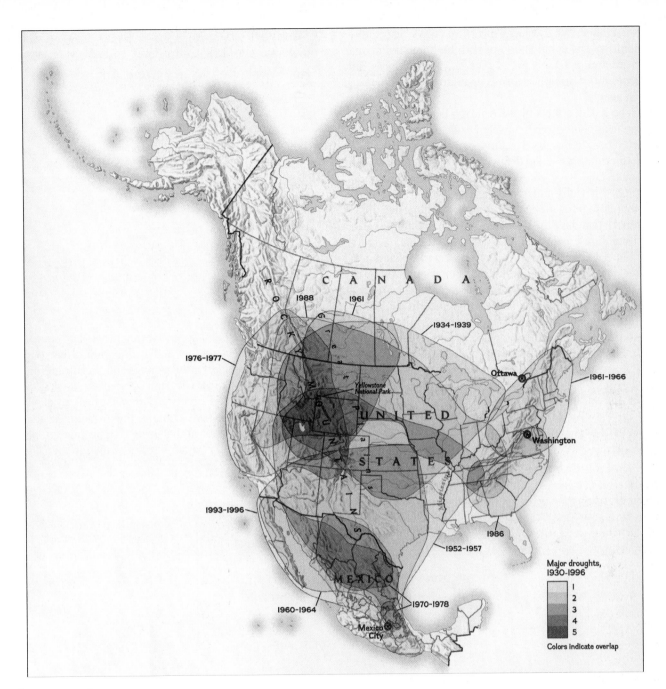

Figure 11.16
Major droughts in North America 1930–1996.
Source: National Geographic Image Collection.

bridge girders, and twisted heavy steel rail lines. Brick sidewalks and roadways heaved, and sidewalks cracked under the intense heat. Surface temperatures on tarred roads exceeded 65°C. In some instances, the softened asphalt melted and flowed freely into ditches. Road crews sanded streets in order to reduce skidding. But mostly it was a killer heat wave. Between 800 and 1,000 Canadians died—mostly the elderly and small infants.

HEAT WAVE IN CHICAGO, JULY 1995

Dry and hot weather in Canada and the central United States are commonly associated with high-pressure atmospheric conditions (Figure 11.14). In July 1995, a strong, upper-level ridge of high pressure sat on top of a slow-moving, hot, humid air mass on the surface. During the three-day period from 13 to 15 July, heat records were broken at numerous locations in the central and northern

Great Plains. What made this heat wave especially difficult was its combination of both high maximum and high minimum temperatures. The surface air mass did not cool much at night because its high humidity held so much heat.

The health effects of the Chicago heat wave became apparent as bodies were recovered from overheated dwellings. When human body temperature reaches 40.5°C, hyperthermia sets in and death becomes a possibility. The most affected were people without access to air conditioning, especially older people; the greater their ages, the higher their death percentages. A troubling statistic is that more than half the deceased lived on the top floor of their buildings, where heat buildup was greatest.

The 1995 heat wave in Chicago also offers an interesting example of changing social behaviour. Although the 1995 heat wave was comparable to heat waves in the 1930s, the number of deaths was far greater. In the 1930s, people were not afraid to sleep on their rooftops, and thousands slept on the beach, whereas in the 1990s people locked themselves in their rooms out of fear of violence.

EUROPE'S HEAT WAVE, 2003

The summer of 2003 brought record-breaking heat waves to Europe, and a delayed recognition of how many people it killed—over 35,000 (Table 11.5). Heat waves dominate

Table 11.5

Heat Wave Deaths in Europe, August 2003

Fatalities	Country
14,802	France
7,000	Germany
4,230	Spain
4,175	Italy
2,045	United Kingdom
1,400	Netherlands
1,316	Portugal
150	Belgium
35,118	Total deaths

the news while they happen, yet their role as silent killers usually does not get much attention. Heat waves mostly kill the elderly, the young, and the ill, and most deaths occur in cities. City areas are *urban heat islands* where buildings and streets absorb solar heat all day and then release stored heat at night, thus robbing residents of the relief that cool nights bring. Night-time temperatures in the city may be 5.5°C warmer than in the nearby

Figure 11.17
European heat wave, July 2003. Red areas are 10°C hotter than in July 2001. Blue areas are cooler.

Figure 11.18

Number of days with temperatures exceeding 30°C, 2050 (red) versus today (green), for several Canadian cities.

Source: © Her Majesty The Queen in Right of Canada, Environment Canada 2008. Reproduced with the permission of the Minister of Public Works and Government Services Canada.

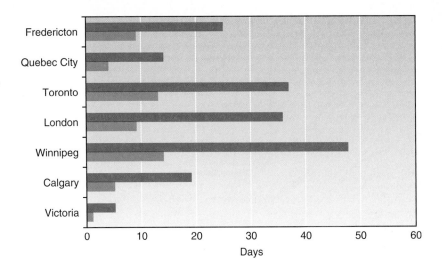

countryside. City dwellers' body temperatures stay higher and under greater stress.

The 2003 European summer heat wave was unique (Figure 11.17). Statistical analysis of temperature records of the last 150 years shows that the 2003 temperatures were unprecedented.

Because climate is likely to continue to warm through the 21st century, more and more heat waves will occur at the same time as the world population grows rapidly and huge numbers of people migrate into cities. Sometime in 2006, the world's population crossed over from being mostly rural to the majority of people now living in cities.

Warming scenarios suggest that hot spells in Canada will become more frequent and intense. By 2050, for example, hot summer days exceeding 30°C are likely to become three or four times more frequent than today in southern Canada (Figure 11.18). For Toronto, the yearly number of hot days, which now is about 12, averaged over 1971–2000, are projected to double by 2030, triple by 2050, and increase five times by 2090. Real scorcher days (above 35°C) would increase from 1 now to 10 by the close of the century.

We need to learn more about how to survive heat waves. Perhaps we are learning to adapt better; in the years following the Chicago and Western Europe heat waves, prolonged and comparable hot spells occurred, but with far fewer deaths. In developed countries, easier access to air conditioned spaces and greater health awareness have contributed effectively to reduce vulnerability to extreme heat.

Mid-Latitude Cyclones

Much of the mid-latitude severe weather in the northern hemisphere occurs via cyclones: air masses rotating counter-clockwise about a low-pressure core. This non-tropical cyclonic activity occurs at a number of scales.

On a relatively small scale, cyclonic airflow characterizes individual thunderstorms within a large frontal cyclone. The radius of a thunderstorm is much smaller than a typical cyclone (e.g., 10 km versus 1,000 km); however, its momentum is greater and its wind speeds are higher. Within a cyclonic thunderstorm, an even smaller-radius rotation, a **tornado**, may spring forth. The radius of a tornado funnel cloud may be only a few percent of that of a thunderstorm, but again, the smaller radius of the spinning tornado brings its mass closer to the axis of rotation, thus causing even higher wind speeds.

On a much larger scale are cyclones linked to jet-stream troughs (Figure 10.18). Cyclones in the northern hemisphere form at the Earth's surface at locations east of the upper-level trough in the jet stream. From the centre of these cyclones is often a cold front extending south and a warm front extending east. A cold front may wedge under a warm, moist air mass, sending it upward to form thick clouds, and, if the air is unstable enough, possibly a line of **thunderstorms**. A warm front may move northeastward, flowing up onto a cooler air body and producing widespread low clouds and precipitation (Figure 11.19).

In Atlantic Canada and the northeastern United States, large-scale cyclones can create potent storms known as *nor'easters*. When a low-pressure system moves up the northeastern United States coastline, its counter-clockwise circulation on its western or landward side draws cold, dry air down from the north toward the storm's centre. Meanwhile, its eastern or seaward side picks up moisture from the Atlantic Ocean to feed into the cyclone. Generally, the larger the temperature gradient between air over a cold landmass and air over relatively warm ocean waters, the more vigorous the storm. Once a nor'easter has developed, it typically begins to track northeastward off the Atlantic coastline, intensifying and picking up energy over the relatively warm coastal waters of the Gulf Stream where the air is heated and lifted to higher altitudes.

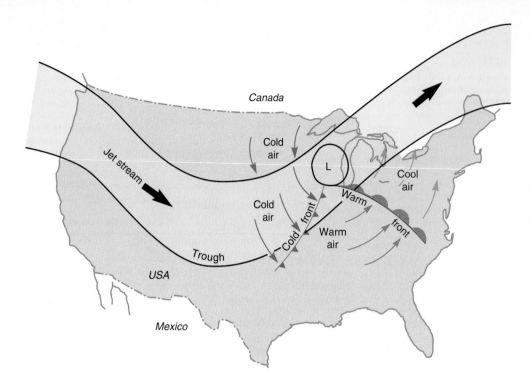

Figure 11.19
A trough in the jet stream helps cause a large-scale frontal cyclone formed of horizontally rotating winds around a low-pressure core. The cold front sweeping down from the north wedges beneath warm air, lifting it to form a line of thunderstorms. The warm front coming from the southwest flows up a gentle slope on top of the cooler air mass to the east to form widespread clouds and rain.

One of the most important factors in a nor'easter's potential destructiveness is the presence of a strong, stable high-pressure system positioned over eastern Canada. The high blocks a developing nor'easter from tracking swiftly up the east coast, thus lengthening its duration near the water. At the same time, the anticyclone funnels in cold air from the northeast, keeping temperatures along the northern Atlantic coast well below freezing.

Nor'easters are far more frequent than hurricanes. During the height of their season (December through March), an average of 30 nor'easters track up eastern North America, often with gale-force or stronger winds and towering waves that batter the coast, causing serious beach erosion, property damage, and even loss of life. Most of the major snowstorms along North America's Atlantic Coast arise from nor'easters.

A very explosive form of nor'easter is a "weather bomb," a powerful, rapidly intensifying maritime storm that seems to pop out of nowhere, making it tough to forecast. The key to weather bombs' identity is the rate at which the storm intensifies. Central pressures must drop at least 2.4 kPa in 24 hours. Some of the more explosive bombs drop at twice that rate. The lower the pressure, the stronger the winds. Weather bombs tend to occur after the hurricane season between late fall and early spring but can be just as powerful and destructive.

Such a storm occurred on 7 November 2001, when the remnants of two hurricanes and a powerful mid-latitude storm from New England converged and then intensified over the Gulf of St. Lawrence. The storm blew out car windows, swamped wharves and fragile sand dunes, and caused blackouts for more than 100,000 hydro customers in Atlantic Canada. Prince Edward Island and Cape Breton Island received the brunt of the storm—sustaining high winds combined with high tides to produce a storm surge of one metre or more, and waves of nine metres. Rocks as heavy as 14 kg were thrown hundreds of metres inland, some landing on golf greens. The Confederation Bridge between New Brunswick and Prince Edward Island was closed to all traffic for the first time ever when winds were clocked at 123 km/h gusting to 155, the strongest ever measured. The storm also tore out chunks of the Canso Causeway connecting Cape Breton Island to mainland Nova Scotia.

Another type of powerful mid-latitude cyclone is a "witches of November" storm over the Great Lakes. November is one of the windiest and stormiest months on the Great Lakes. It accounts for about 10% of the annual traffic on the Great Lakes, but 40% of the shipwrecks. The location of the lakes in the interior of North America, between the source regions of contrasting Arctic and tropical air masses, often brings the region rapidly changing and explosive weather systems. Along the overriding jet stream, developing cyclones track eastward into the Great Lakes where they get an extra shot of energy from the relatively warm lake waters. Lows are often stronger than at other times of the year. At their greatest intensity, these storms reach very low pressures, sometimes rivalling Atlantic hurricanes, and creating tremendous winds and monster waves as much as 12 m high.

THE NORTH AMERICAN EAST COAST "WHITE HURRICANE" OF 1993

Shortly before spring began in 1993, an immense cyclone moved in and covered Eastern North America from Cuba to Nova Scotia and from the Appalachian Mountains to the Atlantic Ocean.

The storm unleashed tremendous forces on millions of residents. Thousands of people were isolated by record snowfalls from Georgia to New England. The highest snowfall amounts recorded exceeded 140 cm. For the first time, every major airport on the east coast was closed at one time or another by the storm. Snowfall rates of 5 to 8 cm/h were common during the height of the storm. Hundreds of roof collapses occurred owing to the weight of the heavy wet snow. In the wake of the storm, bitterly cold conditions pushed into the region, establishing dozens of new daily record lows, including −14°C in Washington, D.C.

The death toll in the United States was 400, more than three times the combined death toll from Hurricanes Hugo and Andrew. In Canada, three storm-related deaths were reported in Quebec and one in Ontario. Up to 42 cm of snow fell in New Brunswick and gusts of 200 km/h whipped across Cape Breton Island. Off Nova Scotia, hurricane-force winds churned up 15 to 20 m seas. A 177 m ship sank in heavy seas 175 km south of Sable Island, Nova Scotia, with all 33 of its crew lost at sea. Twenty-metre waves were reported in the area. A wind gust of 210 km/h was recorded at Grand Etang, Nova Scotia.

Overall damage figures exceeded US$3 billion, making this the fourth-costliest storm in American history. The late-winter cyclone was bigger than the legendary blizzard that struck the northeastern United States on the same days of March in 1888. The 1888 blizzard brought wind gusts up to 135 km/h and snow drifts 6 m deep. In New York City, the heavy snow immobilized the city, leaving about 400 people dead.

Why did such a huge winter storm hit such an unusually large area so late in the season? How did it combine some of the worst aspects of both a blizzard and a hurricane? The weather map for 12 March 1993 shows a large trough in the jet stream and three air masses migrating toward it. The collision of two of these air masses would have made a significant storm, but the conflict between all three created a "storm of the century." The scene was set with an unusually low-pressure zone in the Gulf of Mexico causing big trouble with its warm, moist air and line of violent thunderstorms rotating around it (Figure 11.20). Then a trough in the jet stream, with its

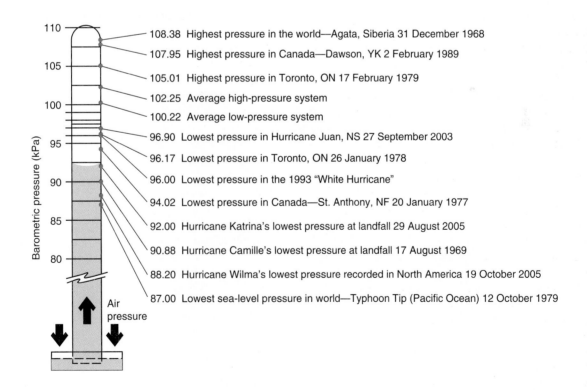

Figure 11.20

Air pressures recorded in a barometer. The barometer is a tube with one end closed, filled with mercury, and turned upside down in a dish of mercury. The mercury in the tube rises and falls depending on the amount of air pressure on the mercury in the dish. Commonly, high pressure indicates clear weather, and low pressure means clouds and rain.

associated very low pressure, created rotation that drew in a fast-moving mass of frigid Arctic air from the north as well as a rainy and snowy east-moving air mass off the Pacific Ocean. The collision among the three air masses began in Florida. The low-pressure zone and three colliding air masses rode up the Atlantic coastline with the jet stream, savaging everything in their path.

BLIZZARDS

A **blizzard** is the most violent winter storm, combining strong winds with cold temperatures (Figure 11.21). Whiteouts, drifting and blowing snow with heavy snow depositions, cause many hardships. A blizzard, however, can occur without new snow; strong winds can pick up and blow snow dropped by earlier storms. In February 1978, the southern side of Regina, Saskatchewan was buried for four days by a blizzard. Snow drifts reached rooftops yet the storm left only a trace of new snow at the airport.

Environment Canada uses different criteria for defining blizzards in different regions. Officially, to be classified as a blizzard, the following conditions must be fulfilled:

- a temperature of less than 0°C (more often below −10°C) or wind chill of −25°C or lower
- wind speed of 40 km/h or greater
- visibility of less than 1 km
- duration of these conditions for at least three to six hours.

Table 11.6

Average Number of Blizzard Hours in a Year for Selected Canadian Cities

Whitehorse	1
Vancouver	0
Yellowknife	4
Edmonton	3
Regina	36
Winnipeg	18
Toronto	2
Ottawa	5
Montreal	11
Quebec City	20
Fredericton	4
Moncton	30
Charlottetown	40
Halifax	9
St. John's	46

Blizzards are often winter's deadliest storms. Fatalities occur (1) from heart attacks while shovelling snow and pushing stuck cars, (2) when automobiles slide and collide, (3) when people slip on ice and fall, or (4) when people get disoriented or lost, and freeze.

Figure 11.21
A blizzard blows through Michigan.
Source: NOAA.

Blizzards in Canada are most frequent in the open prairie but less frequent in the prairie parkland and forests where the force of the wind is broken (Table 11.6). Blizzards in southern Ontario are more frequent downwind of the Great Lakes during bursts of lake-effect snow off open lake waters. Perhaps surprisingly, blizzards are rare in the Western Arctic and Yukon where winds are very light and the snow amount is scant.

Legendary tales are told of pioneer farmers who perished midway between house and barn or of Arctic explorers who died after straying only a metre or two from their campsites. Even today, not a winter goes by without tragic news being heard about travellers succumbing to a blizzard.

The 1977 White Death, Niagara Peninsula
January 1977 began in the grips of a bitter cold wave that swept across the eastern half of the continent on New Year's Day and ended with one of the worst blizzards ever in Ontario and Western and Northern New York State. The extreme cold meant that Lake Erie froze completely some two to three weeks earlier than usual. While the ice-covered lake cut off moisture to passing storms, the frozen surface also became a smooth platform for old snow to accumulate.

In the last week of January, a cold low became established over James Bay, bringing another surge of Arctic air across Ontario. The cold air contained little snow; however, its fierce winds lifted the mounds of snow on Lake Erie and blew it inland into monstrous drifts. The blizzard buried residents of the Niagara Peninsula and Western New York State in their cars and homes. The storm was blamed for three deaths in Ontario and 24 in New York State. Snow on the ground reached to power lines. Monster drifts also closed airports and blocked rail lines. In some frightening scenes, snowploughs sheared off the tops of cars buried along the Queen Elizabeth Way highway.

The 2004 White Juan, Halifax
They dubbed it White Juan—a hurricane disguised as a blizzard. Late on 17 February 2004, an ordinary winter storm centred over Cape Hatteras, North Carolina, suddenly intensified over the Gulf Stream before striking the Maritimes. Its central pressure plunged 5.7 kilopascals in 42 hours, making it one of the most explosive storms ever—even more powerful than its namesake, Hurricane Juan, which had struck the same area five months earlier.

Huge, lumbering White Juan packed quite a weather wallop—heavy snows, fierce winds gusting to 124 km/h and zero visibility. Snow fell at a phenomenal rate of 5 cm/h for 12 straight hours. Blowing snow and high winds maintained blizzard conditions for a day or more and created drifts as tall as 3 m. Halifax, Yarmouth, and Charlottetown broke all-time 24-hour snowfall records,

receiving almost a metre of snow. For Halifax, the snowfall almost doubled the city's previous record for a single day. With over 300,000 people, Halifax is the largest city in the world to ever receive such a dump of snow in one day.

The 1947 Great Prairie Blizzard
Railway officials called it the worst blizzard to affect the railway in Canadian history. At the end of January and the beginning of February in 1947, a monstrous whiteout buried the southern Prairies from Calgary to Winnipeg. In Saskatchewan, all roads and rail lines were blocked for more than ten days. The snow was so deep in places that people could step over the power lines. One train was buried in a snowdrift 8 m deep. Regina was isolated when all rail lines and highways in and out of the city were blocked and all telephone lines were down. Extreme cold air at −43°C arrived on the heels of the storm. Regina faced the worst fuel crisis in its history—a coal shortage that closed all city schools and caused curtailment of heating in offices, businesses, churches, and factories.

ICE STORMS
Forecasting the occurrence and the amount of **freezing rain** is tricky, yet this form of precipitation affects Canadian cities several times a year, most often in the east (Table 11.7). The atmosphere must be properly layered—a layer of warm air aloft with temperatures above freezing, sandwiched between layers of colder air with

Table 11.7

Average Number of Hours of Freezing Rain in a Year for Selected Canadian Cities

Whitehorse	4
Victoria	2
Vancouver	4
Yellowknife	35
Edmonton	21
Regina	35
Winnipeg	31
Toronto	35
Ottawa	64
Montreal	48
Quebec City	54
Fredericton	47
Charlottetown	53
Halifax	33
St. John's	148

Source: Based on *The Day Niagara Falls Ran Dry!* Key Porter Books 1993.

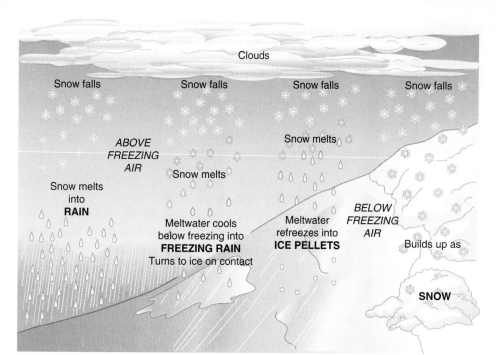

Figure 11.22
Snow may fall through cold air to the ground, or snow may be modified during its fall through different air temperatures into rain, freezing rain, or ice pellets.

(labels within figure)

Clouds

Snow falls   Snow falls   Snow falls   Snow falls

ABOVE FREEZING AIR

Snow melts

Snow melts

Snow melts into **RAIN**

Meltwater cools below freezing into **FREEZING RAIN**
Turns to ice on contact

Meltwater refreezes into **ICE PELLETS**

BELOW FREEZING AIR

Builds up as

SNOW

temperatures below freezing. Rain falls, or snow melts, while falling through the intermediary warm layer and continues as liquid precipitation through the shallow cold layer near the ground. If the surface layer is deep enough to allow the raindrops to refreeze, the liquid drops form tiny ice particles called ice pellets or continue to freeze into snowflakes (Figure 11.22). On the other hand, if the layer is shallow or the drops do not stay in the cold air long enough to freeze, they become supercooled. They reach the ground as supercooled liquid (water droplets at a temperature below 0°C) or as a mixture of liquid and ice. Upon striking a colder object, such as pavement, hydro wires, tree branches, building walls or cars, the supercooled raindrops spread out and freeze almost immediately, forming a smooth thin veneer of slick ice.

How a Thunderstorm Works

Air temperature normally decreases upward from the ground surface through the troposphere at an average rate of about 6°C/km. At this rate, the troposphere is statically stable. On those days when the **lapse rate**, that is, the actual rate of cooling with height, is greater than 6° to 10°C/km, the atmosphere is unstable. The degree of atmospheric instability increases as the temperature differences increase between warm bottom air and overlying cool air. Warm, low-altitude air is less dense and it wants to rise upward. Once vertical lifting begins, the warm air mass will continue to rise as long as it is less dense than the surrounding air.

If heat builds up in dry air near the surface, the warm air will rise and cool adiabatically (with a lapse rate of 10°C/km) after a moderate ascent, and no thunderstorms will form. However, if the air near the ground is both warm and moist, the warm air may rise high enough to pass through the lifting condensation level, allowing condensation of water vapour to begin. This marks the cloud base for the thunderstorm. Once condensation is occurring, the rising cloud also is fuelled by a large and important energy source—release of the latent heat that was absorbed during evaporation. This latent heat provides the fuel to help form thunderstorms, tornadoes, hurricanes, and other severe weather.

The process of vertical transfer of heat in a rising air mass is known as convection. As water vapour in the rising air mass condenses, it releases latent heat, adding to the warmth of the rising cloudy air and helping the cloud top climb even higher.

Most individual thunderstorms form on sunny days in the late afternoon or early evening, when temperatures of the ground surface and lower troposphere are the highest. A thundercloud begins with an initial updraft of warm, moist air, maybe aided by wind pushing up a hill slope or by surface-wind collision. The early stage of thunderstorm development requires a continuous supply of rising, warm, moist air to keep the updraft and cloud mass growing (Figures 11.23a and 11.24).

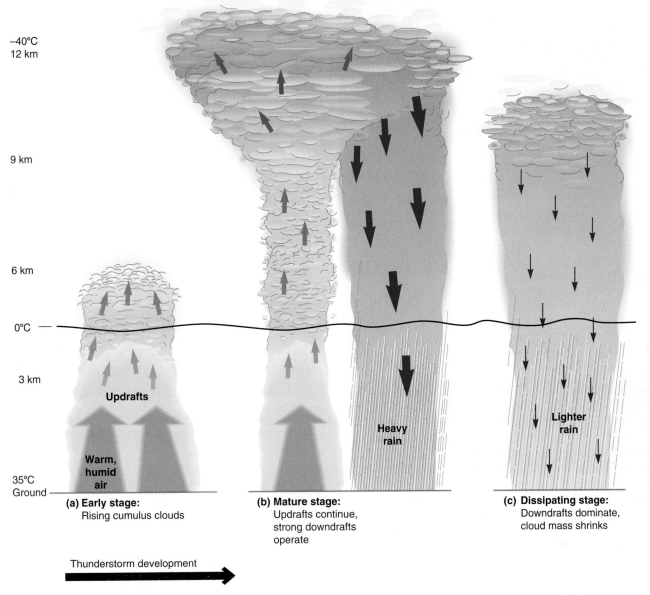

Figure 11.23

Stages in the development of a thunderstorm. (a) *Early stage:* Warm, humid air rises in updrafts; cooling causes condensation to form clouds; air keeps rising as long as it is warmer than surrounding air. (b) *Mature stage:* Ice crystals and large raindrops become too heavy for updrafts to maintain in suspension; ice and rain fall, forcing air to move in downdrafts, while updrafts still pump warm, moist air into the thunderstorm. (c) *Dissipating stage:* Downdrafts dominate, warm and moist updrafts cease, and rain becomes weaker as clouds begin to evaporate.

When the amount of ice 3 crystals and/or water drops becomes too heavy for the updrafts to support, some upper-level precipitation begins. Falling rain causes downward drag, developing downdrafts and pulling in cooler, dryer air surrounding the tall cloud mass. In the thunderstorm's mature stage, the cloud-mass top commonly spreads out as an icy cap (Figures 11.23b and 11.25). Updrafts and downdrafts operate side by side as warm, moist air is rising high at the same time that cool, dry air is descending rapidly. This is the most violent stage of the thunderstorm, with gusty winds pummelling the ground and tossing about any airplane daring to fly through the storm. Rain is heavy, **thunder** and **lightning** are powerful, and ice may pummel the ground as **hail**.

The dissipating stage is reached when downdrafts drag in so much cool, dry air that it chokes off the updrafts

Figure 11.24
Early stage of thunderstorm growth.
Copyright PhotoLink/Getty Images

Figure 11.25
Late in the mature stage of a thunderstorm's existence.
Copyright Royalty Free/CORBIS

of warm, moist air necessary to fuel the thunderstorm (Figure 11.23c). Without new moisture, the tall thundercloud mass evaporates in the surrounding dry air.

Occasionally, a winter thunderstorm arrives when advancing warm air from the south rides above retreating cold air at the surface, as might occur ahead of a warm front. The warm air is slowly but gradually forced aloft. In being lifted, it becomes destabilized. The air is cooled, clouds grow, and occasionally thunder is heard. Generally, you do not see lightning because the widespread low cloud obscures the towering thunderclouds rising from it. A winter thunderstorm or "thundersnow" is much less severe than its summer cousin. They are rare in Canada; for example, over 30 years of records, not a single winter thunderstorm was observed in Edmonton and Regina. For the same period, Winnipeg recorded only four winter thunderstorms. In Eastern Canada, winter thunderstorms are more common because the tropical air associated with these systems is more prevalent. In the East, if you listen for it, you will probably hear thunder about once a winter.

MICROBURSTS: AN AIRPLANE'S ENEMY

In the mature stage of a thunderstorm, violent downbursts of air, sometimes accompanied by rain and maybe hail, strike the ground and spread out horizontally in all directions. If these sudden, strong downrushes of wind are confined to a small area tens of metres to 4 km in diameter, they are called **microbursts**. Because microburst winds often exceed 200 km/h, they can sometimes be mistaken for a weak tornado. Low-level microburst winds present a major aviation hazard when horizontal changes in wind direction and speed are prevalent.

A crude analogy can be made to dropping a water-filled balloon from the roof of a house and watching it splatter with force on the ground. What if the "water balloon" is a heavy ball of wind with rainwater descending at about 270 km/h? The danger to airplanes is obvious. Microbursts are especially hazardous to airplanes during takeoff and landing. The airplane is so close to the ground that the unexpected downdraft of a microburst can push the plane into the ground before the pilot has a chance to react.

Between 1975 and 1985, sudden downburst winds were responsible in aircraft accidents leading to the loss of 500 lives worldwide. One of the worst occurred at New Orleans International Airport on 9 July 1982 during a severe thunderstorm. Shortly after a 4:10 p.m. take-off, Pan American Flight 759 was hit by a downburst that slammed the plane down onto a residential neighbourhood, killing 8 people on the ground and 145 passengers on board the aircraft.

On 2 August 2005, an Air France flight from Paris landed in a driving rainstorm at Lester Pearson International Airport in Toronto. The jet overran the runway, slammed into a ditch, and burst into flames. Miraculously, the more than 300 people aboard survived. By the time the Air France pilot lined up to land, shifting and shearing winds with strong gusts, an intense downpour that reduced visibility, and frequent lightning flashes filled the air at and near the airport. Speculation was that a microburst flowing from a nearby thunderstorm could have either increased the wind ground speed or reduced the airspeed of the plane in the seconds immediately preceding touchdown, forcing the jet to career off the runway into a gully.

Many airports in microburst-prone regions now use Doppler radar to detect microburst conditions in time to warn pilots. Training is given to pilots on how to fly an aircraft out of microbursts.

THUNDERSTORMS IN CANADA

Thunderstorms develop both in isolation and as parts of larger weather systems. The distribution of thunderstorms in Canada shows a non-uniform pattern (Figure 11.26). Southern Ontario has the most thunderstorms; the Arctic and the coasts the fewest. Windsor, Ontario, averages 33 days of thunderstorms per year. Canada's most southern city is the most humid place and has one of the warmest summers—prime ingredients for initiating thunderstorm activity. Further, it is away from the stabilizing effects of the Great Lakes.

Environment Canada issues severe thunderstorm warnings only when severe weather is occurring or is about to occur. The weather service tries to provide lead times of 15 minutes to two hours. Environment Canada usually issues watches first, then warnings. In some situations, however, when severe thunderstorms develop quickly, forecasters skip the watch stage and issue warnings directly.

Severe thunderstorms can wreck havoc on people and

property with their lethal arsenal—heavy rain, flash floods, hail, lightning, and high-speed winds, which can be either straight-line blasts or rotating tornadoes. A severe thunderstorm warning is issued when one or more of the following is expected to occur:

- wind gusts of 90 km/h or more
- hail of 2 cm in diameter or larger
- rainfall of 50 mm or more within one hour or 75 mm or more within three hours.

HAIL

Hailstones are layered ice balls dropped from severe thunderstorms (Figure 11.27). The stones of varying shapes and sizes crash to the ground at speeds exceeding 150 km/h. There are no records of hail killing anybody in Canada. Wildlife and livestock are less fortunate. Once, hailstones pounded a 270-kg hog to death. On 14 July 1953, a hailstorm in Alberta killed 3,000 ducks and thousands of other birds, such as owls and songbirds. Four days later hailstones crushed the skulls of 27,000 ducks in the same area. Hail also takes a tremendous toll on crops, vehicles, and buildings. On 9 August 2007, softball-sized hail struck southern Manitoba, flattening a crop ready to be harvested. In Dauphin, hardly a car or dwelling's roof was left untouched, with repairs totalling several million dollars. It is estimated that it will take up to two years to complete repairs.

Important requirements for hail are (1) large thunderstorms with buoyant hot air rising from heated ground and (2) upper-level cold air creating maximum temperature contrasts, resulting in (3) the strong updrafts needed to keep hailstones suspended aloft while adding coatings of ice onto ever-growing cores. Comparison of thunderstorm frequency in Figure 11.26 with hail frequency in Figure 11.28 reveals a marked difference. Thunderstorms that drop large, damaging hailstones are irregularly distributed in Canada. Thunderstorms are common in Ontario, but the cold air necessary for hail formation is uncommon. Destructive, large hail abounds in the colder Prairies, especially central Alberta.

A cross-section through a hailstone (Figure 11.27) reveals accretionary layers of ice with an onion-like appearance. The layering indicates that the hailstone travelled through parts of the thunderstorm cloud with greater and lesser amounts of super-cooled liquid-water content. A hailstone weighing 290 g (estimated to be 450 g on impact) fell in Cedoux, Saskatchewan on 27 August 1973. It had a diameter of 114 mm, the largest ever documented in Canada. A much larger hailstone, the biggest ever documented in North America, fell in south-central Nebraska on 22 June 2003. It measured 17.8 cm in diameter—almost as large as a soccer ball. Updrafts must be very powerful to keep hailstones this large suspended in the air.

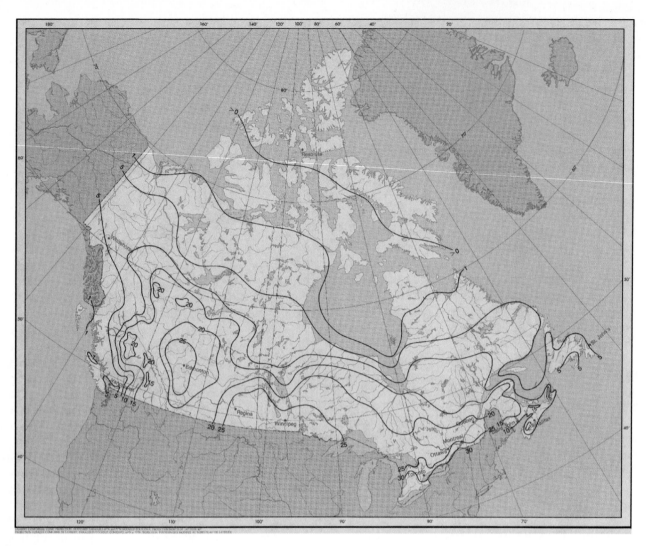

Figure 11.26
Average annual number of days with thunderstorms in Canada.

Source: © Her Majesty The Queen in Right of Canada, Environment Canada 2008. Reproduced with the permission of the Minister of Public Works and Government Services Canada.

Whereas hail is common in Canada, it is relatively rare at any single location. Most southern localities report only one or two days of hail each year (Figure 11.28). Some of the most hail-prone geography in the world, central Alberta's hailstorm alley to the lees of the Rockies gets hit on four or six days each year, although some farms have been hit as many as ten times in one year. May to October is the period of maximum hail occurrences, and nearly three-quarters of all hail falls occur between noon and the dinner hour. The average hailfall usually lasts from six to ten minutes. July is the month of peak hailstorm activity although the most expensive hailstorm in Canada occurred in September. The Labour Day 1991 storm in Calgary caused up to $412 million in insured losses in 116,000 claims—a record insurance loss for any single hailstorm in Canadian history. The 30-minute storm split trees, flooded basements, broke windows and siding, and dented thousands of vehicles. Raging sewer waters blew off sewer covers and plugged catch basins. More than a quarter of the homes in Calgary experienced some property damage. Many aircraft at Calgary International Airport suffered costly hail damage.

To protect property against hail damage, civil engineers and contractors recommend the development of economical building materials for roofs and exterior walls that are resistant to impact by hailstones. To reduce property damage caused by hail, some insurance companies have sponsored cloud seeding, which is aimed at generating small, softer hailstones.

LIGHTNING

Thunderstorms generate lightning (Figure 11.29), and thunder is caused by lightning. Lightning is a major cause of weather-related deaths in Canada during the summer. Hurricanes, tornadoes, and floods are dramatic events that take many human lives in brief, dramatic episodes, whereas a lightning bolt kills people in ones and twos.

Lightning Hot Spots in Canada

At any moment there are 2,000 thunderstorms happening worldwide. Lightning strikes at least 100 times a second, nearly nine million times a day, and more than three billion times a year. According to Environment Canada, lightning flashes occur in Canada about three million times a year. That includes a rate of one every three seconds during the summer months.

Figure 11.27
A broken hailstone shows the layers of its growth.

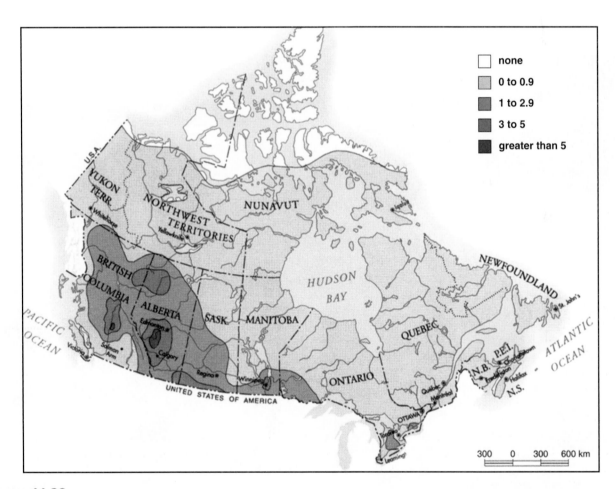

Figure 11.28
Average annual number of days with hail in Canada.

Source: © Her Majesty The Queen in Right of Canada, Environment Canada 2008. Reproduced with the permission of the Minister of Public Works and Government Services Canada.

Where does lightning occur? Its distribution is similar to thunderstorm days.

Flash density averages approximately 0.5 to 2 flashes per square kilometre per year in much of Canada except southern Ontario, which receives approximately 1.5 to 3.5 flashes per square kilometre per year, and most of British Columbia, Newfoundland, and Labrador, and the northern portions of the country, which receive less than 0.5 flashes per square kilometre per year (Figure 11.30). While southern Ontario is the lightning "hot spot" in Canada, it receives much less lightning on average than neighbouring areas of the United States which have warmer climate and more tempestuous weather.

How Lightning Works

You can make your own "lightning." Drag your feet across a carpet and become a negatively charged "thundercloud." Now touch a metal door handle and feel the "lightning" as the negative charges bolt from you to the positive charges on the metal. The lightning of thunderstorms involves a similar flow of electric current as areas with excess positive charges seek a balance with places having excess negative charges. During the buildup of tall clouds, charged particles separate, creating an abundance of positive charges up top and an excess of negative charges down low (Figure 11.31).

The charge imbalance apparently comes about as the freezing and shattering of super-cooled water drops initiates charge separations that are distributed by updrafts and downdrafts within the thundercloud. The charge separations occur during the cloud buildup of the early stage (Figures 11.23a and 11.24), and then lightning bolts forth during the mature stage (Figures 11.23b and 11.25).

A thundercloud interacts electrically with the ground. The abundance of negative charges in the basal part of the cloud induces a buildup of positive charges on the ground surface, because the opposite charges attract each other. Lightning can move from cloud to earth, earth to cloud, or cloud to cloud.

Lightning moves at speeds over 10,000 km/s and typically includes several strokes, all occurring within 0.5 to 2 seconds. Thanks to high-speed photography, it is now possible to explain the basic sequence within a lightning flash. (1) Static electricity builds up within

Figure 11.29
A thunderstorm electrifies downtown Montreal.
Photo: © Desirable Futures.

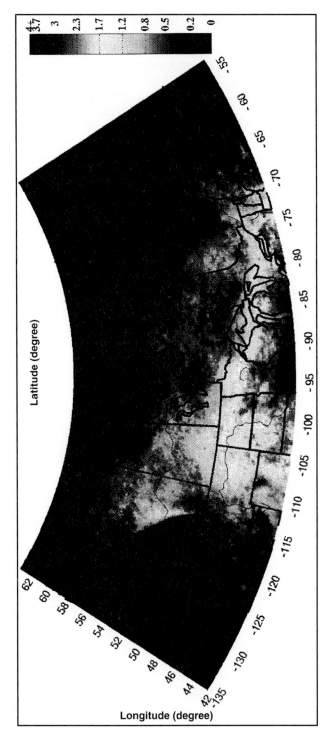

Figure 11.30
Canadian annual lightning flash density average (1998–2005).

jumps as a stepped leader (Figure 11.32b). (4) As the stepped leader nears the ground, the electrical field at the surface increases greatly, attracting streamers of positive sparks upward and connecting with the stepped leader about 50 m above ground (Figure11.32c). (5) The connection closes the electrical circuit and initiates the return stroke, sending positive charges up to the cloud with a brilliant flash (Figures 11.32d and 11.33). (6) More lightning strokes occur as charges flow between the cloud and the earth.

Several different strokes all occur within the one- or two-second event we call a lightning bolt. If you have seen a lightning bolt that appears to flicker, you have witnessed the several different up-and-down strokes that constitute a given "bolt." The electrical discharge of lightning can briefly create temperatures as high as 30,000°C. The high temperatures of lightning flash heat the surrounding air, causing it to expand explosively; this expansion of air produces the sound waves we call thunder.

The 30/30 Lightning Rule

Lightning is one of the most consistent and underrated causes of weather-related deaths or injury in North America. Lightning isn't good at killing you, though. Given that just one lightning bolt contains 100 million volts of electricity, while only 120 volts can kill you; and that more than 30 million lightning bolts strike North America each year, it's surprising that fewer than 100 people are struck dead each year. That number, however, represents more deaths than all other weather forces combined, including hurricanes, tornadoes, and floods.

In Canada, lightning kills an average of 10 people annually and seriously injures about 125 people. That's a one in 240,000 chance of being hit, better than your odds of winning most high-prize lotteries. Lightning mortality has declined significantly over the past century as people moved from rural to urban settings. Falling death rates can also be attributed to better forecasts and warnings, greater awareness of the lightning threat, more substantial buildings available for safe refuge, more structures fitted with lightning rods and conductors to convey the lightning energy to the earth, improved medical care, and more rapid communications.

Whereas the number of lightning deaths has decreased over the years, damages from lightning strikes have been on the increase, which can be attributed mostly to increases in population, more wealth, and more personal possessions. Forest fire managers are keen users of lightning observations and forecasts as indicators of forest fire risks (Figure 14.21). Another major user of lightning data is hydro utilities, where lightning hits can disrupt electrical power distribution. Lightning occurrence is also an indication of severe weather hazards such as microbursts, heavy rains, and tornadoes.

the lower thundercloud and induces opposite charges on the ground. (2) Discharge begins within the cloud and initiates a dimly visible, negatively charged stream of electrons propagating downward (Figure 11.31a). (3) The conductive stream moves earthward in 50 m

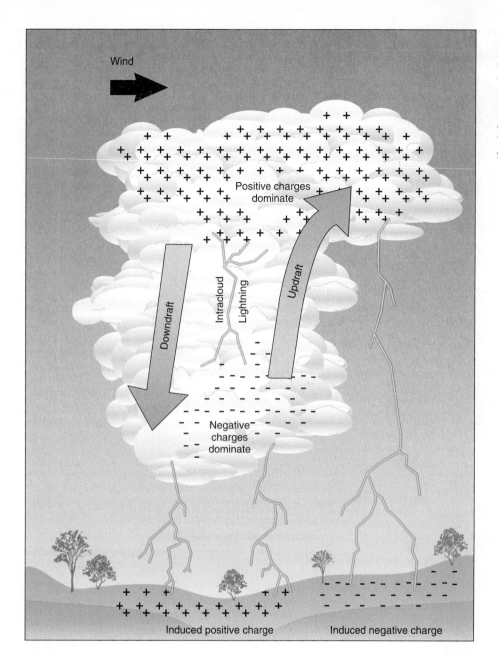

Figure 11.31
Schematic view of charge separation within a thundercloud and the induced charges on the Earth beneath. When electrical potential is great enough, narrow channels of air become ionized, allowing them to conduct the electricity that we see as lightning.

Three-quarters of all lightning casualties occur between May and September (with July the most lightning-prone month) and nearly four-fifths occur between 10 a.m. and 7:00 p.m (Figure 11.34). Most victims are male; ages 10 to 35 account for one-half of the fatalities. Males are killed 5.6 times as often as females, and are 4.9 times as likely to be injured as females. Don't get the idea that males are more magnetic than females or have smaller brains; they are just likely to spend more time outdoors and are often willing to take greater risks.

Each year, about 400 children and adults in the United States and Canada are struck by lightning while working and playing outside at sports events, or attending concerts and assemblies. Wide-open fields and parks are often cited as the most dangerous places to be during a thunderstorm. Sports fields offer a lot of targets for lightning such as poles, wire fences, dugouts, and metal bleachers. The fields themselves are wide open where players and spectators become the tallest objects around. In and around a thunderstorm, swimming and other water-based activities are very dangerous and should be stopped until the threat is over. Water is a good conductor of electrical current and if the lightning should strike the water even at a good distance from the swimmer, he or she could still get a serious shock.

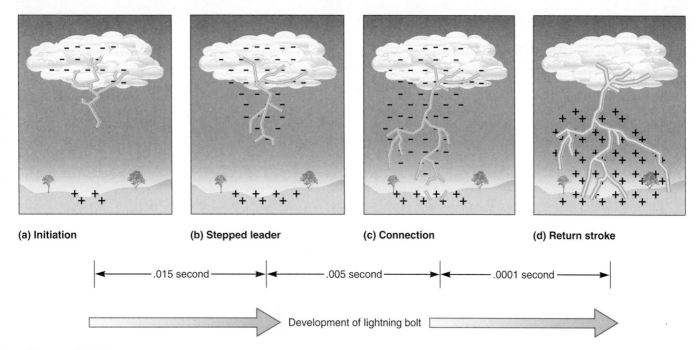

(a) Initiation   **(b) Stepped leader**   **(c) Connection**   **(d) Return stroke**

.015 second   .005 second   .0001 second

Development of lightning bolt

Figure 11.32

Steps in creating a lightning bolt. (a) *Initiation:* Charge separation in cloud builds up static electricity. (b) *Stepped leader:* Negative charges move in dimly visible stream downward in intermittent steps. (c) *Connection:* When leader nears ground, a positive discharge leaps up, completing the attachment. (d) *Return stroke:* The connected path flashes bright as charges exchange between cloud and ground in several events, totalling about 0.5 second.

Source: NOAA.

Figure 11.33

Triple lightning modes. On left, cloud-to-ground followed by extra-bright return stroke from ground. In lower right, ground toward cloud seeking to connect. In middle right, cloud-to-cloud.

Photo: © NOAA.

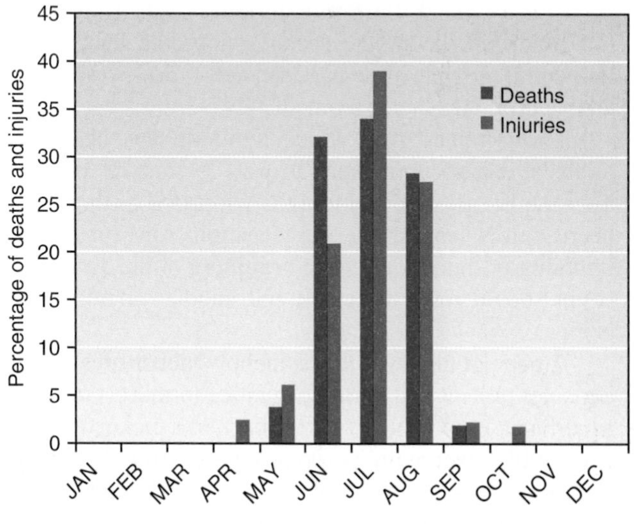

Figure 11.34

Monthly distribution of lightning-related deaths and injuries in Canada (1986–2005).

Source: Brian Mills et al. 2006.

In Greater Depth

What to Do and Not Do in Case of Lightning

DO

- Follow forecasts.
- Get off the phone, unless it's a cordless or a cell phone; 2.4% of victims are hit through phones.
- Clear the lake, pool, and shower. Water is a great electrical conductor. Move away from open water such as swimming pools, lakes, rivers, wet beaches, and piers. If you are in a small boat, go ashore.
- Get in your car, but don't touch anything.
- Stay 5 m apart if you're outside with others; a charge can jump.
- Crouch and ball up. Don't lie flat. Don't put your hands down, cover your ears or head.
- Remember the 30/30 rule.

DON'T

- Blow-dry your hair, make a cake, or do the dishes—stay away from water and wires.
- Surf TV or the Internet—don't rely on surge protectors.
- Watch out the window—stay well inside.
- Shelter under a tree; in a phone booth; or near a fence, shed, tractor, or tent with metal poles.
- Walk under power lines, beside highway guard rails, or on railway tracks.

Lightning tragedies can be avoided. Generally speaking, if you see lightning or hear thunder you are already at risk. Every flash of lightning is dangerous, from the first to the last. It doesn't have to be overhead to be dangerous. Louder or more frequent thunder indicates that the storm is fast approaching, increasing your risk for lightning injury or death. Lightning often strikes as far as 15 km away from any rainfall. Many deaths from lightning occur ahead of the storm because people try to wait to the last minute before seeking shelter. As the jingle goes: if you can see it flee it; if you hear it, clear it.

Environment Canada recommends the 30/30 rule:

Thirty-second flash-to-bang rule: When lightning is recognized, count the seconds until the bang of its thunder. If the time lapse is 30 seconds or less, you should take appropriate shelter immediately.

Thirty-minute rule: Once lightning has been recognized, it is recommended to wait 30 minutes or more after the last flash of lightning is witnessed or thunder is heard before leaving the safe location. Any subsequent lightning or thunder after the beginning of the 30-minute count should reset the clock and another count should begin.

A popular fallacy is that somehow rubber tires or rubber soles protect you during a thunderstorm. It is true that a hard metal-top vehicle, not the back of a pickup truck or convertible (even with its top up), away from the danger of falling trees or hydro poles is one of the safest places to be in a lightning storm. School buses are an excellent lightning shelter that can be utilized for large groups of people. But it is not your all-weather tires that guard you against the risk of lightning. Vehicles are an excellent source of protection because the all-metal steel cage or frame surrounding the vehicle dissipates the current equally before arcing around the tires to the ground, and therefore there is little likelihood that the current will go to the interior.

WINDS

Winds can arrive with tremendous power; they may be hot or cold. The rotating winds of tornadoes capture our imaginations; they are the most feared offspring of a thunderstorm. Tornadoes derive their name from the Spanish verb *tornar,* which means "to turn." In 1888, the Spanish word **derecho**, meaning "straight ahead," was applied to widespread, powerful, straight-line winds. Derechos can be as damaging as a small tornado: they kill people; extensively damage mobile homes and lightly constructed buildings; cause tragic incidents with airplanes, trucks, and cars; and mow down huge tracts of trees.

Derechos

Thunderstorms advancing in a line can have their individual energies combine to form a line of ferocious winds with hurricane-force gusts. An organized line of storms in a region can generate a derecho lasting 10 to 15 minutes.

Derechos commonly extend along a line at least 400 km long with wind gusts of 100 km/h; maximum recorded wind speeds are 240 km/h. In North America, derechos mostly occur in the middle and eastern states, and in southern Ontario.

Ontario-to-New York Derecho, 15 July 1995

In the evening of 15 July 1995, a huge complex of thunderstorms with imbedded tornadoes packing hurricane-force winds and tens of thousands of lightning bolts cut numerous paths of destruction from Upper Michigan across Central Ontario to the Ottawa River Valley. Early the next morning, the storm moved south across the Adirondack Mountains of New York State and off the coast of New England. The 1200-km trek took only 12 hours at an average speed of 110 km/h. Wind gusts in the worst-damaged area were in the 150–200 km/h range. In Ontario, the winds scattered 1-tonne round bales of hay as if they were breakfast cereal, and 13-m trailers were tossed 250 m. Thousands of trees were blown down, with some blocking roadways, severing electrical lines, and damaging or destroying homes and automobiles.

Power outages along the storm band lasted from several days to a week. In some areas, the power grid had to be rebuilt. In New England, millions more trees came down, killing five and injuring 11. Most of the dead were hikers and campers in the Adirondack Mountains. The Ontario–Adirondacks derecho was one of the most costly severe thunderstorm events to occur in eastern North America during the 20th century, creating almost US$0.5 billion (1995 dollars) in damage.

Severe thunderstorms usually occur during the hottest part of the day, in the late afternoon or early evening. Why was this derecho still active in the early hours the next morning? In mid-July 1995, a heat wave was in progress. Late-evening temperatures on 14 July were still around 30°C and the humidity was high. The hot and humid air just above the ground supplied energy to the mass of thunderstorms travelling through the night. At low altitudes, record heat and humidity moved in while, at the same time, the upper atmosphere remained dry and cool. This sharp contrast produced the potential for extremely violent thunderstorms. As the cloud mass raced across Michigan, Ontario, and New York State, it drew the hot, humid air upward until it condensed, releasing its contained energy. Derecho winds flowed down from the fast-moving cloud mass, causing extensive damage.

Tornadoes

A tornado is a rapidly rotating column of air usually descending from a large thunderstorm. Tornadoes have the highest wind speeds of any weather phenomenon. The strongest tornadoes are more intense than the biggest hurricanes, but they affect smaller areas. The Great Plains region of the central North America plays host to about 75% of the tornadoes that occur on Earth. The most violent tornadoes move from southwest to northeast at speeds up to 100 km/h, but with rotating wind speeds sometimes in excess of 500 km/h. Only slightly more than 1% of tornadoes have wind speeds in excess of

Figure 11.35
Tornado in Elie, Manitoba.
Source: Wikipedia Commons, GNUFD.

320 km/h, but they are responsible for over 70% of deaths. The core of the whirling vortex is usually less than 1 km wide and acts like a giant vacuum cleaner, sucking up air and objects (Figure 11.35).

Funnel clouds initially form hundreds of metres up in the atmosphere, and many never touch the ground. Tornadoes may touch ground only briefly, or they may stay in contact for many kilometres, moving along an irregular path with abrupt changes in direction.

HOW A TORNADO WORKS

Weather forecasters know the atmospheric conditions that may spawn a tornado but the actual process that causes a tornado to pop out of one cloud and not another is largely still a puzzle. Only 1-in-100 thunderstorms produce a tornado. Several conditions are necessary to turn an ordinary thunderstorm into a tornado-spinning monster. Typically, in North America, the following conditions occur simultaneously: (1) a low-altitude, northerly flow of warm moist air, often from the Gulf of Mexico, has temperatures at the ground in excess of 24°C; (2) a middle-altitude, cold, dry air mass, often from Canada or the Rocky Mountains, at speeds in excess of 80 km/h; and (3) high-altitude jet-stream winds racing east at speeds in excess of 250 km/h. These three air masses, all moving in different directions, set up shearing conditions, imparting spin to a thundercloud (Figure 11.36).

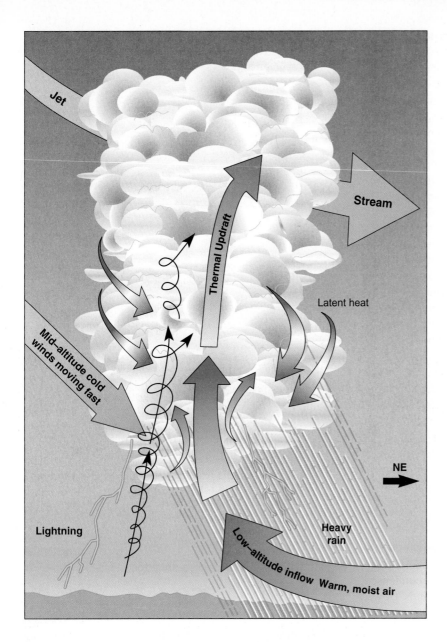

Figure 11.36

Components of a tornado. A warm, moist mass of Gulf of Mexico air collides with a fast-moving mass of polar air, causing updrafts that build up into the polar-front jet stream. Three fast-moving air masses, all going different directions, impart shears, causing rotation. A tornado receives additional energy via lightning and latent heat released by rainfall.

Source: Adapted from J. Eagleman, *Severe and Unusual Weather*, 1983; Van Nostrand Reinhold, New York.

The warm, moist air lifts vertically, releasing its latent heat and forming a strong updraft that is sheared and spun at mid-levels by the fast-moving dry air and then twisted in another direction at its upper levels by the jet stream. The corkscrew motion is enhanced by vertical movements of air: warm air rising on the leading side, with cool air descending on the trailing side. The rotation of the winds is achieved without requiring the Coriolis effect.

But most large thunderclouds do not spin off tornadoes. What is different about those clouds that do? The question cannot be answered exactly, but we are beginning to see patterns. In an ordinary *single-cell thunderstorm* (Figure 11.37a), warm air rises by convection to build a nearly vertical cloud mass. In the cold upper air, water

vapour condenses and rain falls back down through the thundercloud, causing a cool downdraft that blocks the upward flow of energy-carrying warm air.

Sometimes wind shear tilts the thundercloud mass and it may grow into a *supercell thunderstorm* (Figure 11.37b). The tilt allows the warm air to rise in the middle of the cloud, while most of the rain falls in the forward flank of the storm with the associated precipitation downdraft. On the trailing side, downdrafts of cool, drier air exist, and it is between the updraft and the rear flank downdraft that tornadoes usually form. Rotation may develop in a wide zone in the thunderstorm; then, as the rotating core pulls into a tighter spiral, its speed increases dramatically, and its angular momentum is preserved. This principle is analogous to ice skaters spinning with arms outstretched who, pulling their arms toward their bodies, spin faster. In other words, the smaller the diameter of a rotating mass, the faster it spins.

In those instances when a mobile team of tornado chasers is able to get a Doppler radar unit close enough to a tornado, the radar data tell some interesting tales. At least some tornadoes have downward-moving air in the centre surrounded by a cone- or cylinder-shaped funnel that rapidly spirals upward. This indicates that as the tornado is sucking up huge volumes of air plus debris from the ground, some of the air supplied to this megavacuum cleaner comes from a central downdraft.

The rotating wind speeds of a tornado are highest a hundred metres or so above the ground. This is most likely due to the winds at ground level being slowed by the drag resistance of earth, trees, buildings, cars, and such. There is no such thing as a typical tornado; however, the majority are 75 m across, have winds of 175 km/h, move at 60 km/h, stay on the ground for 15 km or less and last for minutes. Fortunately, only 6% of all tornadoes are in the severe category (Table 11.8). Tornadoes range in orientation from vertical to horizontal and assume a variety of shapes.

DEATH AND DESTRUCTION CAUSED BY TORNADOES

Tornadoes cause destruction in several ways:

1. High-wind speeds blow away buildings and trees.
2. The furious winds throw debris that acts like bullets or shrapnel, breaking windows and killing people.

3. When the fast winds lift and blow away a roof, the exposed walls are easily knocked over and the furniture removed.

Who dies during tornadoes? Tornadoes preferentially kill (1) old people, (2) residents in mobile homes and recreational vehicles, (3) occupants of exterior rooms with windows, and (4) those unaware of broadcast tornado alerts. Residents of frame houses can run into interior rooms to gain some protection. But where do mobile-home dwellers run to hide? There are no interior rooms, and who wants to run outside into a severe thunderstorm with heavy rain, lightning, hail, and flying debris? Almost half of those killed by tornadoes die inside their disintegrating mobile homes. Many towns now require that mobile-home communities provide tornado protection with a common basement shelter or an aboveground reinforced concrete shelter building.

Are you safer in a car or a mobile home? Many mobile homes can be tipped over by 130 km/h winds, whereas many modern cars (excluding many SUVs) have low centres of gravity and streamlined shapes that require wind speeds of about 200 km/h to tip over. Also, most new vehicles are equipped with seat restraints and air bags to provide some protection during a rollover or collision. Many mobile-home dwellers facing a tornado threat would do better to run outside and sit inside their cars.

The traditional protection against dying in a tornado has been to go underground, into a cellar. But more and more houses are being built without cellars. What can a homeowner do? A new type of shelter, the "safe room," is being offered by some new home builders in tornado-

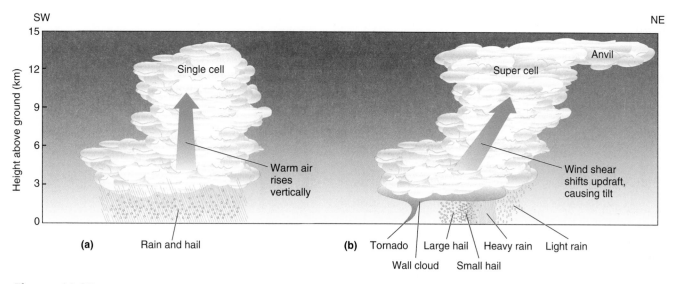

Figure 11.37

Types of thunderstorms. (a) *Single-cell thunderstorm:* Warm, moist air rises vertically, forming rain that falls down through the cloud, cooling it down. (b) *Supercell thunderstorm:* Tilted thunderstorm has rain and hail on leading side with tornadoes on trailing side.

Table 11.8

The Fujita Scale

F0 Light
- Small-scale tornado; winds 64–116 km/h
- 28% of all tornadoes
- Path length: 0–1.5 km and width: up to 15 m
- Damage to roof shingles, signs and billboards, windows, chimneys, and TV antennas
- Breaks twigs and tree branches and pushes over shallow-rooted bushes.

F1 Moderate
- Winds 117–180 km/h
- 39% of all tornadoes but less than 5% of all tornado-related deaths
- Path length: 1.5–5 km and width: 16–50 m
- Damage to sections of roofs; demolishes sheds, garages, and weak outbuildings; overturns mobile homes; pushes moving cars off roads; blows loose objects and lawn furniture around; damages crops and uproots trees.

F2 Considerable
- Winds 181–253 km/h
- 24% of all tornadoes
- Path length: 5–16 km and width: 50–160 m
- Roofs and chimneys torn off homes. Frame homes and structures with weak foundations lifted and moved. Mobile homes destroyed. Rail cars tipped over and vehicles lifted off the ground. Large trees snapped or uprooted. Large objects picked up, becoming battering missiles.

F3 Severe
- Winds 254–332 km/h
- 6% of all tornadoes
- Path length: 16–50 km and width: 160–500 m
- Exterior walls collapse and entire roofs blown off well-made houses. Levels or uproots trees in forests. Heavy vehicles lifted and thrown about. Metal buildings collapse or severely damaged. Woodlots and farmland flattened. Ground furrowed to a depth of 1 m.

F4 Devastating
- Winds 333–418 km/h
- 2% of all tornadoes
- Path length: 50–160 km and width: 500–1500 m
- 70% of all tornado-related deaths occur in F4 and F5 tornadoes
- Well-built buildings including brick homes levelled and debris blown some distance away. Steel and concrete buildings lose roof and walls. Tossed cars become large airborne missiles carried over 100 m. Bark stripped from trees.
- Trees tossed in the air like javelins. Train locomotives overturned.

F5 Incredible
- Winds in excess of 419 km/h
- Less than 1% of all tornadoes
- Path length: more than 160 km and width: 1500–5000 m
- Lasts for only a few seconds but at terrifying wind strength
- Well-built homes disintegrated and their rubble carried great distances. Large buildings such as schools and hospitals lose roofs and walls. Steel-enforced concrete structures badly damaged. Heavy vehicles and appliances fly through the air in excess of 2 km.

Source: Fujita Scale in the SMRP Research Paper, Number 91, published in February 1971 and titled, "Proposed Characterization of Tornadoes and Hurricanes by Area and Intensity."

prone areas of the United States. In the interiors of houses, closets, or bathrooms are being built as safe rooms with 30-cm thick concrete walls, steel doors, and concrete roofs. These safe rooms are reminiscent of bank vaults. Prices range from about $1,000 for a basic safe room all the way past $10,000 for larger, custom models with carpet, lights, phones, and Internet connections. Some can hold up to 25 people.

The Fujita Scale: Classifying Tornado Intensity

The Fujita scale is a well-known scheme for classifying tornado strength according to the potential damage to homes and other structures (Table 11.8). It is a six-point intensity ranking, designated F0 to F5, in order of increasing wind speed and storm damage.

TORNADOES IN CANADA AND THE UNITED STATES

The United States is the tornado capital of the world with a yearly tornado frequency between 1,000 and 1,200. Canada is a distant second with 80 to 100 tornadoes yearly (Figure 11.38). Our country has nevertheless been the scene of several deadly tornadoes (Table 11.9). In Canada, 63% of tornadoes occur in June and July—when contrasting warm/moist and cool/dry air masses are more prevalent (Figure 11.39). Although the number of tornadoes reported in Canada is increasing—most probably due to a combination of better observations and climatic changes—their intensity distribution according to the Fujita scale has remained stable in the last decades (Figure 11.40). A notable exception is the Elie, Manitoba,

Table 11.9

Canada's Deadliest Tornadoes

Date	Location	Fatalities
30 Jun 1912	Regina, SK	28
31 Jun 1987	Edmonton, AB	27
17 Jun 1946	Windsor to Tecumseh, ON	17
31 May 1985	Hopeville to Barrie, ON	12
14 Jul 2000	Pine Lake, AB	12
16 Aug 1888	Eastern Ontario to Valleyfield, QC	11
3 Apr 1974	Windsor, ON	9
20 Aug 1970	Sudbury, ON	6
14 Jun 1892	Ste-Rose, QC	6
6 Aug 1879	Buctouche, NB	6

Source: Updated from Climates of Canada, 1990.

tornado of 22 June 2007, the first officially documented F5 tornado in Canada (Figure 11.35).

The 1912 Regina Cyclone

In late June 1912 a blistering heat wave prevailed over southern Saskatchewan. On 30 June at 4:50 p.m., dark sinister clouds appeared to the southwest. As the clouds approached, they formed a whirling funnel and tornado. It took less than three minutes for the tornado to sweep through Regina, slashing a path of destruction six blocks wide and tearing down about 500 buildings. No structures were immune from the tornado's forces. It picked up small buildings like paper boxes and smashed them into kindling—traces of them were found kilometres away. Magnificent structures such as churches, libraries, and the YMCA were wrecked beyond repair. Even cement foundations were ground into powder. At the rail yards, the tornado demolished the roundhouse and turned over 150 freight cars. Half the business section of the city lay in wreckage. It was reported that the tornado grabbed a woman, stripped off her clothes, even removing her shoes, and carried her 150 m. When it was over, the Regina cyclone had become the worst killer tornado in Canadian history, leaving 28 dead, 300 injured, and 3,000 homeless.

The 1987 Black Friday, Edmonton Tornado

The deadliest Canadian tornado in recent history occurred on 31 July 1987 in Edmonton, Alberta. That Friday began sunny with warm, moist, southerly winds and a hint of stormy weather in the air. As the day wore on, temperatures and humidity rose. Thunderstorms developed over the Rocky Mountain foothills and moved toward the Alberta capital.

At about 3 p.m. the colliding systems triggered a severe thunderstorm that packed baseball-sized hail and torrential rains of 40 to 50 mm. But it was the monster tornado that horrified the community and surprised meteorologists around the world. Never had such a powerful, deadly tornado travelled so far north. The tornado cut a 40 km swath up to 1 km wide and was on the ground for a full terrifying hour. When the horrifying event ended, 27 people were dead, hundreds of others injured, and more than 750 families homeless. Property damage totalled $215 million. The F4 intensity twister packed winds between 330 and 415 km/h. Transmission towers were toppled, cars tossed great distances like a child's toy, trees uprooted, trains derailed, and a giant oil storage tank moved 300 m.

The worst-hit area was the Evergreen Mobile Home Park, in the city's far northeast where 1,700 residents lived. There, 15 residents lost their lives. One woman lost four of her family. More than 200 of the 600 trailers were destroyed or damaged. Some were devastated yet those

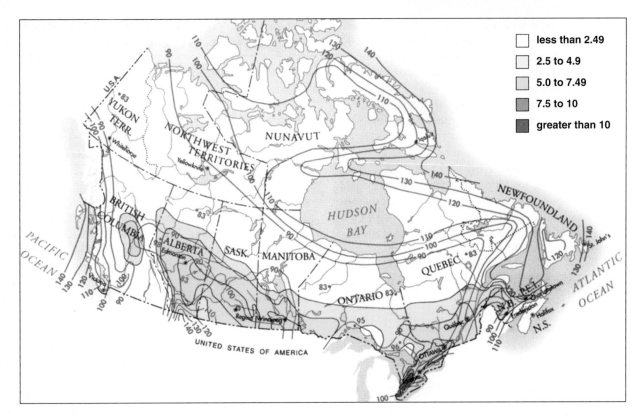

Figure 11.38
Number of tornadoes in Canada per year per 10,000 km². The red contour lines represent the 50-year return period wind speed (km/h).

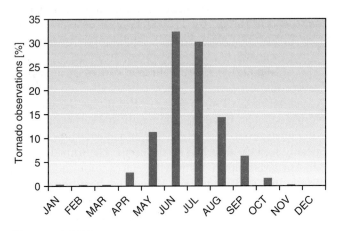

Figure 11.39
Frequency of tornado observations by month in Canada (1980–1997).

Source: Etkin et al. 2001. *International Journal of Climatology.*

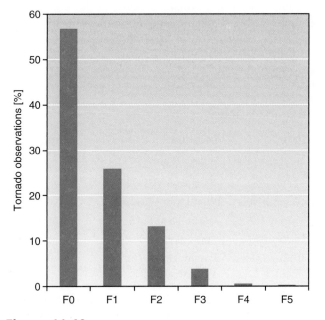

Figure 11.40
Frequency of tornado observations by intensity in Canada (1980–2007).

Source: Etkin et al. 2001. *International Journal of Climatology.* Data updated in 2007.

next door were untouched. Officials were thankful the tornado did not strike two hours later when many more people would have been home from work. Edmonton's Black Friday tornado was Canada's worst natural disaster in 30 years, since Hurricane Hazel claimed 81 lives in 1954.

The 1946 Windsor Tornado

Southwestern Ontario has the highest incidence of tornadoes in Canada because of the presence of warm, moist tropical air capped by cool breezes from the Great Lakes. On average, Essex, Kent, and Lambton counties are struck by "strong" tornadoes—powerful enough to overturn cars and tear off roofs from well-built structures—about once every five years. Weak tornadoes capable of snapping trees and pushing over mobile homes happen almost yearly.

On 17 June 1946, a powerful tornado of F4 intensity began in Michigan around suppertime, hopped the Detroit River, and touched down in Ojibway just southwest of Windsor. It cut a swath of destruction over 35 km long but was entirely spent in less than an hour. Eyewitnesses remembered mostly the sound it made: "roaring like a squadron of planes." Of the 17 deaths, more than half were members of two families. Several victims were decapitated by flying debris or were thrown violently to the ground. The tornado was strong enough to level concrete-block buildings, yet it ignored property next door. Ruined buildings were ground into bits, with the debris dropping all over the tri-county area. Strips of sheet metal roofing with Michigan stampings were found on farms in Blenheim, Ontario, some 85 km away.

The day before, southern air streams had began moving northward from the Gulf of Mexico and reached southwestern Ontario. The day's excessive heat and humidity fuelled an already unstable atmosphere to set off violent storms. Across Essex County, afternoon thunderstorms dumped in excess of 50 mm of rain, flooding farm fields. On the fateful 17 June, with tropical air well entrenched over the Great Lakes, a fresh outbreak of cool Arctic air settled over the entire province. Somewhere west of Windsor, out over the farm fields of southern Michigan, the two air masses collided and unleashed what was to become Ontario's worst-ever killer tornado.

The 1974 Super Tornado Outbreak

One of the great success stories of modern weather forecasting is that fewer people are dying from tornadoes than in past generations. Earlier warnings are now broadcast in a multitude of ways from sirens and weather radios to the Internet. Further, people are better informed about weather extremes and better prepared to deal with the ravages of tornadoes. However, no amount of preparation could protect everyone from the ferocity of the multiple tornado swarm of 3–4 April 1974.

The weather scene on 2 April 1974 included (1) a cold front spreading snow in the Rocky Mountains, (2) a low-pressure system moving east, (3) increasingly humid air over the 24°C water of the Gulf of Mexico, (4) a strong polar jet stream with a bend flowing from Texas to Atlantic Canada, and (5) a dry air mass coming from the

southwest and being drawn into the low-pressure system. As the dry, desert air mass moved toward the Mississippi River, it overrode the moist Gulf air, forming an **inversion layer** that trapped unstable, moist air below.

On 3 April, all the weather systems came together. The unstable, moist air from the Gulf of Mexico began bursting up through the inversion layer, forming huge, anvil-shaped thunderclouds that were set spinning by the other converging air masses. At about 1 p.m., there began the greatest tornado assault ever recorded: in 16 hours, 148 tornadoes touched ground in 13 states east of the Mississippi River and one Canadian province (Figure 11.41). The barrage included six tornadoes of F5 intensity: two in Ohio, two in Alabama, and one each in Indiana and Kentucky. The mighty six were a decade's worth, all in a few hours; each touched ground for over 50 km, and two stayed down for more than 160 km. Some towns were struck twice on the same day. Most of the tornadoes touched down during the warm hours between 4 to 9 p.m.; typical hours for tornado touchdown.

It was the worst North American tornado disaster in 49 years. The destruction wrought by the super outbreak was overwhelming (Table 11.10). In Ontario, the winds lifted a 30-tonne crane off the ground and tore the roof off the Windsor curling club, collapsing an unreinforced wall and burying curlers beneath the rubble. Eight people died in the tragedy.

TORNADOES AND CITIES

Cities create their own weather. In the 1800s, it was recognized that Berlin, London, and Paris were warmer than the surrounding countryside. Urban concrete, asphalt, and stone absorb heat during the day and radiate heat at night. The warm air rising above a city creates its own

Table 11.10

Damages from the Super Outbreak Tornadoes

335	people killed
1,200	people hospitalized
over 7,500	houses destroyed
over 6,000	houses severely damaged
2,100	mobile homes destroyed
over 4,000	farm buildings destroyed
1,500	small businesses destroyed or severely damaged
27,600	families suffered significant losses

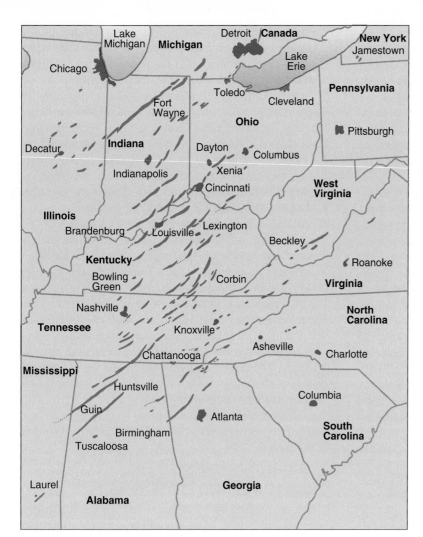

Figure 11.41
Paths etched across the ground by 147 torna-does on 3–4 April 1974. The northeasterly trend is typical. Based on a map prepared by T. T. Fujita at the University of Chicago.

Source: © T.T. Fujita at the University of Chicago.

low-pressure cell, a convecting plume of heat that can rise, cool, condense, and form thunderstorms.

A commonly heard tale is that tornadoes never strike big cities. It is a myth. Of the 1,300 tornadoes in North America each year, most tornadoes occur away from urban areas. Cities cover very little ground in a large region, thus they are small targets. Yet cities are not immune. Recent tornado strikes on American cities include assaults on downtowns and their skyscraper buildings. A Nashville tornado in 1998 sent pedestrians scurrying into high-rise buildings for protection. A year later, the Oklahoma City tornado packed record-high wind speeds of over 500 km/h measured 20 m aboveground using Doppler radar. If there is a capital city for tornadoes in the United States, it would have to be Oklahoma City. Sitting in the heart of tornado alley, Oklahoma City has felt the wrath of at least 103 tor-nadoes between 1893 and 1999 (Figure 11.42).

Of the four deadliest tornadoes in Canada, all touched down in urban areas. In Winnipeg over the past century 11 tornadoes have been spotted in or from the city. In Edmonton, weather records show 13 tornadoes since 1889—all brief and intermittent touchdowns but only one killer, the Black Friday tornado on 31 July 1987.

Volcanism and Weather

Benjamin Franklin recognized in 1784 that volcanism can affect the weather. He suggested that the haze and cold weather in Europe during 1783–84 were due to the massive outpourings of lava and gas at Laki, Iceland (see Chapter 8). How else can volcanism affect the climate? Large, explosive Plinian eruptions can blast fine ash and gas high enough to be above the normal zone of weather. Free from the cleansing effects of rainfall, the volcanic products can float about in the stratosphere for years and interfere with incoming sunlight.

The finest volcanic ash (diameter ~0.001 mm) can stay suspended for years. Most gases blown into the strat-osphere disappear into space, but sulphur dioxide (SO_2)

Figure 11.42
The Oklahoma City tornado of 5 May 1999 left a trail of destruction through Midwest City, killing more than 40 people and setting a wind speed record of 512 km/h.
Source: © TANNEN MAURY/AFP/Getty Images

picks up oxygen and water to form an aerosol of sulphuric acid (H_2SO_4) that may stay aloft for years. The combined ash and sulphuric acid produce **haze**, reducing the amount of sunshine that reaches the troposphere and the ground surface; thus, cooling results.

EL CHICHÓN, 1982

Located in the state of Chiapas in southern Mexico is the relatively small volcano called El Chichón (which translates loosely as "bump"). Four big Plinian eruptions from El Chichón on 29 March to 4 April 1982 blew out about 0.6 km³ of material, leaving a 1 km diameter crater and killing 2,000 people. Although the eruptions were not as big as the Mount St. Helens event in 1980, over 100 times the volume of SO_2 gases was pumped into the stratosphere along with volcanic ash. The cloud of stratospheric gases took 23 days to circle the globe (Figure 11.43). The SO_2 gas combined with O_2 and water vapour, converting to sulphuric acid (H_2SO_4) aerosol. Sunsets were spectacular for months, beginning with a purple glow high over the horizon, changing gradually to surreal yellows and oranges as the Sun set and, finally, a red afterglow when

the sky normally would have been dark. Based on computer models, world temperature from this event should have been lowered by 0.2°C. However, development of a major El Niño event that year, which resulted in warmer global temperatures in the aftermath of the eruption meant that no recognizable temperature result was observed.

The injection of SO_2 gases into the stratosphere by El Chichón in spring 1982 was followed by the strong El Niño phenomenon of 1982–83. Was there a relationship between El Chichón and El Niño? Or was it a coincidence? In 2003, it was suggested that an El Niño was twice as probable in years 1, 2, and 3 following a large, tropical volcanic eruption.

MOUNT PINATUBO, 1991

After a slumber of 635 years, Mount Pinatubo awoke to disrupt life on the Philippine island of Luzon in the spring of 1991. The 1,745 m high summit was blasted to bits and replaced by a 2 km wide caldera as up to 5 km³ of dense magma was blown out as pyroclastic debris. Despite ample warnings before the explosive events, over 300 people died in pyroclastic flows and lahars. Adding

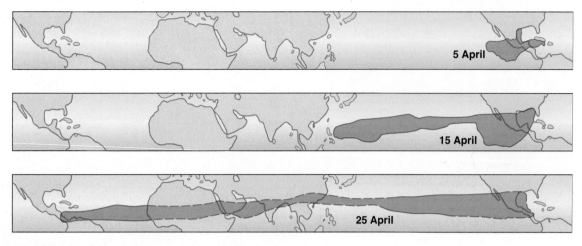

Figure 11.43
The El Chichón gaseous cloud moving west in the stratosphere in 1982.

Adapted from Robock, Alan, and Matson, "Circumglobal transport of the El Chichón volcanic dust cloud" in Science, 221 (1983):195–97.

to the tremendous destruction of property was a major storm that poured torrential rains on the loose pyroclastic debris, setting in motion numerous large-volume lahars.

Of climatic importance were the 20 million tonnes of SO_2 gas blasted into the stratosphere (Figure 11.43)—triple the volume of SO_2 released by El Chichón. The H_2SO_4 aerosols reflected 2 to 4% of incoming short-wavelength solar radiation back to space, causing a 20 to 30% decline in solar radiation directly reaching the ground. Mean global temperatures at the ground surface dropped 0.5°C. The greatest cooling occurred in the mid-latitudes of the northern hemisphere where temperatures declined by 1°C. It would be a year before temperatures return to normal levels. The volcanically induced cooling from SO_2 in the stratosphere more than offset the greenhouse warming that was expected in 1991–92 due to the CO_2 added to the troposphere by humans burning wood, oil, coal, and natural gas.

TAMBORA, 1815

In the early 1800s, Mount Tambora, on the island of Sumbawa in Indonesia, stood 4,000 m tall. After the explosive eruptions of 10–11 April 1815, Tambora was only 2,650 m high and had a caldera 7 km wide and 650 m deep (Figure 11.44). About 150 km³ of rock and magma were blasted out during the eruption, producing 175 km³ of ashes and other pyroclastic debris. The eruption has been called the greatest in historical times, killing about 10,000 people outright by pyroclastic flows and another 117,000 indirectly through famine and disease.

The volcanic ash and aerosols blown into the stratosphere, especially those associated with sulphur dioxide (SO_2), blocked enough sunshine to make 1816 still remembered as "the year without a summer," the "Poverty Year," or "Eighteen hundred and froze to death." Agricultural production was down throughout the world as global temperatures were lowered another 0.3°C during an already cold series of years. Lord Byron spent a cold and darkened summer of 1816 on the shores of Lake Geneva and described it in his poem "Darkness":

The bright Sun was extinguish'd, and the stars
Did wander darkling in the eternal space
Rayless, and pathless, and the icy earth
Swung blind and blackening in the moonless air;
Morn came and went—and came,
and brought no day . . .

On the other side of the Atlantic, in eastern North America, snow or frost occurred in every month of the following year. Over 30 cm of snow fell in southern Quebec in June. In July and August, lake and river ice was observed as far south as Pennsylvania. Dramatic temperature swings were common, with temperature sometimes plummeting from normal or above normal temperatures of 35°C to near freezing in hours. It has been suggested that the Tambora-cooled weather induced the famine in India that year, and weakened the population enough to trigger a cholera epidemic. The disease then slowly migrated around the world, killing people who lived under the harshest, least sanitary conditions.

Toba, Indonesia, About 74,000 Years Ago

Tambora erupted an impressive 150 km³ of material, but if we go back 74,000 years, the eruption of Toba on Sumatra expelled about 2,000 km³ of material. The Toba event is the youngest known resurgent caldera eruption. It is estimated that the Toba ash and H_2SO_4 aerosols formed

Figure 11.44
Vertical eruptions from Mount Pinatubo in June 1991 injected 20 million tonnes of sulphur dioxide (SO_2) into the stratosphere.
Photo K. Jackson/US Air force.

a dense cloud in the stratosphere lasting for up to six years. Global cooling may have been 3° to 5°C for several years. A *volcanic winter* of this magnitude may have triggered additional climate responses that prolonged the cold weather and increased the severe drought, ecological disasters, and famine. It even has been speculated that the Toba eruption effects drove down the global population of humans to just thousands of people.

VOLCANIC CLIMATE EFFECTS

The eruptions of El Chichón, Pinatubo, Tambora, and Toba give an idea of the climatic effects of volcanism. Gas-rich eruptions can decrease the amount of incoming solar radiation and thus cause agricultural production to decline, which in turn can lead to famine, disease, and death. Yet each Plinian eruption affects weather significantly for only a year or two. The rarer resurgent caldera eruptions may cause longer-lasting climate changes. The main variables that must come into play for volcanism to affect climate include

1. The size and rate of eruptions.
2. The heights of eruption columns.
3. The types of gases and the atmospheric level they reach. Sulphur dioxide in the stratosphere reflects sunlight and cools the climate below. Carbon dioxide in the atmosphere creates a greenhouse effect.
4. Low-latitude eruptions spread atmospheric debris across more of the world and have greater global effects than high-latitude eruptions.

Summary

- In the last thousand years, Earth's average surface temperature has fluctuated about 1.5°C. During the 20th century, humans increased global warming via the greenhouse effect as they poured carbon dioxide (CO_2), methane (CH_4), nitrous oxide (N_2O), ozone (O_3) and chlorofluorocarbons into the atmosphere. The 21st century will most likely bring much more warming.

- Climate, grading into weather, changes on the scale of years. In the El Niño condition, warm water in the Pacific Ocean shifts positions, resulting in cooler water off Australia, yielding less rainfall and leading to massive bushfires. At the same time, warm water off the west coast of the Americas may yield heavy rains.

- Most of the death and destruction from natural disasters worldwide comes via severe weather. Developing countries are the worst affected.

- Intense heat waves kill frail members of society through overexposure to elevated temperatures. On a longer timescale, sustained hot, dry weather over a few-year period causes droughts, which can gradually lead to crop failure and famine.
  - In the central Plains of North America, droughts have resulted from high-pressure ridges in the polar jet stream that foster anticyclonic circulation. An anticyclone rotates clockwise with dry air descending down its core, warming further, and evaporating moisture from the lands below.
  - The deadliest Canadian natural disaster in history was the 1936 heat wave.

- Rotating air bodies create some of the most severe weather via thunderstorms, tornadoes, and hurricanes.
  - In the northern hemisphere, rotation is counter-clockwise as cyclonic circulation. Cyclones have a low-pressure core, so surface winds flow inward toward the core, feeding a large updraft of rising air that cools to form clouds and sometimes rain.
  - Many of the largest cyclonic circulations are linked to troughs (large bends concave toward the North Pole) in the polar jet stream.
  - The smaller the radius of a rotating air mass, the faster its wind speeds.

- Intense cyclones a few kilometres across can occur in thunderclouds, commonly producing heavy rain, lightning, thunder, and hail, and sometimes spinning off even smaller-radius rotations—tornadoes. Tornado winds can exceed 500 km/h.

- Volcanism has major effects on weather. When ash and sulphur dioxide (SO_2) are blasted through the troposphere into the stratosphere, they block some incoming solar radiation, leading to cooling.

Terms to Remember

blizzard 320	haze 341	ozone 303
derecho 332	inversion layer 339	teleconnection 310
El Niño 307	La Nada 310	thunder 323
freezing rain 321	La Niña 310	thunderstorm 317
global climate models (GCMs) 303	lapse rate 322	tipping point 306
global warming potential (GWP) 302	lightning 323	tornado 317
hail 323	microburst 324	

Questions for Review

1. Name six greenhouse gases. How do they cause Earth's average surface temperature to rise?
2. How much did global surface temperature rise in the 20th century? How much is temperature projected to rise in the 21st century?
3. What is the difference between a drought and a desert?
4. What are the stages of a famine? How do people react during famine compared to during a tornado, flood, or hurricane?
5. Draw a map showing the polar jet conditions associated with drought in the central Plains of North America.
6. Sketch a series of vertical cross-sections showing the stages of development of a late-afternoon thundercloud. Label the processes occurring in the cloud during each stage.
7. What is the relationship between thunder and lightning?
8. How does hail form? Where does most of the large hail fall in Canada?
9. Why do higher wind speeds develop in a tornado than in a hurricane?
10. What land and air conditions make the central United States the tornado capital of the world?
11. In what direction do most North American tornadoes travel? What controls this?

Questions for Further Thought

1. What changes in the natural environment are likely to happen in the next 40 years? How might your life change because of them?

2. Humans are causing global warming by burning wood, coal, natural gas, and oil and thus returning CO_2 to the atmosphere. What global changes may result?

3. What weather events create billion-dollar disasters?

4. You are hiking in the countryside when a lightning bolt flashes, followed quickly by loud thunder. What should you do?

5. What are the impact of tornadoes on large cities?

6. Is it more dangerous to live in earthquake or tornado country?

7. If major volcanic eruptions occurred nearly every year for a century, what might happen to global climate?

CHAPTER 12

Hurricanes

This is the disintegrating power of a great wind: it isolates one from one's own kind. An earthquake, a landslip, an avalanche, overtake a man incidentally, as it were—without passion. A furious gale attacks him like a personal enemy, tries to grasp his limbs, fastens upon his mind, seeks to rout his very spirit out of him.

—*Joseph Conrad, 1903*, Typhoon

Outline

Hurricane Andrew flung this 1-by-4 timber like an arrow through the trunk of this royal palm tree, 24 August 1992.

Photo: © NOAA.

In August 2005, Canadians were following the Katrina saga through the media. The initial hit on the state of Florida; the rapid increase in strength over the Gulf of Mexico; the violent onslaught on New Orleans. And then, events seemed to shift in slow motion. The lack of a vigorous response led to a disintegration of the social fabric of the community as severe as that of the surrounding urban infrastructure. In her television appearance on *Larry King Live* on 3 September, pop queen Celine Dion expressed a mix of conflicting emotions felt by millions of viewers, and pledged money to the victims.

Maritimers are hurricane-hardened, being on the tail end of the North Atlantic hurricane paths. Halifax, for example, has experienced so many weather-driven crises that it is no longer possible for residents to sue the City for fallen trees and storm water damage. The City is committed to becoming more resilient and its long-term mitigation plan includes burying all wires when modernizing neighbourhoods. The rest of Canada, however, seems to be oblivious to hurricane risk. Hurricanes happen only south of the border, don't they? How many Torontonians remember Hurricane Hazel, which, in one terrible night in October 1954, took the lives of 81 people (Table 12.1)? The event seems to have almost vanished from the collective memory.

Hurricane Katrina, New Orleans, 2005

The 2005 North Atlantic hurricane season was extremely punitive with record numbers of named storms and hurricanes (Table 12.2). An unprecedented four hurricanes

reached category 5, the most destructive level on the hurricane damage scale: Emily (10–21 July), Katrina (23–31 August), Rita (17–26 September), and Wilma (15–25 October).

On 24 August 2005, a tropical air mass over the Bahamas grew powerful enough to be given a name—Katrina. Two hours before reaching Florida on 25 August, Katrina had grown to be a hurricane. Katrina lost strength crossing Florida, but after reaching the warm waters of the Gulf of Mexico, the storm grew rapidly, with wind speeds reaching 280 km/h and its size nearly doubling. By 26 August, computer models identified New Orleans as a probable target with a 17% chance of a direct hit. Many residents were nervous; they knew that most of their city of lay below sea level and that Katrina would bring huge volumes of water. As 27 August dawned, residents saw that Katrina had moved ever closer. More warnings were issued. People began shuttering their homes, grabbing prized possessions, and fleeing. On the morning of 28 August, the situation looked even worse and a mandatory evacuation was ordered for 1.2 million residents. All lanes of all roads out of the area were filled with evacuating vehicles.

Katrina came ashore 55 km east of New Orleans on 29 August near the border between the states of Louisiana and Mississippi (Figure 12.1). Katrina brought enough water inland to breach levees (Figure 12.2) and to overflow canals, flooding low-lying areas that make up 80% of New Orleans (Figure 12.3). At least 100,000 people did not evacuate from New Orleans; more than 1,500 of them died there.

Katrina is the costliest natural disaster in U.S. history. It took until early October to pump the excess water out of the city and expose the houses, many of which were total losses. Damages are estimated at US$135 billion,

Table 12.1

Canada's Deadly Hurricanes (1900–2007)

Date	Name	Fatalities	Coast affected
1900	Galveston hurricane	80–100	Atlantic
1927	"The August Gale"	56	Atlantic
1954	Hazel	81	Atlantic
1959	Unnamed	33	Atlantic
1962	Freda	7	Pacific
1968	Gladys	1	Atlantic
1975	Blanche	1	Atlantic
1984	Ogden	5	Pacific
1989	Gabrielle	1	Atlantic
1990	Bertha	6	Atlantic
1991	Bob	2	Atlantic
2003	Juan	8	Atlantic
2004	Bonnie	1	Atlantic

Source: URL: http://atlas.nrcan.gc.ca/site/english/maps/environment/naturalhazards/naturalhazards1999/majorhurricanes/hurricanes_stats_new.html; (2) Canadian Disaster Database Version 4.4 (see worksheet "Chap1OK", cell G12); (3) Reid, J. 2000. The 1900 Galveston Hurricane in Canada. CMOS Bulletin, Vol. 28, No. 6, p.167–171.

Table 12.2

Records During the 2005 North Atlantic Hurricane Season

Most Numerous

28	Named storms (Old record: 21 in 1933)
15	Hurricanes (Old record: 12 in 1969)
4	Major hurricanes hit the United States (Old record: 3 in 1909, 1933, 1954, 2004)
7	Tropical storms before 1 August (Old record: 5 in 1997)

Costliest

U.S. hurricane: Katrina

Mexican hurricane: Wilma

Figure 12.1
Cutaway view into Hurricane Katrina showing variable rainfalls. Rainfall amounts in centimetres per hour: blue = 0.6, green = 1.25, yellow = 2.5, red = 5.

Figure 12.2
Water flows over a failed levee into New Orleans on 30 August 2005.

Figure 12.3
Hurricane Katrina brought extensive flooding into New Orleans, August 2005.

Source: National Weather Service, National Hurricane Center http://www.nhc.noaa.gov/aboutnames.shtml

but money will not repair the damages. It will take time—years—to restore the city.

WERE THE KATRINA-CAUSED DEATHS AND DESTRUCTION A SURPRISE?

New Orleans has a long history of flooding, destruction, and death from hurricanes. A hurricane like Katrina has been anticipated for decades. The major newspaper in the region, the *New Orleans Times Picayune*, ran an award-winning series of detailed articles from 23 to 27 June 2002 called "Washing Away": "It's only a matter of time before South Louisiana takes a direct hit from a major hurricane. Billions have been spent to protect us, but we grow more vulnerable every day." Special reports included "In Harm's

Way: Levees, our best protection from flooding, may turn against us"; "The Big One: a major hurricane could decimate the region, but flooding from even a moderate storm could kill thousands. It's just a matter of time"; "Evacuation: it's the best chance for survival, but it's a bumpy road, and 100,000 will be left to face the fury."

Thanks to Hurricane Ivan in September 2004, New Orleans had a practice evacuation one year prior to Katrina. But the lessons from the active hurricane season of 2004 were not learned. It is a sad thing to say, but there were no surprises before, during, or after Hurricane Katrina passed alongside New Orleans. The storm, the evacuation difficulties, the levee failures, the flooding, the destruction, the deaths had all been accurately predicted for many years. But the years of advance warnings were to no avail; the drama played out as scripted.

NEW ORLEANS: CAN THIS SETTING BE PROTECTED?

Water has always been part of life in New Orleans. The original French settlement was built on Mississippi River delta swampland surrounded by huge bodies of water (Figure 12.4). Three centuries of floods brought by the river and hurricanes have led to spending billions of dollars to build levees to try to keep water out. The land of New Orleans is made of a loose mixture of mud, sand, and water deposited by Mississippi River floods onto its delta. It is the nature of deltas to subside. Subsidence has lowered part of the city to 6 m below sea level, and the subsidence continues. The levees built to keep Mississippi River water out of New Orleans also prevent deposition of additional mud and sand that would build new land. As levees are built higher and the city sinks lower, a bowl has been created (Figure 12.5), with lake and river water levels higher than city land levels.

What does the future hold for New Orleans? A sinking city. An increasingly elevated Mississippi River. High lake levels. Much destroyed marshland between the Gulf of Mexico and the city. Globally rising sea level. And more hurricanes.

What should be done about New Orleans? Suggestions are numerous. Reduce the size of the city. Rebuild only on ground above sea level. Make New Orleans into an island. Restore marshlands between the Gulf of Mexico and the city. Raise ground level in the city. Construct huge levees and floodgates. Build bigger water-pumping systems.

Hurricane Hazel, Southern Ontario, 1954

Hazel was born offshore West Africa and travelled across the Atlantic Ocean unnoticed. On 5 October 1954, it reached the Caribbean Sea where it was detected by a Hurricane Hunter aircraft. First identified as a tropical storm, Hazel gained strength rapidly and reached hurricane status later that day (Figure 12.6). On October 10, its path veered sharply, heading straight north. Hazel caused nearly 1,000 fatalities in Haiti two days later and, on October 15, flattened the resort town of Long Beach in

Figure 12.4
Mississippi River delta and the low-lying city of New Orleans (top centre). Hurricanes flood much of the city up to 6 m deep.
Photo: © NASA.

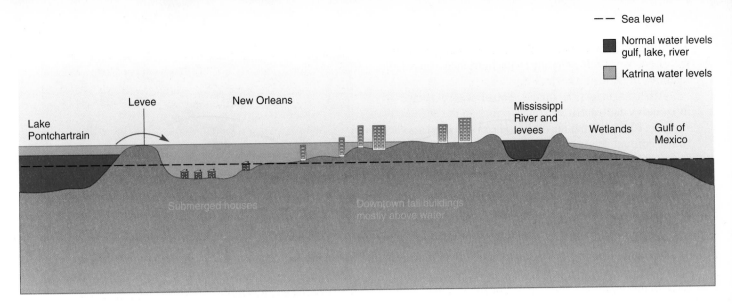

Lake Pontchartrain

Levee

New Orleans

Mississippi River and levees

Wetlands

Gulf of Mexico

Submerged houses

Downtown tall buildings mostly above water

Figure 12.5

New Orleans sits in a bowl between the levees of the Mississippi River and Lake Pontchartrain. Much of the city is below sea level. The land continues to sink, so levees are built higher. Normal level of lake is 1.2 m above sea level.

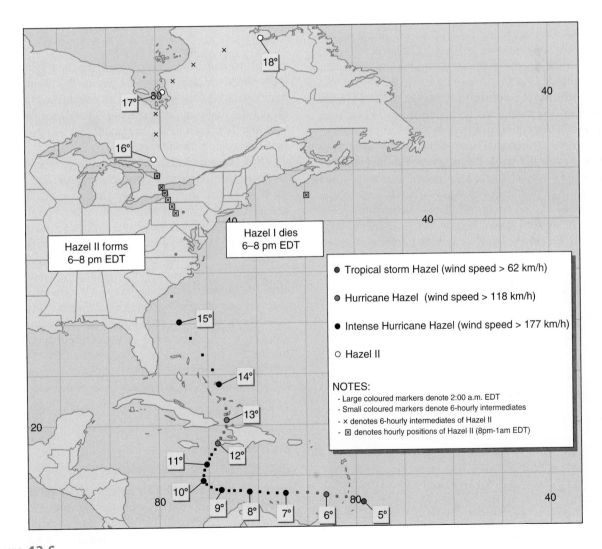

Figure 12.6

Paths of hurricane Hazel I and storm Hazel II (5–18 October 1954).

Source: © Her Majesty The Queen in Right of Canada, Environment Canada 2008. Reproduced with the permission of the Minister of Public Works and Government Services Canada.

North Carolina where only 5 of the 357 buildings along the shore were left standing. The hurricane caused 95 fatalities in the United States.

After its incursion inland, Hazel was expected to lose energy and vanish. On the contrary, in the evening of October 15, Hazel the hurricane (Hazel I) joined another storm coming from the west (Hazel II) and combined forces. The revived weather system now headed directly toward Toronto.

Throughout the day of October 15, meteorologists from the Dominion Weather Office in Malton, Ontario, had been monitoring the situation closely. A special weather bulletin was issued at 9:30 a.m., and an update around noon, both forecasting strong winds. The evening bulletin issued at 9:30 p.m., however, was very bland and didn't foretell the tragic events that would unravel that night: "The intensity of this storm has decreased to the point where it should no longer be classified as a hurricane. This weakening storm will continue northward, passing east of Toronto before midnight. The main rainfall associated with it should end shortly thereafter, with occasional light rain occurring throughout the night. Winds will increase slightly to 45 to 50 mph [72–80 km/h] until midnight, then slowly decrease throughout the remainder of the night."

The centre of the storm hit Toronto at exactly midnight and dumped 183 mm of rain in the following 24 hours, on soil already saturated by a very rainy first half of October. Several rivers and creeks swelled, becoming dangerous torrents (Figure 12.7). The rushing waters of the Humber River, in the west end, threatened several streets that lined the river's floodplains. People had to quickly seek refuge on roof tops. On the small residential street of Raymore Drive in Weston, 14 family homes and 35 residents were engulfed in the flow (Figure 12.8). The current was strong

Figure 12.8
The Humber River washed away the lower portion of Raymore Drive where 35 people perished during the passage of Hurricane Hazel over Toronto.

Source: Reprinted with permission from Dundurn Press Ltd. Copyright 2004.

enough to jeopardize most boats launched into the raging waters, which complicated rescue operations already hampered by darkness. In total, 81 people died in Toronto during the tragic night, including 5 volunteer firefighters who lost their lives while on rescue work. A total of 1,896 families were left homeless.

Jim Gifford, author of *Hurricane Hazel: Canada's Storm of the Century,* a book commemorating the 50th anniversary of the event, ponders: "Could it happen again? Could a storm like Hazel submerge Toronto?" The most significant mitigation measure taken in the aftermath of Hazel has been the acquisition of floodplain land and the alteration of zoning laws to prevent redevelopment. Today, not only is flooding risk reduced, but also Torontonians enjoy an extensive network of green spaces along the main rivers dissecting the city. On the other hand, as Jim Gifford points out, the population of the Greater Toronto Area has increased exponentially since 1954. Basements, which are particularly vulnerable to flooding, were traditionally dedicated to storage in the 1950s but now serve extensively as living space.

Hurricanes

Hurricanes are large **tropical cyclones**. They are heat engines that convert the heat energy of the tropical ocean into winds and waves. They are huge storms that can generate winds over 240 km/h. Hurricanes can push massive volumes of seawater onshore as **surges** that temporarily raise sea level over 6 m; and their heavy rains can cause dangerous floods, killing people well away from the coastline.

Figure 12.7
TTC (Toronto Transit Commission) streetcars carried away by the waters of the Humber River swollen by Hurricane Hazel.

Source: Photography © 2008 Toronto and Region Conservation.

Hurricanes go by different names in different parts of the world. In the Indian Ocean, they are tropical cyclones, and in the western Pacific Ocean, they are **typhoons,** from the Chinese word *t'ai fung,* meaning "strong wind." Hurricanes are named after Hurakan, one of the creator gods of the Mayans, who blew his breath across the water and brought forth dry land. Hurakan was later introduced in the Carib mythology as Huri-can, the god of evil. Nowadays, the diverse manifestations of this angry god are given human names. Andrew, Camille, Hugo, Iniki, Katrina, Mitch, Rita, and their kin share family traits, but each has its own personality. Each hurricane "lives" for enough days that we get to know its individual characteristics.

It is unclear how the practice of naming hurricanes started, but the approach has gained wide acceptance because it is quicker to use and less subject to error than latitude–longitude identification methods. Historians point to Australian meteorologist Clement Wragge (1852–1922), who named hurricanes after women and local politicians he particularly disliked. The practice was revived during World War II when American Air Force and Navy meteorologists named events after their wives (or girlfriends?). The system was formalized in 1953 by the United States Weather Service. Until 1979, only women's names were used. Since then, the World Meteorological Organization oversees the use of pre-selected lists of alternating male and female names, recycled every six years (Table 12.3). The 2008 list will be used again in 2014. Names attached to extreme events are retired: there will not be another hurricane Katrina or Juan. The name Katrina has been replaced by Katia in the 2011 list. In consideration of the devastating impact of Hurricane Juan in the Maritimes in 2003, the name Juan has been retired from the list and replaced by Joaquin. This has been the only time Canada has requested the retirement of a hurricane name.

The Life Cycle of a Hurricane

BIRTH

A hurricane is a storm of the tropics. Heat builds up during long, hot summers, and hurricanes are one means of exporting excess tropical heat to the mid-latitudes. Before a hurricane develops, several requirements must be met: (1) seawater should be at least 27°C in the upper 60 m of

Table 12.3

World Meteorological Organization List of Atlantic Hurricane Names

2008	2009	2010	2011	2012	2013
Arthur	Ana	Alex	Arlene	Alberto	Andrea
Bertha	Bill	Bonnie	Bret	Beryl	Barry
Cristobal	Claudette	Colin	Cindy	Chris	Chantal
Dolly	Danny	Danielle	Don	Debby	Dean
Edouard	Erika	Earl	Emily	Ernesto	Erin
Fay	Fred	Fiona	Franklin	Florence	Felix
Gustav	Grace	Gaston	Gert	Gordon	Gabrielle
Hanna	Henri	Hermine	Harvey	Helene	Humberto
Ike	Ida	Igor	Irene	Isaac	Ingrid
Josephine	Joaquin	Julia	Jose	Joyce	Jerry
Kyle	Kate	Karl	Katia	Kirk	Karen
Laura	Larry	Lisa	Lee	Leslie	Lorenzo
Marco	Mindy	Matthew	Maria	Michael	Melissa
Nana	Nicholas	Nicole	Nate	Nadine	Noel
Omar	Odette	Otto	Ophelia	Oscar	Olga
Paloma	Peter	Paula	Philippe	Patty	Pablo
Rene	Rose	Richard	Rina	Rafael	Rebekah
Sally	Sam	Shary	Sean	Sandy	Sebastien
Teddy	Teresa	Tomas	Tammy	Tony	Tanya
Vicky	Victor	Virginie	Vince	Valerie	Van
Wilfred	Wanda	Walter	Whitney	William	Wendy

the ocean; (2) air must be unstable, warm, and humid; (3) upper-level winds should be weak and preferably blowing in the same direction the developing storm is moving; and (4) there must be a Coriolis effect to spin the system (see In Greater Depth box: Coriolis Effect in Chapter 10).

The 27°C temperature is a real threshold for hurricane development. As the sea-surface temperature increases, the amount of water vapour that air can hold increases exponentially. When the 27°C threshold is exceeded, the amount of latent heat lifted from the tropical ocean becomes large enough to fuel a hurricane. Katrina picked up tremendous amounts of heat from the warm Gulf of Mexico water (Figure 12.9).

Hurricanes differ significantly from storms formed in higher latitudes. Hurricanes have unique aspects: (1) latent heat released by condensation of water vapour inside a hurricane is its main energy source;

(2) hurricanes that move onto land weaken rapidly; (3) fronts are not associated with hurricanes; (4) the weaker the high-altitude winds, the stronger a hurricane can become; (5) hurricane centres are warmer than their surroundings; (6) hurricane winds weaken with height; and (7) air in the centre of the eye sinks downward.

Notice in Figure 12.10 that tropical cyclones form on the west sides of oceans where warm water is concentrated, with two informative exceptions. Hurricanes form off the Pacific Coast of Mexico because a bend in the coastline isolates a pool of warm coastal water from the cold California current. Hurricanes rarely form off Brazil because the South Atlantic Ocean is too narrow, high-altitude winds are too strong, and there are fewer convective precursors to hurricanes.

All hurricanes, cyclones, and typhoons are rotating, low-pressure weather systems with warm cores that

Figure 12.9
Hurricane Katrina grew in strength travelling across unusually warm waters in the Gulf of Mexico. Water temperatures in yellow are 28°C and in red are 32°C and above.
Photo: © NOAA.

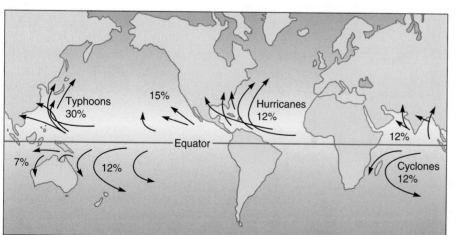

Figure 12.10
Map of common areas where hurricanes form, typical paths they travel, and annual percentage of the Earth's large cyclones occurring in each region. Note that they are called cyclones in the Indian and South Pacific Oceans and typhoons in the west Pacific Ocean.

generally form over warm seawater between 5° to 20° latitude and then travel off to deliver their heat to higher latitudes. Hurricanes do not form along the equator because there the Coriolis effect is zero. The Coriolis effect is so weak within 5° N or S of the equator that there is not enough rotation to build hurricanes. Even an already formed hurricane could not cross the equator because without the Coriolis effect it would lose its rotation.

Each year about 84 tropical cyclones (hurricanes, typhoons, cyclones) form on Earth. North Americans think the North Atlantic Ocean–Caribbean Sea–Gulf of Mexico area is where the action is, but on a global scale, it accounts for only about 10 of the 84 events. The typhoons of the northwest Pacific Ocean hit Japan, China, and the Philippines about three times as often, and the storms can be larger.

DEVELOPMENT

Hurricanes go through four distinct stages of development (Table 12.4). Their development begins with a low-pressure zone that draws in a poorly organized cluster of thunderstorms with weak surface winds; this is a **tropical disturbance** (Figure 12.11a). As surface winds strengthen and flow more efficiently around and into the centre of the growing storm, it becomes a **tropical depression** (Figure 12.11b) and receives an identifying number. The storm surface winds rotate in a counter-clockwise (cyclonic) fashion around a central core in the northern hemisphere and in a clockwise fashion in the southern hemisphere. The converging surface winds meet at the central core, which acts like a chimney, sending warm, moist air flowing rapidly upward toward the stratosphere. The rising moist air cools and reaches its dew point temperature where water vapour condenses, thus releasing prodigious quantities of latent heat. The released heat warms the surrounding air, causing stronger updrafts, which, in turn, increase the rate of upward flow of warm, moist air from below.

The converging winds continue to spiral up the core wall at ever-increasing speeds as the cyclonic system grows in strength. When sustained surface-wind speeds exceed 63 km/h, it has become a **tropical storm** and receives a name (Figure 12.11c). It matures to hurricane status when the surface winds consistently exceed 119 km/h (Figure 12.11d). The strength of a hurricane depends on the speed that surface winds can flow into the central core, race up its sides, and easily flow out and away in the upper atmosphere (Figure 12.12). As the central core or column becomes a more efficient "chimney," the hurricane grows stronger.

Not all coastal residents are hit by the same wind speeds during a hurricane; they vary along the coastline (Figure 12.13). In the northern hemisphere, if you are on the "right-hand side" of the tropical cyclone, you experience the speed of the storm body *plus* the wind speeds (for example, 30 km/h plus 160 km/h equals 190 km/h). If you are on the "left-hand side," you feel the wind speed *minus* the storm motion (for example, 160 km/h minus 30 km/h equals 130 km/h. This explains why, in certain occasions, houses on one side of a street are demolished while houses on the other side suffer only minor damages. Also, on the left-hand side, the winds come off the land, while on the right-hand side, the winds come off the ocean, pushing much more seawater onto the land.

The Eye

As increasing amounts of wind blow faster into the centre of a tropical storm, it becomes difficult for all winds to reach the centre. The result is a spiralling upward cylindrical wind mass in the centre of the storm. When surface-wind speeds reach about 119 km/h, none of the wind reaches the centre of the storm, resulting in the calmer clear area, typically 30 to 60 km in diameter, known as the eye (Figure 12.11d). Because the distinctive eye forms at wind speeds of about 119 km/h, this wind speed defines the threshold where a tropical storm has grown strong enough to be called a hurricane (Table 12.4).

Inside the eye, air sinks. As this cool air descends, it absorbs moisture, leaving the core clear and cloud free to form the "eye" of the hurricane. Sometimes blue sky or stars can be seen through the eye of a hurricane.

The eye wall is the cylindrical-shaped area of spiralling upward winds that surround the eye. The eye wall of a hurricane has the strongest winds; they surround the relatively calm eye. After the short quiet period associated with the passage of the eye, the winds pick up again, this time in the opposite direction as before (Figure 12.14).

Hurricane Energy Release

A hurricane acts as a heat engine, transferring heat from the warm, moist air above tropical seas into the core of the hurricane. As air rises into the hurricane, latent heat is released in staggering quantities. The average hurricane

Table 12.4

Hurricane Development Stages

Development stage	Wind speed [km/h]	Designation
Tropical disturbance	36 or less	Not applicable
Tropical depression	37–63	Number
Tropical storm	64–118	Name
Hurricane	119 or more	

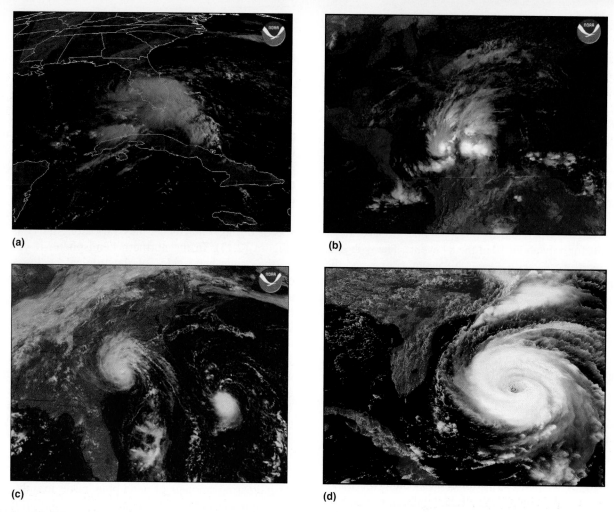

(a)

(b)

(c)

(d)

Figure 12.11

Hurricane development stages. (a) A tropical disturbance moving westward over southern Florida is gradually becoming better organized; (b) Tropical depression south of Kingston, Jamaica; (c) Tropical storm Gaston making landfall northeast of Charleston, South Carolina, in August 2004; (d) Hurricane with a well-developed eye heading toward Florida.

Photos: http://www.noaa.gov. National Oceanic and Atmospheric Administration, 2003 & 2004 Regional Imagery Hurricanes.

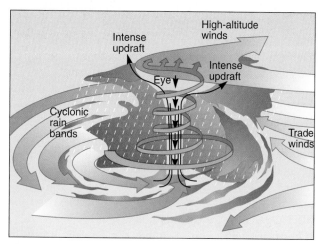

Figure 12.12

Schematic drawing through a hurricane. Low-altitude trade winds feed moisture and heat to the eye. Updrafts rise rapidly up the core (eye) wall and are helped away by high-altitude winds.

Source: © US Department of Commerce.

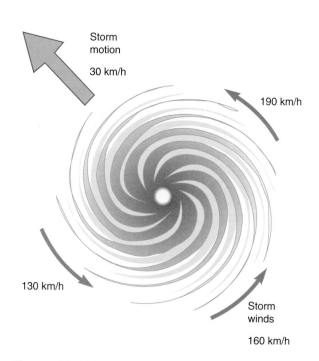

Figure 12.13

Tropical cyclones hit the coastline with different wind speeds. Storm motion (in this example, 30 km/h) and wind speed (in this example, 160 km/h) may combine or subtract.

Figure 12.14
Change in wind direction before (left) and after (right) the passage of the eye of a hurricane.

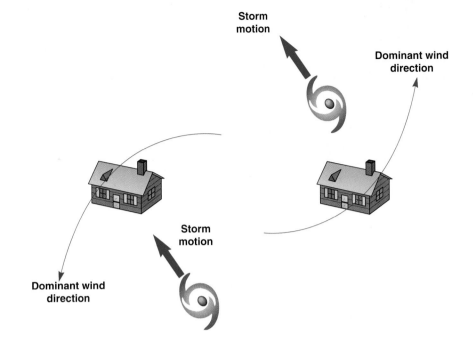

generates energy at a rate 200 times greater than our worldwide capacity to generate electricity. The kinetic energy of winds in a typical hurricane is about half our global electrical capacity. Summing up, the energy released in a hurricane by forming clouds and rain is 400 times greater than the energy of its winds.

The strength of tropical cyclones and the damages they inflict are assessed by the Saffir-Simpson scale (Table 12.5). In category 1, winds damage trees and unanchored mobile homes. Category 2 winds blow some trees down and do major damage to mobile homes and some roofs. In category 3, winds blow down large trees and strip foliage, destroy mobile homes, and cause structural damage to small buildings. In category 4, all signs are blown down; damages are heavy to windows, doors, and roofs; flooding extends kilometres inland; and coastal buildings suffer major damage. In category 5, damages are severe to windows, doors, and roofs; small buildings are overturned and blown away; and damages are major to all buildings less than 5 m above sea level and within 500 m of the shoreline.

DECLINE

Hurricanes decline when they are cut from their main source of energy: warm water. This occurs abruptly when hurricanes ram onshore. It is not so much friction with the land that causes hurricanes to lose strength, a common misconception, but the fact that they become starved for energy. In the last hours of their lives, however, hurricanes venturing inland often cause their maximum destruction as they can be accompanied by storm surges, torrential rains, and severe flooding. In developed countries, deaths by hurricanes have dropped dramatically in the last decades. This trend is reflected in Canadian statistics (Table 12.1). Thanks to the advanced warnings that are now broadcast widely before a hurricane makes landfall, most people take cover or evacuate the low-lying

Table 12.5

Saffir-Simpson Hurricane Damage Potential Scale

	Barometric pressure (kPa)	Wind speed (km/h)	Storm surge (metre)	Damages
Category 1	≥98.0	119–154	1.2–1.5	Minimal
Category 2	96.5–97.9	155–178	1.8–2.4	Moderate
Category 3	94.5–96.4	179–210	2.7–3.7	Extensive
Category 4	92.0–94.4	211–250	4–5.5	Extreme
Category 5	<92.0	>250	>5.5	Catastrophic

areas and save themselves. Although hurricane deaths are down, however, the damages they cause are up. An ongoing trend is for the wealthy to move to the coastline and to build larger and more expensive homes filled with costlier possessions.

Hurricanes can also decline gradually as they travel to northern latitudes. When entering Canadian waters in the North Atlantic, most hurricanes are in the final stage of their lives. Their paths curve eastward, blown by the clockwise winds around the Bermuda High, sometimes reaching all the way to the British Isles (Figure 12.15). In a different scenario, some hurricanes undergo a transformation process known as **post-tropical transition** and unexpectedly gain strength.

Post-Tropical Transition

In the North Atlantic, when hurricanes venture to latitudes beyond 30 and 40 degrees, they move into cooler air and stronger air streams, and accelerate. Some of them undergo a post-tropical transition, a topic of intense research in meteorology in recent years. During post-tropical transition, the well-organized, symmetric cyclonic structure (Figure 12.12) deforms and becomes less compact. An asymmetric structure develops where rain bands are mostly concentrated on the west side and the strongest winds and ocean waves occur on the east side. This explains why Atlantic Canada most often experiences the heavy rains associated with post-tropical cyclones rather than their most punitive winds. Occasionally, a post-tropical cyclone merges with an existing depressionary weather system, and gains strength. Hurricane Hazel is a classic example of this phenomenon.

Storm Surges

Most deaths related to tropical cyclones in the world are associated with sea surges occurring when a cyclone nears and moves on land. Sea level rises for more than one reason. First, winds from the approaching storm push sea **swells** ashore that pile water above the normal tidal levels. Then the arrival of the hurricane brings the storm surge,

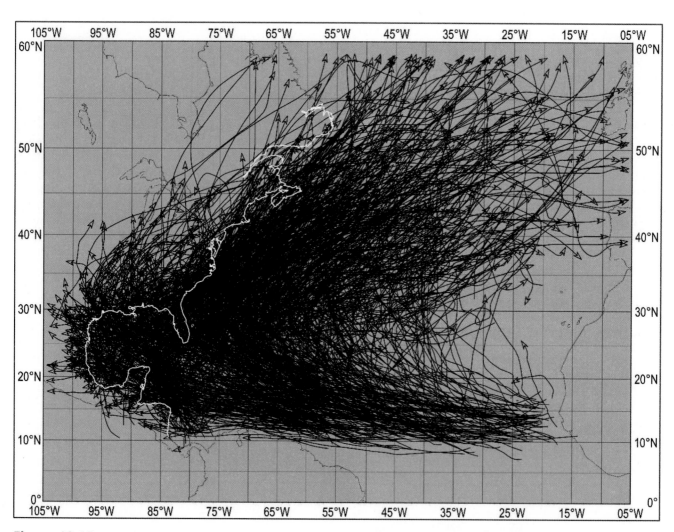

Figure 12.15
Paths followed by 1,325 North Atlantic Ocean hurricanes from 1851 to 2004.
Source: © NOAA.

which is a relatively rapid rise in water level caused by two primary reasons. (1) A mound of seawater builds up beneath the eye because it is a zone of very low-pressure. (2) Even more important than the water mound beneath the eye are the powerful winds boosted by the speed of the oncoming air mass on the side of the storm where speeds are additive (Figure 12.13). In the northern hemisphere, maximum storm surges occur about 15 to 30 km to the right of the path of the eye (Figure 12.16).

The worst time for a storm surge to come onshore is during the already high sea level of an astronomical high tide. On 4 October 1869, the arrival of a hurricane in the Bay of Fundy coincided with the new Moon being at its monthly closest distance from Earth. The combination of the storm surge and the high spring tide resulting in the water level rising nearly 2 m higher than previous records. Several people and animals from coastal farming communities were lost at sea. This event is remembered as the "Saxby Gale" after Lieutenant Stephen Saxby of the British Royal Navy. Lieutenant Saxby, a naval instructor and amateur astronomer, had predicted a year earlier that astronomical forces could produce extremely high tides in the North Atlantic Ocean on October 5.

Why do impacting waves kill so many people? A cubic metre of water weighs 1,000 kg and water is almost incompressible. Being hit by a wall of water is not much different from being hit by a solid mass.

Hurricane Camille is one of three category 5 hurricanes to hit the United States in the 20th century. Camille brought winds gusting over 320 km/h that hit the state of Mississippi in 1969 with a surge of 7.3 m; this caused many of the 256 fatalities. Fatal sites included the three-storey brick buildings of the seaside Richelieu apartment complex where, instead of evacuating, 32 party-hearty people held a "hurricane party" to celebrate the event—it was the last party for 30 of them (Figure 12.17).

Figure 12.16
Elevation of storm surge along a coastline. In the northern hemisphere, the highest water levels occur to the right of the hurricane eye where the winds are strongest (compare to Figure 12.13).

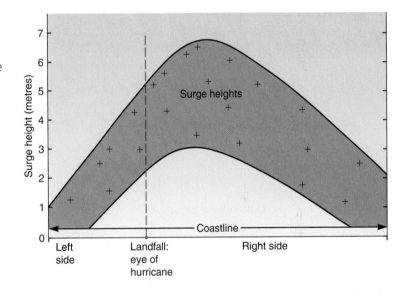

(a)   (b)

Figure 12.17
Storm surge of Hurricane Camille. (a) Before. Richelieu Apartments in Pass Christian, Mississippi, where a hurricane party was held. (b) After. Remains of the building where 30 of 32 partiers died.
Source: USGS

In Greater Depth

Rogue Waves

An ocean is such an extensive body of water that different storms are likely to be operating in different areas concurrently. Each storm creates its own wave sets. As waves from different storms collide, they interfere with each other and usually produce a pattern on the sea surface that is the result of the constructive and destructive interference of multiple sets of ocean waves (Figure 12.18a). However, every once in a while, the various waves become briefly synchronized, with their energies united to form a spectacularly tall wave, the so-called **rogue wave** (Figure 12.18b). Then the moving waves quickly disunite and the short-lived rogue wave is but a memory. But if a ship is present at the wrong time, a disaster may occur.

During World War II, the *Queen Elizabeth* was operating as a troop transport passing Greenland when a rogue wave hit, causing numerous deaths and injuries. On 3 June 1984, the three-masted *Marques* was sailing 120 km north of Bermuda when two rogue waves quickly sent the ship under, drowning 19 of the 28 people on board. In 1987, the recreational fishing boat *Fish-n-Fool* sank beneath a sudden "wall of water" in the Pacific Ocean near a Baja California island.

On 10 April 2005 in New York, 2,300 eager passengers boarded the 295 m long *Norwegian Dawn* for a one-week vacation cruise to the Bahamas. On the return trip, the seas became rough. Then a thunderous disruption shocked people as a freak 22 m high wave slammed into the ship, breaking windows, sending furniture flying, flooding more than 60 cabins, and injuring four passengers. The wave even ripped out whirlpools on Deck 10. Damage to the hull forced an emergency stop for inspection and repairs in Charleston, South Carolina.

On occasion, rogue waves strike the shoreline and carry people away from the beach. On 4 July 1992, a rogue wave 5.5 m high rose out of a calm sea at Daytona Beach, Florida, crashed ashore, and smashed hundreds of cars parked on the beach, causing injuries to 75 of the fleeing people.

Rogue waves have been measured at up to 34 m height. The problems they present also include the steepness of the wave front descending into the wave trough. A small, short boat is manoeuvrable and in good position to ride over the rogue wave, as long as it does not get hit sideways and rolled, or tossed from the front of one wave onto the back of the next wave. Large, long ships face the problems of either being uplifted at their midpoint, leaving both ends suspended in air, or of having both ends uplifted with no support in their middle. Either case creates severe structural strains that break some ships apart.

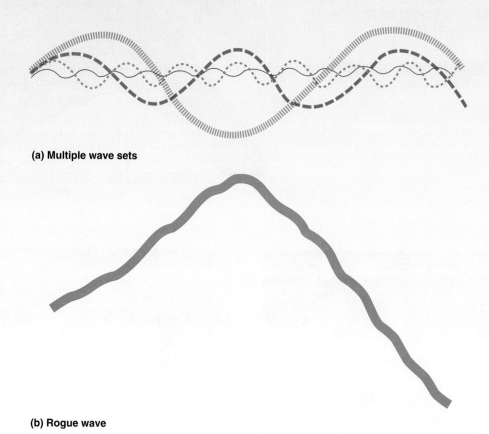

(a) Multiple wave sets

(b) Rogue wave

Figure 12.18 Waves on sea surface. (a) At any time, there usually are several different storms, each producing its own waves of characteristic wavelength. Different wave sets usually interfere with each other. (b) On rare occasions, the various wave sets combine to produce an unexpected giant—a rogue wave.

North Atlantic Ocean Hurricanes

Hurricanes in the North Atlantic Ocean are large, mobile, and long lasting (Table 12.6). Each year witnesses anywhere from 4 to 28 tropical storms and hurricanes in the North Atlantic–Caribbean Sea–Gulf of Mexico region out of which 4 on average affect Canada (Table 12.7). Storms reaching Canada are most often weakened and have lost their hurricane status when they come to shore. A notable exception is Luis, a category 3 hurricane, which made landfall on 11 September 1995 on the Avalon Peninsula of Newfoundland accompanied by 60–120 mm of rain and sustained winds of 195 km/h, causing extensive material damage. A total of 29 cyclones classified as hurricanes have made landfall in Canada between 1886 and 2007. No category 4 or 5 hurricane has made landfall in Canada since Confederation (Table 12.8).

The arrival of rotating tropical-weather systems is an annual media event in North America. Hurricanes form when sea-surface temperatures are warmest, and in the North Atlantic Ocean, this occurs in late summer. The warmest weather occurs earlier in the summer, but sea-surface temperatures are highest at the end of summer because the ocean water with its high heat capacity absorbs solar energy all summer long. The peak of the North

Atlantic hurricane season is between mid-August and late October (Figure 12.19). As the average temperature of the ocean increases from June to September, hurricane paths extend further north along the Atlantic coastline and then gradually retract in October and November (Figure 12.20). All the strongest hurricanes affecting Canada struck in August, September and October, except one (Table 12.8). The most common date for a storm to make landfall in Canada is September 15.

Meteorologists of the Canadian Hurricane Centre, located in downtown Dartmouth, Nova Scotia, monitor all tropical and post-tropical storms, and hurricanes predicted to enter a large response zone within 72 hours (Figure 12.21). The meterologists assess the potential impact of these systems on Canada and issue weather forecasts for an area including Ontario, Quebec, New Brunswick, Nova Scotia, Prince Edward Island, and Newfoundland, and extending 200 nautical miles into Canadian Atlantic territorial waters.

Hurricane Paths

The paths followed by Atlantic hurricanes have been plotted in Figure 12.15. Hurricane paths are difficult to predict in detail because they adjust to other high- and low-pressure atmospheric systems they encounter. But in a broad sense, there are a few main influences on paths. (1) At low latitudes, trade winds blow the tropical cyclone toward the west (Figure 10.8). (2) The Coriolis effect adds a curve to the right that progressively increases in strength with distance from the equator (Figure 10.15). (3) An extensive high-pressure zone called the Bermuda High commonly sits above the North Atlantic Ocean. Hurricane paths vary depending on the size and position of the Bermuda High. When the Bermuda High is small and to the north, hurricanes may curve northward around it and have little or no effects on coastlines (Figure 12.22a). However, when the Bermuda High is strong and extensive, it may guide hurricanes along the east coast of the United States (Figure 12.22b). Sometimes the Bermuda High

Table 12.6

General Characteristics of North Atlantic Hurricanes

Storm diameter	200–1,300 km
Eye diameter	16–70 km
Surface wind speed	≥119 km/h
Direction of motion	Westward then northward
Surface wind rotation	Counter-clockwise
Life span	1–30 days

Table 12.7

North Atlantic Tropical Storms and Hurricanes, 1899–2005

Category	Frequency (Year) Maximum	Frequency (Year) Minimum
Tropical storms and hurricanes	28 (2005)	4 (1983)
Hurricanes	15 (2005)	2 (1982)
Major hurricanes (wind speed >178 km/h)	7 (1950, 2005)	0 Many times
US landfalling tropical storms and hurricanes	8 (1916)	1 Many times
Canadian landfalling tropical storms and hurricanes	5 (1996)	0 Many times

Source: www.nhc.noaa.gov and the Canadian Hurricane Centre.

Table 12.8

Hurricanes Making Landfall in Canada, 1886–2007

Date	Name	Category	Wind speed [km/h]	Province affected
11 Sep 1995	Luis	3	195	NF
22 Aug 1893	1893C	3	185	NS
29 Oct 1963	Ginny	2	167	PEI, NS, NB
25 Aug 1927	1927A	2	167	NS
29 Sep 2003	Juan	2	158	NS, PEI
2 Aug 1908	1908B	2	158	NS
8 Oct 1891	1891F	2	158	NS, NF
12 Sep 2002	Gustav	1	130	NS
19 Oct 2000	Michael	1	139	NF
18 Aug 1893	1893E	1	163	NF
27 Aug 1924	1924B	1	148	PEI, NS, NF
15 Oct 1896	1896E	1	148	NS
15 Oct 1891	1891I	1	148	PEI, NS, NF
8 Sep 1891	1891D	1	139	NS, NF
10 Sep 1969	Gerda	1	130	QC, NF
27 Sep 1937	1937G	1	130	PEI, NF, NS
25 Sep 1936	1936O	1	130	NS
25 Aug 1893	1893D	1	130	QC, NF
22 Aug 1892	1892B	1	130	NF
15 Sep 1996	Hortense	1	120	NS
16 Aug 1971	Beth	1	120	NS, NF
21 Jul 1966	Celia	1	120	QC, NF, NS, NB
8 Oct 1962	Daisy	1	120	NS
29 Sep 1958	Helene	1	120	NF
17 Sep 1940	1940E	1	120	NF, NS
25 Aug 1935	1935A	1	120	NF
8 Aug 1926	1926B	1	120	NF, NS
5 Sep 1925	1925C	1	120	NF
27 Aug 1887	1887E	1	120	NS, NF

Source: © Her Majesty The Queen in Right of Canada, Environment Canada 2008. Reproduced with the permission of the Minister of Public Works and Government Services Canada.

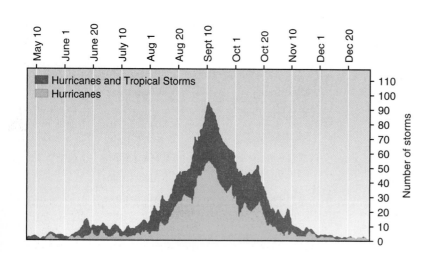

Figure 12.19

Monthly distribution of hurricanes and tropical storms in the North Atlantic Ocean between 1896 and 2006.

Source: National Oceanic and Atmospheric Administration. Monthly distribution of hurricanes in the North Atlantic Source: http://www. nhc.noaa.gov/gifs/peakofseason.gif

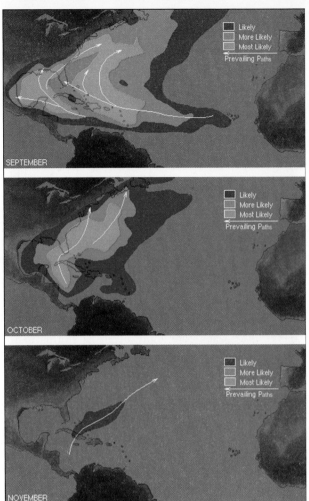

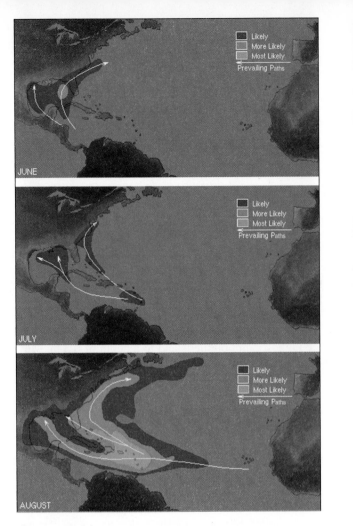

Figure 12.20
Typical hurricane paths for different months during the North Atlantic hurricane season.

Source: National Oceanic and Atmospheric Administration. http://www.nhc.noaa.gov/pastprofile.shtml; "Climatological Areas of Origin and Typical Hurricane Tracks per Month."

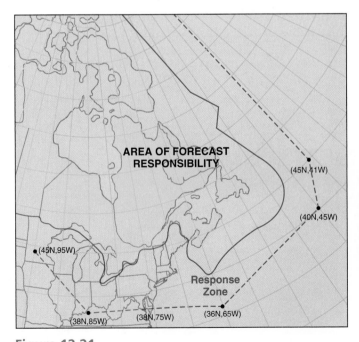

Figure 12.21
The response zone and area of forecast responsibility of the Canadian Hurricane Centre.

Source: National Oceanic and Atmospheric Administration. http://www.nhc.noaa. gov/pastprofile.shtml; "Climatological Areas of Origin and Typical Hurricane Tracks per Month" Canadian Hurricane Centre.

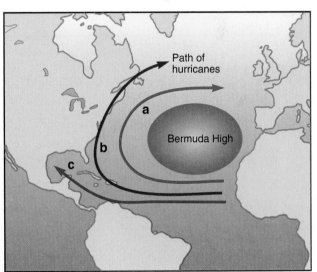

Figure 12.22
Paths of Cape Verde–type hurricanes are influenced by the size and position of a high-pressure zone, the Bermuda High. (a) A small Bermuda High allows hurricanes to stay over the Atlantic Ocean and miss North America. (b) A large Bermuda High may guide hurricanes along the eastern coast of the United States and Canada. (c) When the Bermuda High moves south, it directs hurricanes into the Caribbean Sea and Gulf of Mexico.

North Atlantic Ocean Hurricanes **361**

drifts southwestward toward Florida and helps direct hurricanes into the Caribbean Sea and Gulf of Mexico (Figure 12.22c). When a hurricane travels far enough to the north, then the westerly winds at mid-latitudes will push it to the northeast (Figure 10.8).

The position and strength of the Bermuda High is part of the **North Atlantic Oscillation (NAO)**, which describes the shifting of atmospheric pressures over the ocean. The NAO may strengthen and weaken on a timescale of decades, causing some coastlines to be repeatedly struck by hurricanes for a decade and then escape attack for another decade. For example, in the 1950s, the Atlantic coast of the United States and Canada was hammered by major hurricanes, but in the 1960s and 1970s, it was the Gulf of Mexico coast that was hit most frequently.

CAPE VERDE–TYPE HURRICANES

Atlantic hurricanes commonly begin as storms in the western Sahel region of Africa (Figure 12.30), which lies south of the Sahara Desert. These storms are low-pressure systems that travel westward as **tropical waves** within the trade-wind belt. Upon reaching the warm water of the subtropical Atlantic Ocean, some of these storms strengthen rapidly and may even reach tropical storm status near the Cape Verde Islands (Figure 12.36). These Cape Verde–type tropical cyclones are blown across the Atlantic Ocean by the trade winds between 5° and 20°N latitude. The great distances that these tropical cyclones travel over water warmer than 27°C are a major factor in growing to hurricane strength. Approaching North America, they commonly move north on

clockwise-curving paths due to the general circulation around the Bermuda High.

Galveston, Texas, September 1900

On 8 September 1900, the deadliest natural disaster in the history of the United States struck Galveston, Texas. The Galveston hurricane is a disaster of truly continental proportion. Over a two-week period, the storm unleashed its fury from the Gulf of Mexico to the Grand Banks of Newfoundland.

Galveston is built on a low-lying island, a sandy barrier beach (Figure 12.23). Behind the sandbar island lies Galveston Bay, where trading ships made Galveston the wealthiest city in Texas early in the 20th century. In 1900, the 38,000 residents were given warning of a possible hurricane, and many thousands evacuated the island.

The category 4 hurricane arrived in late afternoon. A high tide and the hurricane surge combined to flood the highest point on the island to a depth of 0.3 m. Moving on top of this elevated sea level were storm waves blown by 210 km/h winds. No place was safe. Wooden buildings were destroyed quickly. Even many of the big brick buildings fell to the high winds and ferocious waves that used the debris of other broken buildings and ships as battering rams to beat down their sturdy walls. Many people crammed into the Bolivar lighthouse to find refuge, sitting on the laps of strangers on the curving metal staircase. They were jammed so close together that no one could move; there was no water to drink and no facilities for relief. Surrounding them was an air of fear permeated with the stench of human waste excreted where people sat or stood for the many hours that the 9 m high

Figure 12.23
An early version of the Galveston seawall. Waves reflecting off the seawall have carried away beach sand.
Photo: © W.T. Lee, US Geological Survey.

waves kept them confined. When finally they could open the massive door, the scene they saw was one of smashed buildings and boats, and thousands of bodies. Later the 6,000 decaying human bodies presented a serious problem—the spread of disease. With much unhappiness, thousands of bodies were barged out to sea and dumped to avoid an epidemic. However, the tides and waves carried the floating bodies back to shore. The survivors had to pile up wood from wrecked buildings and build funeral pyres to consume the corpses.

Although weakened from its incursion onshore, the storm continued to move north through the American Midwest. It then underwent post-tropical transition and veered to the northeast. The remnants of the Galveston hurricane swept through Ontario where they destroyed half of the apple, pear, and peach harvest in the Niagara Peninsula. Before vanishing in the North Atlantic, the storm hit the Maritimes, causing an estimated number of fatalities of between 80 and 100, mostly people perishing in vessels at sea.

Juan, September 2003

Juan formed off the coast of Africa on 14 September 2003, and travelled west across the Atlantic. It was classified as a tropical depression on 23 September southeast of Bermuda, then started its journey toward Canada along an unusually straight south–north path, becoming a

tropical storm on September 25 (Figure 12.24). The next day, an eye developed and Juan was promoted to hurricane status. As the hurricane moved into the warm waters of the Gulf Stream, it strengthened and organized further. It made landfall near the picturesque village of Peggy's Cove at midnight on September 29 as a category 2 hurricane (Figure 12.25) causing widespread structural and vegetation damage in the metropolitan areas of Halifax and Dartmouth. In the following few hours, Juan continued its course due north through rural central Nova Scotia to Prince Edward Island (Figure 12.26), the storm centre passing directly over the Confederation Bridge. It finally started to lose strength when reaching the Gulf of St. Lawrence.

The Canadian Hurricane Centre started to monitor Juan when it transitioned from depression to storm on September 25. By September 27, meteorologists forecast a landfall over or just west of the City of Halifax the next day in the evening. Warnings were issued to alert the population of strong winds and heavy rainfalls. Although no large-scale evacuations were made, local evacuations for low-lying areas were issued on the evening of September 28.

With almost 100,000 trees, Point Pleasant Park in Halifax is a forest within a city. It also offers a perfect vantage point from which curious onlookers would be able to see the hurricane approaching shore. Resisting public

Figure 12.24

The path of Hurricane Juan, September 2003.

Source: © Her Majesty The Queen in Right of Canada, Environment Canada 2008. Reproduced with the permission of the Minister of Public Works and Government Services Canada.

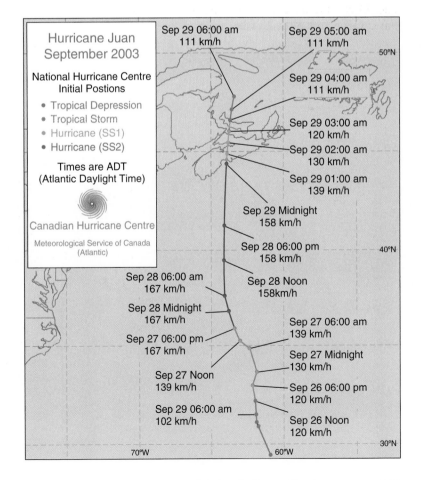

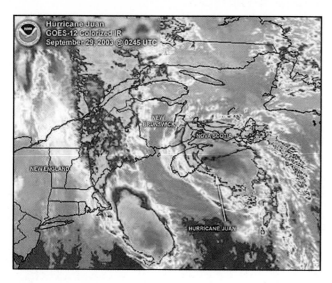

Figure 12.25
Satellite image of Hurricane Juan taken at 11:45 pm on 28 September 2003, just before it made landfall.

Source: National Oceanic and Atmospheric Administration. satellite image of Hurricane Juan Source: URL: http://www.atl.ec.gc.ca/weather/hurricane/juan/satellite_e.html

pressure, the authorities closed the park to the population. This preventive measure probably saved several lives as between 60,000 and 75,000 trees were uprooted by Juan, leaving the park totally devastated.

The storm surge accompanying Juan set a new record water level in Halifax Harbour. Boulders the size of garbage cans were hurled from the harbour to the adjacent boardwalks and piers by the surge. Four independent

unfavourable circumstances contributed to the record: (1) a new Moon on September 25; (2) the position of the Moon at its closest point to the Earth on its orbit; (3) the timing of the daily high tides along the Atlantic coast of Nova Scotia; and (4) hurricane-force winds (Figure 12.27). The first two points are reminiscent of the Saxby Gale.

Although the population was very disciplined and took cover during the hurricane, Juan still took eight lives. Three fatalities occurred where people generally feel the safest—in their home. These indirect deaths were caused by a house fire started by candles during a power outage.

CARIBBEAN SEA–AND GULF OF MEXICO–TYPE HURRICANES

Hurricanes can form above the very warm waters of the Caribbean Sea and Gulf of Mexico at the Intertropical Convergence Zone (ITCZ). The convergence zone occurs where the trade winds meet near the equator (Figure 10.8). The southwestward-blowing trade winds of the northern hemisphere converge near the equator with the northwestward-blowing trade winds of the southern hemisphere. The location of the ITCZ moves with the tilt of the Earth's axis. The average position of the ITCZ is about 5°N latitude, but in January, it mostly lies south of the equator, and, by July, all the ITCZ is north of the equator. Where the airflows converge, a low-pressure area can form with thunderstorms, a large core, and rising moist air that combine to create a rotating tropical cyclone that can strengthen to a hurricane, such as Mitch in 1998.

Figure 12.26
Hurricane Juan devastated rural central Nova Scotia.

Photo: © Her Majesty The Queen in Right of Canada, Environment Canada 2008. Reproduced with the permission of the Minister of Public Works and Government Services Canada.

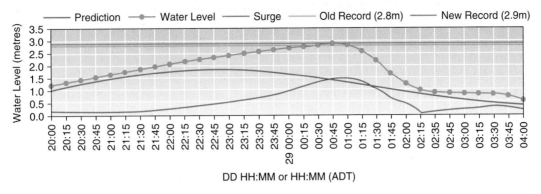

Figure 12.27

Tide gauge data recorded in Halifax Harbour during the passage of Hurricane Juan (orange line). The green line is the predicted water level from astronomical tides. The red line is the difference between the green and the orange line, and corresponds to the storm surge itself. The storm surge raised the previous record water level by 10 cm (blue lines).

Source: © Her Majesty The Queen in Right of Canada, Environment Canada 2008. Reproduced with the permission of the Minister of Public Works and Government Services Canada.

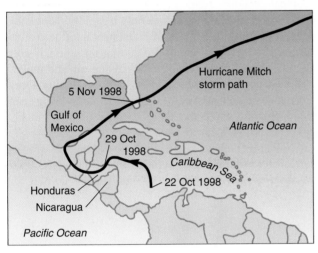

Figure 12.28

Hurricane Mitch began in the Caribbean Sea on 22 October 1998. Mitch stalled offshore from 27–29 October, dumping enormous volumes of rain on Honduras and Nicaragua. On 3 November, Mitch entered the Gulf of Mexico, picked up strength from the warm water before travelling north to Great Britain in the following days.

Mitch, October 1998

In the early morning hours of 22 October 1998, Tropical Depression 13 formed at the ITCZ over the Caribbean Sea north of the Panama–Colombia border (Figure 12.28). The warm Caribbean water supplied so much energy that within 18 hours, it was Tropical Storm Mitch, and in another 36 hours, it was Hurricane Mitch. On October 26, Mitch had grown to be one of the strongest category 5 hurricanes on record with sustained winds of 290 km/h and gusts greater than 320 km/h. Wind speeds remained over 250 km/h for 33 consecutive hours, which is the second longest in the North Atlantic region.

Figure 12.29

Hurricane Mitch stalled offshore and poured huge volumes of rain onto Honduras and Nicaragua, October 1998.

Source: © Laboratory for Atmospheres; NASA GSFC

Mitch was heading toward Cuba but then turned sharply left toward Central America. As landfall for the 37 km diameter eye and the category 5 winds were anxiously awaited, Mitch stalled off the coast of Honduras late on October 27 and stayed there until the evening of October 29, while its winds slowed to tropical storm strength (Figure 12.29). At first reading, this seemed good. The coastline was not attacked, and the powerful hurricane sat offshore while its fierce winds weakened before slowly coming onshore on October 30. But in reality, this scenario was much worse. As the winds subsided and the central pressure increased, the massive volumes of airborne moisture spread over the land and poured down as rain. In effect, Mitch acted like a giant siphon, sucking up water from the sea and dumping it onto the land, especially in Honduras and Nicaragua. Three-day rainfall totals of 64 cm were common, and in some mountainous areas, rainfalls up to 190 cm were estimated. Think of the problems that occur when 1 or 2 m of rainfall must run off the land.

In Honduras, about 6,500 people were killed, 20% of the population was homeless, about 60% of roads and bridges were unusable, and 70% of the crops were destroyed. The president of Honduras, Carlos Flores Facusse, stated that Mitch wiped out 50 years of progress.

In Nicaragua, about 3,800 people were killed. The worst incident occurred 360 km inland from the Caribbean Sea when the crater lake atop Casitas Volcano filled with rainwater and the crater wall failed, sending lahars (mudflows) flowing 23 km downslope to the Pacific Ocean. Four villages were overwhelmed and about 2,000 people were buried beneath mud 2 to 6 m thick.

While many of the people of Central America were still fighting for their lives, Mitch moved out onto the warm water of the southern Gulf of Mexico (Figure 12.28), grew in strength to a tropical storm, crossed southern Florida, and carried its heat and energy across the Atlantic Ocean to die north of the British Isles on November 9.

During a 15-day rampage, Mitch killed over 11,000 people, making it the second deadliest hurricane in the Americas behind only the Great Hurricane of October 1780, which killed a total of 22,000 people on several Caribbean islands. As survivors worked to restore the Nicaraguan economy in the Casitas Volcano area in late 1998 and 1999, they had to cope psychologically with "the return of their dead." New rains eroding the mud deposits kept exposing the bodies of family members and neighbours.

FORECASTING THE HURRICANE SEASON

Progress has been made in forecasting how many Cape Verde– and Caribbean/Gulf of Mexico-type hurricanes are likely to form each year. William M. Gray of Colorado State University has had reasonable success forecasting the number of named tropical storms in the North Atlantic region based on several variables. (1) When the western Sahel region of Africa is wet, then its greater number of thunderstorms provides more nuclei for hurricanes (Figure 12.30). (2) The warmer the sea-surface temperatures, the more energy is available to help tropical depressions grow into hurricanes. (3) Low atmospheric pressure in the Caribbean region aids the formation of tropical cyclones. (4) If La Niña conditions are present in the Pacific Ocean, then west-blowing trade winds help hurricane movement over warm water. But if El Niño exists, then its east-blowing high-level winds tend to disrupt and break apart tropical cyclones. Remember that a tropical low-pressure zone can grow into a hurricane only if rapidly rising moist air releases huge quantities of latent heat into the growing storm. If upper-level winds are cutting into the tall storm clouds, they disrupt the vertically rising air and make it difficult for hurricanes to form. Most North Atlantic Ocean hurricanes travel westward, whereas El Niño brings eastward-blowing winds that disrupt storms and help make a quiet season with few hurricanes.

Wherever they begin over the Atlantic, tropical cyclones reach hurricane strength above the warm waters of the westernmost Atlantic Ocean, Caribbean Sea, and

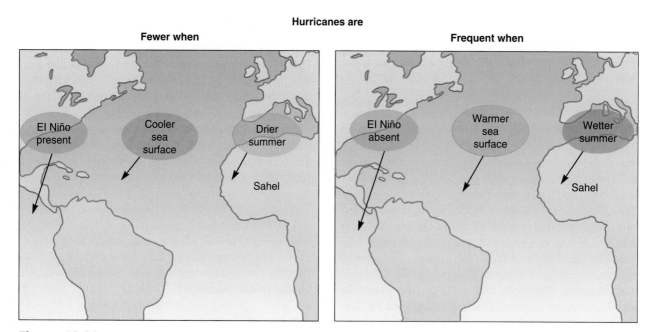

Figure 12.30
The frequency of North Atlantic Ocean hurricanes is affected by climatic conditions.

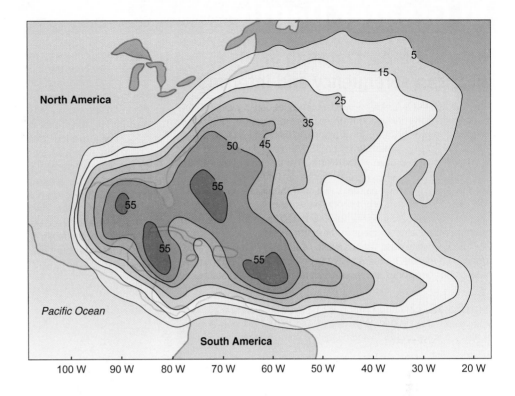

Figure 12.31

Annual probability of a named storm in each area during the June to November season for tropical storms and hurricanes, 1944–99.

Source: © Chris Landsea of NOAA.

Gulf of Mexico. The annual probabilities of a hurricane over the waters of this region are sobering (Figure 12.31). Many of these hurricanes will extend their paths of destruction all the way to the Maritime provinces.

Pacific Ocean Tropical Cyclones

CYCLONES AND BANGLADESH

In the 20th century, seven of the nine most deadly weather events in the world were cyclones striking Bangladesh. The country sits mostly on sediments eroded from the Himalaya Mountains and dumped into the Bay of Bengal as the delta of the Ganges and Brahmaputra Rivers (Figure 12.33).

The nation has densely populated a comparatively small area of less than 150,000 km². Since Bangladesh has a rapidly growing population and scarce land and food, it is little wonder that many millions of people are driven to the rich delta soils that yield three rice crops per year. The delta country is low-lying, most being 30 cm or less above sea level; over 35% of Bangladesh is less than 6 m elevation.

Bangladesh is a nation of water. Over 20% of the entire country is submerged beneath river floods in an average year. In 1988, 67% of the country was covered by river floodwaters. It is little surprise that the national flower is the water lily.

Then come the cyclones that bring surges of seawater of 6 m height, which can flood 35% of the nation.

Bangladesh has a 575 km long coastline shaped like a funnel that catches the cyclones roaring up and over the warm waters of the Bay of Bengal (Figure 12.34). About five cyclones per year enter the Bay of Bengal both before (April–May) and after (October–November) the monsoon season.

On 12–13 November 1970, during the high tides of a full Moon, a cyclone arrived with a surge of 7 m height and winds of 255 km/h. The tall waves drove into the low-lying delta land, killing about 400,000 people and as many large farm animals. On 30 April 1991, a cyclone packing winds of 235 km/h unleashed a surge of 6 m into Bangladesh, drowning 140,000 people and 500,000 large farm animals, and leaving 10 million people homeless.

The population of Bangladesh is projected to double in about 30 years, exposing millions more to the cyclones. As Bangladesh will be more seriously inundated in the future, many Bengalis might choose to relocate in neighbouring countries, fuelling already existing regional geopolitical tensions.

HURRICANES AND THE PACIFIC COAST OF NORTH AMERICA

Each year about 15% of Earth's tropical cyclones of hurricane strength form in the eastern Pacific Ocean, mostly offshore from southern Mexico/Guatemala/El Salvador (Figure 12.10). There are about 25% more hurricanes per year in the eastern Pacific Ocean than in the North Atlantic/Caribbean Sea/Gulf of Mexico. Why don't Pacific Ocean hurricanes strike the west coast of North

In Greater Depth

Role of Global Warming in Hurricane Frequency and Intensity

The year 2004 saw Florida hit by four hurricanes, Japan was struck by a record-breaking 10 typhoons (the old record was six in 1993), and the first documented hurricane (Catarina) in the South Atlantic Ocean made landfall in southern Brazil on 28 March. The year 2005 saw hurricane records broken in the North Atlantic Ocean (Table 12.2). Is this increase in hurricane activity due to human-caused global warming, or is it just a natural variation in hurricane occurrences? The evidence is intriguing but not overwhelming, leading to vigorous discussions. In fact, during the 2006 and 2007 seasons, there were fewer hurricanes than average in the North Atlantic.

Using satellite observations available since 1970, no detectable trends in hurricane frequency have been documented. But has the intensity of hurricanes increased? Several recent studies state that total energy release by hurricanes is increasingly higher, and these authors attribute the increase to global warming. They point to increasing sea-surface temperatures, to increased water vapour in the lower atmosphere, and, since 1950, to increasing lengths of the hurricane season of five days per decade in the Atlantic and 10 days per decade in the northwest Pacific Ocean.

Other respected scientists who point to natural oscillations in ocean and atmosphere circulation that in turn influence hurricanes to vary in multi-decadal cycles (Figure 12.32). These scientists see the record-breaking hurricanes and typhoons of 2004 and 2005 as part of a natural cycle that began in 1995 and should last through the early part of the 21st century.

The relationship between global warming and hurricane intensity is hotly debated now, but as data sets improve in quality and duration in the next few decades, these questions should be answered.

Figure 12.32 Annual energy release by Atlantic hurricanes compared to the 1950 to 2000 median. The 1970–1994 interval is below average and 1995 and ongoing is above average. Source: © NOAA.

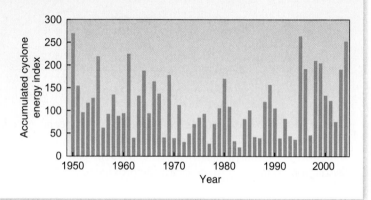

America as often as Atlantic Ocean hurricanes do the east coast? First, the trade winds blow most of the hurricanes westward out into the Pacific Ocean. Second, there is a marked difference in seawater temperatures. Along eastern North America, the northward-flowing Gulf Stream current brings warm water from the Gulf of Mexico up along the Atlantic Coast, while western North America is bathed by cold water of the California Current coming down from Alaska (Figure 10.20). The cold-water current acts as a hurricane defence line. The cold water drains the energy out of any hurricanes that dare to move across it.

Freda, October 1962

The worst hurricane that affected Canada's west coast, Freda, was born near the Philippine Sea in Asia on 28 September 1962. During its 8000 km two-week journey across the Pacific Ocean, Freda was promoted to typhoon (October 4) and then declined back to tropical storm (October 8) and depression (October 10). When approaching the Pacific coast of North America, however, Freda underwent post-tropical transition and merged with another depression. Invigorated with renewed energy, it rapidly gained strength. Freda first struck the northern California coast, its area of influence stretching from San Francisco to northern British Columbia, making it one of the largest storms of the 20th century. On October 12, Freda's low-pressure minimum was centred on Vancouver Island (Figure 12.35) following behind another storm that had raged in the region only a day and a half earlier. Victoria and Vancouver were seriously battered. World-renowned Stanley Park in Vancouver lost of third of its trees during the storm. In total, Freda was responsible for 46 fatalities in the United States and 7 in Canada, with hundreds injured. Damages in British Columbia are estimated at $500 million in 2003 dollars. A long-time resident of Port Moody, British Columbia, recalls a shortage of roof shingles following the event. Many owners could not get matching colours, resulting in a lot of multi-coloured roofs.

Reduction of Hurricane Damages

The effort to reduce the impact of hurricanes on society includes concrete actions in the short and long term. In the immediate event of a hurricane approaching, advance weather forecasts alert people early enough to take cover

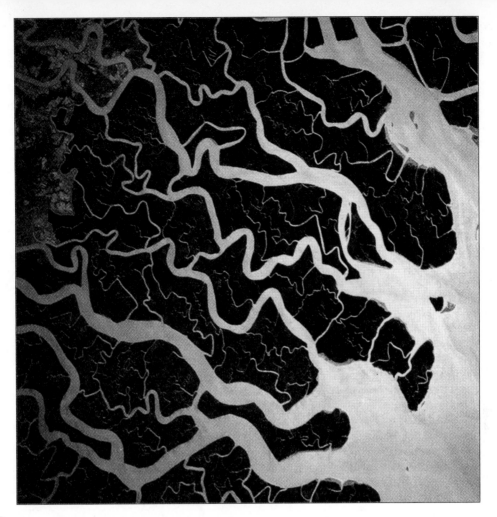

Figure 12.33
Much of Bangladesh is low-lying, river-delta land where cyclone storm surges kill many thousands of people.
Source: © NOAA.

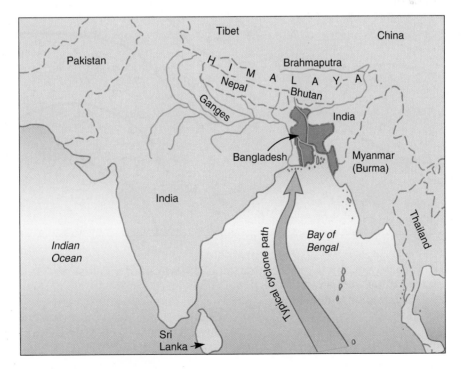

Figure 12.34
Bangladesh sits largely on the low-lying delta of the Ganges and Brahmaputra Rivers built into the Indian Ocean. Cyclones commonly move up the Bay of Bengal into Bangladesh.

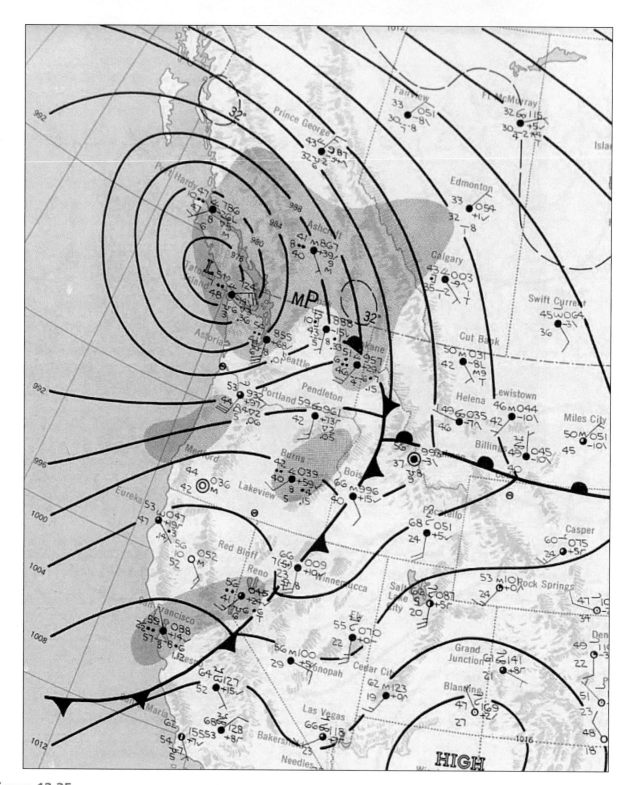

Figure 12.35
Historical weather map showing the remnants of typhoon Freda striking the west coast of Canada and the United States on 12 October 1962.

Source: Wikipedia Commons, U. S. Weather Bureau Daily Weather Maps http://docs.lib.noaa.gov/rescue/dwm/1962/19621013.djvu.

and help to save lives. As important are mitigation measures, including land planning and building codes, introduced to reduce hurricane damage.

LAND-USE PLANNING

Decisions made about land use before development takes place can prevent a lot of damage. Think of the destruction that could be avoided if cities and counties designated that low-lying coastal land and flood plains be used for parks, farm fields, golf courses, nature preserves, or other uses where flooding will not create disasters. At the same time, the higher and more protected land could be zoned for house and building construction.

BUILDING CODES

In 1994, two years after Hurricane Andrew destroyed countless mobile homes in the Florida peninsula, tougher building codes were enacted. The mobile-home industry filed a lawsuit in an unsuccessful attempt to stop the stiffened rules. Nevertheless, when Florida was hit by four hurricanes in 2004, countless old mobile homes were destroyed, but the new ones built to meet the tougher standards fared well. The Florida Manufactured Housing Association admitted that it had been wrong to oppose the new rules.

When hurricane winds destroy a building, commonly, the roof is first lifted off. Then with walls standing exposed and less supported, the winds proceed with their destruction. When hurricane winds push against the outside of buildings, the wind energy needs to be passed from the roof down through the walls to the ground to prevent damage or destruction. This goal can be achieved in several ways. (1) Design better buildings. For example, eliminate or strengthen eaves that project from roofs and make it easier for winds to lift off roofs. (2) Strap roofs to walls. Inside the attic where the roof meets the walls, add numerous hurricane straps to help hold the roof to the walls. The straps are heavy belts of material similar to those used on suitcases or backpacks. Each strap is wrapped around a roof rafter or truss and continues wrapping onto a heavy wood stud of a wall; each hurricane strap is fastened by numerous nails. (3) Ban the common practice of using rapid-fire staples to secure thin asphalt roofing sheets onto plywood. Hurricane winds easily strip off these lightweight, flexible materials and thus gain entry to the house.

Fabian, Bermuda, 2003

Hurricanes are part of life in Bermuda. The archipelago often experiences the side effects of hurricanes swinging around the Bermuda High (Figure 12.22). No such luck this time. At the end of August 2003, Fabian, a Cape Verde–type category 3 hurricane, was forecast to strike Bermuda head on within a few days (Figure 12.36). Cruise ships were redirected. Flights were cancelled. The government mandated the preventive evacuation of people living in flood-prone areas. The eye of Fabian passed 90 km offshore west of Bermuda on September 5 with sustained winds at 190 km/h for several hours. Although Bermudians emerged from the storm to find their coastline modified in several places and the airport causeway severely damaged by the pounding action of the waves, wind damage to buildings was relatively minor (Figure 12.37). Bermuda imposes a strict building code that includes elements from both the islanders' traditional know-how and modern engineering. Walls are made of limestone or concrete blocks, and must be thicker than 20 cm. All windows must be protected by storm shutters. Roofs are made of heavy limestone slates laid on a wooden frame, and are designed with a high pitch (Figure 12.38). Wind deflecting from a steep roof creates loading forces on the windward side that counterbalance lifting forces and help to secure the roof in place (Figure 12.39). Eaves, however, remain vulnerable and that is where most of the damage was concentrated (Figure 12.40). The building code will be revisited to address this issue. A period of mourning followed Fabian. Four lives were lost to the hurricane, a terrible tragedy for the tightly knit Bermudian community of only 60,000 people. Two teenagers had ventured close to shore to see the spectacular waves. They were swept out to sea, together with the two police officers who had come to warn them of danger. Their bodies were never found.

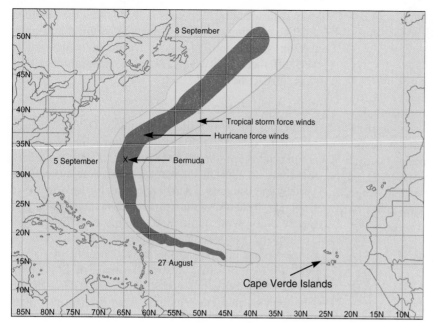

Figure 12.36
The path of Hurricane Fabian,
August–September 2003.

Modified from a United States National Weather Service map.

Figure 12.37
Causeway severely damaged by wave action during Hurricane Fabian, Bermuda.
© Steve Earley

Figure 12.38
(a) Whitewashed roofs are the most distinctive feature of Bermudian architecture. Since Bermudian soils are too porous to retain surface water, roofs are used to collect rain for drinking water. (b) Roofs are made of slates laid on a wooden frame.

Photos: © Claire Samson.

In Greater Depth

What to Do Before, During, and After a Hurricane

The Canadian Hurricane Centre, in collaboration with Environment Canada, is responsible for issuing hurricane warnings for land and sea (Figure 12.41). Marine weather reports are especially important as hurricane fatalities often include sailors caught in rough seas. Hurricanes are forecast one or two days before they strike. Preparation is the key to reducing risk.

Before

Move people and livestock from exposed coastal areas and areas prone to flooding to higher ground. If your house is well built and safely located, take cover at home. Stock water and food that needs little cooking or refrigeration. Check battery-operated equipment. Opening windows on one side of the house during a hurricane to save the roof is an "urban myth"! Close all windows. Protect them with storm shutters or board them up. Remove or secure all items around your home (porch furniture, gardening tools, bicycles, etc.) that could fly in high winds. Secure all boats.

During

Keep well informed of the storm progression by listening to the radio. If the eye of the hurricane passes directly over your region, resist the temptation to venture outside. Quiet conditions will prevail only a few minutes before winds pick up again. Use the telephone only for emergency calls.

After

Inspect your property. Clean out debris. In the unfortunate event of damages, take pictures for insurance claims. Service damaged septic tanks first as they are a health hazard. Pump out flooded basements gradually to avoid structural damage to buildings.

Figure 12.41 The hurricane warning marine flags are two square red flags each with a black square in the middle.

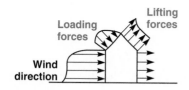

Figure 12.39
Distribution of forces due to wind on a house with a steep roof. Loading forces on the windward side counterbalance lifting forces.
Modified from Rowe (2003) *Roof Damage by Hurricane Force Winds in Bermuda— The Fabian Experience,* September 2003.

Figure 12.40
Roof eave damaged by the high winds associated with the passage of Hurricane Fabian, Bermuda.
Modified from Rowe (2003) *Roof damage by hurricane force winds in Bermuda — The Fabian experience,* September 2003.

Summary

Tropical cyclones are weather systems that convert the energy of warm ocean waters into wind and rain. They are called cyclones, hurricanes, or typhoons in different parts of the world. Four requirements must be met for a hurricane to form: (1) surface seawater temperature of at least 27°C; (2) warm and humid air; (3) weak upper-level winds; and (4) a substantial Coriolis effect. These conditions are encountered in the oceans between 5° and 20° latitude. Hurricanes spin in a counter-clockwise or clockwise fashion in the northern and southern hemisphere, respectively.

Hurricanes go through four stages of development, gradually becoming more structured and powerful. (1) A low-pressure disturbance forms from a cluster of thunderstorms. (2) Winds begin to flow in an organized pattern and the system becomes a depression. (3) The system reaches the status of tropical storm when winds in excess of 63 km/h converge to its centre. (4) When winds exceed 118 km/h, a strong updraft prevents them from reaching the centre. An eye forms and the system reaches hurricane status.

Hurricanes decline rapidly after they make landfall, being deprived of their main source of energy, warm water. However, at mid-latitudes, some hurricanes undergo post-tropical transition, merge with other depressions, and temporarily regain strength.

Even though weather forecasters track hurricanes several days before they make landfall, hurricanes, together with earthquakes, are the deadliest natural disasters worldwide. Storm surges and torrential rains associated with hurricanes can kill thousands of people in low-lying coastal areas.

Atlantic Canada experiences the effects of hurricanes, most often after their transition to post-tropical cyclones, on average four times a year.

Terms to Remember

hurricane   350
North Atlantic Oscillation (NAO)   362
post-tropical transition   356
rogue wave   358

surge   350
swell   356
tropical cyclone   350
tropical depression   353

tropical disturbance   353
tropical storm   353
tropical wave   362
typhoon   351

Questions for Review

1. Rank the following in order of increasing strength: hurricane, tropical depression, tropical storm, tropical disturbance.
2. Why do hurricanes require at least 27°C ocean water temperature to form?
3. Draw a cross-section through a hurricane and explain how it operates. Label the internal flow of winds. What is the "eye"? How is it formed and maintained?
4. Why do hurricanes rotate in a counter-clockwise fashion in the northern hemisphere and in a clockwise fashion in the southern hemisphere?
5. Why are the strongest winds of a North Atlantic hurricane typically on the right side of the storm?
6. Draw a cross-section showing how a hurricane produces a sea surge that floods the land. How high can surges be?
7. Explain the sequence of events that turns an African storm into a hurricane hitting North America.
8. What factors control the path of a Cape Verde–type hurricane from Africa to North America?
9. What is the most common month for hurricanes to strike Canada? The United States? Why?
10. Why do hurricanes strike the Atlantic Coast of North America much more often than the Pacific Coast?
11. Many hurricanes form north of the equator in the North Atlantic, Caribbean Sea, and Gulf of Mexico. Why don't many hurricanes form south of the equator in the South Atlantic Ocean? Can a hurricane form at the equator?
12. Compare a tornado to a hurricane. Which has the most total energy? Which has the highest wind speeds?

Questions for Further Thought

1. Should buildings be allowed in low-lying coastal areas vulnerable to hurricanes? Should governmental relief funds go to homeowners who suffer losses from hurricane surge and waves?

2. If global ocean temperature continues to rise, what effect will it have on hurricane strength? On hurricane frequency?

3. What can be done to strengthen buildings to withstand hurricanes?

4. Compare how many hours in advance we know where a hurricane will strike with how many hours it takes to evacuate a large city.

5. What should authorities do when people refuse to comply with a hurricane evacuation order?

6. How would you react if confronted with a hurricane evacuation order? Is it difficult for people to accept emotionally that they may be endangered?

7. Isn't the American electorate rewarding politicians for flashy initiatives—the NASA Space Program, for example—rather than for investing in long-term plans to protect society, like upgrading New Orleans' infrastructure to withstand strong hurricanes?

8. Where is investment to reduce the impact of hurricanes better directed? On early detection? On hurricane tracking? On building resilient infrastructure? On making emergency management plans?

CHAPTER 13

Floods

Most men will not swim before they are able to.

—*Novalis (Friedrich von Hardenberg, 1772–1801)*

Naturally they won't swim! They are born for the solid earth, not for the water. And naturally they won't think. They are made for life, not for thought. Yes, and he who thinks, what's more, he who makes thought his business, he may go far in it, but he has bartered the solid earth for the water all the same, and one day he will drown.

—*Herman Hesse, 1929, Steppenwolf*

Outline

Record flood levels for the Severn at Ironbridge, England. Flooding is part of the natural rhythm of rivers.

Photo: © Claire Samson

For a period of six years, between 2005 and 2010, a 100-km corridor of land to the south and east of the City of Winnipeg will be the scene of intense activity. Construction teams are at work on the Red River Floodway Expansion Project, one of the largest earthmoving projects in Canada. Manitobans, with support from the federal government, are investing in a major upgrade of the infrastructure that has protected Winnipeg from the floods of the Red River since 1968.

Is the situation worsening in Canada with regard to floods? Statistics show an increasing number of floods throughout the decades of the 20th century (Figure 13.1). This trend is a combination of several factors. The floods tallied in these statistics are events identified as "natural disasters" and might be overrepresented in the second half of the century because of better reporting. Nevertheless, the statistics also reflect the very real trend of increased development on flood-prone lands following growth in the Canadian population. They might also signal long-term changes in climate.

Floods occur in every region of Canada and anytime during the year. However, the classic combination of snowy winters transitioning abruptly into balmy, wet springs causes a cluster of floods during the snowmelt period (Figure 13.2).

Floods in Canada cause few deaths but extensive damage (Figure 13.3). Only one entry in the table of deadliest Canadian disasters (1900–2005) can be mostly attributed to flooding, that of Hurricane Hazel (Table 1.4). On the other hand, floods feature prominently in the table of the costliest disasters (1900–2005) with 7 entries out of 40, including Hurricane Hazel (Table 1.5). A closer look at fatality statistics reveals a different pattern before and after 1950 (Figure 13.4). Deaths due to flooding are probably underrepresented in

the first half of the 20th century. Most deaths in recent decades are isolated cases of people caught in their homes or cars by rapidly rising waters. The 1960–1969 decade was especially deadly, with people losing their lives in five separate events.

Yet Canadians like to be near rivers. They provide food and drink, business and transportation, arable land and irrigation, power, and an aesthetic environment. But being near rivers also means being subjected to floods. To live successfully with floods, we need to understand how streams and rivers operate, starting with Canada's most notorious flood-prone river, the Red River of Manitoba.

The Red River Floodway

The Red River flows northward. The meandering river drains parts of South Dakota, North Dakota, and Minnesota before crossing the U.S.–Canada border into Manitoba where it joins with the Assiniboine River in Winnipeg, before reaching Lake Winnipeg. The list of historical floods on the Canadian side of the Red River basin reads like a litany. There were major floods in 1776, 1826, 1852, 1861, 1916, 1950, 1979, and 1997. Less serious floods occurred in 1882, 1897, 1904, 1948, 1956, 1966, 1969, 1974, and 1996. As described by John McCormick of *Newsweek*, "On the northern plains, nature is less an enemy than a sparring partner, trading rounds in a grudge bout that never ends."

Why are floods so common along the Red River? (1) The Red River valley is geologically young, only about 9,000 years old, and the river has not yet carved a deep valley. (2) The valley is underlain by an impermeable

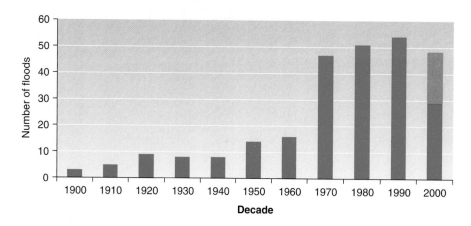

Figure 13.1
Number of floods identified as natural disasters in Canada per decade from 1900 to 2005. Values for the decade 2000–2009 have been extrapolated (in green).

Source: Number Floods Identified as Natural Disasters in Canada per decade, Canadian Disaster Database, http://ww5.ps-sp.gc.ca/res/em/cdd/search-en.asp. Reproduced with the permission of the Minister of Public Works and Government Services, 2008.

Figure 13.2

Number of floods identified as natural disasters in Canada per month of the year from 1900 to 2005. (UNK = unknown or unspecified.)

Source: Number Floods Identified as Natural Disasters in Canada per month, Canadian Disaster Database, http://ww5.ps-sp.gc.ca/res/em/cdd/search-en.asp. Reproduced with the permission of the Minister of Public Works and Government Services, 2008.

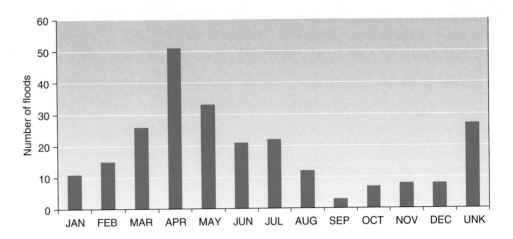

Figure 13.3

Different failure mechanisms of buildings subjected to floods.

Source: Becker, A.B. and Lence, B.J. (2007). "Wood Frame Building Response to Catastrophic Flooding in Aid of Emergency Planning and Mitigation." GEOIDE 9th Annual Scientific Conference, Halifax, Nova Scotia: June 6–8, 2007. Modified from Figure 6 in: Johnstone, W.M., Sakamoto, D., Assaf, H., and Bourban, S. (2005) "Architecture, Modelling Framework and Validation of BC Hydro's Virtual Reality Life Safety Model" in International Symposium on Stochastic Hydraulics (ISSH 2005), May 23–24, 2005, Nijmegen, Netherlands

Fill

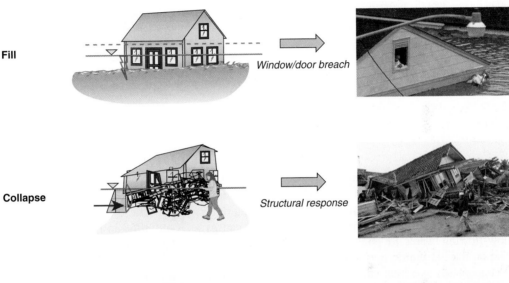

Window/door breach

Collapse

Structural response

Float

Buoyant uplift

Figure 13.4

Number of flood fatalities in Canada per decade from 1900 and 2005. Values for the decade 2000–2009 have been linearly extrapolated (in green).

Source: Number of Fatalities in Canada Per Decade, Canadian Disaster Database, http://ww5.ps-sp.gc.ca/res/em/cdd/search-en.asp. Reproduced with the permission of the Minister of Public Works and Government Services, 2008.

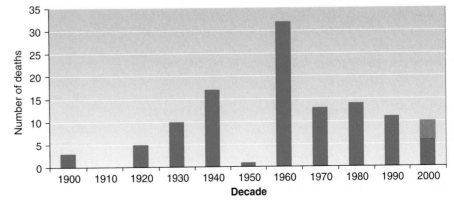

A Different Kind of Killer Flood

Wednesday, January 15, 1919, was unusually hot in Boston. As the temperature climbed higher, the pressure of 12 million kilograms of expanding molasses was too much for its heated tank to hold at the Purity Distilling Company. Steel bolts popped with a sound like gunfire, and the steel panels of the tank burst apart, releasing a flood of crude molasses; 8.7 million litres flowed forth as a 9 metre high brown wave. The flood knocked down supports for the elevated train, pushed houses off foundations, and smothered employees at the Public Works Department, as well as teamsters and their horses unloading goods at the Boston & Worcester and Eastern Massachusetts railroads (Figure 13.5). As the molasses flowed, it cooled and congealed, holding people so tightly in its sticky grasp that rescue workers needed hours to free them. The great molasses flood of 1919 killed 21 people and injured 150. Flood threats are not always obvious.

Figure 13.5 Damage in Boston from the molasses flood of 15 January 1919.

reddish clay layer, which gave the river its name. The clay impedes the infiltration of water into the ground. (3) The slope of the riverbed is very low, averaging only an 8 cm/km drop in elevation. The lack of slope causes slow-flowing water to pool into a broad and shallow lake on the flat prairie during high-water flow. (4) River flow increases as winter snow melts. The meltwater runs northward into still-frozen lengths of the river, where ice jams up and obstructs water flow, causing floods.

THE 1950 RED RIVER FLOOD

The winter of 1950 had been long and severe, covering southern Manitoba under a thick blanket of snow and ice. The spring was equally miserable and late in coming. By April, snow was starting to melt and water levels in the Red River were rising. They were already 8.2 m above normal when, on 5 May, a blizzard struck the region. The precipitation, combined with strong winds, caused several **dikes** protecting Winnipeg to collapse, turning 1,600 km^2 of land into an enormous lake (Figure 13.6). The state of emergency was declared due to "the most catastrophic flood ever seen in Canada." In the largest evacuation due to a natural disaster in Canadian history, 107,000 people were evacuated from Winnipeg (one-third of the city's population!) with the help of the Canadian Army and the Red Cross. The Red River stayed above **flood stage** for 51 days. When the waters finally subsided, Winnipeggers were left with 10,500 damaged buildings and a

bill of $1.1 billion (1999 dollars) in repairs (Figure 13.7, Table 1.5).

The Red River Floodway was built between 1962 and 1968 in response to the flood of 1950. The project cost $63 million at the time. The federal government contributed 55% of the funds, and Manitoba 45%, a significant investment for a province with a modest economy. Premier Duff Roblin showed strong leadership and vision in championing the project against considerable opposition.

The Floodway is simply a trench in the earth diverting excess water, but a trench of gigantic proportions! The 48-km long, 140-m wide channel circumvents Winnipeg to the east, extending from the St. Norbert inlet structure to the Lockport outlet structure (Figures 13.8 and 13.9). The project necessitated the excavation of 75 million m^3 of earth. In fact, at the time, the excavation of the Floodway was the second-largest earthmoving project in the world, next to the Panama Canal.

Under normal circumstances, the Floodway is empty. However, when the Red River starts to overflow its banks and poses a potential threat within Winnipeg, the gates of the inlet structure are partially raised to limit the amount of water flowing in the river through the city and redirect the excess flow into the Floodway (Figure 13.10). In recent years, it has been necessary to use the Floodway every two to three years in the spring.

The original Floodway was designed to protect downtown Winnipeg against an exceptional flood with a

(a)

(b)

Figure 13.6

The 1950 Red River flood on the campus of the University of Manitoba: (a) then and (b) now.

Photos: (a) University of Manitoba Archives & Special Collections, Winnipeg Tribune Photograph Collection, "Flood 1950" (PC 80, 339-I), (b) © Claire Samson.

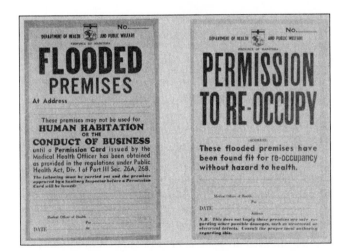

Figure 13.7

Notices issued by the Manitoba Department of Health and Public Welfare during the 1950 Red River flood.

Source: Used with permission of the Library and Archives Canada nlc010739.tif

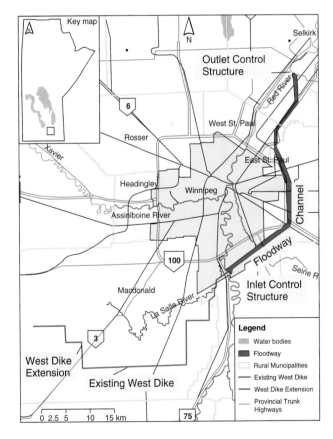

Figure 13.8

Regional map of Winnipeg, Manitoba.

Source: Images courtesy of the Manitoba Floodway Authority

(a)

(b)

Figure 13.9
The St. Norbert inlet structure is being modernized (left) and the Lockport outlet structure is being widened (right) as part of the Red River Floodway expansion project.
Photos: © Claire Samson.

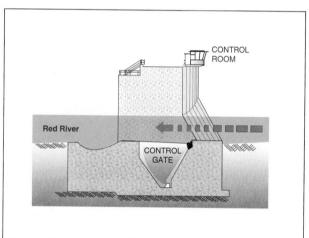

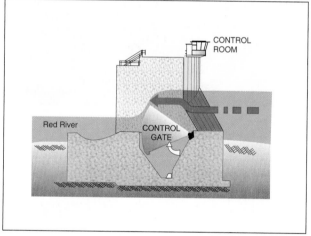

Figure 13.10
Operation of the inlet control structure of the Red River Floodway.
Source: Images courtesy of the Manitoba Floodway Authority.

1-in-225-years return period (Figure 13.23). In 1997, the city narrowly avoided the worst...

THE 1997 RED RIVER FLOOD

In 1997, several variables combined to unleash record floods, which were forecast weeks in advance. (1) The fall 1996 rainfall in the Red River **drainage basin** was about four times greater than average. (2) Cold temperatures in winter 1996 began earlier than normal, thus freezing the water saturated in the soil into an impermeable layer. (3) Winter 2006 was exceptionally snowy. At the end of the season, the snowpack had reached a record thickness of 250 cm. The situation became catastrophic when a late-winter blizzard dropped an additional 50 cm of snow on 4–6 April.

On 8 April 1997, the average regional temperature was –13° C, but on 18 April, it was 14° C. Snow and ice melted, and the ground everywhere was covered by over-land waterflow that overwhelmed the water-transporting ability of the flat-bottomed Red River. As the flood waters slowly flowed northward, they progressively inundated farmland and towns.

The United States National Weather Service issued flood warnings as early as February. Residents of the neighbouring cities of Grand Forks, North Dakota, and the smaller East Grand Forks, Minnesota, on the western and eastern banks of the Red River braced themselves for the events to come. The communities mobilized to erect dikes with sandbags and clay. This haphazard protection was no match for the elements. On 18 April 1997, the Red River poured over the dikes. By the end of the next day, 52,000 residents of Grand Forks and all 8,000 residents of East Grand Forks had been forced to evacuate their homes. Floodwaters interfered with electrical wirings and ignited a fire that spread to three blocks in downtown Grand Forks, leading to the incongruous scene of a flooded city centre with its buildings on fire. In North Dakota, the flood caused overall damages exceeding $1 billion; destroyed potato, sugar beet, and grain crops; prevented planting seeds for the next crop; and drowned farm animals, including 123,000 cattle.

The flood reached its maximum at the U.S.–Canadian border around 26 April, and continued to progress further north. A new lake formed, centred on the town of Morris, south of Winnipeg, which reached 40–50 km wide and over 100 km in length (Figures 13.11 and 13.12). Winnipeggers, however, were protected by the floodway infrastructure that they had wisely invested in. At the peak of the crisis in Manitoba on 4 May, the Red River Floodway was diverting about 1,400 m^3 of water per second around the city (Figure 13.13). It was, however, barely containing the flow. An additional rise of 60 cm in water level would have overwhelmed Winnipeg's network of dikes, including the strategic West dike, which protects the southern edge of town.

THE RED RIVER FLOODWAY EXPANSION PROJECT

What if the Red River reaches a water level higher than in 1997? Studies estimate that a 1-in-700-years flood would necessitate the evacuation of 450,000 Winnipeg residents, and cause damages on the order of $12 billion. This realization prompted the current expansion of the Floodway. The project work plan is ambitious and is calling for a widening of the main Floodway channel and major improvements to the inlet and outlet structures (Figure 13.9). The option of deepening the channel was rejected to avoid any impact on groundwater. Widening, however, comes at a high cost as six bridges over the Floodway, including the Trans-Canada Highway #1 East Bridge, will have to be replaced and raised. The project also includes extending the West dike (Figure 13.11) by 15 km, and raising its height. This part of the project has been set aside for Aboriginal contractors to gain

Figure 13.11
Satellite image of the 1997 Red River flood.
Source: Radarsat.

Figure 13.12
The town of Morris, Manitoba, surrounded by water during the 1997 Red River flood. The ground surface in Morris is lower than the level of flooding. A ring-dike protects the town from flood waters.

Photo: Reproduced with the permission of Natural Resources Canada 2008, courtesy of the Geological Survey of Canada. http://gsc.nrcan.gc.ca/floods/redriver/images_e.php.

Figure 13.13
The Red River Floodway at the inlet structure, in operation during the 1997 flood. The inlet structure is in the centre of the photograph and the flow in the Floodway channel is towards the top of the photograph.

Photo :Reproduced with the permission of Natural Resources Canada 2008, courtesy of the Geological Survey of Canada. http://gsc.nrcan.gc.ca/floods/redriver/images_e.php.

experience and demonstrate their know-how. Overall, the expansion will provide protection for a flood with a return period of 1 in 700 years, an event of larger proportion than the highest flood in historical records, the 1-in-300-year flood of 1826 (Figure 13.23).

How Rivers and Streams Work

A river is simply a large stream. Streams reveal much about their behaviour when examined over their total length.

LONGITUDINAL CROSS-SECTION OF A STREAM

A longitudinal cross-section of a stream's bottom elevation versus the stream's distance from source yields a fairly consistent and revealing relationship (Figure 13.14).

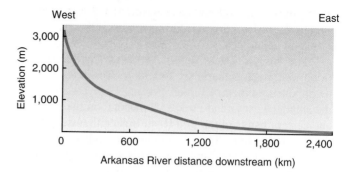

Figure 13.14
Longitudinal cross-section of the Arkansas River bottom from its origin in the mountains of Colorado to its mouth at the Mississippi River. Note the extreme exaggeration of the vertical scale necessary to emphasize the concave-upward profile of the bottom.

Source: Henry Gannett, US Geological Survey.

Using exaggeration of the vertical scale to emphasize the relationship, the bottom profile is seen to be relatively smooth and concave upward with a steeper bottom or slope (higher **gradient**) near the stream source and a flatter bottom (lower gradient) near the stream mouth. Figure 13.14 shows the Arkansas River from the American Midwest, but by changing the scales of elevation and length, this longitudinal cross-section could serve for virtually any stream in the world.

The lessening of gradient in a stream's lower reaches is partly due to the limitations of **base level**—the level below which a stream cannot erode. For a small stream, base level may be a lake or pond into which the stream drains. For many large rivers, base level is the ocean.

Streams have similar longitudinal cross-sections whether they run through the tropics or the deserts, whether they are long or short, and whether they run through hard or soft rocks. The worldwide similarity of bottom profiles of streams implies that some equilibrium processes must be at work.

THE EQUILIBRIUM STREAM

Numerous factors interact to make streams seek **equilibrium**, a state of balance where a change causes compensating actions. To grasp the fundamentals of how streams work, a few key variables must be understood: (1) **discharge**—the rate of water flow expressed as volume per unit of time, (2) available sediment (**load**)—the amount of sediment waiting to be moved, (3) gradient—the slope of the stream bottom, and (4) channel pattern—the **sinuosity** of the stream path.

The greater the discharge, the greater the load of sediment carried. Both discharge and available sediment are independent variables, that is, the stream has no control over how much water it will receive or how much sediment is present. Nonetheless, a stream moves the sediment present with the water provided. Excesses in discharge or load are managed by changing dependent variables, such as gradient and channel pattern.

Case 1—Too Much Discharge

If a stream has too much water, it will flow more rapidly and energetically. The move away from equilibrium triggers responses to correct the imbalance. (1) Some of the excess energy is used in eroding the stream bottom, reducing the vertical drop downstream and causing slower and less-energetic water flow (Figure 13.15). (2) The sediment picked up by erosion adds to the load carried by the stream, thus consuming more of the excess energy. (3) The stream also responds by increasing the sinuosity of its channel pattern through meandering. A meandering stream cuts into its banks, thus using some of its excess energy to erode and transport sediment. Notice how the meandering pattern lengthens the flow path, lowering the stream's gradient and thus slowing water flow (Figure 13.16).

A close look at the meandering process tells us much of value (Figure 13.17). Water does not flow at even depth and power across a stream. Instead, a deeper, more powerful volume of water flows from side-to-side, eroding the river bank on one side and then on the other. This lengthens the path of the stream, decreases the gradient, and slows the water flow. Notice that deposition of sediment occurs on the inside bend of each **meander**, where water is shallower and less powerful. The meandering process can proceed so far that two erosional banks can merge and create a shortcut that straightens the river locally (see centre right of Figure 13.17).

Case 2—Too Much Load

If a stream is choked with sediment and has insufficient water to carry it away, this also triggers a counteraction. The excess sediment builds up on the stream bottom, increasing the gradient and causing stream water to flow faster and thus have more load-carrying capacity (Figure 13.18). Channel pattern responds by straightening to shorten the flow distance and increase gradient. The straighter stream still contains excess sediment, causing the water to pick its way through as a **braided stream** (Figure 13.19).

Another "too much load" situation for a stream is the presence of a lake. For example, if a landslide dams a stream, it adds excess load that the stream will attempt

Figure 13.15

Schematic cross-section of a stream with too much discharge. The excess water erodes the bottom, flattening the gradient and thus slowing water flow.

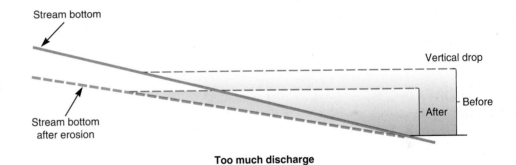

Figure 13.16

(a) Straight stream is the shortest path between two points. (b) Meandering channel lengthens stream, thus reducing gradient and slowing water flow.

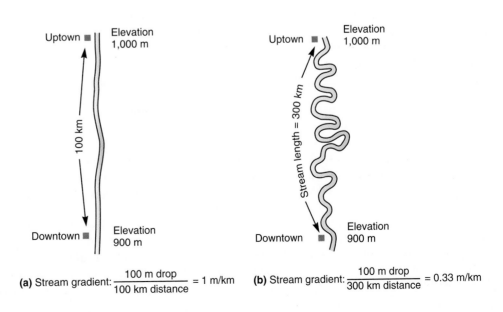

(a) Stream gradient: $\dfrac{100 \text{ m drop}}{100 \text{ km distance}} = 1 \text{ m/km}$ (b) Stream gradient: $\dfrac{100 \text{ m drop}}{300 \text{ km distance}} = 0.33 \text{ m/km}$

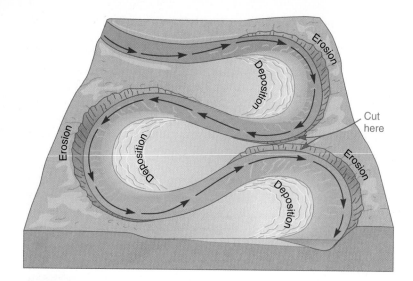

Figure 13.17
In a meandering stream, the outside bank is eroded and steep, while the inside bank grows as sediment is deposited. In the lower meander, notice how the erosional banks have almost met; in many cases, humans have cut through adjacent banks to straighten a river.

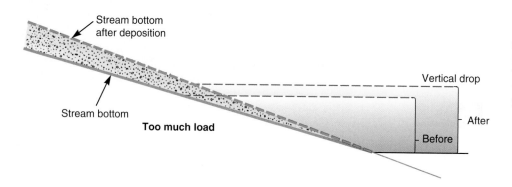

Figure 13.18
Schematic cross-section of a stream with too much load. Excess sediment is dropped on the stream bottom, increasing the gradient and thus speeding water flow.

to carry away. The stream will gradually fill in the lake basin with its load of sediment until flow can reach the dam (Figure 13.20). When the stream is able to flow rapidly over the steep-gradient face of the dam, it does so with heightened erosive power, allowing it to carry away the landslide dam as well as the sediment fill in the lake. In a geological sense, lakes are temporary features that streams are striving to eliminate.

Graded Stream Theory
All streams operate in a state of delicate equilibrium maintained by constantly changing the gradient of the stream bottom, thus sustaining a **graded stream**. Every change in the system triggers compensating changes that work toward equilibrium. A typical stream has too much load and too little discharge in its upstream portions, thus it maintains a braided channel pattern there. In its downstream segments, the typical stream has too much discharge, finer sediments in its load, and less friction, thus it runs in a meandering pattern there. Streams also change their equilibrium states from one season to another and in response to global changes in sea level and to tectonic events.

The Flood Plain

After rainfall, a portion of water infiltrates through the soil and the remaining portion runs off at the surface into streams and rivers. What factors determine the amount of **infiltration** versus **runoff** (Table 13.1)? Water is likely to infiltrate in porous, dry soils over a flat landscape covered with vegetation. This is especially true if the total amount of precipitation is spread over a relatively long period of time. On the other hand, intense precipitation over already-saturated soils on exposed, steep slopes promotes runoff.

Streams occupy less than 1% of the land surface but convey the rainfall runoff from all the land. When discharge temporarily exceeds their capacity to contain the flow, flooding occurs. Drainage basins with a high density of short streams are associated with a higher potential flooding hazard because rain water tends to be captured quickly into streams instead of infiltrating over a long distance before reaching a body of water.

Flood plains are the floors of streams during floods (Figure 13.21). Flood plains, with their thick sediment cover and sheltered surroundings, offer several species a

Figure 13.19
A braided channel pattern occurs as water flows through excess sediment within a fairly straight valley.

Figure 13.20
Schematic cross-section of a landslide-dammed valley. Over time, a stream fills the lake with sediment and then flows across the infilled lake. Flow down the dam's steep face is at high velocity, causing erosion and transport of dam and lake sediment.

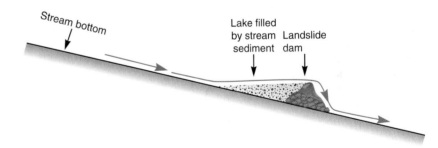

Stream bottom

Lake filled by stream sediment   Landslide dam

Table 13.1

Factors Affecting Infiltration and Runoff

Infiltration	Runoff
←——Increasing soil porosity———	
←——Increasing vegetation cover———	
←——Increasing duration of precipitation———	
——Increasing amount of precipitation——→	
——Increasing soil saturation——→	
——Increasing slope steepness——→	

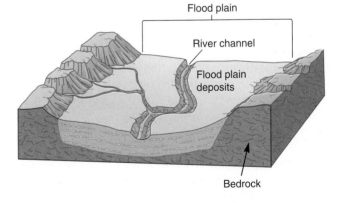

Flood plain

River channel

Flood plain deposits

Bedrock

Figure 13.21
Flood plains are stream floors during floods.

In Greater Depth

Cottonwoods

Cottonwoods (*Populus Deltoides*) are magnificent trees that stand tall in the Prairies where their waxy leaves and thick bark help them to conserve water in spite of the dry environment (Figure 13.22). They owe their name to the white fluffy seeds produced by the female tree in June. Cottonwoods can live for several hundred years, growing massive trunks up to 2 m in diameter. The Plains Indians respected the spirit of old cottonwoods. They used them as burial places, putting their dead on platforms in these trees.

Cottonwoods grow in flood plains. They are never found far from the water edge as their roots must remain in contact with the water table to survive. In fact, the life cycle of cottonwoods has developed in harmony with recurring floods. Following the spring melt in the Rockies, prairie rivers normally flood their banks in late spring or early summer, just in time for the cottonwood seeds to land in the moist, fertile mud. The long-term survival of cottonwood forests is jeopardized by the building of upstream flood control dams, which deprive the trees of that nourishing flux.

Figure 13.22 This cottonwood growing in the flood plain of the Red Deer River in Southern Alberta is over 200 years old.
Photo: © Claire Samson.

nurturing environment (see In Greater Depth box: Cottonwoods). Streams build flood plains by erosion and deposition, and reoccupy their flood plains whenever they see fit. Humans who decide to build on a flood plain are gamblers. They may win their gamble for many years, but the stream still rules the flood plain, and every so often it comes back to collect all bets.

Flood Frequency

Everyone living near a stream needs to understand the frequency with which floods occur. Small floods happen every year or so. Large floods return less often—every score of years, century, or longer. Statistically speaking, the larger the floods, the longer the return period between each. A typical analysis of flood frequency involves a plot of historical data on flood discharge versus return period (Figure 13.23). The longer the historical record of floods in an area, the more accurately the curve can be drawn. With a flood-frequency curve, the return period of floods of a given size can be estimated by reading directly along the horizontal axis the period corresponding to their discharge value on the vertical axis.

Individual flood-frequency curves must be constructed for each stream because each stream has its own characteristic floods. A flood-frequency curve should serve as the basis for designing all structures built on a flood plain and determining where buildings should be located for the highest probability of safety. Planners can decide what size flood (how many years of protection)

to accommodate when determining how the land is to be used.

When designing roads, bridges, and buildings, it is seductive to consider only the smaller floods and save large amounts of money on initial construction costs. However, these initial savings are eaten away by higher maintenance and repair costs. In the long run, it is commonly cheaper to build with respect for large floods; this not only saves money in the future but also eliminates much of the human suffering that occurs when homes and other buildings are flooded.

A designer needs to know the likelihood of a given size flood occurring during the expected usage time of a structure. A common standard for design near streams is protection from the 100-year flood. Flood frequency also can be expressed as the statistical probability of stream discharges of a given size arriving in any year or number of years (Table 13.2). The bigger the flood, the longer the return period and the smaller the probability of experiencing it in any one year. Statistically, the 100-year flood has a 1% chance of occurring any year. What is the probability that a 100-year flood will occur once in 100 years? The obvious answer of once is wrong; from Table 13.2, the probability is only 63%. No flood has a 100% chance of occurring.

We must distinguish between yearly versus cumulative probability. In cumulative probability, the longer the wait for a 100-year flood, the more likely it will occur. Nevertheless, the yearly probability of a flood is the same for any year regardless of when the last flood occurred. The confusion that commonly arises when hearing of the "100-year flood" has led some people to stop using the term

In Greater Depth

Flood-Frequency Curves

We need to know how often a given-size flood may occur in order to intelligently develop land. The process used is statistical. If enough historical records exist for a river, then probable flood frequencies can be estimated.

A relatively simple method for constructing a flood-frequency curve begins by determining the peak discharge for each year. Ignoring the chronological order, rank each annual flood in order from biggest discharge (= 1), second biggest (= 2), etc., on down to the smallest. To plot a curve such as Figure 13.23 for a river of interest, you will first calculate return periods for each year's maximum flood using the formula

$$\text{Return period} = \frac{(N+1)}{M}$$

where N is the number of years of flood records, and M is the numerical rank of each year's maximum flood discharge. After calculating a return period for each year, locate that value (in years) on the horizontal axis (which usually is a logarithmic axis as in Figure 13.23); then move upward until reaching the appropriate discharge value. Stop and plot a point marking the intersection of the return period and discharge values. After plotting a discharge versus return period point for each year, draw a best-fit line through your plotted points.

The flood-frequency curve for the Red River in Manitoba is presented in Figure 13.23. The 1997 flood is the fourth highest in the record. A flood of this size has an estimated return period of 62 years.

How valuable are flood-frequency curves? Their reliability is directly related to the number of years of flood records; the longer the record, the better the flood-frequency curve. In this method, the return period for the largest flood on a river is the most suspect point; it is based on a sample population of one. Advanced statistical methods are available to help plot the upper segments of flood-frequency curves for the rare, extra-large floods.

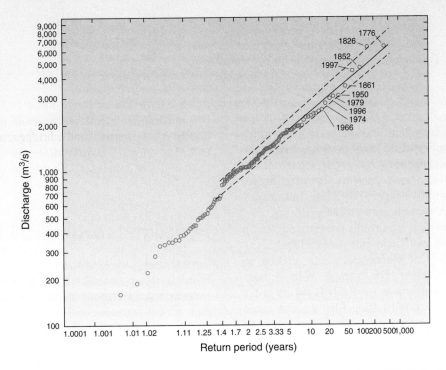

Figure 13.23 Flood-frequency curve for the Red River, Manitoba, for the years 1776, 1826, 1852 1861, 1875 to 1878, 1880 to 1885, and 1892 to 1997. (The ten largest floods have been labelled.)

Source: Reproduced with the permission of Natural Resources Canada 2008, courtesy of the Geological Survey of Canada (GSC Bulletin 548).

and to replace it with "1%-chance flood." A 1% chance flood is a flood event that has a 1% chance of occurring or being exceeded in any given year.

By similar analysis, even though a "150-year flood" may occur one year, it is still possible for another of the same size to come again in the following year or even in the same year. For example, in 1971, the Patuxent River between Baltimore and Washington, DC, in the United States had a flood that was 1.6 times bigger than its calculated 100-year flood. The next year, in 1972, the Patuxent River conveyed a flood that was 1.04 times as big as its 100-year flood. A 100-year flood, or any other size flood, is a statistically average event that occurs by chance, not at regular intervals (Table 13.2). As the adage states: "Nature has neither a memory nor a conscience."

Table 13.2

Cumulative Probabilities of Floods (Percentage Chance of This Size Flood Occurring)

Return Period (Years)	Any 1 Year	10 Years	25 Years	50 Years	100 Years
2	50%				
5	20				
10	10	65	94	99.9	
20	5	40	71	90.5	
50	2	18	40	63	86
100	1	9.6	22	39	63
200	0.5	5	12	22	39
500	0.2	2	5	9.5	18
1,000	0.1	1	2.5	4.8	9.5
2,000	0.05	0.5	1.2	2.3	5
5,000	0.02	0.2	0.5	1	2
10,000	0.01	0.1	0.25	0.5	1

Source: B. M. Reich, *Water Resources Bulletin*, 9 (1973), 187–88.

Flood Styles

Worldwide, river and coastal flooding affects more people than all other natural hazards. Floods are intricately related to several other natural disasters. They can trigger mass movements, and be triggered by mass movements, storms and cyclones, tsunami, and volcanic activity.

Floods are unleashed by several phenomena, which can be grouped into two main categories (Table 13.3). (1) Hydrometeorological floods occur in relation to specific weather conditions. For example, a local thundercloud can form and unleash a flash flood in just a few hours. Abundant rainfall lasting for days can cause regional floods that last for weeks. The storm surges of tropical cyclones flood the coasts. The breakup of winter ice on rivers can pile up and temporarily block the water flow, and then fail in an ice-jam flood. (2) Flooding also occurs when there is a local obstruction to flow. Natural dams made by landslides, glaciers, or lahars fail and unleash floods.

Table 13.3

Flood Styles

1. Hydrometeorological floods	Rainfall
	Snowmelt
	Rain-on-snow
	Ice jam
2. Natural dams	

In Canada, most floods are caused by hydrometeorological mechanisms, often working in combination. April and May are particularly vulnerable (Figure 13.2) when abundant rain coincides with the spring melt.

Hydrometeorological Floods

RAINFALL FLOODS

Rainfall floods occur when the rate of precipitation exceeds the infiltration capacity of the ground. Water runs off into streams and rivers, which swell and soon overflow.

A rainfall flood can take the form of a dramatic flash flood, the result of torrential rainfall over a relatively small area. Flash floods develop in a matter of a few hours, sometimes unexpectedly. The hamlet of Buffalo Gap, Saskatchewan, holds the Canadian flash-flooding record. On 30 May 1961, 254 mm of precipitation—a mix of rain and hail—fell in less than one hour! An agent of the Saskatchewan Wheat Pool reported: "Pigpens, full and empty, gas barrels, toilets, timbers, C.P.R. [Canadian Pacific Railway] ties and telegraph poles went through the town like sail boats." A day after the storm, hail was still piled a metre deep.

Southern Ontario, with its oppressive summer heat and high humidex ratings, which fuel thunderstorm activity, has witnessed a few events. From 19 to 20 July 1989, for example, 450 mm of rain fell in Harrow, near Lake Erie. More recently, in the late afternoon of 19 August

2005, a swarm of thunderstorms dumped on the City of Toronto 153 mm of rain, accompanied by quarter- to golf-ball sized hail, causing flash flooding of creeks and ravines, sewer backups, and infrastructure damage. According to the Insurance Bureau of Canada, the bill for this tempestuous event exceeded $500 million, which is more than 2.5 times Ontario's losses during the infamous ice storm of 1998.

Flash floods can be deadly. Several flood fatalities in recent years in Canada have occurred when cars were swept off the road by flood waters. Not enough people appreciate what a shallow-water flood can do to a car (Figure 13.24). Flowing water about 0.3 m deep exerts about 2,250 newtons of lateral force. If 0.6 m deep water reaches the bottom of a car, there will be a buoyant uplift of about 6,500 newtons, which helps the 4,500 newton lateral force in pushing or rolling the car off the road. Many automobile drivers and passengers are swept away by floodwater less than a metre deep.

The 1972 Rapid Creek Flood, South Dakota

The 1972 Rapid Creek flood was a landmark event in our thinking about flash floods and vulnerability. The Black Hills are one of the most beautiful sites in the United States; they host nearly 3 million tourists a year. At the foot of the Black Hills sits Rapid City, first settled south of Rapid Creek in 1876. The early inhabitants were wary of the Rapid Creek flood plain, and the wisdom of their caution was borne out by a large flood in 1907. However,

as the city's population grew, the peaceful, meandering stream became a magnet that induced development on the flood plain. In 1952, Pactola Dam was built 16 km upstream to provide flood protection and a reserve water supply for Rapid City. The dam eliminated most small floods, giving people a false sense of security. By 1972, the flood plain was host to numerous houses, mobile-home parks, shopping centres, car lots, and other urban structures serving residents in a city approaching a population of 50,000.

On 9 June 1972, southeast winds bringing moist air from the Gulf of Mexico met a cold front coming from the northwest. The moist air turned upward to build 16 km high thunderheads that remained stationary due to weak upper-level winds. Shortly after 6 p.m., heavy rain began to fall; up to 38 cm fell in less than six hours, but most of the rain fell downstream from Pactola Dam. Rain runoff filled Canyon Lake, built on the western edge of Rapid City. The spillway at Canyon Lake Dam became plugged by automobiles and house debris, causing the lake level to rise an additional 3.6 m. Then the dam failed at about the same time as the natural flood crest arrived, thus unleashing a torrent of water on Rapid City. The river reoccupied its flood plain with vengeance, leaving destruction totalling $664 million in 2002 dollars. Floods in the region killed 238 people, and destroyed 1,335 homes and 5,000 vehicles.

This time the lesson was learned by many. Canyon Lake Dam and many bridges were redesigned and rebuilt to prevent debris accumulations. Rebuilding was

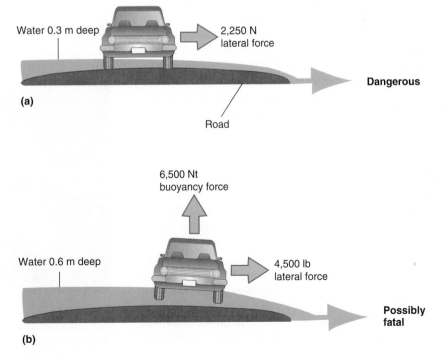

Figure 13.24
Do not drive through a flood. (a) Flood water 0.3 m deep exerts 2,250 new-tons of lateral force. (b) Flood water 0.6 m deep both buoyantly lifts and laterally pushes a car.
Modified from US Geological Survey Fact Sheet 024–00.

Water 0.3 m deep

2,250 N lateral force

Dangerous

Road

(a)

6,500 Nt buoyancy force

Water 0.6 m deep

4,500 lb lateral force

Possibly fatal

(b)

not permitted on the portion of Rapid Creek flood plain inundated in 1907 and 1972. It is now a long greenway featuring a golf course, picnic areas, bike and jogging paths, recreation areas, ponds and ice-skating rinks, low-maintenance grasslands, and an area reseeded with native vegetation: in short, the greenway is now being used for activities that will not be harmed by the occasional flood.

The 1996 Saguenay Flood, Quebec

The Saguenay flood of 1996 was a major natural disaster and the costliest flood in Canadian history. It was not, however, solely due to extreme weather conditions. The event illustrates the complex interaction between the forces of nature and human modifications to the environment.

On 18 July 1996, a large cyclonic depression started forming over the North Atlantic Ocean, offshore of New England. The weather system operated as a huge engine, evaporating warm water from the Gulf Stream and condensing rain droplets over the Saguenay region of Quebec. How much water can the soil of the boreal forest possibly absorb? Between 19 and 21 July, the region received a total of 279 mm of rain, most of which fell in a 36-hour period. It was the equivalent of 10 buckets of water emptied over every square metre of soil.

Such a deluge causes rivers to adapt by overflowing their banks. In the Saguenay, they did this with a vengeance. Several rivers re-occupied ancient channels that had been diverted by urban intervention, in a process called **avulsion** (Figure 13.25). Some eroded their banks severely, sending waterfront properties down into the river channel.

The precarious situation was further complicated by the fact that the area is covered by a network of more than 2,000 dams and earthen dikes. All this haphazard infrastructure is managed by various organizations, dedicated to different uses, and in various states of maintenance. Kenogami Lake was one of the many reservoir lakes whose level was artificially controlled by a dam. At the request of recreationists, the water level in Kenogami Lake had been kept high since the spring. At the onset of the crisis, there were only 160 cm between the lake and the crest of the dam. In the early hours of 20 July, technicians realized that the dam would not resist much longer the influx of water into the reservoir. They increased the evacuation of water, creating an artificial flood downstream in the Rivière aux Sables and Rivière Chicoutimi (Figure 13.26).

The floods created chaos in the region, with 1,700 houses and 900 cottages destroyed (Figure 13.27). More than 15,000 people had to be evacuated from their homes. Ten people lost their lives, including two children who died when a mud flow buried their home. The house of Mrs. Jeanne d'Arc Lavoie-Genest, which resisted the flood, has been preserved in downtown Chicoutimi as a symbol of the resilience of the people of the Saguenay (Figure 13.28).

Figure 13.25
Post-flood Rivière à Mars, Saguenay region, showing channel avulsion and bank erosion.

Photo: Reproduced with the permission of Natural Resources Canada 2008, courtesy of the Geological Survey of Canada (Photo 1997-42X by G.R. Brooks). http://gsc.nrcan.gc.ca/floods/saguenay1996/photo1_e.php.

Figure 13.26
The City of Jonquière dam along Rivière aux Sables was overtopped during the 1996 Saguenay flood.

Photo: Reproduced with the permission of Natural Resources Canada 2008, courtesy of the Geological Survey of Canada (Photo 1997-42L by G.R. Brooks). http://gsc.nrcan.gc.ca/floods/saguenay1996/photo4_e.php.

Figure 13.27

The large number of damaged properties made the Saguenay flood the costliest in Canadian history.

Photo: Reproduced with the permission of Natural Resources Canada 2008, courtesy of the Climate Change Impacts and Adaptation Program. http://adaptation.nrcan.gc.ca/perspective/intro_2_e.php.

May it also serve as a reminder for more cautious land use and urban development practices in the future.

Ancient Tales of Deluge

In almost every part of the world, tales are told of ancient deluges far greater than any seen in modern times. In India, it is said that Vishnu, the god of protection, used one of his 10 lives to save Mother Earth from a great flood. China celebrates Yu the Great, who helped protect the people from the overwhelming floods of the Huang (Yellow) River. American Indian origin mythologies begin with an Earth completely flooded. In Babylonia, clay tablets record the Gilgamesh Epic, which tells of the great flood where Utnapishtim built an ark that sailed for seven days and seven nights and saved his kin and cattle. The Genesis book of the Bible tells of Noah building an ark to save his family and pairs of all the animals from 40 days and 40 nights of rain that covered the world with water for 150 days. These sagas tell of events that occurred around 6000 BCE to 1000 BCE. Were floods larger in those times? Or are these tales of rare events with very long recurrence intervals—the "1,000-year" inundation floods?

The flood of the Gilgamesh Epic, and possibly the Bible, may have occurred within the Tigris and Euphrates Rivers (in modern-day Iraq), which flow across an extensive, low-lying plain to enter the Persian Gulf (Figure 13.29). Long-duration rains pouring onto the mountains of Iran and Turkey shed runoff, creating massive flood crests that inundate the flood plains of the lower Tigris and Euphrates Rivers. It is on these fertile flood plains that people congregate to reap the agricultural rewards. A long-lasting flood would submerge the "whole world" of their existence.

SNOWMELT FLOODS

Snowmelt floods develop over several weeks. Technological advances, including satellite imagery and distributed networks of river gauges, allow better forecasts of the time and height of flood waters. In well-studied drainage basins, computer models can simulate the response of the different streams and rivers to different weather scenarios.

The floods of the Red River are classic examples of regional snowmelt floods, compounded with the occasional ice jam. Hydrologists knew in December 1996 that the 1997 spring melt in the Red River valley would be

Figure 13.28

The house of Mrs. Jeanne d'Arc Lavoie-Genest, nicknamed "La petite maison blanche" ("the small white house") now stands alone in a park. The neighbouring houses were washed away during the 1996 Saguenay flood.

Photo: © Pascal Tremblay

www.revolution-saglac.com

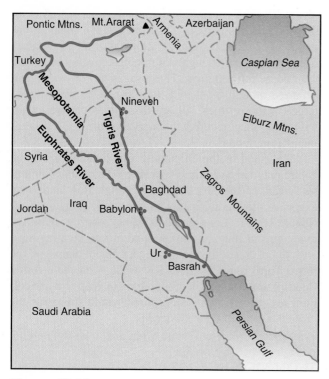

Figure 13.29
Map of the Euphrates and Tigris River plains, the site of the Babylonian (Gilgamesh Epic) and possibly the Hebrew (Noah's ark) flood tales. The lower flood plain receives long-lasting inundation floods from extended heavy rains in the mountains of Turkey and Iran.

problematic. On 23 April, almost two weeks before the actual peak in water level, Manitoban provincial authorities ordered a mandatory evacuation of thousands of homes in the Red River Valley, a decision still questioned. For several residents, the forced evacuation meant that they were relegated to the role of bystanders and could not do anything to save their homes.

Better forecasting of snowmelt floods has reduced the loss of life. But it is interesting to note the twin trends of better forecasting and engineering offset by ever-greater dollar losses during big floods. We know more, yet suffer greater damages.

RAIN-ON-SNOW FLOODS

Rain-on-snow floods are a combination of rainfall and snowmelt floods. They are likely to occur in the fall along the west coast, or during a mild spell in winter or in the spring elsewhere in Canada, when temperatures are hovering around 0° C. Two factors coincide to create the problem: rain adds to the snowmelt to generate a large quantity of water, and, at the same time, the frozen soil is almost impermeable to infiltration. The result is excess water pooling at the surface.

Another problem is associated with rain on snow. A water-saturated snowpack becomes very heavy and can add a dangerous load on structures. We have seen this situation before: just imagine replacing volcanic ash with wet snow in Figure 7.20!

ICE JAM FLOODS

Ice jams are a spring "classic" in many drainage basins across Canada. With the return of milder temperatures, river ice breaks into pieces and moves downstream with the current. Problems occur when they start to pile up, obstructing the flow of water. Water levels rise upstream and the river may overtop its banks. Ice jams of several kilometres in length are common (Figure 13.30).

Rivers flowing from south to north—the Red River of Manitoba, the Mackenzie River in the Northwest Territories, and the St. Lawrence River and several of its tributaries in Ontario and Quebec—are particularly vulnerable to this style of flood. Break-up starts earlier in the south, sending large pieces of ice toward the north where the still-frozen ice acts as a plug. The supply of upstream ice and the thickness of the intact ice are the key variables in this scenario. Several other factors might compound the problem. Bends and other variations in the shape, depth, and gradient of the river channel can create favourable circumstances to the formation of ice jams, as can human-made obstacles like bridges and piers (Figure 13.31).

At critical times in the St. Lawrence River, ice breakers continually fracture the ice to prevent the onset of a jam. In smaller rivers, a mix of ice blasting and ice cutting is used to breach the ice cover and to fragment ice blocks into smaller, more mobile, pieces.

Figure 13.30
Ice jam at Hay River, Northwest Territories, in spring 2005.
Photo: Robyn Andrishak, Research Engineer, University of Alberta.

Figure 13.31

Ice blocks jamming against bridge pilings on Hay River, Northwest Territories, spring 2007.

Photo: Robyn Andrishak, Research Engineer, University of Alberta.

WORLD DISTRIBUTION OF HYDROMETEOROLOGICAL FLOODS

It is interesting to examine the flooding styles of the world's largest drainage basins (Figure 13.32). Rainfall floods occur most often (20 of 38) and include the record flood of 1953 in Brazil when the Amazon River reached a peak discharge of 370,000 m³/s. Rainfall floods are mainly concentrated between 35 degrees of latitude north and south, and are associated with torrential tropical rains. Snowmelt floods dominate in the northern latitudes. Canada contributes 4 data points to this inventory: the drainage basins of the St. Lawrence, Nelson, and Mackenzie rivers, and that of the international Yukon River flowing from the Canadian Rockies to the Bering Sea through Alaska. All are characterized by snowmelt flooding.

Figure 13.32

Geographical distribution and peak discharges for 38 of the world's 45 largest drainage basins.

Sources: O'Connor and Costa, 2004, USGS Circular 1245; Dery et al., 2005, *Journal of Climate*.

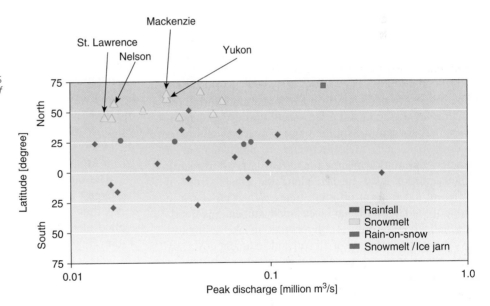

Natural Dams

The category "Natural dams" groups several flooding mechanisms in which an obstacle is blocking the flow of water. This blockage can result from mass movement (see "1971 and 1993 Lateral Spreads, Lemieux, Ontario" in Chapter 9), lava flows, or the advance or retreat of glaciers.

The complex relation between glaciers and liquid water can take several forms. In jokulhlaups, subglacial volcanic activity triggers the rapid melting of glaciers (see "Jokulhlaup of 1996" in Chapter 8). In some cases, very large glacial lakes are formed when deep valleys are blocked by tall glaciers for an extended period of time. These lakes might overflow, or breach their ice dams or retaining moraines.

When natural dams fail catastrophically, they trigger **outburst floods**. Outburst floods are the sudden release of large quantities of water with peak discharges typically one order of magnitude greater than that of hydrometeorological floods. Their force of impact causes enormous damage downstream. Table 13.4 lists the 11 known historical floods with peak discharges equal to or greater than 100,000 m³/s. Although not quite as common as hydrometeorological floods, natural dam floods account for 4 out of 11 entries. All natural dam floods listed were outburst floods.

Table 13.4

Largest Historical Floods

Date	Flood/River	Country	Peak Discharge [million m³/s]	Flood style
1841	Indus River	Pakistan	0.54	Landslide dam
1953	Amazon River	Brazil	0.37	Rainfall
1918	Katla	Iceland	0.30	Jokulhlaup
1963	Amazon River	Brazil	0.25	Rainfall
1976	Amazon River	Brazil	0.24	Rainfall
≈1450	Columbia River	United States	0.22	Landslide dam
1967	Lena River	Russia	0.19	Snowmelt and ice jam
1962	Lena River	Russia	0.17	Snowmelt and ice jam
1948	Lena River	Russia	0.17	Snowmelt and ice jam
1870	Yangtze	China	0.11	Rainfall
1986	Russell Fiord	United States	0.10	Ice dam

Hydrometeorological floods
Natural dams

Source: J.E. O'Connor and J E. Costa, 2004, USGS Circular 1254.

QUATERNARY ICE-DAM FAILURE FLOODS

The biggest floods known on Earth occurred during the melting of the continental ice sheets during the Quaternary period from 1.8 million years to a few thousand years ago. Glacial meltwater tends to pond in front of glaciers due to downwarped land (isostatic adjustment). Thousands of lakes formed along the glacial front in different locations at different times. When ice dams in front of the largest glacial lakes failed, stupendous floods resulted whose passage is still recorded in lake sediments; by countryside stripped of all soil and sediment cover; by high-elevation flood gravels; by an integrated system of braided channels (a megabraided stream); by abandoned waterfalls; by high-level erosion; and by large-scale sediment deposits.

The failure of an ice-dammed lake can send so great a volume of water running over and eroding the land that it can make changes in the paths of rivers. In North America, the meltwater floods varied in their paths among the following: the Mississippi River to the Gulf of Mexico, the St. Lawrence and Hudson Rivers to the North Atlantic Ocean, the Mackenzie River to the Arctic Ocean or via the Hudson Strait to the Labrador Sea.

The discharge of a huge volume of cold, low-salinity glacial meltwater could change the global circulation of deep water through the world ocean (Figure 2.29). The deep-ocean circulation is driven by regional differences in heat and salinity of ocean water, and this could be changed by a huge influx of cold, fresh meltwater. A change in ocean circulation would in turn make changes in global climate. At 12,900 years ago, climate cooled about 5° C in the event known as the Younger Dryas (Figure 10.35). This dramatic plunge back into colder temperatures is thought to have been caused by a gigantic meltwater flood through the St. Lawrence River into the North Atlantic Ocean.

The outbursts from glacial meltwater lakes created the largest known floods in Earth's history. In the span of a few thousand years, the massive continental ice sheets melted in gigantic quantities, raising sea level by some 130 m (Figure 10.36).

Mitigation of Flood Hazards

Mitigation strategies to reduce society's vulnerability to flood hazards have been in two main categories: structural and non-structural.

Structural mitigation initiatives include the erection of major infrastructures like floodways, dams, and flood barriers; building **levees** along rivers to contain floodwater inside a taller and larger channel; and engineering projects to increase the water-carrying ability of a river channel via straightening, widening, and deepening, as well as removing debris.

Non-structural responses include more accurate flood forecasting through use of satellites and high-tech equipment, zoning and land-use policies, insurance programs, evacuation planning, and education.

What to Do Before, During, and After a Flood

Before

If you live in a flood-prone area, consider taking a few practical steps to make your home more resilient. For example, put sealant around basement windows and at the base of ground-level doors. Put in drains moving rainwater away from the building. Install a sump pump and zero-reverse-flow valves in basement floor drains.

If a flood is forecast and there is enough time, turn off the basement furnace and the outside gas valve. Electricity and water do not mix! Safeguard all electrical equipment. Move valuables above ground level.

If there is immediate danger of flooding, shut off the electricity. Plug basement sewer drains and toilet connections with a wooden stopper.

During

Listen to the radio to stay informed of the latest developments.

Never cross a flooded area. If your car stalls in raising waters, abandon the car.

After

Be aware of potential electrical shocks when re-entering your home. Wear rubber boots.

Flood water can be heavily contaminated with sewage and other pollutants, posing a serious health hazard. Dispose of any food items if they have been exposed to flood waters. Do not move back into your house until every flood-contaminated room has been thoroughly cleaned, disinfected, and surface-dried. Because some items (appliances, carpets, furniture, etc.) require specific care, you might need the help of a qualified professional.

DAMS

The construction of dams is a common method used to lessen the threat of flooding. Dams act as dampers by holding water in large reservoirs and releasing it at a safe rate. The presence of a dam gives a feeling of protection that invites many people to settle in the "protected" flood plain lying downstream. But dams do not provide absolute flood control. They offer some flood protection—if their reservoirs are not filled to capacity or if they do not fail.

All dams have life spans limited by the durability of their construction materials and style, and the rate at which stream-delivered sediment fills in their reservoirs. Despite all the massive dams and extensive reservoirs, major floods still occur downstream due to overtopping and to heavy rains that fall below the dam.

THE LONDON FLOOD BARRIER, ENGLAND

Although located up the Thames estuary, some 50 km inland from the sea, central London has been flooded repeatedly in history. It happened last in 1928 when 14 people drowned. A similar event is unimaginable today. Beside major museums, art galleries, and institutional buildings, central London includes the "City," the world's most strategic financial district. It also features cultural icons like Big Ben and the Tower of London.

What makes London vulnerable to flooding? (1) Central London is built on a bed of clay and is gradually subsiding under the weight of its infrastructure. Several highly populated neighbourhoods are barely above sea level. (2) Tectonic forces are inexorably tilting southeast England downward into the sea. The net result is a rise of the tide levels relative to the land of 60 cm per century. Storm surges are a particular threat. When they coincide with high astronomical tides, large quantities of water enter the Thames estuary, which acts as a bottleneck, causing a rapid increase in water level.

Since 1984, London has been protected by the Flood Barrier (Figure 13.33). This major infrastructure consists of 10 concrete buttresses spread across the half-kilometre width of the Thames. Not unlike the inlet structure of the Red River Floodway (Figure 13.10), the most important

Figure 13.33
The London Flood Barrier under normal conditions. Radial gates are kept underwater so they do not interfere with maritime traffic.
Photos: © Claire Samson.

features of the barrier—the radial gates—are normally submerged, allowing maritime traffic on the Thames. When dangerous weather conditions are forecast, the gates are raised, some three to four hours before the predicted peak of the incoming surge. The gates effectively form a continuous steel wall facing downriver, ready to stem the high tide.

Experts fear that by 2030, the existing Flood Barrier may no longer be able to cope with the increased flood threat due to climate change and its associated rise in mean sea level and more vigorous storm activity. Plans to build a 16-km-wide barrier further east in the Thames estuary are under consideration.

LEVEES AND SANDBAGGING

Levees confine floodwater by increasing the height of the channel through which the water flows. Higher levees create higher river levels. Levees prevent rivers in flood from flowing laterally to spread out their water; instead, they are confined and forced to rise vertically until ultimately overtopping the levees. As levees become saturated, the river finds weak spots, compromising the levees by wave attack, erosion by overtopping, failing by slumping, and undermining by piping (Figure 13.34).

There is a continuing debate regarding the value of levees. On one side, critics suggest that the cost of building more levees and dams may be higher than the value of the buildings they are protecting. Plus, the presence of structures advertised to control floods creates a sense of security that stimulates further development of the flood plain—development that likely will be flooded. These critics recommend lowering or removing levees along farmland to increase wetland habitat and restore the flood plain. Allowing floods to spread out and dissipate their energies over a wide expanse of land would also lower flood heights in the levee-protected major cities and towns.

However, proponents of levees say that the billions of dollars in flood damages would have been many billions more without the levees. When a big flood is on the way, a common response is to quickly build temporary levees using hastily filled bags of sand and mud. Some of the sandbag levees do lessen damages but others do not. Even when sandbag levees fail, it is commonly observed that there is a real therapeutic value gained by people working together in a project for the common good.

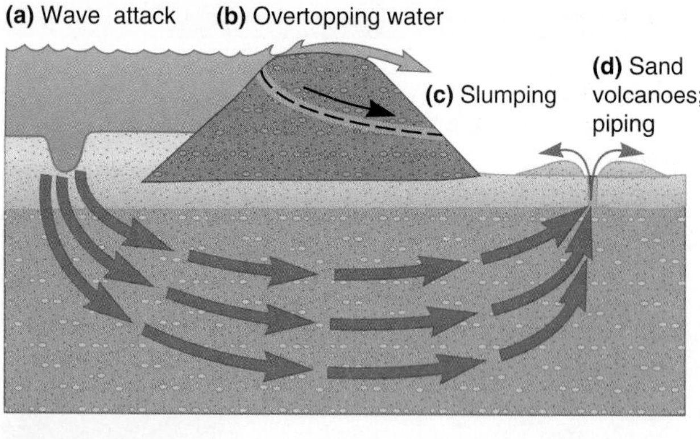

CHANNELIZATION

Humans try to control flood waters by making channels (1) clear of debris, (2) deeper, (3) wider, and (4) straighter. A typical channelization project involves clearing the channel of trees, debris, and large boulders to reduce channel roughness and then increasing the channel capacity by digging it deeper, wider, and straighter by creating shortcuts across meander bends. All these activities make it easier for water to flow through the channel (Figure 13.35).

Figure 13.35
The concrete-lined channel of Forester Creek, El Cajon, California. In response to flood damage, several cities in Southern California not only cleared, straightened, and deepened their river channels, but also lined them with concrete to further reduce friction and speed flow. As long as flood volumes stay smaller than channel capacity, then there are no urban floods. It should be noted, however, that concrete-lined channels obliterate the habitat of all riverine plants and animals. The "soul" of a community is less well served by a concrete ditch than a tree-lined stream.
Photo: © Pat Abbott.

(a) Wave attack   **(b)** Overtopping water

(c) Slumping

(d) Sand volcanoes; piping

Figure 13.34
Levees are attacked by several processes: (a) wave attack; (b) erosion by overtopping; (c) slumping of the levee mass; and (d) subsurface erosion (piping).

THE HUANG AND YANGTZE RIVERS, CHINA

The Chinese have cohabited for millennia with mighty, flooding rivers. China's two greatest rivers, the Huang (Yellow) and Yangtze, flow west to east, capturing the flow of a myriad of tributaries along a journey of several thousand kilometres. As explained by Simon Winchester in his travel book *The River at the Centre of the World*, four "curses" make the evacuation of the runoff captured in the massive drainage basins of the Huang and the Yangtze especially challenging. (1) China receives a large amount of precipitation every year, far more per square kilometre than North America or Europe. (2) Precipitation is geographically concentrated in a small portion of the drainage basins, in the west and south of the country. The rainy season, the summer monsoon, is (3) short in duration and (4) coincides with the spring melt of the Himalayan glaciers.

The Huang River is reputed to have killed more people than any other natural feature; it is also known as the "River of Sorrow" or the "Unmanageable." In the lower 800 km of its course, it flows over flood plain and coastal-plain sediments. Attempts to control river flow and protect people and property go back at least as far as the channel dredging of 2356 BCE. Levees are known to have been constructed since at least 602 BCE. In the last 2,500 years, the Huang River has undergone ten major channel shifts that have moved the location of its mouth as much as 1,100 km (Figures 13.36 and 13.37).

In 1887, the Huang overtopped 22 m banks, "discovered" lower elevations, and began flowing south to join the Yangtze River. The 1887 floods drowned people and crops, creating a one-two punch of floods and famine that were responsible for over one million deaths.

In 1938, the Huang River levees were dynamited in the war with Japan, resulting in another million lives lost to flood and famine. Today, the riverbed is 20 m higher than the adjoining flood plain! The Huang River "wants" to change course, but the Chinese keep building levees

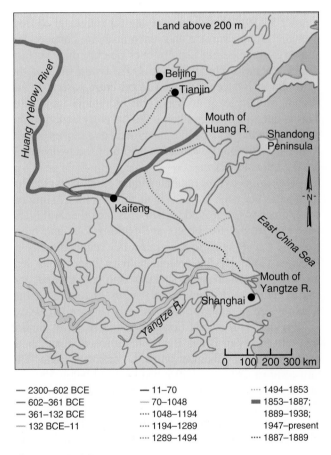

Figure 13.36
Locations of lower Huang (Yellow) and Yangtze Rivers.
Source: © Czaya.

Legend:
— 2300–602 BCE
— 602–361 BCE
— 361–132 BCE
— 132 BCE–11
— 11–70
— 70–1048
···· 1048–1194
···· 1194–1289
···· 1289–1494
···· 1494–1853
▬ 1853–1887; 1889–1938; 1947–present
···· 1887–1889

Figure 13.37
Delta of Huang River, China.
Photo: NASA.

to make it stay where it does not want to be. How long can the river be confined? The Chinese have tried to control the Huang for well over 4,000 years with limited success.

The situation is equally worrying along the Yangtze. The Yangtze is 1,000 km longer than the Huang, and has many more tributaries, including giant rivers. The 20th century has been exceptionally trying. Few natural disasters compare in magnitude with the Central China Flood of 1931. Several cycles of rapid flooding followed by episodes of total immersion affected 28 million people. Nearly 4 million people died in the ensuing famine. In 1954, flood waters covered Wuhan, a city of 8 million people, for over three months. In 1998, a flood in the same area caused damage on the order of billions of dollars and affected more than 2.3 million people.

Completed in 2006, the massive concrete structure of the Three Gorges Dam now stands on the Yangtze west of the city of Yichang. The dam, originally envisaged by Sun Yat-Sen in 1914, was primarily intended to provide flood control. The storage capacity of the dam reservoir is 22 km^3, which should reduce the frequency of downstream floods from 1 in 10 years to 1 in 100 years. When its turbines become fully operational in 2011, the Three Gorges Dam will also be the largest hydroelectric dam in the world and a critical source of power for China's manufacturing industry. However, critics argue that important human, environmental, and cultural impacts of the project have been ignored to bolster economic pursuits. They question the durability of the dam's flood protection, given the rapid accumulation of sediments in the reservoir. The Three Gorges Dam project has forced more than one million residents to relocate, and the local society is showing signs of dislocation, such as an increasing number of abandoned infants, and vagrancy. Has flood control been achieved at an excessive cost to society?

Urbanization and Floods

As more people move near rivers and streams, they encounter unexpected problems. Yet some of the problems are due to human activities that increase both flood heights and frequencies.

HYDROGRAPHS

A **hydrograph** plots discharge versus time, recording the passage of water volumes flowing downstream

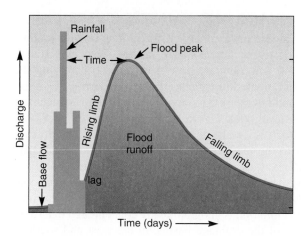

Figure 13.38
A hydrograph showing discharge (vertical axis) versus time (horizontal axis). Precipitations are drawn in green. Commonly, stream flow rapidly increases from surface runoff, as shown by a steep rising limb reaching a peak flow. From the peak, discharge decreases slowly as infiltrated rain flows underground and feeds the stream.

(Figure 13.38). There is a time lag for rainwater to flow over the ground surface and reach a stream channel, but stream surface height usually rises quickly once surface runoff reaches a channel; that is, the rising limb of the hydrograph is steep. When a flood crest passes downstream, stream level does not fall as rapidly as it rose. This is due to the stream being fed water by underground flow of rain that soaked into the ground and moved slowly to the stream; that is, the falling limb of the hydrograph has a gentle slope.

The flood hydrograph in Figure 13.38 is typical of rural areas but what happens in an urban setting? Humans cover much of the ground with houses and other buildings, pave the ground for streets and parking lots, and build storm-sewer systems to take rainwater runoff directly to streams. Covering the ground with an impervious seal prevents rainwater from soaking into the ground and causes rainwater to flow rapidly across the surface, thus reaching the stream ever more quickly (Figure 13.39).

Figure 13.40 shows flood hydrographs from similar size rainstorms in Brays Bayou in Houston, Texas, both before and after urbanization in the drainage basin. The rainstorm of October 1949 mostly soaked below the surface and its water flowed slowly underground to feed the stream. Following urbanization, the rainstorm of June 1960 produced a flood hydrograph with a very different shape. This is a proverbial good news–bad news situation for city dwellers. The good news is that the urban flood lasted only 20% as long; the bad news is that it was four times higher. The roofing and paving that accompany growing urbanization cause many areas to receive more severe floods.

FLOOD FREQUENCIES

Another way of looking at flood runoff within urban areas is to see how urbanization affects the frequency of floods. Roofing and paving the ground increase the surface runoff of rainwater, thus causing higher stream levels in shorter times; that is, runoffs become flash floods. Figure 13.41 shows the effects of building storm sewers (percentage of area sewered) and of roofing and paving (percentage of area impervious). The various curves corresponding to different urbanized conditions plot to the left of the curve for an unurbanized setting, that is, at shorter flood return periods.

Even well-planned communities can experience unanticipated floods. As population grows and development moves up the river basin, the increase in ground covered by buildings, roads, and parking lots means that floods will occur more frequently. Remember that wherever urbanization is increasing, the floods of today will be smaller than the floods of tomorrow.

Figure 13.39
Roads, especially those located in topographic lows, are vulnerable to temporary flooding during heavy rains, the paved surface impeding infiltration.

Photo: © Claire Samson

Figure 13.40
Flood hydrographs for similar-size runoffs in Brays Bayou in Houston, Texas, before and after urbanization. In the rural setting, much of the rainfall soaks into the ground. After urbanization, the roofs and pavement covering the land prevent infiltration, and most rain quickly runs over the surface of the ground, creating much higher floods.

Source: K. Young, *Geology: The Paradox of Earth and Man.* Boston: Houghton Mifflin, 1975.

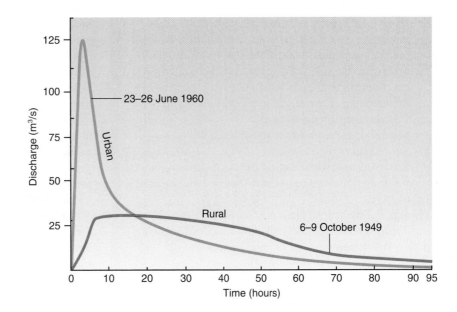

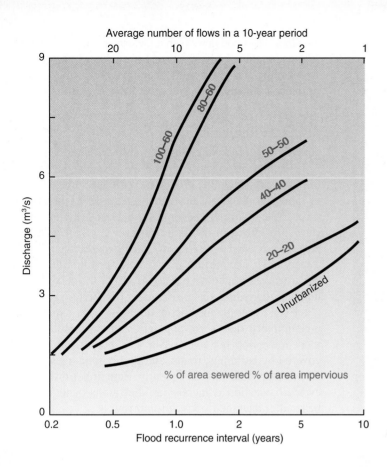

Figure 13.41

Flood-frequency curves for small drainage basins in various stages of urbanization. Floods occur more frequently as storm sewers, roofs, and pavement increase. For example, a discharge of 3 m³/s has a return period of 4 years in the unurbanized setting. The same discharge has shorter return periods as urbanization intensifies: 1.75 years (20–20); 0.9 years (40–40); 0.7 years (50–50); 0.5 years (80–60); 0.45 years (100–60).

Source: L. B. Leopold, "Hydrology for Urban Land Planning," in US Geological Survey Circular 554, 1968.

Summary

- Floods occur when the infiltration capacity of the soil is exceeded. Water runs off at the surface of the ground to reach streams and rivers, which swell and overflow their banks.
    - Hydrometeorological floods are caused by excess rainfall or snowmelt, or both. Rainfall floods are mostly associated with torrential tropical rains. Snowmelt floods affect northern countries and tropical countries with high mountain ranges, especially in the spring. They are the dominant flood style in Canada's large drainage basins.
    - Natural dams, earth material displaced during mass movements or by glaciers, for example, can block the flow of water. When natural dams fail catastrophically, high-impact, devastating outburst floods are triggered.
- Flood plains are flattish areas used as stream floors during floods. Streams routinely adopt new courses in their flood plains. Development on flood plains is risky as nature eventually takes back its rights.
- Small floods happen frequently; large floods happen uncommonly. Statistical analysis of successive flooding episodes is used to assess the return period and severity of floods in a given area.

- Humans have occupied flood-prone land for millennia. Efforts to control river flow in the long term have had various levels of success. Levees keep elevating river channels perilously higher and higher above the flood plain. Some dams gradually choke under excess sediments. On the other hand, small-scale channelization and large-scale floodways and barriers have been effective in handling high water flow in times of crises.
- Urbanization has increased society's vulnerability to floods. In rural settings, a heavy rain supplies water to a stream quickly by overland runoff and slowly by underground seepage. After urbanization occurs, pavement and roofs seal off most of the ground, increasing the amount of surface runoff. The result is flooding of a greater frequency and severity than a region's pre-urbanization history would have predicted.
- Floods cause much human suffering and infrastructure damage in a time span of a few days to a few weeks. In the longer term, they can be responsible for famine when agricultural lands have been submerged and harvest is compromised. They are also often followed by epidemics, with polluted flood waters serving as vectors for infectious diseases.

Terms to Remember

Questions for Review

1. Draw a map showing the channel pattern of a stream having excess discharge. Explain the processes involved to restore equilibrium.
2. Geologically speaking, lakes are temporary features. Draw a cross-section of a lake and use stream equilibrium processes to explain how lakes are gradually removed over long periods of time. Are human-made reservoirs also temporary?
3. Draw a cross-section of a meandering river and explain flood plains. Label where it is safe to build.
4. Draw a flood-frequency curve and explain its use in planning.
5. How often does a 100-year flood occur on a stream?
6. Draw a cross-section through a levee and explain the processes pushing it toward failure.
7. Draw a hydrograph record for a two-week-long flood in a rural setting. What controls the shape of the hydrograph; that is, what is happening on the rising and falling limbs? Now draw the hydrograph resulting from the same-size rainstorm after the land has been urbanized.
8. What activities are typically involved when humans modify stream channels to provide flood "control"? Use equilibrium stream processes to explain the changes in stream flow characteristics after channelization.
9. Explain the steps leading to the large floods of the Quaternary period.

Questions for Further Thought

1. Are all floods bad?
2. Make a list of appropriate uses for a flood plain. Make a list of inappropriate uses. Should urban development on flood plains be halted?
3. How long does flooding last?
4. Why are some urban areas receiving more frequent floods and higher peak flows than at any time in their history?
5. What kind of damage can flood cause to buildings?
6. How can communities increase their resilience to floods?
7. Are floodways, like the one around Winnipeg, a good idea for everyone?
8. What can be the adverse consequences of flooding on health?

Fire

"On a trail you set a fire and the following year, when you return to the same trail and there's new growth, that's where all the moose are. As I burned there in the fall, I would return in the spring—maybe five moose."

—Member of a First Nations community in northwestern Alberta, recorded by T.A. Ferguson, and reported in: Henry T. Lewis and Theresa A. Ferguson. 1988. Yards, corridors, and mosaics: How to burn a boreal forest. Human Ecology 16(1): 55–77.

Outline

Helitorch burning-out operation (use of a backfire) on a forest fire north of Thunder Bay, Ontario, 2006.
Photo: Mitch Miller/Ontario Ministry of Natural Resources.

Fire is so familiar; it is both friend and foe, slave and master. Fire is a natural force, yet it has been used by humans for many thousands of years. Humans developed the ability to artificially generate fire, and the control and use of fire has been a major factor in the development of the human race. The control of fire for warmth allowed humans to migrate into cold climates and build diverse and successful civilizations. Fire for cooking greatly increased the number of foods available and improved their taste, ease of digestion, nutrition, sanitation, and preservation. Fire has long been used to drive game out of hiding during hunting and to scare away predatory animals during the night. Fire aided agriculture by clearing the land of trees and creating fertilizer with its ashy residue. With the help of fire, humans have been able to expand farmland and pasture against both climatic and vegetational gradients.

The possibilities of fire have also stimulated creative thinking, which in turn has spurred human development. One invention has followed another. The use of fire to harden materials led to the creation of pottery, cookware, weapons, and more. The ability to produce ever-higher temperatures led to the creation of the smelting and use of metals. The use of fire provided the benefits of sterilization, which advanced public health. Fire controlled inside machinery supplies much of the energy that underlies our civilization. The heat from the burning of oil, coal, and natural gas is converted into the electrical and mechanical energy that powers our industries, the lighting and heating of our homes, and our ability to travel quickly to any point in the world.

Wildfire is common throughout the forested regions of Canada, and although it is often depicted as a destructive force (Figure 14.1), it is a natural ecosystem process that is essential to the health of many forests. Fire, for example, provides the heat that is required to melt the waxy resin that seals serotinous cones of jack pine that is prevalent throughout the boreal forest. It also burns

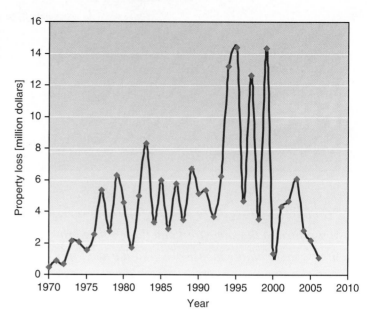

Figure 14.1
Value of property destroyed by forest fires in Canada, 1970–2006.

the dead pine needles and moss that grows beneath jack pine stands and thereby prepares a seed bed on which the seeds released from those cones can germinate. The exclusion of fire from the boreal forest would lead to a reduction in the abundance of jack pine and other species and set the boreal forest on an unnatural path. The complex mix of social, economic, and ecological costs and benefits of fire pose significant challenges to fire and forest managers who seek to achieve an appropriate balance of the beneficial and detrimental impacts of fire. Climate change will make it even more difficult for them to do so in the future.

Most of the fires that occur in Canadian forests are caused by people, but lightning-caused fires account for most of the area burned (Figures 14.2 and 14.3).

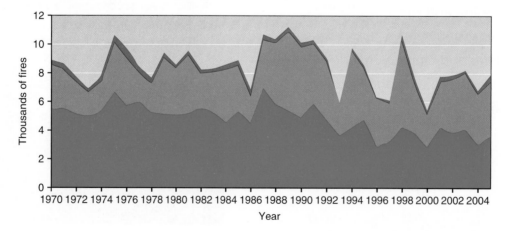

Figure 14.2
Number of forest fires in Canada (1970–2005) by cause: human activities (blue); lightning (green); unknown (red).

Sources: Canadian Forest Service and National Forestry Database.

Figure 14.3

Area burned across Canada (1970–2005) by cause: human activities (blue); lightning (green); unknown (red).

Sources: Canadian Forest Service and National Forestry Database.

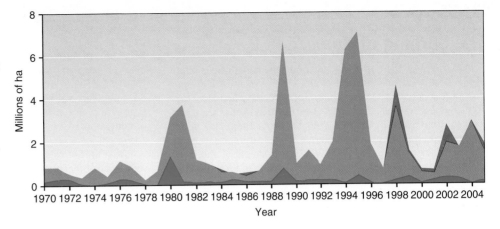

In 2005, for example, lightning ignited 47.3% of the fires but those fires burned 73.5% of the area burned that year (Table 14.1). That apparent discrepancy is due, in part, to the fact that lightning fires tend to arrive in clusters generated by the passage of storms, and they can overtax the capabilities of fire-suppression resources more readily than human-caused fires, which tend to occur at a more uniform rate over time. Also, most human-caused fires occur near populated areas or along roads or railways. They are more readily detected and reported than lightning fires, some of which occur in more remote areas where they burn undetected for longer periods and are therefore larger and more difficult to control when the suppression forces arrive at the scene (Figure 14.4).

What Is Fire?

Fire is the rapid combination of oxygen with carbon, hydrogen, and other elements of organic material in a reaction that produces flame, heat, and light. In effect, the burning of forest vegetation is the **photosynthesis** reaction in reverse.

In the photosynthesis reaction, plants take in water (H_2O) and carbon dioxide (CO_2) and use solar energy to build organic material, their tissue. Oxygen is given off as a by-product of the reaction. The molecules of plants are tied together by chemical bonds between atoms. These bonds store some of the Sun's heat as chemical potential energy. An example of the photosynthesis reaction is:

$$6CO_2 + 6H_2O + \text{heat from the Sun} \rightarrow C_6H_{12}O_6 + 6O_2$$

Table 14.1

Canadian Forest Fires by Cause, 2005

Cause	Number of Fires	Percentage of Fires by cause	Area Burned (ha)	Percent Area Burned by Cause
Human Activities				
Recreation	921	11.7	23,384	1.2
Resident	1,291	16.4	4,769	0.3
Forest industry	149	1.9	5,559	0.3
Railways	138	1.8	7,979	0.4
Other industry	340	4.3	851	0.0
Incendiary	478	6.1	9,010	0.5
Miscellaneous known causes	304	3.9	18,285	1.0
Total human activities	3,621	46.0	69,837	3.7
Lightning	3,719	47.3	1,386,402	73.5
Unknown cause	525	6.7	429,058	22.8
Total	7,865		1,885,297	

Source: National Forestry Database.

In Greater Depth

The Burning of Rome, 64 CE

A famous fire of the ancient world consumed Rome, the capital of the most powerful empire of its time. The popular myth about the fire tells of a vain and bored Emperor Nero, who fiddled while Rome burned. As usual, the truth, as best as we can know it, is a bit different from the myth. On 19 July 64, fire broke out in the Circus Maximus and was swept by strong winds through the small, closely packed buildings along the narrow, winding streets of the city. Upon hearing news of the fire, Nero left Antium and returned to Rome. For six days and seven nights, the fires moved up and down the hills of Rome until only four of its 14 districts were unscathed. Gone were mansions, shrines, and temples built over the centuries; also destroyed was Nero's palace on the Palatine Hill.

Although no eyewitness accounts remain, both Tacitus and Suetonius, writing two and three generations later, describe the actions of Nero that provoked the rage of the populace. Nero is possibly the only ruler of a major empire who considered himself to be primarily a singer and stage performer. During the emotional time of the long-lasting fire, Nero donned his singer's robes, played his lyre, and sang a lengthy song of his own composition called "The Fall of Troy." Expressing his emotions musically during the tragic fire was perceived as callous, and stories spread until Nero was even rumoured to have started the fire. In the absence of contemporary manuscripts, the truth shall probably never be known.

After the fire, Nero quickly rebuilt the Circus Maximus, religious shrines, and other public facilities. He personally paid to have debris from the fire cleared and provided bonuses to building-site owners who quickly completed houses and blocks. For the reconstruction, Nero ordered measures to reduce the probability of future city-destroying fires. Rome was rebuilt with broad streets, spacious and detached houses, and heavy usage of massive stone; households were required to have firefighting apparatus in an accessible place. This story from 2,000 years ago is amazingly similar to events in the news today.

Figure 14.4
Photograph of a tree that was struck by a lightning that travelled down the bole of the tree and ignited a fire in the duff layer at the base of the tree, Fort Frances District, northwestern Ontario.

Photo: © Jennifer Beverley, Canadian Forest Service.

The organic molecule ($C_6H_{12}O_6$) in this equation is glucose, which approximates that of cellulose, the main component of wood.

In the fire reaction, plant material is heated above its **ignition temperature** and oxygen begins combining rapidly with the organic material. The old chemical bonds between carbon and hydrogen are broken, new bonds form between carbon and oxygen and between hydrogen and oxygen, and the stored energy is given off as heat during the fire. The fire equation is identical to the photosynthesis equation, except that it runs in the opposite direction:

$$C_6H_{12}O_6 + 6O_2 \rightarrow 6CO_2 + 6H_2O + \text{released heat}$$

In effect, the solar energy stored by plants during their growth is returned to the atmosphere during fire. We earlier viewed plate tectonics as causing the buildup of stresses that are released during earthquakes; by analogy, photosynthesis causes the buildup and storage of chemical potential energy in plants that is released during fires.

The Need for Fire

Through photosynthesis, plants grow and collectively produce large volumes of trunks, branches, leaves, needles, grasses, and such. The mass of organic material is recycled by the combined effects of slow decomposition through rotting and digestion plus the rapid burning through wildfire. Decomposition requires warmth and moisture to operate efficiently. In a tropical rain forest with abundant warmth and moisture, rotting can decompose the dead vegetation and recycle the nutrients for the production of

Historical Canadian and American Forest Fires

Most Canadian forest-fire management agencies were established in the early 1900s in response to tragic forest fires that burned large areas and took many lives in Canada and the United States during the 19th century and the early part of the 20th century.

The 1825 Miramichi fire burned more than 1,214,000 ha of uncut forest and spruce budworm–killed stands in the Miramichi River Valley in the province of New Brunswick and the state of Maine. Many small logging and settler fires that had been left to burn unattended and a severe summer drought and high winds supported the spread and merging of many of those fires into a large fire that killed 160 people.

The Peshtigo fire burned 1,530,000 ha in eastern Wisconsin and western Michigan in October 1871. Many uncontrolled logging and settler fires that were burning under severe drought, high temperature, and strong wind conditions grew together and burned through red and white pine stands, some hardwoods, and large slash areas. More than 1,500 lives were lost.

In 1910 the Rainy River fire resulted when three railway locomotive fires and one settler fire joined to eventually burn 121,500 ha in northwestern Ontario and Minnesota. The fire resulted in the loss of 42 lives in the United States.

The 1916 Cochrane and Matheson fire in northeastern Ontario formed when many small unattended fires fed by a prolonged drought, high temperatures, and strong winds joined to burn 344,000 ha of predominately spruce and jack pine stands. The 233 lives lost make this the worst forest fire ever experienced in Canada.

---

new plant material via photosynthesis; there is no need for wildfire to recycle materials (except in cases such as after a hurricane destroys large numbers of trees). In the deserts, there is little moisture for either plant growth or decomposition, so fire does not need to be frequent.

In many environments, fire is necessary to recycle nutrients and regenerate plant communities. Fire-dependent ecosystems include grasslands, seasonal tropical forests, some temperate-climate forests, and the Mediterranean-climate shrublands.

In the Mediterranean climates, such as in the Californias, Australia, and South Africa, the wet winters are too cold and the warm summers too dry for rotting to recycle the products of photosynthesis; consequently, wildfire must be frequent. In these areas, fire is necessary for the health of plant communities. Many of the plant species must have the smoke and/or heat of fire to germinate their seeds, to control parasites, and to influence insect behaviour. Thus fire is necessary; it is nature's way of cleaning house.

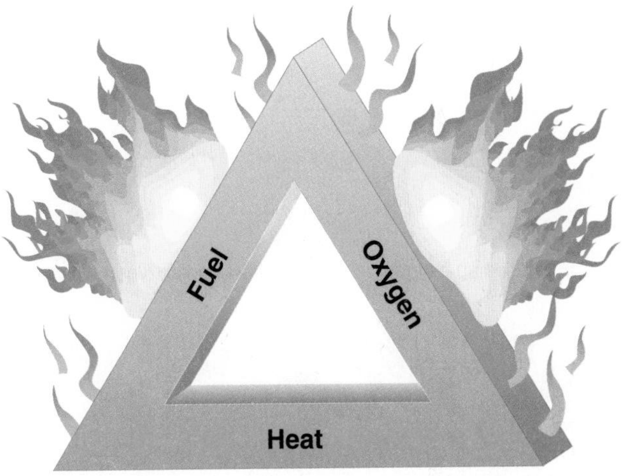

The Fire Triangle

A fire may begin only when **fuel**, oxygen, and heat are present in the right combination. These three critical components are referred to as the fire triangle (Figure 14.5). Oxygen makes up 21% of the atmosphere, so as long as a steady supply of air is available, then heat and fuel are the most important factors. Heat during summers and droughts both warms up and dries out vegetation, making it easier for a lightning strike to ignite a fire. Given the common presence of oxygen and heat, the occurrence of fires is limited mainly by the amount of fuel available.

Any combustible material is fuel. Common categories of fuel include grasses, shrubs, trees, and **slash**, the organic debris left on the ground after logging or

Figure 14.5
The fire triangle. When all three sides are present, a fire results; eliminate one side and the fire cannot burn.

windstorms. As the human population spreads into wildlands, houses have become a fifth category of fuel.

The fire triangle also is useful for visualizing how to fight a fire. Remove one of the sides of the fire triangle, and the fire collapses. Firefighters spray water on a fire to reduce its *heat*. Air tankers drop reddish-orange viscous fluids (commonly referred to as fire retardant) in front of a fire to coat the unburned vegetation and block *oxygen* from contacting the plant. Dry chemical extinguishers using "Purple K" (potassium bicarbonate) kill fires by disrupting the chemical reaction. Firefighters commonly bulldoze and remove vegetation to eliminate *fuel*. Fuel also may be reduced by setting **backfires** (Figure 14.7 and photo of chapter opener). A backfire is lit by firefighters in front of the advancing wildfire. As the wildfire

An Ancient View of Fire

The Greeks developed influential theories concerning fire. The synthesis by Aristotle in the 4th century BCE was taken seriously for nearly 2,000 years. In this view, all matter on Earth was made of varying proportions of four elements: air, earth, fire, and water. The behaviour of matter varied according to the relative abundances of two opposing qualities: hotness versus coldness and wetness versus dryness. The four elements combined these qualities as follows:

air—hotness and wetness
earth—coldness and dryness
fire—hotness and dryness
water—coldness and wetness

The elements were not thought by the Greeks to be identical to everyday materials but rather were essences or purer forms. Their relative qualities may be plotted against temperature and humidity (Figure 14.6).

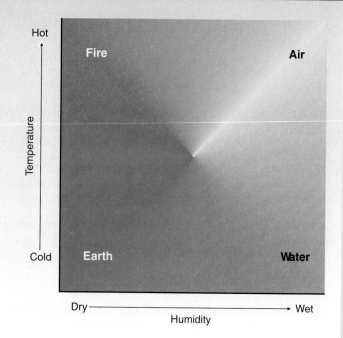

Figure 14.6 The four elements of Aristotle.

① Fire uses up oxygen   ② Fire draws in oxygen which. . .   ③ . . .draws in backfire

Fire direction   **Backfire**

Figure 14.7
How to fight a fire with fire. Light a backfire in front of an advancing wildfire.

draws in oxygen, it also draws in the backfire, thus eliminating fuel in front of the advancing wildfire.

The presence of **ladder fuels** allows small ground fires to quickly carry upward into tall trees and create major wildfires. Vegetation of varying heights makes it easy for fire to climb from grasses to shrubs to trees similar to climbing up the rungs of a ladder (Figure 14.8). How can the ladder fuel threat be reduced? Cut and prune vegetation to create vertical separations between layers.

With the emergence of humans and our ability to both make fires and fight the flames, the old natural balance has changed. No longer does fuel supply simply accumulate until ignited by a lightning strike. Now humans extinguish many small fires, causing the build-up of tremendous volumes of dead-plant fuel that can ignite and cause fires bigger than we can handle. Humans interfere with the natural cycle of plant growth and fire, but we don't control it.

Figure 14.8
Ladder fuels. Vegetation of varying heights allows fire to climb from grasses to treetops.

The Stages of Combustion

Before a fire breaks out, a *preheating* phase occurs where water is expelled from plants, wood, or fossil fuels by nearby flames, drought, or even a long summer day. The water in wet wood has such a high capacity to absorb heat that the wood becomes extremely difficult to ignite. To burn, wood not only needs to be dry, but also to have its temperature raised considerably. For example, the cellulose in wood remains stable even at temperatures of 250°C; however, by 325°C, it breaks down quickly, giving off large amounts of flammable gases.

The thermal degradation of wood involves the process of **pyrolysis.** During pyrolysis, the chemical structure of solid wood breaks apart and yields flammable hydrocarbon vapours along with water vapour, tar, and mineral residues. If oxygen is present when the temperature is raised, then the pyrolized gases can ignite and **combustion** begins. In *flaming combustion,* the pyrolized surface of the wood burns fast and hot; this is the stage of greatest energy release in any fire. The released heat is carried via convection through air flowing up and away from the fire; heat is transferred in **radiation** as electromagnetic waves or particle waves; in conduction the heat energy is transmitted downward or inward through physical contact; and in **diffusion,** heat is in particles that move from hotter to cooler areas (Figure 14.9).

The phases of a fire are well known to anyone who starts logs burning in a campfire or fireplace. The preheating phase is usually accomplished by lighting newspaper or kindling with a match to dry out the logs and raise their surface temperature. When kindling burns beneath logs and is supplied with an efficient air flow carrying abundant oxygen, then the cellulose and lignin in the logs decompose and give off gases in the process of pyrolysis. As the logs heat, they expand in volume and form cracks that release gases to the surface to feed the flames. Where cracks do not form, the wood will "pop" and throw out sparks and embers.

Because of the poor conductance of heat in wood, the interior of a log remains below the combustion point even when the exterior is engulfed in flames. For a log to burn completely, there must be enough outside heat (from embers below, adjoining burning wood, etc.) conducting into the log to continue the pyrolizing process; it is the gases from pyrolysis that fuel the surface flames that slowly eat into the heart of the log. The radiant and convective heat that keeps the logs hot enough to continue burning is also the heat that warms us.

In nature, the flaming combustion stage involves a flaming front that passes by and leaves behind *glowing combustion.* In a fireplace, the active flames disappear, but the wood surface glows. In each case, the wood now burns more slowly and at a lower temperature as the fire consumes the solid wood instead of pyrolized gases. The

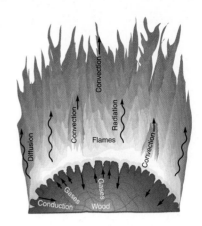

Figure 14.9
Schematic cross-section of a burning log. Heat moves inward by conduction, decomposing the cellulose and lignin of wood into gases (pyrolysis) that move through cracks to fuel flames at the log surface. Heat flows outward by (1) diffusion of particles from hotter to cooler areas, (2) radiation from flames and from hot surfaces, and (3) convection of hot, lightweight buoyant gases that rise upward.

process is a slower **oxidation** of the charred remainders left by the flames.

All the stages of a fire occur simultaneously in different areas of a wildfire (Figure 14.10). The character of a wildfire and the area it covers depend on several factors, described next.

The Spread of Fire

Wildfires occur in different styles: (1) they may move slowly along the ground with glowing combustion playing an important role, (2) they may advance as a wall of fire along a flaming combustion front, or (3) they may race through the treetops as a crown fire.

The spread of fire depends on (1) fuel—the types of plants or other material burned, (2) weather—especially the strength of winds, (3) topography—the shape of the land, and (4) behaviour within the fire itself.

FUEL

The energy release in a fire strongly depends on the chemical composition of the plants and organic debris. For example, the eucalyptus family of trees and shrubs has a high oil content that allows easy ignition and intense heat of burning. In the world before global travel and trade, eucalyptus was confined to Australia, but it has been exported in abundance to many areas where it thrives like a native plant. The eucalyptus fire hazard is now a significant threat in Southern California, North Africa, India, and the Middle East.

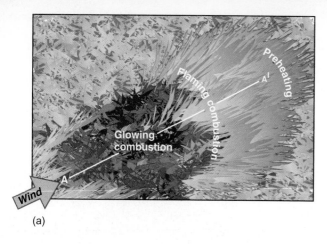

(a)

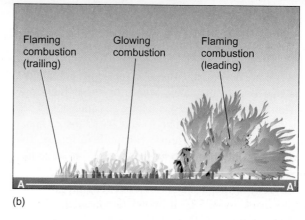

(b)

Figure 14.10
The stages of fire are shown in horizontal or map view (a). Line AA¹ on the map is shown in cross-section view in (b).

WEATHER

Many of the worst fires in history were accompanied by strong winds. Winds bring a continuous supply of fresh oxygen, distribute heat, push the flames forward, and bend them toward preheated plants and other fuel. If winds are absent, a vertical column of convected heat dominates, and the fire may move very slowly (Figure 14.11a, type I). If winds are fast, they push the fire front rapidly ahead and prevent a vertical convection column from forming (Figure 14.11f, type VI). Strong, gusty winds and fire whirls both pick up flaming debris and burning embers called **firebrands** and drop them onto unburned areas, starting new blazes.

TOPOGRAPHY

The topography of the land has numerous effects on fire behaviour. Before a fire, the topography sets up microclimates that result in different plant communities that will burn with different intensities. Winds blowing over rugged topography develop turbulence. Canyons with steep slopes and dense vegetation cause high levels of radiant heat that consume virtually all the organic matter in the canyon (Figure 14.11g, type VII). Fire burns faster up a slope because the convective heat rising from and above the fire front dries out the upslope vegetation in an intense preheating phase; in effect, a chimney is created up the slope, allowing fire to move quickly (Figure 14.12).

FIRE BEHAVIOUR

The strength of a fire is partly created by its own actions. The vast quantities of heat given off by a fire create unstable air. Heat-expanded air is less dense and more buoyant; thus, it rises upward in billowing convection columns (Figures 14.11a–e, types I–V). The rising columns of hot, unstable air may spin off fire whirls (Figure 14.13). Winds sucked into the base of a fire whirl bring oxygen to feed the flames, while huge quantities of heat race up the column, venting above as in a megachimney. Fire whirls are commonly 10 to 50 times taller than their diameters, and they may spin at speeds of 250 km/h. Fire whirls may carry fiery debris and drop it kilometres away, starting new fires.

A fatal example showing the strength of a fire whirl occurred on 24 April 2000 near Winkler, Manitoba. A fire burning 90,000 bales of flax straw spun off a fire whirl that lifted a man and his pickup truck and carried them 50 m away before dumping their remains onto a field.

Forest and Wildland Fuels

The rate of spread, depth of burn, and other important characteristics of a forest fire are heavily influenced by type of forest vegetation or fuel in which it is burning. Some forest types (e.g., coniferous species such as jack pine and black spruce) burn readily while others (e.g., aspen and other hardwood species) usually burn very slowly with little flame. It is therefore not surprising that forest-fire specialists often view forest vegetation in terms of its fuel properties.

Fire behaviour specialists who study the burning of wood chips, wooden dowels, and dead pine needles in the laboratory have identified many chemical and physical properties of the fuel particles and the fuel bed that influence how quickly a fire will spread. Some of the many fuel attributes they have identified as being important include their chemical composition, specific heat capacity, fuel particle length, fuel particle cross-sectional area, fuel loading (mass of fuel per unit area), depth, bulk density, and of course, moisture content. Although such fuel-type characteristics can be measured in the laboratory, it is difficult to measure them in the forest and it would simply be impossible to do so in front of an active wildfire. They have therefore developed **fuel models** that are used to classify *forest types* into *fuel types* that are relatively homogeneous with respect to important fuel attributes.

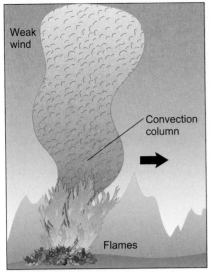

(a) Type I

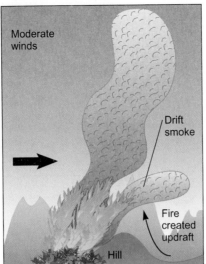

(b) Type II

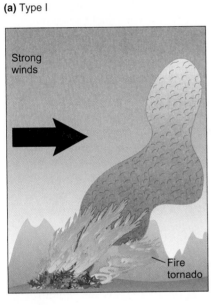

(c) Type III

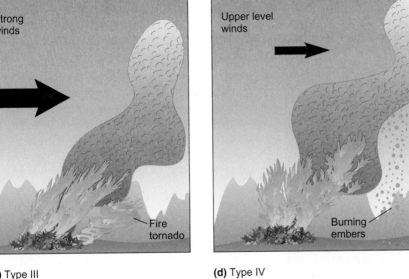

(d) Type IV

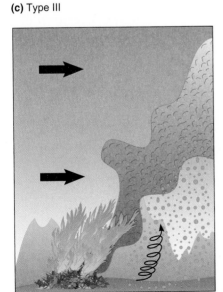

(e) Type V

(f) Type VI

(g) Type VII

Figure 14.11
Some fire types. (a) Type I has a tall convection column and weak winds that push the column at a moderate rate of spread. (b) Type II has a tall convection column that moves rapidly upslope. (c) Type III has a powerful convection column pushed by surface winds; fire tornadoes are spun off. (d) Type IV has a convection column distorted above the ground surface by strong winds; glowing embers are dropped. (e) Type V has a convection column bent by winds of differing speeds. (f) Type VI is a wind-driven fire that spreads rapidly; the winds are too strong for a convection column to function. (g) Type VII shows the effects of topography.

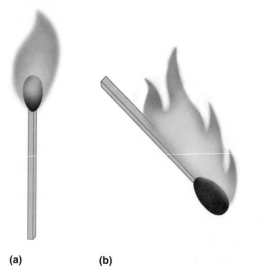

(a)   **(b)**

Figure 14.12
How fires burn on slopes. (a) An upright match burns slowly downward, similar to fire on top of a hill. (b) A sloping match burns rapidly upward, similar to fire up a hill.

Figure 14.13
Fire whirls form as hot, rising air spins and carry the flames upward.

Figure 14.14
C-1 Spruce-lichen woodland fuel type.

Photo by Nikname.

Figure 14.15
C-7 Ponderosa pine/Douglas fir fuel type.

Photo by Marc Shandoro.

The Canadian Fire Behaviour Prediction (FBP) system has 16 fuel types that are divided into 5 general categories: coniferous, deciduous, mixed-wood, slash, and open. The coniferous fuel types include C-1 Spruce-lichen Woodland (Figure 14.14), C-4 Immature Jack or Lodgepole pine, and C-7 Ponderosa pine/Douglas fir (Figure 14.15). The slash category includes S-1 Jack or Lodgepole pine logging slash and the open category includes O-1b standing grass. Fire behaviour specialists conduct experimental burns under different fire weather conditions and then develop mathematical models that can be used to predict the rate of spread and other fire behaviour characteristics as a function of the **fire-danger rating** codes and indices. Analysts who predict fire behaviour to support fire-suppression operations use the fuel-type system to classify the forest vegetation in front of active fires and predict how fast and far they will spread given the observed or forecast fire weather.

Fire Weather

The probability that a lightning discharge that strikes a tree and travels down its trunk to the ground will ignite a fire depends on the moisture content of the organic layer at the base of the tree. The chance that a discarded cigarette or hot metal fragment from a railway brake shoe will ignite a fire depends upon the moisture content of the dead grass or pine needles on which they fall. Since fuel moisture is influenced by temperature, relative humidity, rainfall, and wind, weather has a very significant influence on fire occurrence and fire behaviour processes as well as fire management operations.

Weather affects fire at national, regional, and local scales. Much of Canada is influenced by a predominately westerly flow of weather systems off the Pacific Ocean so sea surface temperature in the Pacific can influence weather and fire activity across parts of Canada. From time to time, zonal upper atmospheric flows are interrupted by upper-level ridges that steer moisture-bearing storm systems north and south of the ridge and contribute to the drying of downstream regions.

On a local scale, lightning can ignite fires and daily weather has a profound influence on any fires that do occur. Fuel moisture influences fire behaviour but once the fuel is dry enough to support sustained combustion, short-term changes in wind speed and direction can have dramatic impacts on fire behaviour. Fire spread rates are particularly sensitive to wind, and large fires are usually the product of one or more wind-driven isolated events, each of which may persist for one or more days.

Winds associated with the passage of fronts often change their directions dramatically over short periods of time. Thunderstorm downdrafts can also produce sudden changes in wind speed and direction in the vicinity of a fire. The convection columns that become established over intense fires can interact with upper-level winds and bring low-level jets down toward Earth's surface where they interact with and produce dramatic increases in fire spread and intensity. Such changes can alter the direction and rate of fire spread and thereby pose both control and safety problems for firefighters.

Days when the relative humidity is low and temperatures and wind speeds are high are cause for concern for forest-fire managers, particularly if such days are preceded by prolonged periods of drought and accompanied by daytime heating or frontal thunderstorms. It is therefore not surprising that fire management agencies devote a great deal of time and effort to monitoring weather, and they make very extensive use of weather forecasts to help predict when and where fires will occur and how they will behave in the days ahead.

FIRE IN THE CANADIAN BOREAL FOREST

The Canadian boreal forest stretches from the Alaska–Yukon border to the east coast of Newfoundland as it forms a link in the circumpolar boreal forest that spans the globe. It is a predominately coniferous forest that is populated by white and black spruce, and tamarack, with balsam fir and jack pine in the east and Lodgepole pine in the west. White birch, trembling aspen, balsam poplar, and other deciduous tree species occur there, primarily in mixed-wood stands. The forest floor is usually covered with a **duff** layer that depending upon its moisture content, can support smouldering or flaming combustion.

Fire is most common in the southern half of the boreal forest, where large-stand replacing fires, which can burn tens or hundreds of thousands of hectares, destroy existing stands and initiate the growth of new even-aged stands in their wake. The boreal forest is home to many forest insects, one of which is the spruce budworm. Spruce budworm population levels surge and subside over time across the boreal forest in cycles that have yet to be fully understood. When these populations surge, they destroy balsam fir and other conifers, which then serve as highly flammable fuel.

Lightning is common across the boreal forest and serves as a source of ignition to ensure fire continues its important natural role. Lightning fires tend to occur in spatial and temporal clusters that fire managers often refer to as fire flaps. Lightning fires are usually ignited

The Canadian Forest Fire–Danger Rating System

Weather affects fire behaviour both directly (fire speed rates increase as the wind speed increases) and indirectly (fires spread faster and burn more intensely as fuel moisture content decreases. Fuel moisture rises and falls from day to day in response to variation in temperature, relative humidity, wind speed, and rainfall. Fire behaviour is therefore influenced by not only the current weather but also the cumulative effect of past weather on the current fuel moisture content. Forest-fire researchers have therefore developed fire-danger rating systems that distil daily temperature observations into relatively simple measures of the impact of weather on fuel moisture, fire occurrence, and fire behaviour.

Canadians are familiar with the "humidex," which is used to describe how uncomfortable they will feel given the temperature and relative humidity during the summer months, and the "wind chill factor," which is a measure of how cold they will feel given the temperature and wind during the winter. The Canadian Forest Fire–Danger Rating System (CFFDRS) is in essence, the forest-fire manager's "humidex."

The CFFDRS includes six codes and indices based on daily observations of rainfall, temperature, relative humidity, and wind speed. The Fine Fuel Moisture Code (FFMC) is a measure of the moisture content of litter and other cured fine fuels like dry needles and dead leaves on the forest floor, and is used to predict when and where people-caused fires might occur. The Duff Moisture

Code (DMC) is a measure of the moisture content of the moss and underlying decomposing organic layer (what fire managers refer to as the duff layer) and is coupled with measures of lightning activity to predict daily lightning fire occurrence. The Drought Code (DC) is an index of the moisture content of the deep organic layers and is used to predict how deep fires will burn and how much time and effort will be required to extinguish them.

Fires spread faster as the Initial Spread Index (ISI) increases and consume more fuel as the Buildup Index (BUI) increases. The Fire Weather Index (FWI) is a measure of fire intensity and also serves as an aggregate measure of fire danger that is used to communicate the need for caution to the public (Figure 14.16). Most Canadian forest-fire management agencies use the FWI to set the pointer on the "Fire Danger Today is ..." signs that are common along highways that pass through forested areas (Figure 14.17). Maps of the CFFDRS codes and indices portray fire danger on provincial (Figure 14.18) and national scales.

A new fire-danger rating code, the sheltered duff moisture code (SDMC), has been introduced recently. The SDMC is a measure of the moisture content of the duff layer at the base of a tree, the point at which a lightning strike is most likely to reach the ground and ignite a fire. Since higher SDMC values denote drier duff layers, lightning that strikes a high–SDMC area is more likely to ignite a fire than lightning that strikes a low–SDMC area. The two maps in Figure 14.19 indicate that most of the lightning-caused forest fires ignited in the province of Ontario on 9 August 2001 were ignited by lightning that struck high–SDMC areas.

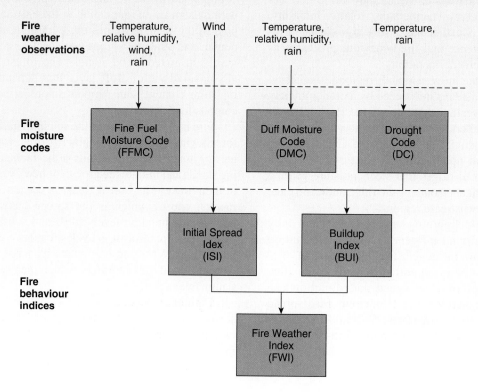

Figure 14.16 Structure of the Canadian Fire Weather Index system.

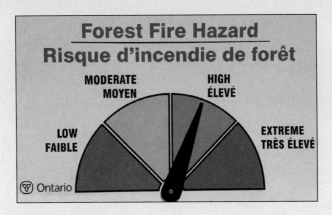

Figure 14.17 Roadside fire prevention sign to communicate current fire danger to the public in Ontario.

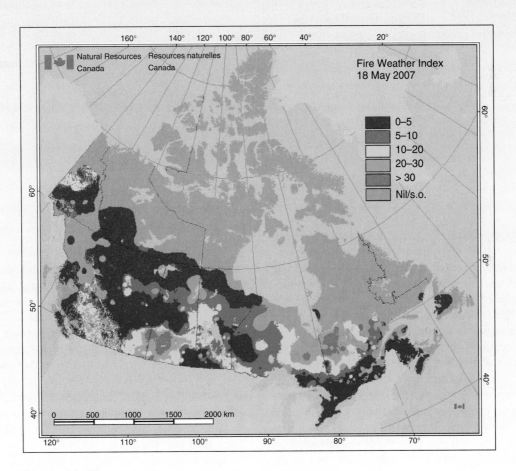

Figure 14.18 Map of the Fire Weather Index across Canada on May 18, 2007.

continued

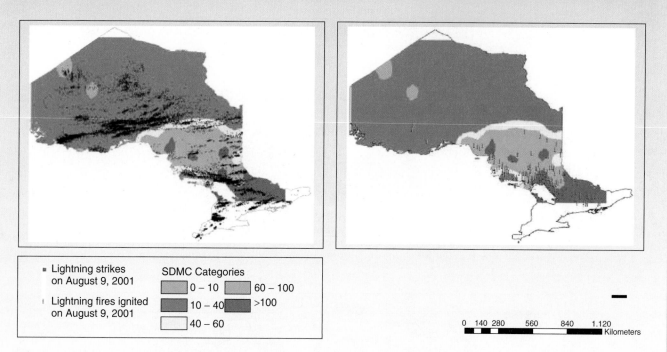

Figure 14.19 Lightning activity and lightning fire occurrence in Ontario on August 9, 2001. The map on the left is colour coded to indicate the sheltered duff moisture code (SDMC) and where lightning occurred that day. The map on the right indicates that most of the lightning fires that occurred that day occurred where lightning struck areas that had a high SDMC.
Source: B.M. Wotton of the Canadian Forest Service.

in the duff layer where they may smoulder for several days until the top of the duff layer and the surface litter layer become dry enough to support the spread of a surface fire (Figure 14.20a). As the surface fire grows in intensity, the energy that it releases preheats the lower branches of the over-story pine and spruce trees, causing individual trees to sporadically burst into flame—what fire specialists refer to as candling or torching (Figure 14.20b). If the surface fire continues to grow in intensity and there are sufficient ladder fuels present to help the fire move from the surface into the crowns, then more and more crowns become actively engaged in a slow-moving crown fire (Figures 14.20c–e). If winds are strong enough, they will penetrate the crowns to accelerate the spread of the surface fire, which will then torch even more trees. Winds above the crowns will bend the flames that extend above the crown and enhance the preheating of unburned crowns (Figure 14.21). This supports the initiation of an active crown fire that extends from the surface through the crown with flames that can reach

30 m or more in height and begins to move as a continuous crown fire front that can spread as fast as 50 m/min or more (Figure 14.22). As winds push burning dry needles, dead leaves, and other fine debris ahead in fluidized waves, they pull firebrands into the fire plume or convection column. The winds then blow those flaming firebrands ahead of the active fire front where they drop and ignite spot fires well ahead of the main fires, often more than a kilometre ahead. This allows the crown fire to easily spread across fire lines, roads, and small lakes and rivers. Firefighters cannot attack crown fires but they sometimes deploy sprinklers connected to power pumps to protect homes and cottages that lie in the fire's path. They then pull back and curtail their suppression activity until rain and/or a change in wind direction or speed slow the fire to a point where it is safe enough to deploy firefighters on the fire perimeter.

Large, intensely burning fires often form large mushroom-shaped convection columns that can extend several kilometres into the atmosphere where they

(a)

(d)

(b)

(e)

(c)

Figure 14.20

Sequence of photographs illustrating the development of a crown fire in an immature jack pine stand in the Blind River district northeast of Sault Ste. Marie, Ontario. (a) Shortly after ignition; (b) early stages of torching; (c) early stages of crown fire; (d) advancing crown fire; (e) established crown fire.

Photos: B.J. Stocks, Canadian Forest Service, Natural Resources Canada.

Figure 14.21
Crown fire in immature jack pine forest.
Photo by David L. Martell, University of Toronto.

Figure 14.22
Crown fire in the boreal forest near Red Lake, Ontario.
Photo: B.J. Stocks, Canadian Forest Service, Natural Resources Canada.

affect local wind patterns and inject smoke and other particulates that can be transported long distances (Figure 14.23). People living in eastern Canada often observe intensely orange sunsets. These are produced by smoke emitted from forest fires burning in northwestern Ontario, and the northern boreal forest portions of the prairie provinces, northern Alberta, Yukon, and the Northwest Territories.

Figure 14.23
Established convection column over a forest fire in northwestern Ontario.

FOREST FIRE IN BRITISH COLUMBIA

The forests of British Columbia are shaped by the predominately westerly flow of weather systems off the Pacific Ocean that interact with mountain ranges aligned in a north-south direction to produce areas with above average rainfall, dry rain shadows, and changes in elevation. This broad range of climatic and topographic features supports very diverse forests; Canada is divided into 194 ecoregions and 46 of them are located in British Columbia. Those 46 ecoregions vary significantly with respect to fuel and weather, and some of them seldom burn while others support extreme fires. British Columbia's renowned temperate rainforests, which dominate much of Vancouver Island, Haida Gwai, and the coast of mainland British Columbia, for example, are characterized by very large Douglas fir and Sitka spruce trees that seldom burn. Much of the southern Interior, on the other hand, is covered by grasslands, Lodgepole pine, and Ponderosa pine stands that burn readily under the hot dry conditions that are considered by many to pose the greatest challenge to forest-fire managers in Canada. The 2003 fire season is a stark example of what can happen when people live near flammable wildland urban interface (WUI) areas, that is, localities where infrastructure is built close to or within undeveloped land.

Firestorm 2003

The 2003 fire season was the worst ever experienced in British Columbia. More than 2,500 fires burned more than 260,000 ha across the province, but those figures alone reveal little of the human cost of several significant fires that occurred in WUI areas in the southern Interior. Three pilots involved in fire operations lost their lives, 334 homes were destroyed, and more than 45,000 people were evacuated. Many businesses were disrupted and some were destroyed. The monetary cost of the fire loss is estimated to have been roughly $400 million.

A provincial Review Team chaired by the Honourable Gary Filmon, former premier of Manitoba, was assigned the task of reviewing the response to the 2003 WUI fires and developing recommendations for improvement in time for the next fire season. The team found that the 2003 fire season was the result of abnormally hot dry weather that exacerbated a prolonged drought coupled with fuel buildups, which set the stage for fast-moving intense fires. The team identified the 15 fires described in Table 14.2 as "Major Interface Fires."

Environment Canada described the weather conditions that set the stage for the 2003 fire season in these terms: "During most of the summer, a large Pacific high-pressure area anchored near the coast kept precipitations away from British Columbia. At some weather stations in the Interior, temperatures soared to 40°C. In Kamloops, temperatures rose above 30°C on 19 days in July and 20 days in August; normal for each month is 11 [days]. Kelowna recorded the driest June-July-August period since records began in 1899 and set a record with 44 consecutive rainless days. On the coast, Victoria had its driest summer since record keeping began in 1914 with a paltry 8.2 mm of rain. The forests in the south were tinder-dry and the forest floor volatile—a spark away from igniting. Then came flashes of dry lightning, strong gusty winds and a bit of human carelessness." (*Firestorm 2003—Provincial Review*, 18.)

Seventy years of fire suppression, a reduction in the use of prescribed fire attributed to a number of factors including public concern about smoke, and a lack of adequate funds and trained personnel contributed to fuel buildups that resulted in the encroachment of forests onto grasslands and increased presence of Douglas fir in the understory of many forest stands.

Figure 14.24
Photograph of part of the area burned by the 2003 McLure fire in British Columbia.
Photo: © David Martell.

Table 14.2

Major Interface Fires of Summer 2003 in British Columbia

Start Date	Fire Name	Location	Final Size (ha)
July 22, 2003	Chilko Fire	Chilko Lk. Aloxis Cr.	29,202
July 31, 2003	McLure Fire	McLure, Barriere	26,420
August 16, 2003	Okanagan Mt. Park Fire	Kelowna	25,600
August 1, 2003	McGillvray Fire	Chase	11,400
August 16, 2003	Lamb Creek Fire	Cranbrook	10,979
August 16, 2003	Venables Fire	Chase	7,635
August 17, 2003	Ingersol Fire	SW of Nakusp	6,700
August 1, 2003	Strawberry Hill Fire	Kamloops IR	5,731
August 20, 2003	Kuskanook Fire	North of Creston	4,832
August 22, 2003	Vaseaux Fire	OK Falls	3,300
August 14, 2003	Plumbob Fire	Cranbrook	2,870
August 2, 2003	Cedar Hills Fire	Falkland	1,620
August 6, 2003	Bonaparte Lake Fire	Bonaparte Lake	1,500
July 17, 2003	Anarchist Mt. Fire	Osoyoos	1,230
August 20, 2003	Harrogate Fire	Radium	1,018

McLure Fire

The McLure fire, which burned near the communities of McLure and Barriere, north of Kamloops, was detected on 30 July under extreme fire weather conditions (Figure 14.24). The Fire Review Summary prepared by the Protection Branch of the British Columbia Ministry of Forests reports that the fire was ignited at approximately 12:40 p.m. and was reported a few minutes later at 12:55. Suppression action by air tankers began at 1:47 p.m. and was continuous until 9:10 that evening when the fire was estimated to be 195 ha in size. The assessment at dawn on 31 July was that the fire could potentially be contained during the day. Unfortunately, a significant weather cell passed near the fire at 3:00 p.m. and the fire grew under winds of 50 to 60 km/h. In the following hours, the fire grew to 3,400 ha and moved to the north and east to threaten the communities of Louis Creek and Exlou. Embers from the fire began dropping into the community of Barriere at 1:30 a.m. on 1 August and during that afternoon the fire destroyed 73 homes and a major sawmill. The fire was 6,629 ha in size at 10:00 that evening. Suppression action continued but the fire continued to grow, reaching an estimated area of 16,640 ha at 3:00 a.m. on 6 August. The fire grew to 25,811 ha from 6 to 10 August but no more structures were lost during that period. The fire eventually grew close to its final size of 23,345 ha on 4 September and was finally brought under control at a final size of 26,420 ha. In total, the fire caused the evacuation of 3,800 people (880 of whom were evacuated a second time) from McLure, Barriere, and Louis Creek.

Okanagan Mountain Park Fire

The 2003 Okanagan Mountain Park fire, what many Canadians think of as the Kelowna fire, was the most destructive Canadian forest fire in recent history (Figure 14.25).

Figure 14.25
Okanagan Mountain Park fire, August 2003.
Source: © 2008 Daily Courier

The fire burned more than 250 homes and at one point nearly one-third of the residents of Kelowna had been evacuated from their homes. What follows is based on the Fire Review Summary prepared by the Protection Branch of the British Columbia Ministry of Forests.

The fire was ignited by lightning at 1:55 a.m. and reported at 2:05 in the morning of 16 August, and it grew to 5 ha in size by 3:00 that morning. When the fire was first reported, it was 6 km from the nearest structures in Narmata and 10 km from the nearest homes in Kelowna. Air tankers worked the fire until 11:15 when it was reported to be a relatively low intensity Rank 1 fire. When the air tankers returned to their base for refuelling they were dispatched to other, higher-priority fires. The winds picked up at about 12:30 and spot fires materialized north of the main fire. Helicopters bucketed those spot fires, and air tanker action resumed at 1:55. Air tanker operations continued until 7:05 p.m. but ceased then due to flight crew safety concerns regarding low visibility due to smoke and falling light levels. The fire was reported to have burned through the retardant dropped by air tankers consistently throughout the day. Suppression action continued on the following days but the fire continued to grow and reached more than 9,000 ha by 20 August.

On 21 August the fire was spotting up to 100 m in front of the main fire. It began threatening Kelowna and 21 structures were lost. A cold front was forecast to pass through the area on 22 August and at 2:00 p.m. that day, crews were pulled off the northeast flank for safety reasons. At 4:45 the fire blew up, pushed by 75 km/h winds. Burning firebrands the size of dinner plates were being carried 6 to 8 km from the main fire. The winds did not subside until 3:00 a.m. on 23 August, at which point more than 250 homes had been lost. The first significant precipitation fell on the fire on 8 September, and the fire was eventually extinguished at 25,912 ha.

CALIFORNIA

Many people move to California because the weather is warm all year; it is said of California that "the four seasons do not exist there." Others say California does have four seasons—flood, drought, fire, and earthquake. A few weeks of winter rain sets plants into a fast-growth mode. Then, months of warmth and drought kill the annual plants and dehydrate the perennials, setting the stage for fire.

Oakland and Berkeley Hills

Rising behind the cities of Oakland and Berkeley are steep hills where million-dollar homes command sweeping views over San Francisco Bay. The hills are covered with trees and shrubs that allow the homeowners to live in the woods and get away from it all. However, these WUI areas are at terrible threat from fire.

A five-year-long drought in the late 1980s dried shrubs and trees in the hills. A December 1990 freeze killed many ornamental plants, only to be followed by a rainy March that set grasses into rapid growth. Then drought quickly returned for the rest of 1991. The volume of dead and dehydrated vegetation was dangerously high. On Saturday, 19 October 1991, a fire of suspicious origin started near the top of the hills. Firefighters fought the blaze and controlled it in three hours with 2 ha burned. The fire site was in an area of Monterey pine trees with a 0.3 m duff layer. Firefighters know duff as a problem; it burns on top but smoulders below the surface, where oxygen is in short supply. Water extinguishes the surface flames, but also can combine with ash to form a crust over smouldering combustion. The firefighters left early Saturday evening, planning to return on Sunday morning to "mop up" the smouldering duff.

However, on Sunday, strong winds also showed up at 10:45 a.m., bringing low humidity, a 36°C day, and wind speeds averaging 27 km/h with gusts up to 40 km/h. The winds picked up sparks from the duff and started a fire in a steep-walled canyon. By 11:15 a.m., the flames had raced up the slopes of the confining canyon and leapt over the rim toward Oakland. The blaze was already out of control. Flames in grass ignited the fuel-rich **chaparral** vegetation, which fed the fire into the low branches of Monterey pine and eucalyptus trees, which in turn sent flames climbing up the "fuel ladder" to set off a crown fire that moved through the treetops at over 6 km/h. Erratic winds pushed the fire in changing directions. The flames reached 1,100°C and quickly grew to **firestorm** status, creating its own winds, towering convection columns, and fire whirls. In its first hour of existence, the fire consumed 790 homes. Winds grew to speeds of 32 km/h with gusts up to 80 km/h, pushing flames across an unbroken chain of dry vegetation and combustible homes. Burning embers carried by the winds started new blazes.

The winds spread the fire and pushed the flames all day long. Fortunately, the firestorm never spread out of the hills into the more densely populated cities of Oakland and Berkeley. While the fire was out of control, plans were being made to evacuate hundreds of thousands of people from the cities, an effort that would have been desperate at best. But before the plans could be implemented, the winds died down and shifted direction in the early evening, finally giving firefighters a chance to control the flames. During the day, 25 people were trapped and killed, 150 were injured, and 2,449 single-family dwellings were destroyed, along with 437 apartments and condominiums. In all, 650 ha were burned, and property damages exceeded $1.5 billion.

This firestorm presents another opportunity to examine how we fight fires. We commonly think of the fire triangle (Figure 14.5) and try to deprive the fire of its heat or fuel or oxygen. This strategy works well for small- to moderate-size **fuel-driven fires**. But when winds blow strongly, fires grow large rapidly. Catastrophic firestorms are **wind-driven fires**. When the winds blow, the fire goes, and only a change in the weather will stop it.

Southern California

Southern California has a long dry season, chaparral vegetation, and hot, dry winds—it is a land born to burn.

On Wednesday, 27 October 1993, wind-felled power lines created sparks that the winds fanned and carried as flames far and wide through the flammable chaparral. Fires also began when the winds picked up flames from a transient's campfire; several more were set by arsonists. The winds died down on Friday, 29 October, allowing firefighters to gain control of some fires but not all.

Then, on Tuesday night, 2 November 1993, resurging winds hit speeds up to 80 km/h, and the flames took off for another two days (Figure 14.26). Fires burned clear to the ocean despite the best efforts of firefighters; surfers rode waves in front of bushes burning on the beach. The only firebreak that could stop the advance of the flames was the Pacific Ocean.

The massive firestorms spun off whirls that sent embers leaping large canyons in a single bound to start new blazes. The flames consumed whatever they wanted. Firestorms are not stopped by humans; they go as long as the wind blows. When these fires finally ended, 3 people were dead, 200 were injured, 1,150 homes were destroyed, and damages exceeded $1 billion. Over 87,000 ha were charred. Despite the horror of this event, it is not a rare one. Every year brings the possibility of similar conflagrations.

The fire peril is evident enough that some people design their houses to withstand fires (Figure 14.27). The choice is yours—either pay higher construction costs to fireproof your home, or pay the entire cost to rebuild your home, and life, after a fire.

Figure 14.26
Firestorm racing through chaparral-covered hillslopes as a wall of flame up to 14 m high.
Photo © L.A. Times.

Figure 14.27
Houses designed to withstand fire remain unharmed while their million-dollar neighbours are nothing but ashes, near Las Flores Canyon in Malibu, California.
Photo: © Patrick Downs, L.A. Times

Figure 14.28
Twelve mistakes, or how to sacrifice your house to the fire gods. (1) House is located on a slope. (2) House is made of wood. (3) Wooden deck hangs out over the slope. (4) Firewood is stored next to the house. (5) Roof is made of flammable wood shingles. (6) Tree limbs hang over roof. (7) Shrubs continue up to house. (8) Large, single-pane windows face the slope. (9) Unprotected louvers face the slope. (10) No spark arrester is on top of chimney. (11) Narrow road or driveway prevents access of fire trucks. (12) Wooden eaves extend beyond walls.
Source: © National Fire Protection Assoc.

Home Design and Fire

Not all of the death and destruction from fires can be called "natural disasters." Poor decisions on landscaping, home design, and construction materials are partly to blame (Figure 14.28). Many homes are made of wood or roofed with wooden shake shingles. Wooden decks extend out over steep slopes and help fire to concentrate heat, igniting the houses. Natural and planted vegetation commonly continue from the wildland right up to houses or drape over the roofs. All of these flammable materials act to convey fire into and through houses.

A house can catch on fire in different ways. (1) Flames can travel to the house by burning through vegetation or along a wood fence. (2) Flames do not have to reach the house; they can generate enough radiant heat to ignite the exterior of the house or even the curtains hanging inside windows. (3) Firebrands carried by wind can be dropped on or next to the house. Compare the combustion potential of the two houses pictured in Figure 14.29.

Now stand outside, look at your house and ask yourself—what could catch on fire? Then eliminate the hazard. All it takes to ignite a house is one vulnerable point where combustion can occur. It is possible to build a house and landscape the property so that a fire will pass by (Figure 14.30).

The houses that flames pass by commonly have clay- or concrete-tile roofs, stucco exterior walls, double-pane windows, few overhanging roofs or decks, and fire breaks of cleared vegetation extending at least 10 m from the house. Houses built on slopes need even larger areas of cleared space (Figure 14.31). If you plan to build a house in the woods or along a WUI area, the decisions you make about construction materials and landscaping may well determine whether your house will end up as fuel for flames or remain your home (Table 14.3). Even little decisions about landscaping can determine whether your house burns or endures (Figure 14.32).

Fire Suppression

In August 1910, over 1.2 million ha of forest in the Bitterroot Mountains of Idaho and Montana burned in a firestorm known as the Big Blowup. The fire destroyed towns, killed 85 people, and provoked the U.S. Congress into authorizing expenditure of federal money to fight forest fires. And so began the policy of aggressively suppressing forest fires with well-trained armies of professional firefighters.

During the 20th century, people were taught to hate fire and to stamp it out quickly. Fire-suppression tactics and equipment improved during the century, resulting in dramatic reductions in the number of hectares burned. Over the decades, forests were transformed by the fire-suppression practices. Forests that once held 75 big trees per hectare were accustomed to having ground fires move

(a)

(b)

Figure 14.29
(a) Bad house—easy to burn. Note wood exterior walls, wood eaves, wood shingle roof, overhanging eucalyptus tree, and tree litter on roof. (b) Good house—difficult to burn. Note stucco walls, boxed eaves of stucco, tile roof, no trees or shrubs next to house, and no litter.
Photos: © Pat Abbott.

Figure 14.30
The fire-safe house. Use fire-resistant materials to build your house, then landscape without providing fuel for flames, and a wildfire can pass by without harm.
Photo: © San Diego County.

Figure 14.31
Buildings at the top of a slope need setbacks to help avoid the increased heat flow by convection and radiation. The defensive space includes a vertical zone around the building that has no tall trees.

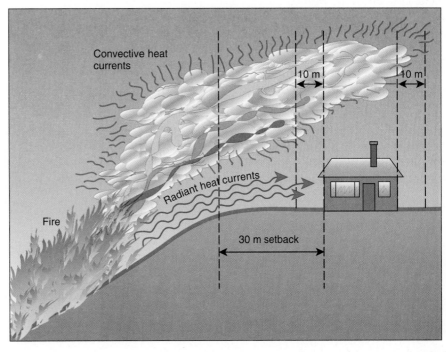

Table 14.3

How to Protect Your House from Wildfire: A Must-do List

Roof The roof is the most vulnerable part of your house because of wind-blown burning embers. Build or reroof with lightweight materials that will not burn. Remember to remove branches hanging over your roof and sweep off accumulated leaves, needles, and other plant debris. Place screens over all vents.

House Build or remodel with fire-resistant materials. The ultimate foolishness is to build a wood house among abundant trees and shrubs that are designed to burn.

Decks The undersides of above-ground decks, balconies, and eaves must be covered with fire-resistant materials.

Windows Use only double- or triple-paned windows to reduce the potential of breakage during a fire. Eliminate wood shutters. Beware of the new-style white plastic window frames; they have melted and allowed fire into homes.

Flammables Be sure to place natural-gas tanks and firewood piles at least 10 m from your house.

Trees Hold back fire from your house by (1) reducing the number of trees in densely wooded areas and (2) cutting off branches within 2 m of the ground so grass fires cannot climb up to the treetops.

Yard Create a defensible space by (1) replacing fire-loving plants with fire-resistant plants and (2) removing all dry grass, dead brush, and leaves at least 10 m from your home, or 30 m if you are on a slope. Replace wood fences with concrete block or metal fences.

Community planning Place golf courses, grass ball fields, and open-space parks between houses and the wildland so they can serve as fire breaks or buffers.

Figure 14.32
Right versus wrong is illustrated above a busy street in San Diego, California. Unaware homeowner on the left has dead grasses on a slope leading up to dead trees and an overhanging wood patio. Aware homeowner on the right has planted nonbonding succulent ice plant on the slope leading up to a concrete-block wall.
Photo: © Pat Abbott.

quickly through grasses and thin litter on the forest floor without harming most of the big trees. However, after years of limiting fires, some of these forests now support 750 to 7,500 trees per hectare plus an understory of shrubs. When lightning ignites fires in these dense forests, the flames burn slowly and intensely, killing the big trees. The widespread recognition of the fire problem for dense and crowded forests led to a dilemma: Should the dense forests be thinned? Should natural fires be allowed to burn? Affirmative answers to these questions led to the following events.

YELLOWSTONE NATIONAL PARK

Yellowstone is the oldest national park in the United States; it was authorized on 1 March 1872. The park aver-

ages about 15 fires per year started by lightning. This is not an unusual number of fires, considering that Earth as a whole is estimated to have about 9 million lightning discharges per day.

Not all lightning strokes have the same fire-igniting potential. The most capable are "hot strokes," which are cloud-to-ground discharges of high amperage and longer duration. About 1 in 25 lightning strokes matches these characteristics. Whether a fire is ignited depends on what the lightning hits. A hot stroke may start a fire if it strikes kindling, such as dry grass, rotten wood, or "organic dust" mechanically blasted into the air by the force of the lightning strike. The policy of Yellowstone Park from the 1880s to the 1970s was to extinguish all fires as soon as possible. But fire is a natural process. So the question arose, "Who can better manage these wildlands—humans or nature?" Nature became the answer in the 1970s, so the policy was changed to one of putting out human-caused fires but leaving natural fires alone to run their course. Lightning-caused fires burn the forest irregularly; they cause formation of a mosaic of meadows, burned-over ground, and forests ranging from young to mature to old growth. The different areas provide a diversity of environments, supporting various communities of plants and animals.

Following the policy change, between 1976 and 1987 there were 235 lightning fires. A typical fire burned about 40 ha, only eight fires burned more than 400 ha, and the largest burned 3,000 ha. The policy change was judged to be a great success. Fires were occurring in moderate amounts and were promoting ecological diversity. Then came 1988.

The winter of 1987–88 was a dry one. Lightning started fires as usual in June 1988, but this year, no rains followed as in the previous six June–July intervals. By late July, over 6,800 ha had burned, and the decision was made to extinguish the blazes and suppress any new fires regardless of their origin. But the situation had additional complexities: (1) many forest stands had been killed by infestations of mountain pine beetles, (2) nine decades of fire suppression had created an extensive buildup of dead wood on the ground, and (3) moisture levels in dead wood had dropped from the usual 15 to 20% down to 2 to 7%.

As firefighters struggled to control the situation, the weather worsened as a wave of high temperatures arrived with sustained high winds. In the 24 hours of 20 August 1988, more square kilometres of Yellowstone Park burned than the total area burned in any preceding decade.

Despite the continuing efforts of firefighters, the blazes did not weaken until the arrival of mid-September snows, and the flames did not quit until winter conditions prevailed in November. The weather controlled the flames that humans could not. At the fire's conclusion, more than 500,000 ha lay burned, including almost half of Yellowstone Park (Figures 14.35 and 14.36). In the previous 116 years, a total of only 59,000 ha had burned.

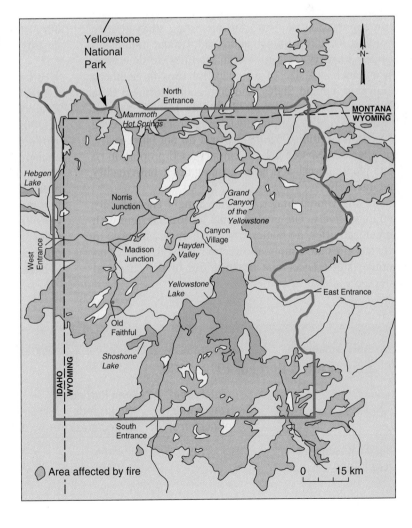

Figure 14.33
View of all of Yellowstone National Park in late 1988 (see map in Figure 14.34).

Figure 14.34
Area burned by the Yellowstone fires of 1988 (see photo in Figure 14.33).

Ten Years Later

The fires of 1988 drastically changed the look of Yellowstone National Park. Thousands of hectares of charred trees held the bodies of 269 elk, nine bison, six black bears, four deer, and two moose. The fires killed trees but opened land to increased sunlight and nutrients that brought forth grasses, wildflowers, and shrubs. Trees are recolonizing the burnt ground with seedlings of lodgepole pine, Engelmann spruce, subalpine fir, and Douglas fir. Standing dead trees continue to fall and thus enrich the soil as fungi, bacteria, beetles, ants, and other organisms decompose their remains. The pre-1988 Yellowstone is gone, but the living and functioning ecosystem is going through many interesting changes and time will allow a return to the past.

CALIFORNIA VERSUS BAJA CALIFORNIA: PAY NOW OR PAY LATER

Many people hold the view that humanity is separate from the environment, that humans are supposed "to be fruitful, multiply, and subdue the Earth." Many seek to control nature for their own benefit. This includes building houses wherever it strikes their fancy. Fires? No problem, we will just extinguish them before they cause any damage. But what is the long-term effect of short-term suppression of fires? An interesting study by fire ecologist Richard Minnich addressed this question using Landsat imagery ("photos" from satellites) to determine the number and size of all chaparral fires in Southern California, United States, and contiguous northern Baja California, Mexico, from 1972 to 1980. The life cycle of the chaparral plant community takes it through a sequence of fire susceptibility. Younger plants do not burn easily, but after 40 years of growth, an increased proportion of dead-plant material acts as fuel, aiding fire to burn readily and intensely.

In the United States, fires are fought energetically and expensively. The goal is to not let fire interfere with human activities, no matter how much money it costs. In Mexico, fires are simply allowed to burn with little or no human interference. The fire histories of the chaparral areas in the United States versus those in Mexico show interesting differences (Table 14.4).

In the United States, fires that break out during the cooler, wetter months are quickly extinguished. Thus, most of the chaparral is allowed to grow older and more flammable. Then, when the hot and dry winds come blowing from the continental Interior (commonly in September, October, and November), firestorms are unleashed that firefighters are powerless to stop, and great numbers of hectares burn. Southern California has fewer fires but more large ones (Figure 14.35).

In Mexico, the fires are smaller because older chaparral is commonly surrounded by younger, less flammable plants. This distribution creates an age mosaic that mixes volatile, older patches with younger, tougher-to-burn growths. Fires are more numerous in Baja California, but they are smaller and more of them occur during the cooler, wetter months (Figure 14.35).

For the 1972–80 period, the percentage of chaparral area burned in the United States and Mexico was about the same. This is despite the enormous expenses and valiant efforts made in the United States to suppress fire. The U.S. fire-control efforts have reduced the number of fires but not the amount of area burned. In Southern California, the monster firestorms pushed by dry, hot winds burn tremendous numbers of hectares, killing people and destroying thousands of buildings.

The Cedar Fire in San Diego County, Southern California, October 2003

Fire potential in San Diego County was high in the fall of 2003. Huge areas of chaparral had been allowed to grow old and increase their volume of fuel; 48% of the chaparral was more than 50 years old and another 31% was more than 20 years old. Plant flammability had been further increased by five years of drought and the low-moisture conditions of a long, hot summer. When stressed by lack of water, the branches of many chaparral plants die, strips of bark fall, and leaves drop. A mature plant can have half of its tissue dead, oil-rich, and ready to burn. The buildup of fuel is made even more critical by

Table 14.4

Chaparral Areas Burned, 1972–1980

	Total Area (thousands of hectares)	Area Burned (thousands of hectares)	% Area Burned	% Burned after September 1	Number of Fires
Southern California	2,019	166	8.2	72	203
Baja California	1,202	95	7.9	20	488

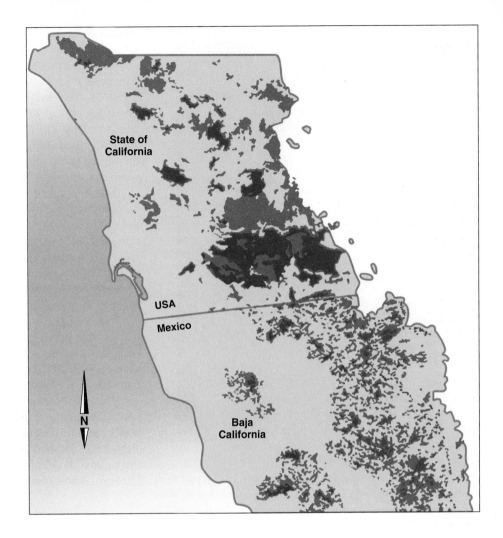

Figure 14.35
Fire burn areas in California and Baja California between 1938 and 1972. Notice the huge areas burned by some California fires. See the larger number of burn areas in Baja California but their smaller sizes.

Source: © Richard A. Minnich, University of California–Riverside.

thousands of homes built in isolated spots within the sea of chaparral; houses built of fuel and placed within a sea of fuel, setting up an impending tragedy (Figure 14.38).

And then it started. A lost and confused hunter lit a signal fire to guide rescuers to him. His flames rose into air with 4% humidity and were pushed westward by winds blowing 32 to 64 km/h. The wind-driven flames and flying embers burned 114,000 ha, destroyed 2,232 buildings, and killed 15 people.

But it could have been worse. For example, the fire front moving southwest ran into a young fuel area, the 4,190 ha burned by the Viejas fire in January 2001. These less-than-3-year-old plants stopped the fire in some areas, and reduced flame height and heat in others, allowing firefighters to prevent the fire from moving into the city of Chula Vista. Also, after the winds reversed, the fire front moving east encountered the prescribed burn areas of 2001, 2002, and 2003. The resulting young fuel mosaics there stopped the flames from entering the community of Pine Valley. It is estimated that the Cedar fire would have burned more than 160,000 ha if it had not run into

these recently burned areas with their young, low-fuel chaparral plants.

AUSTRALIA

Australia is bedevilled by bushfires, major conflagrations swept by high winds through eucalyptus forests that are fire-adapted and fire-maintained. Most eucalyptus trees and bushes have highly flammable oil in their branches and bark. Some trees invite fire by shedding their bark in long, thin strips; the dry strips of bark are kindling that ignites easily and burns fast. Eucalyptus makes good wood for your fireplace, but in a natural setting, the trees may be heated so hot that their sap boils and whole trees explode in flame. This presents obvious problems for houses and towns in the path of a eucalyptus-fuelled bushfire. The bluegum eucalyptus is described by Robert Sward:

Deadly beauty,
Much to admire.
Until it falls
Or catches fire.

Figure 14.36
The houses on this promontory were destroyed by fire in 2003. Surrounded on three sides by chaparral, the houses were built using wood exteriors and roofs, and landscaping with flammable plants.

Fire is not a problem for the plant species. Most eucalyptus varieties are designed to burn hot and fast; it is then that their fruit opens and releases unburned seeds to germinate in the fire-cleared ground. The fast-moving fires may burn down trees, but many of the resilient plant species simply send up shoots from their stumps or roots and grow to full-size trees again in several years.

The worst bushfires in history correlate with drought and wind. Many of these weather episodes occur when an El Niño–Southern Oscillation circulation system is operating in the oceans (Figures 11.9, 11.10 (left), and 11.11b). When the ocean waters off Australia are cooler, evaporation and precipitation are reduced. The lessened rainfall creates drought that can extend through an entire southern hemisphere winter. Bushfire conditions may start with a high-pressure system off southern Australia. As the high-pressure zone moves slowly eastward, it induces air masses over the central desert to blow southeastward from the Interior toward the heavily populated southeastern region of Australia. As the winds descend from the high desert, they warm, producing temperatures around 40°C, humidities of less than 20%, and speeds of at least 60 km/h.

The El Niño–Southern Oscillation of 1982–83 was particularly strong, and the Australian summer was the driest in recorded history. On Wednesday, 16 February 1983, strong, hot, dry winds from the Interior were reinforced by the jet stream in the upper atmosphere. Adelaide, the capital of South Australia, and Melbourne, the capital of Victoria, were ringed by fires pushed by the southeastward-blowing winds.

In mid-afternoon, a cold front swept through the area, dropping temperatures 10°C. However, the cooler winds did not subdue the fires but instead changed their direction of movement to the northeast and increased their speed. The winds were blowing 70 km/h with gusts up to 170 km/h, and the fire front advanced at speeds up to 20 km/h. The firestorms were so strong that their winds snapped tree trunks.

When the fires were finished, 76 people lay dead, 3,500 had suffered injuries, and 2,500 houses and 20 towns were gone. The livestock toll was also great as more than 300,000 sheep and 18,000 cattle perished along with uncounted numbers of native animals.

The bushfire hazard is ever present. The hot, dry, fast winds returned to Sydney in January 1994 and December 2001, again leaving dead bodies and hundreds of incinerated homes behind. In January 2003, a lightning-started fire pushed by 60 km/h winds entered the capital city of Canberra, killing four people and destroying 380 houses.

Forest Fires and Climate Change

Since climate influences forest vegetation, and weather influences fire occurrence and fire-behaviour processes, climate change is expected to have a significant impact on fire activity in the forested regions of Canada and elsewhere.

Fire researchers have studied the impact of weather on fire occurrence and fire behaviour and some of their understanding of the relationships between them are described in the form of mathematical relationships between, for example, the average number of people-caused fires per day in a region and the Fine Fuel Moisture Code, one of the components of the Canadian Fire Weather Index system described above (Figure 14.16). Fire researchers work with climatologists to project how the fire-danger rating indices for an area will change under different CO_2 scenarios and how such changes in fire danger will influence fire activity under climate change.

Some of the early studies indicated that fire-season severity (which is based on the Fire Weather Index) will increase by roughly 45% under doubling CO_2 conditions, and the fire seasons will increase in length. It is important to note, however, that the impact of climate change on fire-season severity is expected to vary regionally, with some areas experiencing increased activity and others lower activity. Other studies have focused on fire occurrence and predicted people-caused fire occurrence might increase by roughly 20% under those same conditions. The area burned by lightning fires is expected to increase as well. Collectively, these studies suggest that fire weather will intensify, more fires will occur, and more area will burn.

IS THERE ANY EVIDENCE CLIMATE CHANGE HAS ALTERED CANADIAN FOREST-FIRE REGIMES?

Both temperatures and forest-fire activity have been rising in parts of Canada in recent decades and many observers are quick to point to increased forest-fire activity as an early sign of climate change. Unfortunately, although climate change is widely believed to be contributing to increased forest-fire activity in Canada, it is very difficult to determine the extent to which such increases are or are not due to climate change.

Fire occurrence and fire-behaviour processes are influenced by not only fuel, weather, and topography but also people who establish homes and cottages in WUI areas, build forest-access roads, harvest forest stands, and engage in human activities that lead to people-caused fire occurrence. People also attempt, with considerable success, to suppress many of the fires that do occur. It is therefore difficult to assess the extent to which fire activity in a particular area is or is not influenced by climate change.

However, recent studies have attributed increased warming during the fire season and increased area burned in the fire-prone regions of Canada to human emissions of greenhouse gasses and sulfate aerosols. More recently, researchers identified areas in the forests of the Northern Rockies of the United States in which large fire activity appears to be related to increased spring and summer temperatures and an earlier spring snowmelt. Such results lend credence to the belief that climate change will have a significant impact on Canadian forest-fire regimes.

POTENTIAL IMPACT

The projected increases in fire activity that are expected to result from climate change will have significant social, economic, and ecological impacts on Canadian forests and the people who live and work in and near them. Given the current structure and composition of our forests, land-use patterns, and fire management strategies, it is reasonable to assume that more timber will be lost to fire and that more communities, particularly small, relatively isolated communities in the far north, will be threatened by fire. Some studies have suggested that increased burning will release more greenhouse gases, which in turn may lead to even more warming, while others have suggested that burning of parts of Canada's northern boreal forest may lead to more sun being reflected by the snow during the winter months, thereby mitigating warming. Some have suggested that our forests be used to sequester carbon while others have expressed concerns that such strategies are short-sighted; as the fuel build ups, such strategies will simply delay and exacerbate the inevitable. Clearly, there is an urgent need to develop a better understanding of forests and fire, and how they will be shaped by, and in turn influence, climate change.

The Similarities of Fire and Flood

Stephen J. Pyne has pointed out that floods can serve as a metaphor for fire. Fires and floods seem so different, yet they have some general characteristics in common.

- Both fire and flood are closely related to weather, plant cover, and topography.
- Both fire and flood are at their strongest when atmospheric conditions are extreme. Fast, dry winds push flames, while heavy rains feed floods.
- Both fire and flood move across the landscape and through human developments as waves of energy. A fire front is a wave of chemical energy released from temporary storage in organic matter. A flood crest is a wave of mechanical energy unleashed when the potential energy of a high topographic position is converted to the kinetic energy of motion.
- Both fire and flood become more turbulent the faster they move and the bigger they grow.
- Both fire and flood can be described by their size and frequency. As a first approximation, the bigger the fire or flood, the longer the return period until the next big one. Both fire and flood are effectively understood as 50-year, 100-year, or other recurrence-time events.
- Both fire and flood are aggravated by human activity. Fires are made more intense by buildings placed in dense growths of plants and by our habit of quickly suppressing small fires, thus allowing organic debris to build into large masses that provide fuel for gigantic firestorms. Floods are made more destructive by buildings placed on flood plains and by levees built to protect against floods that inadvertently might cause record-high flood levels.

Summary

- Fire is the rapid combination of oxygen with carbon, hydrogen, and other organic material in a reaction that produces flame, heat, and light. Fire is photosynthesis run in reverse.
- Fire is a natural process that is essential to the health of many ecosystems, including Canada's forests. Fire recycles nutrients and plays a key role in the reproductive cycle of some plants.
- Fire develops in three stages, which can occur simultaneously in different areas of a wildfire:

  1. In the preheating stage, water is expelled from wood, plants, or fossil fuels by flames, drought, or hot weather.
  2. In the pyrolysis stage, when temperatures exceed 300°C, wood breaks down and gives off flammable gases. If oxygen is present, these gases can ignite and combustion begins.
  3. In the combustion stage, the pyrolizing woods first burn in flames. Released heat keeps the wood surface hot through conduction, diffusion, radiation, and convection. After the active flames pass, glowing combustion slowly reduces the solid wood to ash.

- The spread of fire depends on

  - Types of plants or fuel burned.
  - Strong winds bringing oxygen and pushing flames forward. In fact, fires heat air, which rises buoyantly and creates its own winds.

- Topography, which helps control plant distribution, and channels fire in preferential directions. A steep slope acts like a chimney that fire races up.
- Fire threats are greatest in areas with big contrasts between wet and dry seasons. A wet season triggers voluminous plant growth. Then dry conditions dehydrate plants, making it easier for ignition to occur.
- Given the type of vegetation and meteorological conditions, fire specialists use mathematical models to predict fire behaviour. Results are communicated to the public using a simple index that rates fire hazard as low, moderate, high, or extreme.
- Buildings can be constructed to withstand fire. Traditional structures can be made safer by eliminating flammable vegetation and woodpiles near them, avoiding wood-shingle roofs and overhanging wood balconies or decks, and using double-pane glass in windows and doors.
- Fires cannot be prevented, only deferred. Allowing natural fires to burn helps prevent buildups of extensive debris that can fuel a firestorm during heavy winds.
- In Canada, a majority of forest fires are caused by people but lightning-caused fires, occurring mostly in remote areas where immediate remedial action is difficult, account for most of the area burned. Several climate-change scenarios predict that forest-fire activity will intensify in the future.

Terms to Remember

backfire   409
chaparral   423
combustion   411
diffusion   411
duff   415
fire   406
firebrand   412

fire-danger rating   415
firestorm   423
fuel   409
fuel model   412
fuel-driven fire   423
ignition temperature   408
ladder fuel   410

oxidation   411
photosynthesis   407
pyrolysis   411
radiation   411
slash   409
wind-driven fire   423

Questions for Review

1. How many forest fires occur and how much area do they burn on average in Canada each year?
2. Why do lightning-caused fires burn a disproportionate amount of the area burned by forest fires in Canada?
3. Write a chemical reaction equation that describes how a fire burns woody material.
4. Compare fire to photosynthesis.
5. Explain the process of pyrolysis.
6. Explain the differences between conduction, diffusion, radiation, and convection.
7. Compare the conduction of heat in wood versus metal.
8. What is the difference between flaming combustion and glowing combustion?
9. Will a typical wildfire burn faster upslope or downslope? Why?
10. Explain how a wildfire can create its own winds.
11. What difficulties are presented when duff catches fire?

Questions for Further Thought

1. Explain how to build a campfire. Explain the fire processes occurring at each stage of your campfire.
2. Make a detailed list of actions you could take to make your current residence safer from fire.
3. If you were designing your dream house on your dream lot, what features could you incorporate into the house and landscape design to better protect your house from destruction by fire?
4. Evaluate the wisdom of quickly suppressing a local wildfire during a time of cold weather with low wind speeds.
5. Should homeowners in houses surrounded by flammable vegetation in wildlands pay the same fire insurance premiums as homeowners in the city?
6. Prescribed fire is sometimes used to reduce hazardous fuel buildups but the smoke emitted from prescribed fires bothers many people. Discuss how fire and forest managers might resolve such problems.
7. Suppose Canadian governments decided to sequester carbon in our forests. How might that affect forest-fire management and Canadian firefighters?

The Great Dyings

History fades into fable; fact becomes clouded with doubt and controversy; the inscription moulders from the tablet; the statue falls from the pedestal. Columns, arches, pyramids, what are they but heaps of sand; and their epitaphs, but characters written in the dust?

—Washington Irving, 1820, *The Sketch Book*

Outline

A slice through the chambered spiral shell of a *Nautilus,* a relative of the octopus

Source: Kaz Chiba/Getty Images.

Recorded human history tells of horrifying natural disasters. Earthquake and flood disasters have each killed more than 750,000 people, single cyclones have drowned at least 500,000, and individual volcanic eruptions have killed tens of thousands. Nevertheless, historical disasters such as these do not compare to the vast scale of extinctions documented in the fossil record. The human tragedies wrought by natural disasters involve individuals of a **species**, not an entire species or millions of species. Several times since the start of the Paleozoic 543 million years ago, the majority of the species on Earth became extinct in geologically short times. These great dyings or mass **extinctions** are the biggest natural disasters known to have occurred on Earth. How do we know about the lives of extinct species? We interpret the fossil record.

Fossils

Fossils are evidence of former life. Two common requisites for organisms to become fossilized are (1) possession of dense, robust hard parts such as teeth, shells, or bones, and (2) rapid burial, which protects deceased organisms from being scavenged and disintegrated. Fossilization occurs in numerous ways.

Sharks are cartilaginous fishes; they have no bones. The fossil record of sharks is dominated by their hardest part—teeth (Figure 15.1).

Hard shells are built by many invertebrate animals such as oysters, snails, clams, sea urchins, and barnacles. Clams (bivalves) are well represented in the fossil record; they have hard shells and they bury themselves while alive (Figure 15.2).

Figure 15.1
A fossil shark tooth.

Photo: © Jim Linna/Photodisc/Getty Images.

Tree trunks and branches can be buried by floods carrying mud or sand. After burial, their organic material can be slowly replaced by minerals contained in underground water to make petrified wood (Figure 15.3).

Dinosaurs are known to us primarily by their original hard parts—their fossil bones, skulls, and teeth. Dinosaur fossils may be found in a jumbled mixture dropped by a river in flood (Figure 15.4). The fossil bones are carefully removed from the rock and then assembled like a jigsaw puzzle to show us extinct dinosaurs (Figure 15.5).

Dinosaurs are also known in indirect ways. Figure 15.6 shows numerous dinosaur footprints impressed on mud that transformed into solid rock over geological time; are

Figure 15.2
Many shells of shallow-marine clams of Pliocene age, about 3 million years old.

Source: The McGraw-Hill Companies/John A. Karachewski, photographer.

Figure 15.3
Petrified tree logs of the genus *Araucaria,* Late Triassic age, Petrified Forest National Park, Arizona. The genus still lives today, more than 200 million years later.

Photo: © Dr. Parvender Sethi.

Figure 15.5
An Allosaurus skeleton from 150 million years ago. University of Utah Museum.

Photo: © Pat Abbott.

Figure 15.4
Dinosaur bones washed and deposited in a sandy river in Late Cretaceous, Dinosaur Provincial Park, Alberta.

Photo QT Luong/terragalleria.com.

Figure 15.6
An Early Cretaceous dinosaur trackway thousands of metres in length from the Gorman Creek Formation, Kakwa Provincial Park, British Columbia. A high diversity of dinosaur tracks are recorded at this locality, discovered in 2000.

Source: Richard T. McCrea , Peace Region Palaeontology Research Centre www. tumblerridgemuseum.com.

Figure 15.7
A 26-million-year-old scorpion trapped in amber (fossil tree sap).
Photo: © Pat Abbott.

Figure 15.8
The 2,000-year-old Lindow man was well preserved in a British Isles peat bog.

they fossils? Yes, the term *fossil* is simply evidence of former life. Because of fossil footprints paleontologists have been able to deduce that some species of dinosaurs travelled together in herds.

Visualize a hot day where sap oozes and flows down the trunk of a tree. Sometimes the sticky sap will overrun and trap an insect such as a scorpion (Figure 15.7). The enclosing sap prevents scavengers, water, and oxygen from getting to the scorpion's remains and destroying them. The sap hardens and fossilizes, and is known as amber.

Sometimes fossilization can be spectacular. (1) Thousands of years ago some individuals fell into or were buried in swamps and peat bogs whose dark waters were devoid of oxygen and scavengers. Their bodies have been preserved much the way leather is tanned to preserve it for use in clothes and furniture. The process preserves even small details (Figure 15.8). (2) As glaciers retreat, the frozen bodies of animals such as mammoths become exposed. Even though they died thousands of years ago, there still is flesh left on their bones and food in their stomachs. (3) A Celtic miner killed in a salt mine collapse in Austria had his body preserved until discovery 2,300 years later.

These are just a few examples of the record of life on Earth. Plant and animal species have appeared, changed, and gone extinct, only to be replaced by other species.

Early Understanding of Extinctions and Geological Time

In 1786, French paleontologist Georges Cuvier proved that extinction of species had occurred. He demonstrated that the skeletons of mammoths (Figure 15.9) were distinctly different from those of living elephant species and

Figure 15.9
Once there were many species of mammoths; now there are none.

yet mammoths no longer live; thus, mammoths had gone extinct.

Cuvier also was impressed with the profound changes in the sedimentary rock record. Fossils made sudden first appearances, were found in abundance in overlying rock layers, but then were not found in higher rock layers (Figure 15.10). Cuvier recognized that entire communities of plants and animals often died out in geologically short lengths of time.

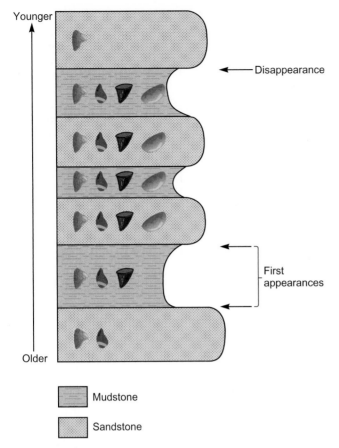

Younger

Disappearance

First
appearances

Older

Mudstone

Sandstone

Figure 15.10

A vertical sequence of sedimentary rock layers illustrates the laws of superposition (the lower the layer, the older) and faunal succession (older forms of life die out and new forms develop).

Figure 15.10 also illustrates Steno's 1669 law of superposition, which explains that younger layers of sediment are deposited on top of older layers. Thus, in a non-overturned sequence of sedimentary rock, the lowest layer is the oldest, and each bed encountered moving up the sedimentary section is progressively younger. Robert Hooke (1635–1703), also known as the Father of Microscopy because he built the first microscope, was the first to suggest the existence of extinction events, as he found that some fossils had no living relatives. He also proposed that fossils could be used as dating tools to correlate rock in different regions.

In 1799, English civil engineer William Smith published a list describing the sequence of sedimentary **strata** and associated fossils in the area of Somerset, England. He indicated clearly that specific intervals of sedimentary strata could be recognized over broad areas by the unique assemblages of fossils they contain. This is called the **principle of faunal succession**; it explains that strata of like age can be recognized by the like assemblage of fossils they contain.

Fossils collected from older rock layers (lower by superposition) are older and more different from present-day organisms than are fossils collected from younger rock layers (higher by superposition). Because the older fossils are more unlike living organisms, we can conclude that new forms of life have developed. William Smith used his principle of faunal succession to make geological maps of England and Wales, which were published in 1815. Geologists throughout the world reacted to the work of Steno, Hooke, Cuvier, Smith, and others by recording the order of sedimentary strata and the sequence of fossils they contained. All over the world, sedimentary strata were classified and subdivided in vertical columns based on their differing fossil assemblages. The sequences of sedimentary rock and fossils in different parts of the world cover different intervals of Earth history. Where fossil assemblages in different areas were found to be the same, the rocks that contain the fossils were considered to be the same age. By 1841, the co-occurrences of fossils had been compiled to erect a standard geological column for the world; this was an early version of the geological timescale that we use today (Figure 15.11).

Beginning in the 20th century, geologists added quantification to the fossil record using dates determined from radioactive elements in igneous rock associated with fossil-bearing sedimentary rock (see In Greater Depth box: Radioactive isotopes in Chapter 2). The ongoing refinements of the geological timescale involve geologists and **paleontologists** studying rock and fossils throughout the world.

BRIEF HISTORY OF LIFE

The fossil record documents the appearances and disappearances of millions of life forms (Figure 15.11). There have been remarkable changes in life on Earth. As described by T. A. Conrad: "Race after race resigned their fleeting breath—the rocks alone their curious annals save."

Archaea are one of the three major branches of life, along with bacteria and eukarya (which includes plants and animals). At 3.85 billion years ago, archaea were alive, reproducing and evolving. They obtained energy by breaking the chemical bonds within molecules such as CO_2, H_2O, and N_2. Archaea today are found down to 3.5 km below the surface under pressures of over 20,000 kPa and in hot springs and deep-ocean spreading centres with temperatures up to 113°C, but they are killed by oxygen. These organisms may be relatives of the earliest life forms on Earth.

Over 3.5 billion years ago, photosynthetic bacteria were removing some of the abundant carbon dioxide (CO_2) from Earth's atmosphere and combining it with water using the Sun's energy. This process called photosynthesis gives off oxygen (O_2), and thus began the radical transformation of the Earth's atmosphere that ultimately led to its present composition (Table 10.2).

Eon	Era	Period		Millions of years ago	Major appearances
Phanerozoic	Cenozoic	Quaternary		0.2 / 2.6	Humans
		Tertiary		3.5 / 65	Direct human ancestors / Flowering plants in abundance
	Mesozoic	Cretaceous		142	
		Jurassic		206	Birds
		Triassic		253	Mammals and dinosaurs
	Paleozoic	Permian		290	
		Carboniferous	Pennsylvanian	323	Reptiles
			Mississippian	360	
		Devonian		417	Amphibians (vertebrates on land)
		Silurian		443	
		Ordovician		495	Land plants
		Cambrian		543	Fishes
Pre-Cambrian	Proterozoic	Ediacaran		620 / 1,000	Great diversification and abundance of life in the sea / Sexual reproduction
				2,500	
	Archean			3,600 / 4,000	Oldest fossils / Oldest Earth rocks
Hadean				4,570	Origin of Earth

Figure 15.11

Geological timescale based on superposition of sedimentary rock layers and the irreversible succession of fossils. Numerical ages were measured on igneous rock found in association with fossil-bearing sedimentary rock. Note: diagram is not to scale. The Precambrian and Hadean eons have been much reduced to fit in this figure.

Organisms of these early times reproduced by simple division of their cells. Thus, if a **gene** had an advantageous mutation, it was limited to passing it on to a single line of offspring. By 1 billion years ago, sexual reproduction had appeared. This allowed cells to share and mix genetic material and thus speed evolutionary changes by thousands of times.

During Earth's early history, organisms lived primarily below the surface in the oceans and within sediment and rock. As oxygen (O_2) given off during photosynthesis built up to a large volume in the atmosphere, some was altered to ozone (O_3), thus building a shield from the Sun's lethal ultraviolet radiation. With a protective atmospheric shield, more multicellular life could come out into the shallower water, and eventually onto land. Marine rock from 620 million years ago contains the oldest known fossils of multicellular animal life, including nearly all the major body plans (that is, the basic layouts of living organisms including the number of limbs and their symmetry) that exist today.

About 543 million years ago, life on Earth began a 40 million-year-long burst of remarkable evolutionary change (called the Cambrian Explosion). From this time onward, the fossil record improves because many of the new groups of organisms began creating hard parts, such as shells, which preserve well as fossils. The initial development of hard parts has been referred to as "the world's first arms race" wherein organisms covered their bodies with armour, possibly as protection against predators.

Moving on through time (up the sedimentary rock sequence), the Earth has continued to fill with new forms of life (Figure 15.11). For example, the waters became home to fish, while plants moved out of the water and spread across the lands. Later on, vertebrate animals appeared on land followed by amphibians, then reptiles, and finally mammals and birds. The **evolution** and increasing diversity of taxa are continuing, as are extinctions.

Today, life is almost everywhere—in waters ranging from 0°C to above boiling, on land, in the air, in the soil, in ice, around deep-sea volcanic vents, within the pores of rock buried several kilometres deep, and inside other organisms. The overall trend has been an increase in the diversity and abundance of life, but there have been major setbacks and reorganizations. Figure 15.12 plots the number of

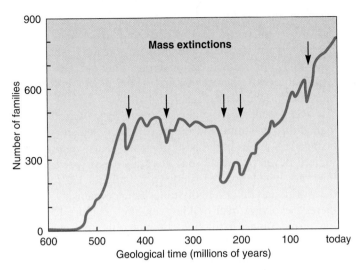

Figure 15.12
Number of families of marine animals with hard skeletons versus geological time. The overall increase in families with time is interrupted by extinction events.

families of marine animals with hard skeletons that have lived during the last 600 million years. Over time, there has been an obvious growth in the number of families; this growth reflects the increase in diversity and abundance of marine life. However, there also have been marked die-offs in which a large number of families became extinct within relatively short time intervals of a few million years. To better understand these dramatic extinction events, it is necessary to look at events on the species level, which is the level most affected by extinctions.

Species and the Fossil Record

The classification of life is a topic hotly debated today. However, the basic terminology laid out by Swedish botanist Linnaeus (Carl von Linne, 1707–1778) provides us with terms still widely used. He organized life into kingdoms and then subdivided successive categories down to species (Figure 15.13). Overviews of life history tend to focus on larger groupings in the hierarchy, such as the families in Figure 15.12. However, it is at the species level where both evolution and extinction occur.

A species is a population of organisms so similar in life habits and functions that they can breed together freely and produce reproductively viable offspring. Members of a species share a common pool of genetic material (**genome**). A species may migrate over a broad geographical area, causing reproductive isolation between local populations in widely separated areas. As genes mutate and are recombined in sexual reproduction, geographically segregated (relict) populations within a species may begin to develop differences in behaviour and anatomy that over time produce enough changes to create new species. This is the process of evolution defined by Wallace and Darwin wherein changes in the genetic pool of a population lead to the origins of new species. A species is the smallest biologically real and distinct unit of individuals that share a common ancestor not shared with other organisms. Each species is unique; each new species is never entirely the same as any previous one.

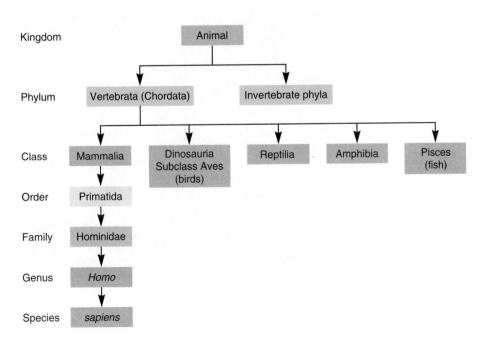

Figure 15.13
A partial hierarchy of life using humans as an example.

Species are subject to many environmental changes. Oceans recede and expose land, climates change from hot to cold and from wet to dry, volcanoes spew out great volumes of magma and gases and then quiet down, and earth movements create uplift and subduction; the physical, chemical, and biological conditions on Earth change both locally and globally. Some species are flexible enough to handle environmental fluctuation, but other species are not and thus become extinct singly, in relay, or in groups. Extinctions of species are an ongoing fact of life on Earth.

Causes of extinction are complex and vary among events, but they combine to create a relatively constant background level of extinction; there are always some species going extinct. The fossil record speaks clearly: each species is nonrecurring; once a species dies out, it never reappears although other taxa may assume very similar body plans.

Over 99.9% of all plant and animal species that have ever lived on Earth are extinct. At present, species diversity on Earth is estimated to range from 40 to 80 million; but consider that these large numbers are less than 0.1% of the species in Earth history. It is increasingly noted that extinctions clear out living space (habitats) thus providing new opportunities for different organisms to evolve new ways of life and to occupy vacated **niches** in the environment, thereby creating more niches. For example, the extinction of most dinosaur species (except birds) 65 million years ago opened up opportunities for ways of life that mammals adopted during the following several million years. The constant elimination of old species and refilling of their vacated spaces in the environment by new species has created an incredible variety of life forms during Earth's history, increasing diversity fourfold since Cambrian time. Major groups of new organisms have usually arisen, not as better competitors that eliminated already living species, but as groups of opportunists that extended into vacant environments and adopted new ways of life.

Mass extinctions are relatively uncommon events; they cause worldwide elimination of numerous species, thus opening up a wealth of niches for new organisms to fill via the evolutionary process. Following a mass extinction, life on Earth takes on a different appearance as the surviving species are joined by numerous new species in the following several million years.

The Tropical Reef Example

Reefs are structures built by organisms such as corals, clams, and others. The reef framework is full of open spaces used by organisms such as red algae, worms, and bryozoa to build their skeletons and shells, and in so doing they add more strength to the reef. The tropical oceans today are host to massive reefs, which have porous, wave-resistant frameworks, creating shelters (new niches) occupied by numerous other species, both within the reefs themselves and in the quiet, protected areas behind the reefs (Figure 15.14).

The fossil record indicates reefs have waxed and waned through time, and the associated organisms have changed. At times in the past, tropical oceans were home to well-developed reefs, but there also have been long intervals when no reef-framework builders existed in the world, and other lengthy times when organisms were merely evolving reef-building abilities (Figure 15.15). Each time a mass extinction eliminated the reef builders of its day, there followed a long interval of time before other creatures were able to fill the environmental void. Each time reefs reappeared in the world, they were built by a different group of organisms.

Figure 15.14
A coral reef in the Red Sea.
Photo: © Pat Abbott.

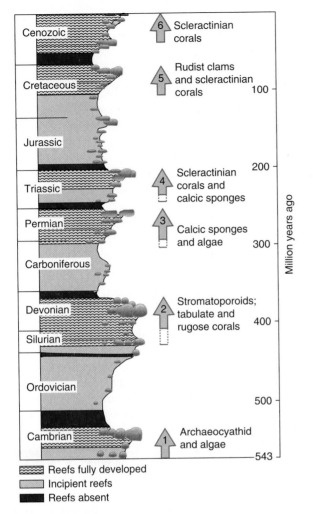

Figure 15.15
Geological column showing the distribution of reef-building organisms and their biozones. Six major successions are shown, terminated by mass extinctions. Species are different in each reef phase.

Background Extinction and Mass Extinctions

Extinction occurs on the species level. When so many individuals of a species die that reproduction fails, then the continuity of their kind is stopped, and extinction occurs. The average "life span" of a species is about four million years. Because there are so many millions of fossil species, plotting all of their extinctions through geological time is difficult. However, at the next hierarchical level—the genus—a major effort was carried out by U.S. paleontologist John Sepkosk, and published in 1986. The times of extinction were plotted for about 25,000 genera of marine invertebrates and protozoa (kingdom Protista). The plot of generic extinctions versus time produces a highly variable, jagged line that obscures trends (Figure 15.16). Note that the level of background extinctions was around 50% during Cambrian time (543 to 495 million years ago) when so many new life forms appeared and extinctions were common. Ignoring the peaks and valleys of the solid line, it can be seen that background extinctions have declined with time to around 5 to 10% in the last 10 million years.

Against this declining rate of background extinction, there are marked spikes on Figure 15.16 that identify mass extinctions; each spike records a significant increase in the number of extinctions of organisms that occurred in a geologically short length of time. The biggest extinction events coincide fairly well with divisions in the 19th-century geological timescale (Figure 15.11), but new perspectives are also needed. A new approach to assessing the frequency of mass extinctions is used by U.S. paleontologist Dave Raup (Figure 15.17). His analysis follows the same logic used in analyzing the size and frequency of floods (Figure 13.23). Numbers of extinctions are plotted

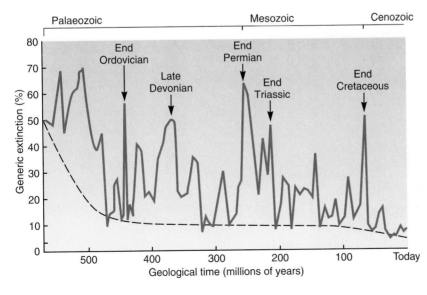

Figure 15.16
Extinction patterns of genera of marine invertebrates and protozoans versus time. The percentage of extinctions was calculated by dividing number of extinctions by number of genera alive at that time. Heavy dashed line represents background extinctions.
Source: © J. J. Sepkoski.

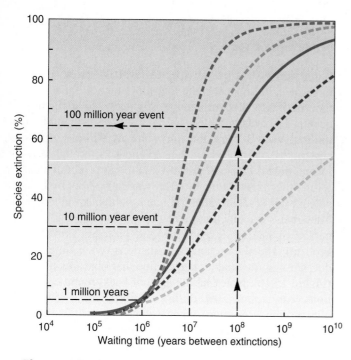

Figure 15.17
Extinction-frequency curves. The purple curve is a best-estimate curve. For example, approximately every 100 million years (10^8 years), up to 65% of species may die out.

against recurrence intervals, producing an extinction-frequency curve. The curve allows estimates of how often a certain size mass extinction might occur.

Possible Causes of Mass Extinctions

There are numerous possible causes of mass extinctions that drive large numbers of species into extinction all around the Earth. They include the long-lasting and far-reaching effects of plate tectonics, voluminous volcanic outpourings, climate changes, asteroid and comet impacts, and biological processes.

THEORY OF PLATE TECTONICS

The rate of seafloor spreading varies, the number and size of continental landmasses differ over time, and the rise and fall of the sea level changes the percentage of land versus sea. Today, the oceans cover about 71% of the Earth's surface, and land comprises 29%. Figure 15.18 shows that the world shoreline lies on top of the gently sloping continents. A sea-level drop could increase the percentage of land on Earth to upwards of 40%, or a sea-level rise could drop the percentage of land to around 17%. Changes of these magnitudes have happened in the geological past, and they have had significant effects on life.

Theory of Seafloor Spreading Rates

The volume of magma rising through spreading centres varies over geological time. During times of more rapid spreading, the volcanic mountain chains at the spreading centres greatly increase in mass and volume with new rock that retains warmth and buoyancy (Figure 15.19). The increased volume of oceanic crust occupies a higher topographic position relative to the stable continents, thus reducing the volume of space available to hold water in the ocean basins. The effect of more rock mass in the ocean basins is similar to you dunking your body in a bathtub full of water. What happens in each case is that displaced water spills over the sides—of the bathtub onto the floor or of the ocean basins onto the continents.

For example, during mid-Cretaceous time, from 110 to 85 million years ago, the tempo of seafloor spreading is thought to have greatly increased. A large volume of new oceanic crust caused the oceans to spill

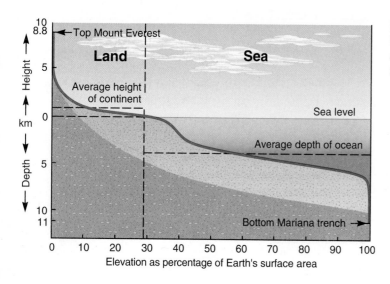

Figure 15.18
Elevations of land and depths to seafloor as percentages of Earth's surface area.
Source: © 1976 John Wiley & Sons.

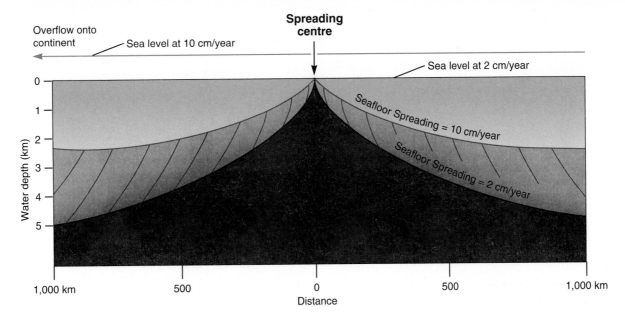

Figure 15.19
Comparative volumes of volcanic mountains at spreading centres. When spreading rates are higher, the greater volume of volcanic rock causes ocean water to spill out of the ocean basins and over the edges of the continents.

over onto the continents and flood the interior of North America (Figure 15.20). At that time, global sea level was over 200 m higher than today, the area of shallow seas was almost doubled, the amount of exposed land was severely reduced, and world climate was warmer due to the abundance of shallow seas. Many of the species that flourished under these conditions were probably severely affected when the oceans pulled back from the continents: the area of shallow seas was sharply reduced, the land area and its interconnections grew, and climates changed.

Theory of Glacial Ice and Sea-Level Changes

The water that falls as snow to build glaciers comes from the oceans via evaporation. The bigger the glaciers, the lower the sea level. Today, about 25 million km^3 of ice ride on the continents, mostly on Antarctica and Greenland. If all of this ice were to melt, world sea level would rise about 70 m.

Just 20,000 years ago, during the most recent expansion of the continental glaciers (Figure 10.33), about three times as much ice (75 million km^3) sat on the continents. Building glaciers this voluminous requires that sea level be drawn down about 140 m from today's levels. The total change in sea level from the glacial peak of 20,000 years ago to a world free of continental glaciers would see a sea-level swing of about 210 m; this would greatly change the proportions of land to sea (Figure 15.18).

The sea-level changes due to the presence or absence of continental glaciers and the variations in seafloor spreading rates operate independently. They can cancel each other out, or they can combine to cause great rises

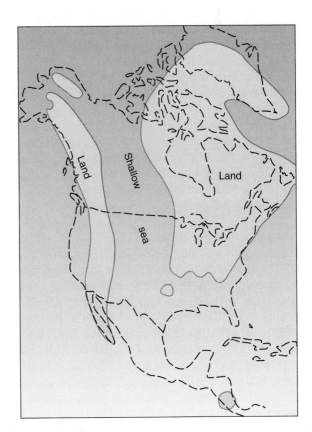

Figure 15.20
The proportions of land and sea in North America 100 million years ago.

and falls of sea level that put major stresses on life. The result of their changes is a world with ever-changing sea levels (Figure 15.21).

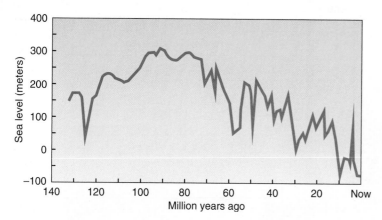

Figure 15.21
Sea-level changes in the last 133 million years.
Source: Based on data from Haq et al., 1987.

Theory of Continent Size

In Late Permian–Early Triassic time (about 260 to 240 million years ago), the continents were combined into the supercontinent Pangaea (Figure 3.18). By 200 million years ago, Pangaea was being dismembered by the seafloor spreading that has produced the numerous continents of today. The breakup of the supercontinent Pangaea greatly lengthened the world's shoreline, reduced the areas of climatically harsh continental interiors, and made other habitat changes in which species either flourished or went extinct (Figure 3.19).

Surface areas being equal, a large, combined landmass will have fewer species than several smaller, isolated landmasses. Today, for example, the isolated landmasses of Australia, New Zealand, Madagascar, and Africa all have very different species from each other and from the rest of the world. If these four landmasses were recombined, there would be numerous extinctions as the different species would compete for the shared food supply and living space.

Theory of Polar Position

The shifting of continents plays a role in the climatic conditions on Earth. It is only when large landmasses have moved near the North or South Poles that enough falling snow accumulated into the massive ice sheets that bury entire continents and plunge the Earth into an Ice Age (Figure 10.33). During an Ice Age, climatic extremes affect the majority of the Earth, with colder and warmer intervals alternating as glacial ice sheets advance and retreat with associated changes in sea level. Major shifts in climatic belts place great stresses on many species.

POSSIBLE VOLCANIC CAUSES

In the past, immense volumes of basaltic lava flowed out and covered millions of square kilometres of the Earth in geologically brief time spans. Magma pours out onto stable tectonic plates as continental flood basalts (see Chapter 7) and onto the ocean floor, forming oceanic plateaus.

For example, the Ontong Java oceanic plateau was created about 120 million years ago when 36 million km^3 of lava poured forth in less than 3 million years to cover an area equivalent to two-thirds of Australia. It is estimated that world sea level rose about 10 m due to this volcanic outpouring alone. The rate of lava emission at Ontong Java was equivalent to the present annual outpourings of magma from *all* the world's spreading centres combined.

Fluctuations in Atmospheric and Oceanic Chemistry

Leading on from the possible volcanic causes of mass extinction, outpourings of flood basalt are generally accompanied by massive volumes of gases. In subsea eruptions, the oceans absorb and dilute some of the gases; however, ocean-water acidity and oxygen concentrations can change. With continental flood basalts, all the gases, including potential greenhouse gases, are pumped into the atmosphere. Some of the warmest climatic intervals in Earth history have accompanied flood basalts. For Ontong Java, average annual temperatures may have increased up to 13°C. Temperature increases this large can create extreme physiological stresses on some species.

CLIMATIC CHANGES AS POSSIBLE CAUSES OF MASS EXTINCTIONS

Climates change for numerous reasons (see Chapters 10 and 11). Each single change triggers a complex network of both negative and positive feedback responses. From the preceding volcanism example, the following sequence of responses could occur: (1) concentrated volcanism emits tremendous volumes of gases, (2) the composition of the atmosphere changes, (3) the altered atmosphere changes the heat balance of the Earth via the greenhouse effect, and (4) the global climate undergoes significant changes. Some of the volcanic gases may dissolve in the ocean and change its composition at the same time that increased climatic warmth raises the temperature of the ocean. The oceanic changes then trigger more atmospheric and climatic changes. Every environmental change has multiple reactions.

The climatic history of the Earth shows drastic changes from cold (Ice Ages) to warm (Torrid Ages). Change can be too rapid for many species to adapt. For example, many forms of life are unable to cope with cooling and desiccation, and eventually face extinction.

THEORY OF OCEANIC COMPOSITION

The world's oceans are chemically connected to their dissolved salts and bottom sediment, the continents, and the atmosphere. Numerous buffer systems using negative feedback work to maintain a dynamic equilibrium composition for the ocean. However, on some occasions, the buffering systems are overcome. The resultant changes in ocean composition can be lethal to some species.

Today, the oceans are circulated by the worldwide movements of water layers of differing densities (Figure 2.29). Near the poles, the cold surface waters of the seas are so dense that they sink and flow through the deep oceans. The deep waters are well oxygenated, and the ocean floors are rich with life.

However, during some of Earth's warmest climatic intervals, the polar waters were too warm to sink. At these times of lessened circulation of water, the decay of organic matter on the ocean floors robbed the bottom waters of their oxygen. The decay process uses oxygen to digest organic matter, and carbon dioxide is released as a by-product. The process is photosynthesis in reverse and is analogous to our human digestive tract; we inhale oxygen to burn (digest) our food and then exhale carbon dioxide as a waste product. During portions of Late Devonian (375 to 360 million years ago), Pennsylvanian/Permian (323 to 253 million years ago), Jurassic (170 to 160 million years ago), and Cretaceous time (124 to 83 million years ago), warm waters at the bottom of the ocean became depleted in oxygen (**anoxic**), causing extinction of **benthic** species. Salinity changes can be lethal also. For example, during intervals of glacier retreat in an Ice Age, the catastrophic emptying of glacial meltwater lakes can quickly cover the surface of the ocean with cold freshwater (low salinity). The cold freshwater is lethal to many sea-surface species used to warmer temperatures and higher salinities. During another event, the northward tectonic movement of Africa closed the Mediterranean Sea from the Atlantic Ocean during parts of Late Miocene time (7 to 5.3 million years ago). Evaporating water from the sealed-off Mediterranean basin increased the water salinity to crisis levels for most aquatic species.

POSSIBLE EXTRATERRESTRIAL CAUSES OF MASS EXTINCTION

Life on Earth is also subjected to bombardment by space debris (Figure 15.22). Large bodies, such as asteroids and

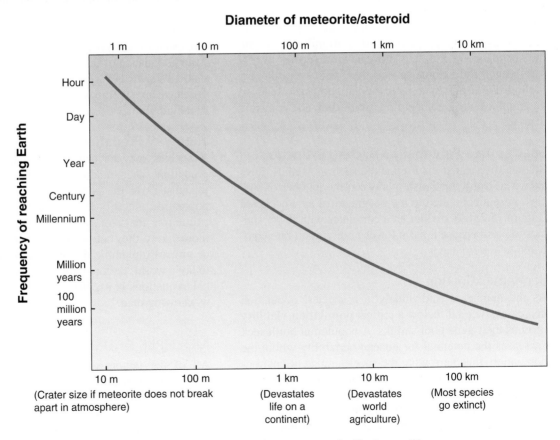

Figure 15.22
Relationships between meteorite/asteroid diameters, crater sizes, and their effects on life.

comets, hit the Earth with tremendous force (see Chapter 16). When an object 10 km in diameter strikes the Earth, it is likely to cause wildfires and/or a tsunami, acid rain, and a huge dust cloud that blocks sunlight and creates weeks or months of dark winter. When the dust settles, voluminous gases may remain aloft, creating a green-house rise in temperature. Events such as these would be traumatic for much of the life on Earth.

Earth is constantly being bombarded by cosmic rays from outer space and by the subatomic debris emitted from the incinerator that is our Sun. The influx of high energy radiation and tiny particles varies as the Sun's intensity changes or when a **supernova** (stellar) explo-sion occurs at astronomically close distances. Earth's magnetic field provides a protective envelope that diverts or entraps most of the incoming subatomic particles, but the strength of the magnetic field varies markedly over time. During intervals of a weakened magnetic field, the amount of radiation received increases significantly. It has been hypothesized that during these times, the cos-mic-ray bombardment causes increases in life-altering genetic mutations. As logical as the cosmic-ray hypoth-esis sounds, however, no correlation to the fossil record has yet been demonstrated.

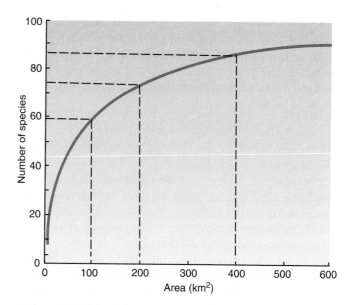

Figure 15.23
A species-area curve showing the numbers of species on islands of increasing size. Note that doubling the area does not double the number of species.
Source: © 1976 John Wiley & Sons.

POSSIBLE BIOLOGICAL CAUSES OF MASS EXTINCTION

The diversity of species on Earth is so great that it cannot yet be defined. Estimates of the number of species alive at the present time range from 40 to 80 million. Despite the abundance of life, it is difficult for a species to per-sist through time. Some species go extinct every day for biological reasons, such as low population size, reduced geographical area, competition, **predation,** and epidemic disease.

Species Area Potentially Affecting Extinction
Studies of isolated environments, such as islands, have shown a strong relationship between the number of spe-cies present compared to the geographical area occupied (Figure 15.23). A smaller area correlates with fewer spe-cies in part because it has a lower immigration rate com-pared to larger islands.

Random Extinction
As the number of individuals in a species' population decreases, they fall below a critical **population viability level** as their gene pool shrinks. A population bottleneck decreases the potential for genetic variability within the population, thus narrowing the species range of environ-mental tolerance. The species then falls below the popula-tion viability level, below which there is no recovery (the species becomes subject to extinction). For example, the African cheetah suffered a severe population bottleneck

approximately 10 000 years ago, and genetic variabil-ity within individuals today is believed to be so narrow that a rapid environmental change would drive them to extinction.

The number of individuals in a species may grow and the species may spread over a wide area. However, there is no abundance or distribution level that can ensure per-manent survival of a species. As changes restrict the geo-graphical area within which a species lives and the number of its individuals decreases, extinction is imminent.

Theory of Predation and Epidemic Disease
A species may be driven into extinction by excessive predation. The predators do not have to do the whole job, just drive the population of a species to below its population viability level, and the species will fall into extinction. Predators may be large carnivores; however, more likely they are small life forms, such as bacteria or viruses (epidemic disease is a form of predation). In today's world, the predator responsible for most biologi-cal extinctions is us, *Homo sapiens,* which means "wise or knowing man."

MULTIPLE CAUSES OF MASS EXTINCTION
All of the factors described and others contribute to extinctions. Any one of these factors operating alone can cause the local stress that drives one or a few species into extinction. This is the process of ongoing disappearances that make up background extinction. However, to wreak

the havoc that ends the existence of numerous species around the world probably requires two or more of the causes described to occur either simultaneously or closely spaced in time and on a global scale. The best way to analyze the combined killing effects is through examination of specific mass extinctions.

Examples of Mass Extinctions

After life made its explosive leap forward beginning about 543 million years ago (Figure 15.12), there were numerous extinction events, each of which decimated many of the species of its time (Figure 15.16). After each great dying, many of the world's environmental niches were vacated, thus clearing the stage for the next set of actors to appear. To illustrate the multiple causes of these great dyings, three examples from different times will be examined: (1) End Permian, (2) End Cretaceous, and (3) Quaternary.

THE "MOTHER OF ALL MASS EXTINCTIONS" (251.4 MILLION YEARS AGO)

In Permian time, the seas were full of animals that lacked mobility; there were reef-building tabulate corals and solitary rugose corals, crinoids on stalks fastened to the seafloor, encrusting bryozoans (colonial coral-like animals), and brachiopods (shelled creatures resembling clams) lying on the seafloor. The marine animals mostly stayed in place, either waiting for prey to pass by or else quietly filtering the water for food. On land, there were amphibians as big as pigs and **therapsids** (mammal-like reptiles), some the size of hippopotamuses.

Although they did not know it, most of these species were doomed, as Earth's largest wave of extinction lay ahead in the closing five million years or less of Permian time. On land, just one of four amphibian orders and only one of 50 reptile genera survived the Permian Period. The die-offs were so drastic that 96% of marine species went extinct along with 75% of terrestrial vertebrate families. These extinctions included taxa already in decline and resulted in a fundamental change in the taxonomic composition of marine life from the "Paleozoic fauna" of crinoids, bryozoans, corals, and brachiopods, to the "modern fauna" we see today comprising bivalves, echinoids, and gastropods. Global changes were so dramatic that they are described in a "horrible luck" hypothesis in which a multitude of problems arose at the same time and combined their effects to trigger the mass extinctions. What were the events that combined to make life so difficult? It was a combination of several changes, each operating on a different timescale.

Formation of the Supercontinent Pangaea

As Paleozoic time was drawing to a close, the continents of the world were being pushed together into one supercontinent stretching from north to south across the face of the Earth (Figure 3.18). The uniting of the continents closed most of the equatorial sea, thus severely reducing the area of shallow tropical oceans and resulting in overcrowding among warm-adapted shallow marine species, possibly causing extinction.

Sea-Level Fall

Seafloor spreading apparently slowed its pace during Permian time. As spreading centres were fed less magma, the volcanic ridge masses shrank in size, thus increasing the capacity of the world ocean basin (Figure 15.19). With a larger ocean basin, seas retreated from the continents; sea level dropped about 200 m; and shorelines moved seaward as much as 1,900 km. After the shoreline retreat, the total area of shallow seas, whether of warm or cool water, was greatly reduced, thus probably pushing more species into extinction.

Climate Changes

The formation of a single supercontinent affected climate. There was less shoreline, which meant that greater percentages of land were located away from the ameliorating effects of the ocean. The continent itself was elevated above the former sea level, causing the interior landmass to suffer climatic extremes. The aridity of the interior indicated by large evaporite deposits led to the spread of deserts with wind-blown sand dunes, likely decreasing optimal areas of habitation for many species.

Ocean Composition Changes

Toward the close of Permian time there was an abrupt warming event, bringing to a close a very long Ice Age. It has been suggested that as cold polar waters disappeared, ocean circulation slowed, and excessive amounts of organic matter were oxidized, probably depleting atmospheric oxygen levels from 30% to less than 15%. Much of the deep ocean became sluggish. Stagnant bottom water became anoxic, thus killing many deep-water organisms. Climatic changes during times of oceanic stratification can cause oceanic overturning and upwelling (see Lake Nyos in Chapter 8), causing shock and death to surface-water organisms.

Siberian Traps Flood Basalt

As more and more species fell into extinction as a result of environmental pressures, a massive volume of flood basalt extruded during the geologically brief interval of a million years in Siberian Russia. Up to 3,000,000 km^3 of basaltic lava flowed out to bury 3,900,000 km^2 of land. With Siberia then in northern latitudes, the lavas likely flowed out on top of permafrost, thus converting frost to water vapour. Direct heating of permafrost would release tremendous quantities of methane that were frozen in hydrates. A huge volume of gases erupted simultaneously, including CO_2 emitted directly into the atmosphere. The abundance of atmospheric methane, carbon dioxide, and water vapour would have warmed climate worldwide by increasing the greenhouse effect, and also caused acid rain.

Duration of the Extinction Events

The end-Permian extinction events were probably very short. Newly determined radiometric ages from Chinese scientist Yu-Gan Jin and colleagues indicate the climactic extinction occurred at 251.4 (+/−0.3) million years ago.

Organic-rich sedimentary rock in China contains a marked drop in the ratio of heavy carbon atoms to light carbon that occurred in less than 165,000 years, and maybe 10,000 years. The change in carbon isotopes tells of a collapse of biological productivity in a geologically short time. Were environmental pressures accelerated by a rapid event such as the impact of a carbon-rich comet? This question is currently under study.

Life at the End of Permian Time

Many changes occurred as the Permian Period was closing: (1) tropical seas were virtually eliminated after a long Ice Age; (2) the extent of shallow marine water was reduced worldwide; (3) only one major landmass existed, which placed species-area pressures on terrestrial life (Figure 15.23); (4) lands were marked by great deserts; (5) deep ocean water probably became anoxic, CO_2-rich, and subject to upwelling; and finally, (6) the climate warmed, perhaps as a result of flood-basalt volcanism and accompanying greenhouse gases.

The oceans were home to abundant corals, brachiopods, bryozoans, fusulinid foraminifera, crinoids, and ammonoids. The lands were populated by diverse, large amphibians and therapsids. All of these successful lineages either were exterminated or their diversity was drastically reduced. The Permian mass extinction left an impoverished global fauna; however, favourable pre-existing dispositions within the remaining species allowed them to evolve into new life forms that spread throughout the world in Mesozoic time. The immobile organisms of the Permian ocean were replaced by increased diversities and abundances of armoured snails, deep-burrowing clams, and free-swimming predators, such as cephalopods and reptiles. The hardy survivors of the Permian extinction were better suited to life in the new conditions and filled more niches in the Mesozoic ocean than had their Paleozoic predecessors. Most surviving terrestrial reptiles may have been more homeothermic and had more efficient respiratory systems. From these survivors arose the dominant terrestrial life of Mesozoic time—the fabled dinosaurs.

CLOSE OF CRETACEOUS (70 MILLION YEARS AGO)

Following the Permian extinctions, the surviving species were few in number, but in the following millions of years, new species originated and the diversity and volume of life increased significantly.

Life in the Mesozoic

In the Triassic oceans, invertebrate life included abundant molluscs—bivalves (clams, oysters), snails, and ammonoids (hard-shelled, coiled squid-like animals)—as well as new types of reef-building corals. By mid-Triassic time, there were numerous vertebrate species, including bony fishes, crocodiles, turtles, frogs, rodent-like mammals, and dinosaurs. By mid-Jurassic time, some small dinosaurs evolved into birds. All of these lines of organisms were hit hard by Triassic, Jurassic, and Early Cretaceous extinctions. Yet, despite these setbacks, the major lines kept evolving new species. Late in Cretaceous time, the North American heartland was covered with herds in a scene reminiscent of Africa today, except that the large animals were dinosaurs rather than mammals. The North American dinosaur herds in Late Cretaceous time included herbivorous ceratopsians (analogous to rhinoceros) and noisy, trumpeting hadrosaurs (analogous to antelope and wildebeest) that were preyed upon by tyrannosaurs (analogous to lions). Overhead were large flying pterosaurs (analogous to vultures and eagles). In the oceans were large marine reptiles including ichthyosaurs (analogous to dolphins) (Figure 15.24).

Plant life had become very different in Late Cretaceous time as the flowering plants (angiosperms) had evolved. Due to hardwood trees, grasses, and other flowering plants reproducing rapidly, they quickly colonized bare ground and competed for light, water, and nutrients. They expanded by competitive displacement of the existing vegetation of ferns and gymnosperms (flowerless seed plants). Gymnosperms' conifer seeds take a long time to develop, so many niches were lost to the flowering plants. Today, the conifers mainly survive only in temperate, cold, or dry areas. At present, there are over 500 species of gymnosperms, comprising less than 5% of the diversity of living land plants, but there are more than 250,000 species of angiosperms.

The K/T (Cretaceous-Tertiary) Extinction (65 Million Years Ago)

By the Late Cretaceous, the world was about to undergo radical changes that would reshape the character of life on Earth again. In the previous several million years of Cretaceous time, many groups of plant and animal life, whether on land or in the seas, were losing species to extinction. It appears that slow-acting changes elevated the level of background extinction. This deteriorating suite of environmental conditions was worsened by

Mesozoic Era

65 million years ago

Cenozoic Era

Ceratopsian—*Triceratops*

Duckbill dinosaur—*Parasaurolophus*

Tyrannosaurus rex

Pterosaur—*Pteranodon*

Ichthyosaur

Time interval when many environmental niches were empty

White rhinoceros

Wildebeest

Lioness

Vulture

Spotted dolphin

Figure 15.24

In Mesozoic time, dinosaurs thrived on land and in the air while large reptiles lived in the sea. Then, 65 million years ago—mass extinction! After a few million years, large animals again filled the same places in the environment, but this time they were mammals and birds.

volcanism and an asteroid impact that ended the Cretaceous Period.

The number of extinctions included over 35% of genera and 65% of species. In the oceans, the reptiles and ammonoids went extinct, and significant die-offs occurred in species of bony fishes, sponges, sea urchins, foraminifera, snails, and clams. On land, many species of mammals and reptiles and all the dinosaurs (except birds) plunged into extinction. Land plant life took a heavy hit as shown in the fossil pollen and spore record. In the North American fossil record, fern spores increase from about 25% to nearly 100% of the fossils, suggesting a massive disturbance (burn-off?) with a slow recovery. The extinction of tiny floating organisms (plankton) in the oceans was overwhelming; the events affected both primary producers (photosynthesizers) and grazers with calcareous and siliceous skeletons. About 60% of these little creatures apparently died out right at the end of Cretaceous time; although individually insignificant, they amounted to an immense biomass (at least 40% of Earth's total biomass). The survivors of the K-T extinction can be loosely grouped as insectivores, and include birds, mammals, and amphibians.

Many studies have concentrated on the dinosaur abundance during the Maastrichtian (71–65 million years ago) in order to answer questions about their demise. Unfortunately the dinosaur fossil localities dating from this time period are limited to North America, immediately imposing a sampling bias. Two theories have come from data collected from these localities—a gradual decline in dinosaurs and dinosaur diversity, or a sudden disappearance—and the debate is ongoing.

What were the changes that led to the massive end-Cretaceous extinction? Probably long-lasting changes in sea level and climate finished with flood-basalt volcanism and an asteroid impact.

Sea-Level Fall

During mid-Cretaceous time, sea level stood high as the ocean flooded low-elevation portions of the continents (Figure 15.20). The final 18 million years of Cretaceous time was marked by a significant marine regression: climates cooled, vegetation suffered, and animal life declined.

Deccan Traps Flood Basalt

The Deccan traps are the remains of a massive outpouring of basaltic lava that erupted from the Réunion hotspot as India drifted over it. The west-central Indian and Pakistani landscape is made of thick piles of hardened lava that give a stair-step feel to the topography (trap is Dutch for "staircase"; deccan is Sanskrit for "southern"). The original area covered by Deccan flood basalt is difficult to estimate due to erosion and subsidence below sea level. Flood basalts present in west-central India cover $500,000 \text{ km}^2$ and the volume of lava extruded probably exceeded 1.5 million km^3. The lavas poured forth probably in less than a million years beginning about 65.5 million years ago. The climatic effects from atmospheric composition changes and temperature increase would probably have been felt worldwide, similar to the Siberian traps flood basalt at the close of Permian time. In the last 250 million years, 10 out of 11 flood basalt events have been the common link in clusters of extinction events.

Chicxulub Impact

On the Yucatan peninsula of Mexico, oil drillers in the 1950s encountered shattered rock about 2 km below the surface. The shattered region apparently resulted from an asteroid impact that occurred 64.98 (+/−0.06) million years ago, some 300,000 years before the extinction event. The feature is called the Chicxulub impact structure, using the Mayan word for "devil's tail" (sanitized translation). The bull's-eye of the structure lies below the surface north of Merida, capital of the state of Yucatan (Figure 16.40).

The chain of effects on life caused by this asteroid impact are still being determined. Despite the popularity of this event with the media and its easy description—big asteroid hits Earth and the dinosaurs all die—there is still controversy about the timing of the impact and whether independent factors were also involved in causing the mass extinction. Impacts are the topic of Chapter 16.

The worst-case scenario for the Cretaceous impact is that an asteroid of 10 km in diameter plunged through the atmosphere faster than 10 km/s. Its impact with Earth set off a fireball of 1,000 km radius; its intense wind and searing heat ignited wildfires that especially affected vegetation in nearby North America. The impact created an earthquake with a magnitude greater than 11 on the Richter Scale and a tsunami with waves up to 2 to 3 km high. The impact blasted a hole in the Earth up to 60 km deep, sending off a horizontally directed base surge of melted and pulverized rock material and a plume of vaporized water and rock that shot up into the stratosphere. Some of the gases and water vapour fell as acid rain, which may have destroyed the planktonic protists and algae in the surface waters of the oceans. The cloud of pulverized dust and ash from the fireball blocked the incoming energy from the Sun for over six months and plunged Earth into a long, dark "winter" in which photosynthesis was virtually stopped. After the dust settled, the greenhouse-effect gases remained aloft, thus replacing the nuclear winter with a few years of elevated temperatures. Life that had survived months of "winter" freezing then had to live through years of "summer" weather. As a result, the die-offs would have been overwhelming. The scenario is easy to visualize—probably too easy—but it remains difficult to rigorously demonstrate the detailed effects of the impact at this time.

When conditions ameliorated, the surviving organisms found themselves in an emptied world where all sorts of opportunities existed to evolve new ways of life, and evolve they did. Flowering plants expanded rapidly, new forms of birds filled the air, more efficient reef-building corals (scleractinians) seized the opportunity, and mammals took over the land vacated by the dinosaurs. Mammals had existed as long as the dinosaurs, but always as little squirrel or shrew-like creatures that occupied different niches to the dominant dinosaurs. But given the opportunity, the mammals grew into large herbivores that were preyed upon by large carnivores (Figure 15.24); they entered the seas (whales and seals) and even flew through the air (bats). The extinction event led to the evolution of new mammalian forms, including us, *Homo sapiens*.

Living Fossils

The Permian/Triassic and Cretaceous/Tertiary mass extinctions were mind-boggling eliminations of species. However, no matter how difficult those times were, there were survivors. In fact, numerous species survived both of these mass extinctions and are familiar life forms to us today; they are living fossils.

We are familiar with the 5% of shark species that are large enough to have surfers racing for the shoreline (Figure 15.25). There is good reason for this: evidence (in the form of denticles) that sharks and other **chondrichthyans** have been swimming the oceans dates from 455 million years ago (Late Ordovician), and they have proved successful predators since then. Some shark species today are facing their biggest threat of extinction, and the cause is humans.

If we were to walk on the continents 275 million years ago, there would be no flowering plants in existence, but we would see plants familiar to us today such as conifers, ferns, and horsetail and scouring rushes (*Equisetum*). Trees living 235 million years ago and still common today include the *Araucaria* (e.g., the Norfolk Island "pine"), gingko (*Gingko biloba*), *Metasequoia*, and cycads (e.g., *Cycas revoluta*) (Figure 15.26). *Cycas revoluta* is commonly sold today as "Sago palm"; it has a trunk that looks like a large pineapple and leaves that are palm-like.

Perhaps the most astounding of all living fossils is the example of a colonial **cyanobacterium** *Eoentophysalis* from cherts of the Belcher Islands of Hudson Bay, Northwest Territories, that existed 2.15 billion years ago (Figure 15.27a). It is living today as the identical-sized and -shaped colonial *Entophysalis* (Figure 15.27b).

QUATERNARY EXTINCTIONS

The fossil record tells of significant die-offs of large-bodied animals in the last 1.5 million years. This has occurred during the advances and retreats of the continental glaciers during our present Ice Age (Figure 10.30). Are the extinctions of large-bodied animals (over 45 kg) just the elevated background extinction associated with severe climatic changes? Or did other causes combine with climate change to push even more than the expected number of species over the brink into extinction? The concentrations of extinctions suggest multiple causes. What is the suspected additional cause that has spelled doom for so many large animals? *Homo sapiens*. The present Ice Age coincides with the growth and worldwide spread of the human population and the increasingly sophisticated abilities of human hunters. Testing of this "**blitzkrieg**" or "overkill" **hypothesis** has raised questions, including

Figure 15.25
Modern-appearing sharks have been swimming in the seas for over 350 million years.
Photo: © Pat Abbott.

Figure 15.26
A cycad (*Cycas revoluta*) similar to
its 230-million-year-old relatives.
Photo by Pat Abbott.

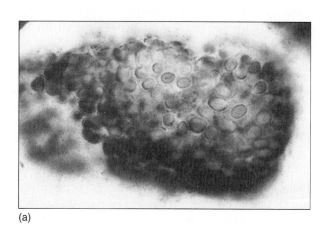

(a)

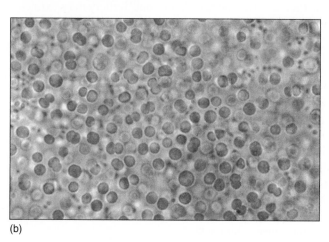

(b)

Figure 15.27
(a) 2.15-billion-year-old colonial cyanobacteria called *Eoentophysalis* from Belcher Islands, Northwest Territories.
From H. J. Hoffmann, in Prothero D. W. 2004 *Bringing Fossils to life: An Introduction to Paleobiology,* McGraw Hill.
(b) The cyanobacteria *Entophysalis* today looks like its 2.15-billion-year-old relative.
From J. William Schopf, in Prothero D. W. 2004 *Bringing Fossils to life: An Introduction to Paleobiology,* McGraw Hill.

the timing of extinctions and human intervention, and the influence of the relatively rapid climate change on the evolutionary trend toward dwarf life forms in the postglacial period.

The fossil record of large-bodied animal extinctions shows variations during the last 100,000 years (Table 15.1). Large animals (excluding bison) were decimated in the Americas and Australia. Comparing the impact of removal of elephants (by poaching) on the vegetation, and subsequent land use by other animals, to past events suggests that extinction of mastodons and mammoths could have caused a chain reaction, indirectly causing the extinction of smaller mammals. African animals fared best; this may be because humans originated and evolved in Africa and the animals there had already coexisted with humans for many thousands of generations. For islands and continents (except Asia) extinctions appear to follow the arrival of human immigrants—wherever humans went, extinctions followed (Figure 15.28 and Table 15.2). Studies by Michael Beck, who analyzed archeological and paleontological data to test the hypothesis of human-induced extinction in

Megatherium
Giant ground sloth

Mammuthus columbi
Imperial mammoth

Arcdotus simus
Short-faced bear

Glyptodont
Armadillo

Smilodon
Sabre-toothed cat

Figure 15.28
The earliest humans migrating to the Americas 13,000 years ago found many species of large land mammals—but the animals went extinct shortly thereafter.

Table 15.1

Extinctions of Large-Bodied Animals

	Genera Extinct in Last 100,000 Years	Genera Still Living	Genera Gone Extinct (%)
Africa	7	42	14
North America	33	12	73
South America	46	12	79
Australia	19	3	86

Source: © Martin and Klein (1989).

Table 15.2

Human Migrations and Large-Animal Extinctions (number of years before present)

	Appearance of Humans	Concentrated Extinctions
Africa	~ 200,000	—
Europe	over 100,000	12,000–10,000
Australia	~ 56,000	~ 46,000
North America	13,000	12,000–10,000
South America	13,000	12,000–8,000
Madagascar	1,500	by 500
New Zealand	1,000	900–600

Source: Beck (1996).

Alaska, Yukon, and the Northwest Territories, predicted that extinctions should occur over time from northwest to southeast. Results indicated that the last recorded dates and localities did not follow this pattern—the opposite was true in most cases. It was concluded that rapid climate change and overkill could not be refuted as possible causes of extinction, but current data did not support the overkill theory.

Were the documented climate changes enough to have caused the extinctions? Several points argue against climate acting alone. (1) Many more large-animal genera went extinct than plant genera. This is contrary to expectations: why should animals die off faster than their food supply? (2) Large mammals should not have been that much affected by climate change because they were **homeotherms**. (3) Retreat of glaciers in the last 11,000 years increased the amount of habitable land,

In Greater Depth

La Brea Tar Pits, Los Angeles, California

In the heart of downtown Los Angeles lies one of the most spectacular fossil localities in the world—the La Brea Tar Pits. In the last 40,000 years, individuals from more than 660 species of organisms became stuck and entombed in the sticky asphalt. The tar pits formed where oil from underground reservoirs seeped upward through fractures in overlying rock to reach the surface. The natural gas and lighter-weight oils evaporated, leaving behind sticky, high-viscosity asphalt in pools.

If an animal steps into the asphalt, it usually cannot get out (Figure 15.29). Why would sinking into a few centimetres of asphalt be enough to trap a large mammal? Visualize this sce-

nario: You step into an asphalt pool and sink above your ankles. When you lift one foot to escape, what does your other foot do? It pushes down into the asphalt. You are trapped. Escape is even more difficult for a four-legged animal such as a mammoth.

What would a trapped animal do? Probably scream as loud as it could. Who would answer the distress call? Mostly carnivores and scavengers. More than 85% of the larger-bodied mammal fossils found at La Brea are carnivores (Table 15.3). This is a curious fact since ecosystems have herbivores in abundance and a lesser number of carnivores that feed on them. Apparently each herbivore trapped in the asphalt attracted hungry carnivores. This interpretation is supported by the bird fossils, which are mostly predators and scavengers such as vultures, condors, and eagles.

So far, 59 species of mammals have been found but much more work remains to be done. In addition to the animals listed in Table 15.3, there are mammal fossils of bears, mammoth, mastodon, deer, tapir, and peccary. The list of larger-bodied mammals is incomplete without mentioning the partial skeleton of a 9,000-year-old human. This is significant. Human beings were living in the area while the extinction of large-bodied mammals was occurring.

Figure 15.29 Statue of an extinct mammoth trapped in an asphalt deposit at the La Brea tar pits in Los Angeles, California.
Photo: © Pat Abbott.

Table 15.3

Percentages of Larger Mammals at La Brea (based on more than 3,400 specimens)

Dire wolf	48
Sabre-toothed cat	30
Coyote	7
Bison	5
Horse	4
Sloth	3
Large cats	2
Camel	1
Antelope	1

which should cause an increase in large-animal species, not a decline. (4) There were no equivalent extinctions of large-bodied animals during earlier phases of our present Ice Age.

Australia

Humans migrated to Australia 56,000 (+/−4,000) years ago. The new arrivals found 24 genera of large-bodied animals and by some accounts, they co-habited for some 15,000 years. By 46,000 years ago, 23 of the genera (marsupials, reptiles, bird) were extinct; only one genus of large kangaroos survived. How did it happen? The extinctions occurred during a short time in all climate zones and habitats. The die-offs occurred tens of thousands of years before the extinctions in the Americas, Madagascar, or New Zealand, suggesting that the Australian extinctions were a regional problem; they were not part of a global event. The most likely cause for the extinctions was humans overhunting naive, large-bodied herbivores (plant eaters), which in turn helped cause the carnivores (meat eaters), who preyed on the herbivores, to die out for lack of food.

In Greater Depth

The Rewilding of North America

North America lost many of its large-bodied vertebrate species around 13,000 years ago. An innovative concept has been put forth by Josh Donlan and 11 co-authors in *Science* in 2005—the rewilding of North America. Their plan calls for restoring large populations of vertebrates living wild in North America by introducing species closely related to extinct North American vertebrates. Some areas could return to conditions similar to those found by the humans who migrated here 13,000 years ago and then quickly spread through the Americas. Some species could run wild, whereas others would need to be confined in large fenced areas such as exist in Texas today.

Here are a few examples of species suggested for the rewilding:

1. The 50-kg Bolson tortoise (*Gopherus flavomarginatus*) survives in a small area of Mexico but is critically endangered. It could be reintroduced to Big Bend National Park and the American desert.
2. Horses and camels originated in North America. They could be returned to their evolutionary homeland using similar species. Good candidates for horses are the critically endangered Asian asses (*Equus hemionus*) and Przewalski's horse (*Equus przewalskii*). For camels, there are the critically endangered Bactrian camels (*Camelus bactrianus*), now found wild only in the Gobi Desert. They could substitute for the extinct North American *Camelops*.
3. Five species of elephant relatives (now extinct mammoths, mastodons, and gomphotheres) lived in North America. They could be replaced by Asian and African elephants.
4. Some top carnivores would need to be controlled in fenced preserves. The now-extinct American cheetah (*Acinonyx trumani*) could be replaced by the endangered African cheetah (*Acinonyx jubatus*). It is thought that the still-existing pronghorn antelope (*Antilocapra americana*) gained its astonishing speed by having to share the land with the American cheetah. The extinct American lion (*Panthera leo atrox*) could be replaced by its smaller relative, the African lion (*Panthera leo*).

The rewilding concept generates lots of thoughts. Proponents say (1) Similar projects are being done in North America by expanding the ranges of bison and wolves. (2) It would undo some of the harm done by humans over the millennia. (3) It would save some of today's species from extinction. (4) It would enhance biodiversity and evolutionary potential. (5) Ecotourism would bring income to the Great Plains and desert areas.

Opponents say (1) The introduced animals will not be genetically identical to the extinct species. (2) Habitats have changed over the millennia. (3) There is the possibility of disease transmission. (4) Every major action brings unexpected consequences.

Madagascar and New Zealand

Humans have been documented to be the exterminating agent in extinctions on Madagascar, Mauritius, New Zealand, Hawaii, and Chatham Island. The first humans to reach Madagascar and New Zealand found that the largest animals living there were flightless birds (Figure 15.30). On Madagascar, the largest elephant bird species stood 3.4 m tall and weighed up to 500 kg. On New Zealand, the largest moa species reached 4 m tall but was not as heavy. Humans killed the big birds and stole their eggs, driving them into extinction. Relatives of these extinct birds include the ostrich (over 2 m tall and 140 kg) of Africa, the rhea of South America, and the emu of Australia. The appearance of humans using spears, fire, and hunting dogs was overwhelming to large animals unprepared for them. Humans did not have to do all the slaughter themselves. Destroying their habitat and driving their numbers below a critical threshold sealed the animals' doom.

It appears that the heavy effects of humans on the environment are *not* something that arrived with the Industrial Revolution; rather, they seem to have accompanied every human advance from toolmaking, to control of fire, to agriculture, to taming of companion animals. The rate of human-induced or -related extinction has increased during the last 12,000 years. The role of life history, biology and physiology of the organisms under changing environmental conditions (including the influence of humans) should not be ignored. Furthermore, it can be

Figure 15.30
The first humans to reach Madagascar and New Zealand found that the largest animals living there were flightless birds. The humans drove the birds into extinction.
Drawing by Jacobe Washburn.

argued that extinction events tend to target large species, leaving smaller-body-mass taxa unaffected or in marginal decline. The past two centuries have seen even faster rates of extinction (for example, in bird and frog populations) that, if continued for another two centuries, could equal the greatest mass extinctions of the geological past.

Living Fossils   **457**

Summary

- As part of the evolution of life on Earth, different species have inhabited the planet from as early as 3.85 billion years ago. Although limited in sampling and biased toward life forms with hard parts, the fossil record reveals the increasing complexity of life with time.
- Over 99.9% of all plant and animal species that have ever lived are now extinct. Superimposed on this background trend, mass extinctions are rare, global events wherein large percentages of Earth's species die off over a relatively short period of time.
- Causes of mass extinctions include variations in land-to-sea percentages, climate change, asteroid and comet impacts, and biological processes.
    - The horizontal and vertical movements of the Earth's surface due to plate tectonics and glaciations, respectively, change the size and distribution of the continents, resulting in major stresses on life.
    - Volcanic causes of extinctions are mostly related to eruptions of flood basalts. Gas emitted during these voluminous outpourings can create a greenhouse effect and change the chemistry of the atmosphere and oceans.
    - Impacts of large asteroids and comets can cause earthquakes and tsunami, and disturb climate.
    - Biological causes, including predation and diseases, are also significant.
- In several cases, multiple causes working in combination have culminated in mass extinction.

Terms to Remember

anoxic   447
archaea   439
benthic   447
blitzkrieg hypothesis   453
chondrichthyan   453
cyanobacterium   453
evolution   440

gene   440
genome   441
homeotherm   455
niche   442
paleontologist   438
population viability level   448
predation   448

principle of faunal succession   439
reef   442
species   436
strata   439
supernova   448
therapsid   449

Questions for Review

1. Give examples of species that have become extinct. What percentage of species in Earth's history has become extinct?
2. Explain the law of superposition and the principle of faunal succession.
3. What is the oldest fossil found on Earth? How old is it?
4. Explain the concept of species.
5. Sketch an extinction-frequency curve. How is it similar to a flood-frequency curve?
6. Why does sea level change during intervals of rapid seafloor spreading?
7. How much can sea level rise and fall due to seafloor spreading? due to continental glaciation? Are these numbers additive or subtractive?
8. Discuss the species-area effect. Apply it to a discussion of species diversity on Pangaea.
9. Explain the effects on world climate of (a) intervals of rapid seafloor spreading, (b) continental glaciation, (c) continents united into a single landmass, and (d) a flood-basalt episode.
10. In what ways could a massive outpouring of flood basalt affect the existence of species on Earth?
11. In what ways can ocean composition change to affect the existence of species on Earth?

Questions for Further Thought

1. How does the principle of faunal succession provide support for the theory of evolution?
2. How does a mass extinction set the stage for increased diversity of life?
3. What types of organisms are likely to increase their population greatly during times of rapid seafloor spreading? What types are likely to suffer the most?
4. Are we alive in the midst of a mass extinction event? In what ways are humans playing a role in mass extinction?
5. Why was Asia an exception in the study of human intervention in Quaternary extinctions?
6. What are the pros and cons of the plan for the rewilding of North America?

CHAPTER 16

Hazards from Space

The universe as Hardy understood it was governed, not by a benevolent god, but by mindless and indifferent chance. All living things were subject to the same injustices, and man and nature could therefore reveal the same philosophic themes, could stand as metaphors for each other. There was one natural world, and man was simply one of the unfortunate creatures in it.

—Samuel Hynes, 1967, Introduction to Thomas Hardy, 1872,
Under the Greenwood Tree

Outline

Imagine the effects of a large asteroid slamming into Earth at high velocity.
Photo: © NASA

Space Weather Hazards

Illuminated by the Sun, planet Earth moves rapidly through space. From its position in the universe, however, the third rock from the Sun is vulnerable to several hazards. The Sun occasionally showers Earth's magnetosphere with charged particles that can trigger malfunctions in technological systems. On rare occasions, Earth crosses path with asteroids and comets with devastating consequences.

SOLAR ACTIVITY

The Sun sends a stream of subatomic particles called the **solar wind** in all directions. Two mechanisms are responsible for strong gusts of solar wind: coronal holes and coronal mass ejections. In both cases, the hot, turbulent upper fringes of the Sun's atmosphere are released in space, gravity not being strong enough to hold them. Coronal holes are localized phenomena producing high-speed streams of **plasma**. Coronal mass ejections are star-scale events sending out clouds of plasma and are often accompanied by bursts of radiation released in the vicinity of sunspots (Figure 16.1). The number of sunspots follows an approximately 11-year cycle. The previous maximum occurred in 2001 and the next is anticipated for 2012.

By analogy with meteorological effects, the changing environmental conditions in space due to the varying solar activity are referred to as space weather. Several satellites and a network of ground stations monitor solar activity, and the information is used to compute space weather forecasts. In Canada, space weather forecasts are produced by the Canadian Space Weather Forecast Centre (CSWFC) operated by Natural Resources

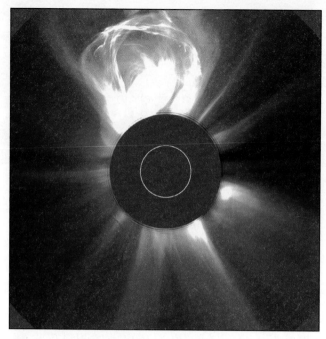

Figure 16.1

The coronal mass ejection of 27 February 2000 captured by the SOlar and Heliospheric Observatory (SOHO) satellite in orbit around the Sun. Direct light from the Sun is blocked in this picture with the Sun's relative position and size indicated by a white circle.

Photo: Courtesy of SOHO/consortium. SOHO is a project of international cooperation between ESA and NASA.

Canada in Ottawa. Integrating data from a dozen stations scattered across Canada, the CSWFC produces long-term and short-term forecasts of geomagnetic activity expected in the polar cap, auroral, and sub-auroral zones (Figure 16.2).

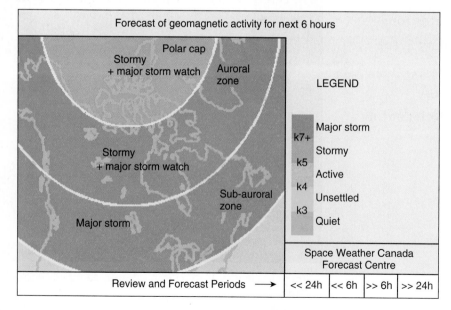

Figure 16.2

Forecast of geomagnetic activity for a "stormy" day.

Source: Reproduced with the permission of Natural Resources Canada 2008, courtesy of the Canadian Hazards Information Service. http://www.spaceweather.gc.ca/forecastmap_e.php.

MAGNETIC STORMS

The physicists of the 19th century unravelled in their laboratories the interrelation between **magnetism** and electricity. They found that magnetic field variations induce electrical currents in a medium. Induced currents then generate their own magnetic field. These laws describe the phenomenon of electromagnetic induction.

The laws of electromagnetism apply at planetary scale. The solar wind takes two to five days to reach Earth. As part of Earth's response to solar wind disturbances, electric currents are produced in the ionosphere, some 100 km above Earth's surface. These fluctuating ionospheric currents might cause rapid geomagnetic field variations. If so, Earth experiences a magnetic storm, which typically lasts 24 to 48 hours. During that time, electrical currents, referred to as **telluric currents**, are induced at the surface and in the subsurface of Earth. They are also generated along conductive networks like power transmission lines, telephone lines, and pipelines, which act like giant antennas. Magnetic storms are most frequent near the peak of the sunspot cycle and during its declining phase (Figure 16.3).

EFFECTS ON TECHNOLOGICAL SYSTEMS

The effects of space weather on technological systems can be grouped into three broad categories: (1) failures directly linked to bombardment by charged particles, (2) problems associated with disturbances in the ionosphere, and (3) electromagnetic induction effects (Figure 16.7).

The high-energy electrons and protons of the solar wind travel in interstellar space at a velocity of approximately 500 m/s. The first targets they might hit as they get closer to Earth are satellites in orbit. The direct impact might cause physical damage to onboard circuitry, or charges might accumulate until a sudden discharge bakes electronic components. Solar wind particles can inflict the

same type of damage at lower altitude or on the ground, although this is much rarer as the atmosphere provides shielding. In August 1989, the Toronto Stock Exchange halted trading for three hours when particles disrupted the charge on a few microchips, causing the highly improbable failure of three disc drives in succession and the sophisticated financial computer system to crash.

Radio signals in the 3-30 megahertz frequency band can be sent around the curve of Earth because of reflections from the ionosphere. During magnetic storms, the ionosphere becomes disturbed and can absorb signals instead of reflecting them, resulting in loss of communications. However, the Global Positioning System (GPS) uses much higher frequency radio signals from satellites that pass through the ionosphere. Nevertheless, during ionospheric disturbances, delays in signal propagation can cause errors in GPS positioning.

The telegraph was the first technological system involving long conductors deployed on Earth's surface, and it is no surprise that the link between geomagnetic activity and technical problems was first noticed by telegraph operators. They observed that disturbances were often accompanied by fluctuations of compass needles and aurora sightings. Magnetic storms also affect the telephone network, including submarine cables. Telluric currents induced by geomagnetic activity are the culprit as they interfere with the normal flow of electrical current in these systems. During the magnetic storm of 10 February 1958, transatlantic phone communication proceeded as alternately loud squawks and faint whispers as the telluric currents acted with or against the cable supply voltage.

Steel pipelines are another example of a large conductive network. It is common practice to impress onto them a small, constant negative voltage as a mean of preventing corrosion. During magnetic storms, telluric currents cause this system to go out of range, leaving the

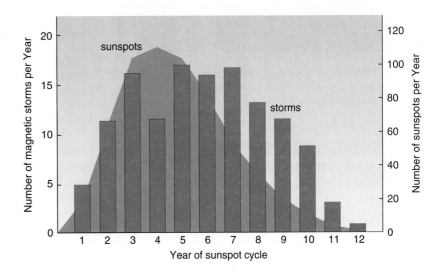

Figure 16.3
Number of magnetic storms (red) and sunspots (green) in each year of the solar cycle (1868–1996).
Source: Natural Resources Canada.

In Greater Depth

Earth's Magnetic Field

Anyone who has ever held a compass and watched the free-turning needle point toward the north has experienced the magnetic field that surrounds Earth. The Chinese invented and were the first to use magnetic compasses, and the compass was known in Europe as early as 1190. In 1269, Peter Peregrinus of Maricourt described experiments on a sphere of lodestone (magnetite, a magnetic iron oxide mineral) and also gave instructions on building a compass. It was 14th-century European travellers to Asia, however, who are mostly responsible for bringing and disseminating the knowledge of the Chinese about the compass in Europe, where it was developed into the navigational tool that helped late–15th century explorers make their voyages of discovery.

Earth's magnetic field defines a large region of space, the magnetosphere, where it offers protection from the solar wind by deflecting particles (Figure 16.4). The magnetosphere is an asymmetric shield, with the magnetic field compressed on the dayside and drawn out into a long tail on the night side. At closer distance, the magnetic field operates as if a gigantic bar magnet is located in the core of Earth (Figure 16.5). The magnetic pole and geographic North Pole do not coincide, but the magnetic pole axis has apparently always been near the rotational pole axis. At the beginning of the 20th century, there was a 20° difference between the north poles. At the present time, the south magnetic pole is 24° from the geographic pole. Notice in Figure 16.5 that the inclination of the magnetic lines of force with respect to Earth's surface varies with latitude. At the magnetic equator, the magnetic lines of force are parallel to Earth's surface (inclination of 0°). At high latitudes, the angle of inclination continuously increases until it is perpendicular to the surface at both the north and south magnetic poles (inclinations of 90°). Between

55° and 70° latitude, the magnetic lines of force guide some solar wind particles toward the upper atmosphere where they excite atoms which, in turn, release energy by emitting light. This phenomenon gives rise to aurorae.

In reality, the interior of Earth is much too hot for a bar magnet to exist. Magnetism in rock is destroyed by temperatures above 550°C, and temperatures in Earth's core are estimated to reach 5,800°C. The origin of Earth's magnetic field involves movements of the iron-rich fluid in the outer core, which generates electric currents that in turn create the magnetic field. The flow of fluid iron in the outer core has regions of turbulence including motions as complex as whirlpools. Fluid iron is an excellent conductor of electricity. The molten iron flowing around the solid inner core is a self-perpetuating dynamo mainly deriving its energy from the convection of heat released by the crystallization of minerals at the boundary of the inner and outer cores.

Figure 16.4 Artist's rendition of Earth's magnetosphere deflecting the solar wind. The boxed area is shown in more detail in Figure 16.5.
Source: Heliophysics/NASA.

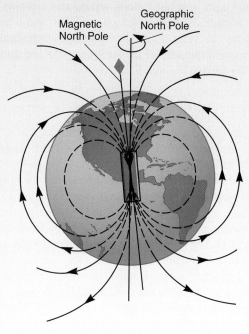

Figure 16.5 Schematic diagram of Earth's magnetic field. The bar magnet pictured does not exist, but it would create the same magnetic field achieved by the electrical currents in Earth's liquid, iron-rich outer core. Notice that (1) the magnetic pole and the rotational pole do not coincide, (2) the magnetic lines of force are parallel to Earth's surface at the magnetic equator and perpendicular at the magnetic poles, and (3) the lines of force go into Earth at the North Pole and out at the South Pole.
Source: © 1976 John Wiley & Sons.

pipeline temporarily unprotected. The cumulative effect of many storms over years might eventually comprise the integrity of the pipeline.

THE 1989 HYDRO-QUEBEC POWER BLACKOUT

The six million residents of Quebec spent most of the day on 13 March 1989 without electrical power and without much explanation as to the origin of the failure. The next

morning, the headline of the Montreal daily *The Gazette* read, "Hydro blames Sun for power failure" (Figure 16.8).

The chain of events leading to the blackout had started four days earlier with a powerful coronal mass ejection. When the ejected particles reached Earth's magnetosphere, they triggered one of the worst magnetic storms of the 20th century. Telluric currents of considerable intensity were induced on the 1,000 km–long power transmission lines linking southern Quebec to the hydroelectric dams of the James Bay area. All transmission

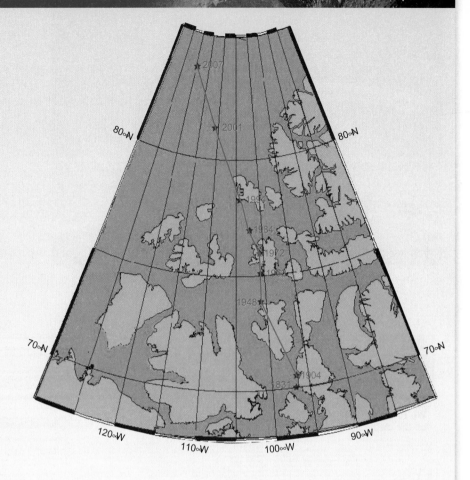

Figure 16.6 Path of the north magnetic pole since its discovery in 1831 to the last observed position in 2007.

Source: Reproduced with the permission of Natural Resources Canada 2008, courtesy of the Geological Survey of Canada. http://gsc.nrcan.gc.ca/geomag/nmp/long_mvt_nmp_e.php.

A closer look at Earth's magnetic field yields several problems awaiting resolution. The simplified magnetic field portrayed in Figure 16.5 does not show the complexities that occur over years and centuries as the magnetic field's strength waxes and wanes. More than 170 years of intensity measurements document variations in the strength and stability of the magnetic field. At present, the field strength is 10% weaker than in the year 1845, but it is still about twice as strong as the long-term average.

The magnetic north pole was first discovered in 1831 on the west coast of the Boothia Peninsula of what is now Nunavut and has moved 1,600 km across the Canadian Arctic since then (Figure 16.6). In recent decades, the magnetic pole has moved northwest at rates of 10 to 50 km per year and will reach Siberia in approximately 50 years if it continues at the same speed and direction.

Every several thousand to tens of millions of years, a highly dramatic change occurs in the magnetic field: the magnetic polarity reverses. In a reversal, the orientation of the magnetic field flip-flops from a north (normal) polarity to a south (reverse) polarity or vice versa. It has been 780,000 years since the last long-term reversal. Models run on supercomputers indicate that reversals take a few thousand years to complete. During a reversal, the magnetic lines of force become twisted and tangled but the magnetic field does not entirely disappear. Its strength is reduced to about 10% of normal.

The change in orientation of the magnetic field leaves its imprint in rock, where geologists (paleomagnetists) can read it. The paleomagnetic history contained in the rock has provided the most important evidence of seafloor spreading; it also has allowed charting of the paths of continents as they have moved through different latitudes. In addition, the record of magnetic reversals provides the data for a magnetic timescale, a third geological timescale. (The first timescale is based on the irreversible sequence of occurrence of fossils in sedimentary rock, and the second timescale is founded on the decay of radioactive elements.)

lines to Montreal became unstable, control systems failed and, in a chain reaction, the entire Hydro-Quebec grid collapsed.

This is how the engineers at the control centre described the event:

> Telluric currents induced by the storm created harmonic voltages and currents of considerable intensity on the La Grande network. Voltage asymmetry on the 735-kV network reached 15%. Within less than a minute, the seven La Grande network static var [Volt-Amperes Reactive] compensators on line tripped one after the other . . . With the loss of the last static var compensator, voltage dropped so drastically on the La Grande network . . . . that all five lines to Montréal tripped through loss of synchronism . . . , and the entire network separated. The loss of 9,450 MW of generation provoked a very rapid drop in frequency at load-centre substations. Automatic underfrequency load-shedding controls functioned properly, but they are not designed for recovery from a generation loss equivalent to

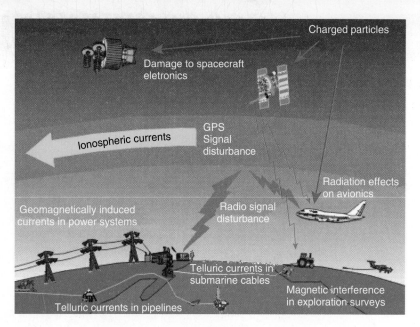

Charged particles

Damage to spacecraft eletronics

GPS Signal disturbance

Ionospheric currents

Radiation effects on avionics

Geomagnetically induced currents in power systems

Radio signal disturbance

Telluric currents in submarine cables

Magnetic interference in exploration surveys

Telluric currents in pipelines

Figure 16.7
Effects of space weather on technological systems.

Source: Reproduced with the permission of Natural Resources Canada 2008, courtesy of the Canadian Hazards Information Service. http://www.spaceweather.gc.ca/effects_e.php.

Figure 16.8
Cover page of the Montreal daily *The Gazette* on 14 March 1989.

Source: *The Gazette* (Montreal).

Hydro will be kept on short leash: Bourassa

Hydro blames sun for power failure

It says solar storm overloaded system

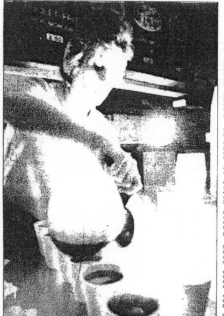

about half system load. The rest of the grid collapsed piece by piece in 25 seconds.

Through the technical jargon, we can feel their anxiety as they were helplessly losing control of a very complex system.

Significant economic loss resulted from the nine-hour blackout that nevertheless served to increase the utility companies' awareness of geomagnetic hazards. It is now common practice to reduce the power on transmission lines when a magnetic storm warning is in effect.

Impact Scars

Could a comet or asteroid impact destroy the human race? The statistics in Table 16.4 suggest that it is possible.

Impact scars are often called **astroblemes**, or, literally, star wounds (the Greek word *astro* means "celestial body" and *blema* means "wound" from a thrown object). A good place to see impact scars made by collisions with space debris is the surface of the Moon (Figure 16.9). In its first few hundred million years of existence, the Moon was a violent place as millions of objects slammed into it. The intense bombardment apparently occurred as a sweeping up of debris left over from the formation of the planets. The Moon's surface still displays tens of millions of ancient impact craters, some with diameters of hundreds of kilometres (Figure 16.9). Flood basalts poured forth on the Moon from about 3.8 to 3.2 billion years ago. They created the dark-coloured **maria** (*mare* is Latin for "sea") so prominent on the Moon's surface today. The maria have relatively few impact scars on them, thus providing evidence that the period of intense bombardment was over before 3.8 billion years ago.

For over 3 billion years, the Moon has been essentially "dead"; it is an orbiting museum showing only the scars of its ancient past. The Moon has no plate tectonics, no water or significant agents of erosion, and no life. About the only event that disturbs the cemetery calm of the Moon is the occasional impact of an asteroid or comet.

Why are impact craters so common on the Moon but so rare on Earth? The Moon is geologically dead, so impact scars remain. But Earth is dynamic: it destroys most of the record of its past. Plate-tectonic movements consume impact scars during subduction and crumple them during continent collisions. The agents of erosion work to erase all impact craters on Earth. Nevertheless, some impact scars have avoided destruction, especially the geologically younger ones. Figure 16.10 shows the Manicouagan crater of northern Quebec. The site was confirmed as an impact crater in 1963 when **shock minerals** were discovered in its vicinity. The water reservoir of the Daniel-Johnson dam (Figure 5.28) has revealed its structure spectacularly.

Figure 16.9
The Moon's surface is ancient and pockmarked by numerous impact craters. Notice the large Orientale multi-ring basin. Its outer ring is 1,300 km across; on Earth, it could stretch across the Prairies, from Winnipeg to the Rockies.
Photo: © NASA.

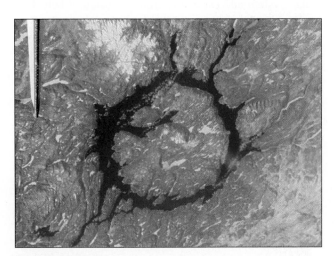

Figure 16.10
The Manicouagan impact crater formed about 214 million years ago in Late Triassic time, in northern Quebec. It is 75 km across but probably exceeded 100 km before glacial erosion stripped away its upper levels.
Photo: © NASA.

Sources of Extraterrestrial Debris

Space debris that collides with Earth comes primarily from fragmented asteroids and secondarily from comets. The pieces of asteroids and comets that orbit the Sun are called **meteoroids**. When meteoroids blaze through the Earth's atmosphere as a streak of light or **shooting star**, they are referred to as **meteors**. The objects that actually hit Earth's surface are called meteorites. The main types of meteorites are either stony or iron-rich (Figure 2.10). Although most space objects that reach Earth's atmosphere are stony meteorites, they are not very abundant on the ground. Stony meteorites are less commonly collected because (1) they break up more readily while passing through Earth's atmosphere, (2) those that reach the ground are weathered and destroyed more rapidly, and (3) they are not as easily recognized as iron-rich meteorites. Thus, most of the collected meteorites are iron-rich meteorites.

ASTEROIDS

The Solar System has eight planets in orbit around the Sun. The four inner planets are small, close together, near the Sun, and rocky. The four outer planets are larger, spaced far apart, lie at great distances from the Sun, and are composed mainly of hydrogen and helium gas surrounding rocky cores; they commonly are orbited by icy moons and rings of icy debris with compositions of water (H_2O), ammonia (NH_3), carbon dioxide (CO_2), and methane (CH_4). Between the inner and outer planets lie the asteroids, a swarm of small (under 1,000 km diameter) rocky, metallic, and icy masses.

Meteorites appear to come from the inner part of the Solar System and especially from the asteroid belt (Figure 16.11). Asteroids are small bodies orbiting the Sun. The three largest asteroids make up about half the combined total mass of all asteroids; they are Ceres, Pallas, and Vesta, with respective diameters of 933, 523, and 501 km. There are more than 200 asteroids with diameters greater than 100 km, about 1,000 with diameters greater than 30 km, and another million with diameters over 1 km. If all the asteroids were brought together they would make a planet about 1,500 km in diameter; this body would have less than half the diameter of our Moon.

The asteroids lie mostly between Mars and Jupiter in a zone where an additional planet might have been expected to form. Many asteroids are similar to the ingredients from which the planets were assembled via low-velocity collisions. However, the asteroids were apparently too strongly influenced by the gravitational pull of Jupiter and thus have been unable to combine, or recombine, to form a planet. The gravitational acceleration caused by the massive planet Jupiter creates asteroid velocities that are too fast and individual collisions that are too energetic to allow the asteroids to collide, unite, and stick together to form a planet.

Notice that the asteroids are concentrated in belts and that there are gaps between the belts (Figure 16.11). The gaps occur at distances related to the orbit time of Jupiter. The asteroids rarely collide, but when they do, their collisions may be spectacular impacts at 16,000 km/h. The force of these smash-ups may bump an asteroid into one of the gaps in the asteroid belt. An asteroid nudged into a gap experiences an extra gravitational acceleration from Jupiter that makes its orbital path more eccentric, and thus, it becomes more likely to collide with a planet.

A recent photo of the asteroid Ida shows it has impact craters and its own moon, named Dactyl (Figure 16.12). When Ida and Dactyl collide with a planet, craters will form simultaneously in two different areas. This observation may explain some of the double-impact sites found on Earth (Figure 16.13).

Recent radar data show that some asteroids are not solitary, solid masses but rather are made of two or more similar-size bodies bound together by gravitational attraction. Calculations indicate that the amount of energy needed to break up an asteroid is much less than the amount of energy required to scatter all its fragments. Thus, an asteroid may be broken into pieces during a collision, and then the pieces may be held together by gravity, creating a loose collection of rocky debris—a rubble pile.

The realization that collisions have made some asteroids into rubble piles raises interesting questions. Did some of the impact craters on Earth form within hours of

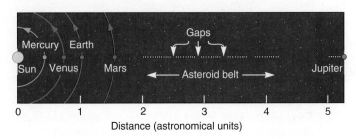

Figure 16.11
The Solar System from the Sun to Jupiter. The asteroid belt is composed of millions of rocky and metallic objects that did not combine to form a planet. One astronomical unit equals 150 million km, the distance between the Sun and Earth.

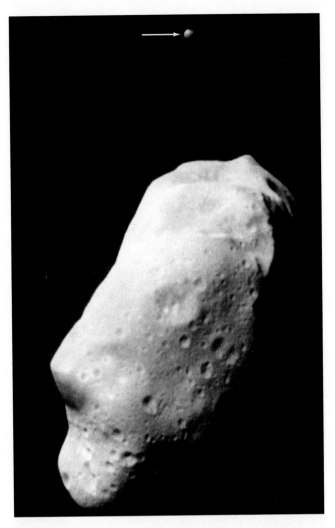

Figure 16.12
The asteroid Ida is 56 km long and pockmarked with impact craters. Travelling with Ida is its near-spherical moon Dactyl with dimensions of 1.2 × 1.4 × 1.6 km.
Photo: © NASA.

Figure 16.13
Space shuttle view of the Clearwater Lakes double impact sites, northern Quebec. About 290 million years ago, a two-part asteroid hit the ground. The western crater is 32 km across and has a central uplift. The eastern crater is 22 km across; its central uplift is below water level.
Photo: © NASA.

each other when a multi-chunk asteroid hit the surface? Removing the effects of 214 million years of plate tectonics places three impact sites along a 4,462 km–long line parallel to the ancient 22.8°N latitude. Saint Martin in Manitoba (40 km diameter), lines up with Manicouagan in Quebec (100 km diameter), and both line up with Rochechouart in France (25 km diameter). If these three impacts occurred hours apart, then life on Earth must have suffered a terrible blow.

Beside the objects orbiting the Sun in the asteroid belt, there are three groups of asteroids whose orbits intercept the orbits of Earth or Mars (Figure 16.14). These near-Earth asteroids are sources for large asteroids and meteorites that occasionally slam into Earth's surface. They include the Apollo, Aten, and Amor asteroid groups. There are more than 1,000 mountain-size Apollo

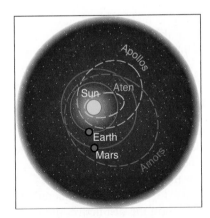

Figure 16.14
Earth's orbit around the Sun is intersected by the Apollo and Aten asteroids. The Amor asteroids cross the orbit of Mars and pass near Earth.

asteroids and a more modest number of Aten asteroids that could hit Earth. The Amors pass near Earth but cross the orbit of Mars. An impact with the red planet could send debris toward Earth. With so many asteroids whizzing about, we are lucky that space has such an immense volume and that Earth is such a small target.

COMETS

Comets are commonly divided into short- and long-period classes. A short-period comet makes a complete orbit in less than 200 years. There are at least 800 of these short-period comets. Some of them are found in the **Kuiper belt**, a flattened disk of comets with orbits ranging from near Neptune out to about 50 astronomical units (an astronomical unit is 150 million km, i.e., the distance between Earth and Sun). The Kuiper-belt comets probably are debris left over from the formation of the outer icy planets. They are the icy bodies that never collided and accreted onto a larger planet, analogous to the asteroid belt of rocky bodies that never accreted onto the inner rocky planets. There may be a billion Kuiper-belt comets greater than 5 km in diameter.

Most of the short-period comets were captured by the gravitational pulls within the Solar System. These comets have had their orbits changed and it is only a matter of time until they meet their fate by (1) erosional destruction or (2) colliding with a planet or the Sun.

The long-period comets have orbits lasting longer than 200 years. The Solar System is surrounded by about a trillion (10^{12}) long-period comets, icy objects whose orbits take them *far* beyond the outermost planets of our Solar System. This vast and diffuse envelope of encircling comets is known as the **Oort cloud**. The Oort cloud has more than 200 comets with diameters greater than 500 km with common travel velocities of 240,000 km/h. They can enter the Solar System at any angle and potentially strike a planet, including Earth.

Most of the comets we see have wildly eccentric orbits that bring them in near the Sun at one end of their orbit (**perihelion**), but they swing out beyond the outermost planet at the other end of their journey (**aphelion**) (Figure 16.15). A comet may travel 100,000 astronomical units away during its orbit.

Comets are called "dirty snowballs" to describe their composition of ice and rocky debris. When an incoming comet passes Saturn on its journey toward the Sun, it begins to be affected by sunlight and the solar wind. Material from the frozen outer portion of a comet sublimates directly to vapour, thus liberating gases and trapped dust to form the distinctive luminous "tail" of a comet (Figure 16.16). The term *comet* is derived from a Greek word for "long-haired." The nearer an icy comet approaches the Sun, the larger its tail becomes. As the comet curves around the Sun, its tail rotates also, always pointing away from the Sun. A comet that has lost most

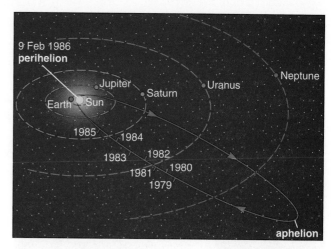

Figure 16.15
Orbit of Halley's comet during its 76-year round trip. Halley's elongate elliptical orbit is steeply inclined to Earth's orbit.

Figure 16.16
Halley's comet viewed from Easter Island, 8 March 1986.
Photo: © NASA.

of its ices over time will have a dim and small tail, the remaining rocky body being quite similar to an asteroid. Despite their visibility in the sky, comets are surprisingly small; most have heads less than 15 km in diameter.

The Swift-Tuttle comet is one of the oldest known short-period comets with sightings spanning two millennia. Observed in 1737 and 1862, its return was predicted for 1982. The comet, however, did not show up until 10 years later; the reasons for the delay are unclear ... Between 8 and 14 August each year, Earth passes through the debris left behind by the comet on previous orbits, which gives rise to the Perseid meteor shower. Generations of Canadians have enjoyed the beautiful spectacle of the Perseids against the night sky at their cottages. Contrary to earlier announcements, which predicted a close call, the trajectory of the Swift-Tuttle comet on its next passage near Earth in 2126 will avoid the planet by a comfortable 24 million km. The Swift-Tuttle comet, however, is on an orbit that will almost certainly cause it to crash into Earth or the Moon eventually.

The most famous of the comets is the one carrying Edmund Halley's name, the man who calculated its orbit in 1682 and predicted its return to the inner Solar System. Halley's comet travels from near the Sun (its perihelion) to beyond Neptune (its aphelion). The orbit of Halley's comet takes from 74 to 79 years, averaging 76 years (Figure 16.15). Near Neptune, the comet travels at 1.5 km/s, but it speeds up to 55 km/s as it nears the Sun due to the Sun's immense gravitational attraction. On its round-trip journey, Halley's comet spends only about 15 months inside the orbital region of Jupiter, but this is where its size is reduced most and its tail develops and glows bright before it returns to the deep freeze of its outer orbit. The latest visit of Halley's comet was in 1986, and, with some luck, you will get to see it on its next visit.

The ices of comets contain carbon compounds, some of which are important building blocks of life on Earth.

For example, Halley's comet contains carbon (C), hydrogen (H), oxygen (O), and nitrogen (N) in ratios similar to that in the human body. Many scientists think that the compounds used to build life were brought to Earth by comets. Are we the offspring of comets?

Rates of Meteoroid Influx

An estimated 100 billion or more meteoroids enter Earth's atmosphere every 24 hours. All this incoming debris adds from 100 to 1,000 tonnes of material to Earth's surface each day.

The numbers of incoming objects are directly related to their size; the smaller the meteoroids, the greater their abundance (Figure 16.17). Earth is largely protected from this bombardment by its atmosphere. At about 115 km above the ground, the atmosphere is dense enough to cause many meteoroids to begin to glow. A typical meteor is seen about 100 km above the ground and has largely or entirely vaporized before reaching 60 km above the surface.

Figure 16.17
Return period of impact events versus size of impacting space debris.

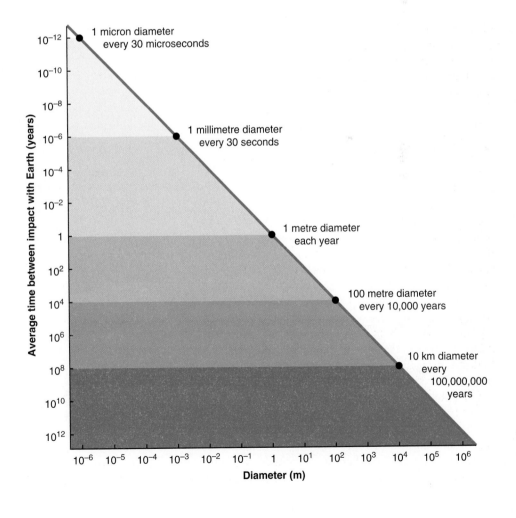

In Greater Depth

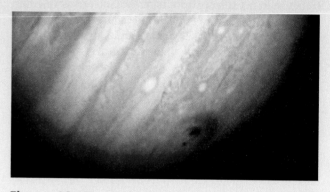

Shoemaker-Levy 9 Comet Impacts on Jupiter

A once-in-a-lifetime event occurred during the week of 16–22 July 1994, as a series of comet fragments plunged into Jupiter. The comet was named after its discoverers: geologists Eugene and Carolyn Shoemaker and comet hunter David Levy. In 1992, the comet had flown too close to Jupiter, and the planet's immense gravitational attraction pulled in the comet and broke it into pieces. In 1994, the broken-up comet was stretched out like a string of beads as it again approached Jupiter. In succession, 21 large fragments plunged into Jupiter's dense atmosphere at speeds up to 60 km/s. Each impact caused (1) an initial flash as a fragment collided with the heavy atmosphere, (2) a superheated fireball of hot gas rising upward as a plume thousands of kilometres above Jupiter's clouds, and (3) radiation as the plume crashed back down at high velocity.

The largest fragment (G) apparently was only 1 km across, yet it left an impact scar larger than the diameter of Earth (Figure 16.18). Each impact caused a rising plume of hot gas that expanded and cooled as it rose (Figure 16.19). Although the impacting fragments were small and penetrated only into Jupiter's upper atmosphere, the impact energy released by fragment G was equivalent to about 315 million World War II atomic bombs.

Figure 16.18 Impact scar of Shoemaker-Levy 9 comet fragment G on Jupiter (in lower right of photo), 17 July 1994. To lower left of G is the smaller impact scar of fragment D.
Photo: © NASA.

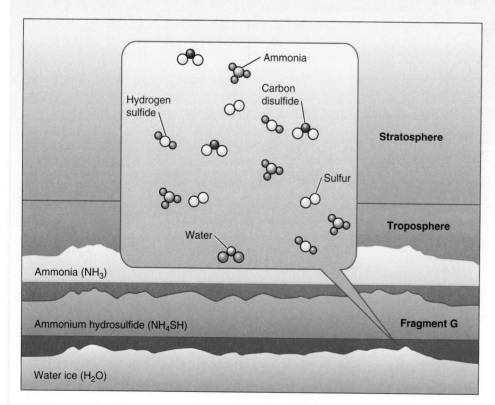

Figure 16.19 Path and impact plume of Shoemaker-Levy 9 comet fragment G plunging through cloud layers thought to make up Jupiter's upper atmosphere.

Earth is also protected from meteoroids by the very great speeds with which they hit the atmosphere—from 11 km/s to over 30 km/s. At high impact speeds, the low-viscosity atmosphere behaves more like a solid. Remember how hard the water in a pool or lake feels when you hit it doing a belly flop? Meteoroids hitting the atmosphere at incredible velocities experience a similar effect; they may be destroyed on impact with the atmosphere, deflected into space if their angle of approach is low enough, or slowed down due to friction. Incoming objects weighing more than about 350 tonnes are big enough to be largely unaffected by the atmosphere. Both the smallest (see below) and the largest meteoroids pass through the atmosphere with little change. However, the intermediate sizes may suffer significant alterations.

COSMIC DUST

The littlest meteoroids are so small that they pass downward through the atmosphere effectively unchanged and settle onto Earth's surface as a gentle rain. Particles with diameters around 0.001 mm have so much surface area compared to their volume that their frictional heat of passage is radiated as quickly as it develops, and they escape melting.

SHOOTING STARS

Incoming debris the size of sand grains, with diameters around 1 mm, typically flame out as shooting stars—flashes of friction-generated light about 100 km above the ground that blaze for about a second. A shooting star melts in the atmosphere, and tiny droplets fall to Earth's surface as little spheres of glassy rock.

METEORITES

Meteoroids weighing 1 g or more will pass through the atmosphere and fall onto the surface of Earth (Figure 16.20). During their meteoric phase, the frictional resistance of the atmosphere may raise their surface temperature to 3,000°C (about one-half the temperature of the Sun's surface) and cause their exteriors to melt. Melted surface material is stripped off to feed the glowing tail of a fireball, lighting up the sky. The stripping process also removes heat and thus protects the interior of meteorites from melting. On the ground, meteorites can be recognized by their glazed and blackened outer crusts. Friction with the atmosphere also slows meteorites; they typically hit the ground at only 320 to 640 km/h.

The number of humans killed by meteorites is . . . zero! In 1954, Ann Hodges of Sylacauga, Alabama, experienced a close call. A 4 kg stony meteorite crashed through the roof of her home, bounced off several walls, and then hit her and severely bruised her hip. She sur-

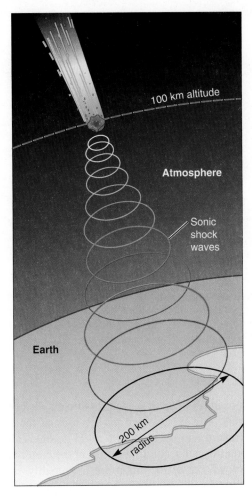

Figure 16.20
A meteor hitting the top of the atmosphere sends off sonic shock waves. To be heard on the ground, the incoming meteor must be at least as big as a basketball.

vived the ordeal and the intruder is now on display at the University of Alabama's Museum of Natural History.

The Crater-Forming Process

The amount of energy released by an asteroid or comet impact depends on the body's speed and size. Asteroids may impact at 14 km/s and long-period comets at 70 km/s.

The impact of smaller meteorites creates *simple craters* with raised rims and concave bottoms lacking central uplifts, such as Meteor Crater, Arizona (Figure 16.21) and Pingualuit Crater in northern Quebec (Figure 16.39).

The impact of larger bodies (Figure 16.22a) forms *complex craters* with central uplifts and collapsed outer rims. Large impacts generate so much heat and pressure that much of the asteroid and crater rock is melted and vaporized (Figure 16.22b). In an instant, temperatures may

Figure 16.21
View northwest of Meteor Crater, Arizona. Notice the upturned rock layers in the crater rim, the little hills of ejected debris surrounding the crater, and the individual blocks of resistant rock (e.g., limestone) strewn about the plateau.
Photo: © John S. Shelton.

reach thousands of degrees, and pressure may exceed 100 gigapascals. The shock wave pushes rock at the impact site downward and outward in a rapid acceleration of a few kilometres per second. The rock in the crater and the debris thrown out of the crater are irreversibly changed by the short-lived high temperature and pressure. Rock is broken, melted, and vaporized; new minerals, such as diamond, are created; and a common mineral such as quartz will have its atomic structure transformed by the high-pressure impact into its high-density form as the mineral stishovite.

Still within the initial second, a release or dilatation wave follows into Earth and catches up with the accelerating rock, causing a deflection of material upward and outward, forming a central uplift on the crater floor (Figure 16.22c). The crater that exists in this split second is transient and soon to be enlarged.

As the crater is emptied of vaporized and pulverized asteroid and rock, the fractured walls of the transient crater fail and slide in toward the centre of the crater (Figure 16.22d). This is the final enlarged crater with an upraised centre, surrounded by a circular trough and then by an outermost fractured rim. The outer circle of the final crater may have a diameter 100 times wider than the crater is deep.

The Manicouagan impact crater shows an upraised central area surrounded by a circular trough (Figure 16.10). An outer circle of a final crater may have existed at higher elevations at Manicouagan but has been eroded away by post-impact continental glaciation. Similar features are seen on other planets as well. The Yuty crater on Mars (Figure 16.23) has a well-developed central peak surrounded by a circular trough. Apparently, subsurface ice deposits were melted at Yuty, yielding muddy, liquefied ejecta that flowed over the adjacent area. Similar features would form on Earth if impact occurred on the frozen ground of northern Canada, Siberia, or Alaska.

The impact process may be visualized in miniature using a falling drop of water hitting a still body of water (Figure 16.24). At the point of impact, water springs upward, ripples and troughs surround the impact, and a spray of fine water shoots upward and outward. Although the water quickly returns to its normal still condition and retains no evidence of impact, rock altered by impact remain in its broken, melted, and shocked states for the rest of its existence.

METEOR CRATER, ARIZONA

The world's classic simple crater lies on an arid portion of the Colorado Plateau in north-central Arizona. Meteor Crater, also known as Barringer Crater, is over 1 km wide, excavated nearly 185 m below the plateau, and surrounded by a rock rim rising 30 to 60 m above the countryside (Figure 16.21).

What is the evidence demonstrating that the crater formed by meteorite impact? (1) The crater is steep-sided and closed; (2) the rim of surrounding rock was created by uplifting the horizontal sedimentary-rock layers of the region and tilting them away from the crater; (3) little hills of rock outside the crater rim are inverted piles of the rock sequence exposed in the crater walls; (4) huge blocks of limestone are strewn around outside the crater; (5) the crater floor holds a 265 m thickness of shattered rock; (6) numerous pieces of nickel-iron metallic meteorite with a combined weight of nearly 30 tonnes have been collected in the area; and (7) several features indicate the occurrence of high temperature and pressure, such as unusual varieties of quartz (the minerals stishovite and coesite), cooled droplets of once-melted metal, fused masses of sand grains, and **shatter cones** (a structure cones inside cones) that form under pressure.

There also is negative evidence that argues against other processes being responsible for the crater. (1) There is no volcanic material within or nearby, and thus, the crater is not the mouth of a volcano. (2) There are no features to argue for a solution-collapse process of subsidence similar to sinkholes.

When all the evidence is considered, the words of Sherlock Holmes in "The Adventure of the Bruce-Partington Plans" apply: "Each fact is suggestive in itself. Together they have a cumulative force." In sum, the evidence at Meteor Crater, Arizona, is overwhelming; the site has become the most-photographed meteorite crater in the world.

Figure 16.22

Formation of a complex crater. (a) An incoming meteoroid heavier than 350 tonnes may be moving faster than 50,000 km/h. (b) The impact shock causes such high temperatures and pressures that most of the meteoroid and crater rock are vaporized and melted. (c) The release wave following the shock wave causes the centre of the floor in the transient crater to rise. (d) The fractured walls fail and slide into the crater, creating a wider and shallower final crater.

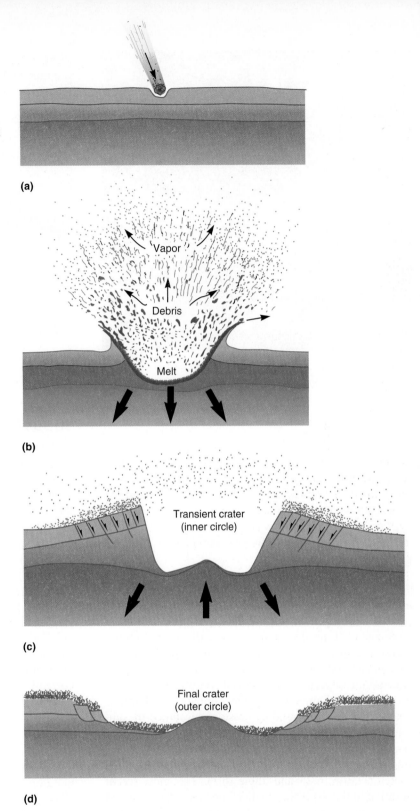

(a)

(b)

Vapor

Debris

Melt

(c)

Transient crater
(inner circle)

(d)

Final crater
(outer circle)

Meteor Crater formed about 50,000 years ago when a nickel-iron metallic meteorite came blazing through the atmosphere. The meteorite had a diameter of about 30 m, weighed around 110,000 tonnes, and hit the ground travelling about 12 km/s. The enormous energy of impact was largely converted into heat, which liquefied about 80% of the meteorite and the enveloping ground in less than a second. About 100 million tonnes of rock were pulverized in this Arizona event, generating about double the energy released by the Mount St. Helens volcanic

Figure 16.23
The Yuty crater on Mars has a well-developed central peak and surrounding circular trough.
Photo: © NASA.

Figure 16.24
Drop of water hits a body of water. Note the central rebound.
© Stockbyte/PunchStock.

eruption. The shock wave levelled all trees in the region, wildfires broke out, and dust darkened the sky.

The Great Canadian Impact Crater Tour

Meteoroids with weights greater than 350 tonnes are not slowed down much by the atmosphere. The big ones hit the ground at nearly their original speed, explode, and excavate craters. Typically, craters have a diameter 20 times larger than that of the impactor. A crater larger than 5 km in diameter does not normally contain meteoritic material because the impactor has vaporized entirely on contact.

The record of crater-forming impacts on Earth is sparse. Craters are erased by erosion, consumed by subduction, mangled by continent collisions, and buried beneath younger sediment. So far, there are 164 known impact craters including 58 in Canada and the United States (Figure 16.25 and Table 16.1). The most recent addition to the list is the small Whitecourt crater, located north of Edmonton, discovered in 2007 by Dr. Chris Herd of the University of Alberta. A large number of craters have been preserved in Canada because of the uneventful recent geological history of a large part of its territory, the Canadian Precambrian Shield.

We have already visited the Charlevoix (see Chapter 5), Manicouagan (Figure 16.10), and Clearwater Lakes (Figure 16.13) impact craters. Let's take a tour and explore a few more Canadian impact sites.

SUDBURY AND WANAPITEI, ONTARIO

Sudbury is the site of the largest and oldest (1850 ± 3 Ma) impact crater in Canada, and the fourth oldest in the world (Figure 16.26). Gravity data outline the Sudbury structure as an elliptical anomaly, approximately 50 km wide (Figure 16.27a). Removing the effects of almost two billion years of tectonic deformation, scientists of the Geological Survey of Canada have reconstructed the feature at the time of the impact (Figure 16.27b). Their results unmistakably unveil the circular shape of the original impact crater. Another piece of evidence points to the impact origin of Sudbury: the presence of well-developed shatter cones in the area (Figure 16.28).

Today, the floor of the Sudbury crater is occupied by bucolic farmland. The Sudbury area is also home to the world's largest nickel deposit. The price of nickel is currently very high due to strong demand from the international manufacturing industry. Could the wealth that miners are extracting from the ground be of extraterrestrial origin? Proponents of the hypothesis point out that iron-rich meteorites can contain up to 20% nickel. Was the Sudbury impactor an iron- and nickel-rich meteorite that brought to Earth large quantities of the metal? Actually, recent isotopic analysis of the Sudbury ore indicates that the nickel was there in the first place, disseminated in the rock of the Canadian Precambrian Shield. The melting due to the impact concentrated the metal. Approximately 25% of impact sites worldwide have associated economic mineral deposits.

The young Wanapitei crater (37.2 ± 1.2 Ma) lies entirely inside the limits of the original Sudbury complex

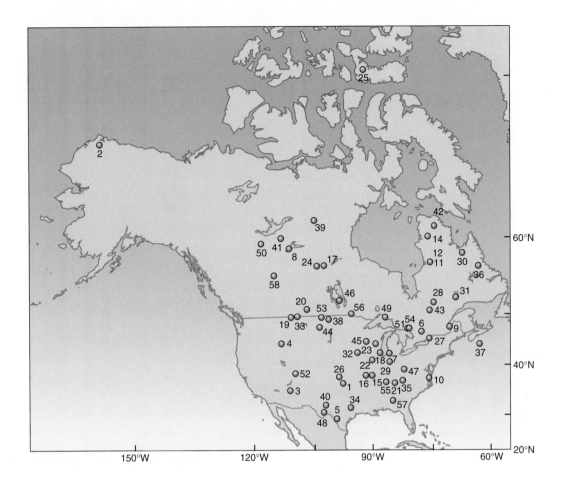

Figure 16.25
Impact crater locations, Canada and the United States. See Table 16.1 for names, sizes, and a.
Source: Planetary and Space Science Centre, University of New Brunswick.

crater. It is a crater within a crater. The crater is located under the waters of Lake Wanapitei and was first identified by a gravity survey (Figure 16.29). The local gravitational acceleration is less than in surrounding areas because rock fractured by impact is less dense than unaltered rock.

HOLLEFORD, ONTARIO

Impact scars in the landscape are often difficult to identify from the perspective of an observer on the ground; however, aerial and satellite photos are invaluable tools for identification. The Holleford impact crater (550 ± 100 Ma), located 27 km northwest of Kingston, Ontario, was discovered in 1955 during a systematic examination of aerial photographs for circular features of possible impact origin. The crater depression stands out against the farmland grid (Figure 16.30).

SLATE ISLANDS, ONTARIO

The Slate Islands are a small group of islands located offshore from Terrace Bay, Ontario, in Lake Superior. The complex shape of the islands suggests a violent, complicated geological history (Figures 16.31 and 16.32). The Slate Islands lie in the centre of concentric underwater features: a trough where the water depth is in excess of 250 m and larger ridge where the water depth is less than 100 m. The ridge is thought to correspond to the rim of the original crater, formed approximately 450 million years ago.

The first mention alluding to the Slate Islands as an impact site is a paper written in *Nature* by Professor Henry Halls of the University of Toronto in 1975. In summer 1973, Professor Halls, who has devoted his life to the study of the flood basalts of the Lake Superior region (Figure 7.30), was mapping lava flows when he discovered **brecciated** rock at several sites on the islands

Table 16.1

Names, Sizes, and Ages of North American Impact Craters

	Crater Name	Location	Diameter (km)	Age (Millions of Years)
1	Ames	Oklahoma	16	470 ± 30
2	Avak	Alaska	12	> 95
3	Barringer	Arizona	1.18	0.049 ±
4	Beaverhead	Montana	60	~ 600
5	Bee Bluff	Texas	2.4	< 40
6	Brent	Ontario	3.8	396 ± 20
7	Calvin	Michigan	8.5	450 ± 10
8	Carswell	Saskatchewan	39	115 ± 10
9	Charlevoix	Quebec	54	342 ± 15
10	Chesapeake Bay	Virginia	90	35.5 ± 0.3
11	Clearwater East	Quebec	26	290 ± 20
12	Clearwater West	Quebec	36	290 ± 20
14	Couture	Quebec	8	430 ± 25
15	Crooked Creak	Missouri	7	320 ± 80
16	Decaturville	Missouri	6	< 300
17	Deep Bay	Saskatchewan	13	99 ± 4
18	Des Plaines	Illinois	8	< 280
19	Eagle Butte	Alberta	10	< 65
20	Elbow	Saskatchewan	8	395 ± 25
21	Flynn Creek	Tennessee	3.8	360 ± 20
22	Glasford	Illinois	4	< 430
23	Glover Bluff	Wisconsin	8	< 500
24	Gow	Saskatchewan	5	< 250
25	Haughton	Nunavut	24	23 ± 1
26	Haviland	Kansas	0.01	< 0.001
27	Holleford	Ontario	2.35	550 ± 100
28	Ile Rouleau	Quebec	4	< 300
29	Kentland	Indiana	13	< 97
30	La Moinerie	Quebec	8	400 ± 50
31	Manicouagan	Quebec	100	214 ± 1
32	Manson	Iowa	35	73.8 ± 0.3
33	Maple Creek	Saskatchewan	6	< 75
34	Marquez	Texas	12.7	58 ± 2
35	Middlesboro	Kentucky	6	< 300
36	Mistastin	Newfoundland/Labrador	28	36.4 ± 4
37	Montagnais	Nova Scotia	45	50.50 ± 0.76
38	Newporte	North Dakota	3.2	< 500
39	Nicholson	Northwest Territories	12.5	< 400
40	Odessa	Texas	0.16	< 0.05
41	Pilot	Northwest Territories	6	445 ± 2
42	Pingualuit	Quebec	3.44	1.4 ± 0.1

Continued

Table 16.1

Names, Sizes, and Ages of North American Impact Craters

	Crater Name	Location	Diameter (km)	Age (Millions of Years)
43	Presqu'ile	Quebec	24	< 500
44	Red Wing	North Dakota	9	200 ± 25
45	Rock Elm	Wisconsin	6	< 505
46	Saint Martin	Manitoba	40	220 ± 32
47	Serpent Mound	Ohio	8	< 320
48	Sierra Madera	Texas	13	< 100
49	Slate Islands	Ontario	30	~ 450
50	Steen River	Alberta	25	95 ± 7
51	Sudbury	Ontario	250	1850 ± 3
52	Upheaval Dome	Utah	10	< 170
53	Viewfield	Saskatchewan	2.5	190 ± 20
54	Wanapitei	Ontario	7.5	37.2 ± 1.2
55	Wells Creek	Tennessee	12	200 ± 100
56	West Hawk	Manitoba	2.44	100 ± 1.5
57	Wetumpka	Alabama	6.5	81 ± 1.5
58	Whitecourt	Alberta	0.036	0.001

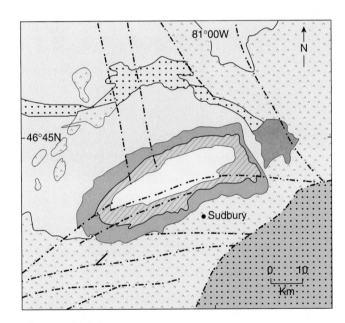

Figure 16.26
Simplified geological map of the Sudbury and Wanapitei impact sites. The elliptical Sudbury structure, including the Sudbury igneous complex (red), the Onaping formation (orange), and the Onwatin and Chelmsfor formations (yellow), stands out against the rock of the Superior province of the Canadian Precambrian Shield (blue). The younger rock of the Grenville Province is shown in green, and Lake Wanapitei in grey. Regional faults are represented by dash-dot-dash lines. The original Sudbury impact site was larger and circular. It has eroded away and deformed over geological time.

Modified from R.A.F. Grieve, *Impact Structures in Canada,* 2006.

(Figure 16.33). Subsequent laboratory analyses of the volcanic rock and breccias revealed that the field samples carried a distinct magnetic direction that had been acquired by the rock almost instantaneously. Prof. Halls concluded that this paleomagnetic signature was due to the same sudden event that had created the breccias.

BRENT, ONTARIO

The Brent impact crater (396 ± 20 Ma) is located in the boreal forest, near the northern boundary of Algonquin Provincial Park in Ontario. The remnants of the original 3.8 km wide crater is a 3.0 km wide and 60 m deep depression occupied by two kidney-shaped lakes (Figure 16.34). Twelve boreholes were drilled into the structure in the 1950s and 1960s (Figure 16.35). They revealed that the crater is filled with approximately 260 m of sedimentary rock deposited long after the impact. Beneath the sedimentary rock, a 600 m layer of shocked rock overlays a thin lens of impact melt rock, which is found immediately above the fractured Precambrian basement. Chemical analyses suggest that the Brent impactor was a large stony meteorite.

HAUGHTON, NUNAVUT

The Haughton impact crater (23 ± 1 Ma) lies on Devon Island, a large uninhabited island in the Canadian Arctic, where shatter cones where discovered in 1974 (Figures 16.36 and 16.37). Cold, dry, windy, rocky and dusty,

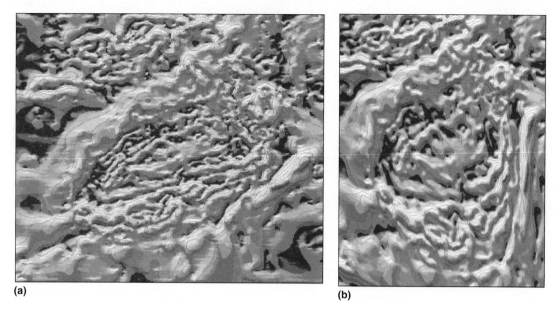
(a)   **(b)**

Figure 16.27
Gravity data from Sudbury, Ontario (a) before and (b) after correcting for the tectonic deformation that took place since the impact some 1.85 billion years ago.

Source: Reproduced with the permission of Natural Resources Canada 2008, courtesy of the Geological Survey of Canada. http://gdcinfo.agg.nrcan.gc.ca/app/sudbury1_e.html

Figure 16.28
Shatter cones from Sudbury, Ontario. Their shapes have been enhanced by white chalk marks. Each feature is a few centimetres across.

Photo by Wanda Carter.

Figure 16.29
Flying over Lake Wanapitei, Ontario. The smooth, semicircular northern shore of the lake is evidence of its impact origin.

Source: Claire Samson.

the Haughton impact site has been described as "Mars on Earth." With its summers lasting just five weeks at an average temperature of only 2°C and its geographic remoteness, it is indeed an analogue of the conditions found on Mars. The Mars Institute and the SETI (Search for Extra-Terrestrial Intelligence) Institute are exploiting the opportunity and operate a research station at the Haughton crater, under the umbrella of the Haughton-Mars

Project. The station is the focal point for multidisciplinary research on the effects of impacts on Earth and on other planets, life in extreme environments, and technologies for future planetary exploration by robots and humans. A key contribution is the Arthur Clarke Mars Greenhouse project led by Dr. Alain Berinstain of the Canadian Space Agency (Figure 16.38). The experiment aims to develop a robust, autonomous greenhouse for growing plants as potential food crops as though it were part of a base on Mars. The project started with a single test crop, lettuce, but has since then diversified its menu offerings to radish and zucchini.

Figure 16.30
Aerial photograph of the Holleford impact crater, Ontario.

Source: National Air Photo Library, Centre for Topographic Information, Natural Resources Canada, Image A17775.

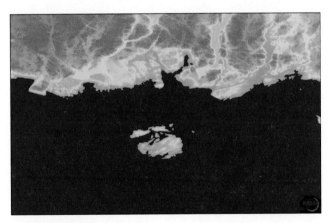

Figure 16.31
Digital elevation model of the Slate Islands, Lake Superior, Ontario.

Source: Planetary and Space Science Centre, University of New Brunswick.

Figure 16.32
South shore of Patterson island, Slate Islands, on a stormy day.

Photo by Henry Halls, University of Toronto.

Figure 16.33
The shock wave from the impact at Slate Islands has broken existing rock into angular fragments and generated abundant shatter cones (the arrow points to a small portion of a shatter cone).

Photo by Henry Halls, University of Toronto.

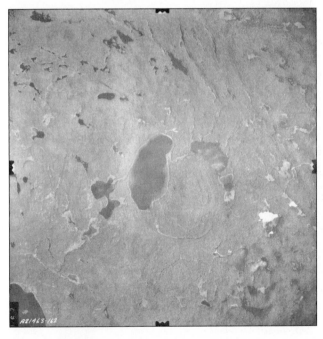

Figure 16.34
Aerial photograph of the Brent impact crater, Ontario.

Source: National Air Photo Library, Centre for Topographic Information, Natural Resources Canada, Image A21463.

PINGUALUIT, QUEBEC

Pingualuit (1.4 ± 0.1 Ma) is a classic example of a simple crater (Figure 16.39). It was first recognized in 1943 when a pilot flew over. *Pingualuit* means "large hill" in Inuktitut. The crater is a conspicuous landmark in the flat tundra and is an important archeological site. The Pingualuit impactor is inferred to have been 100–150 m

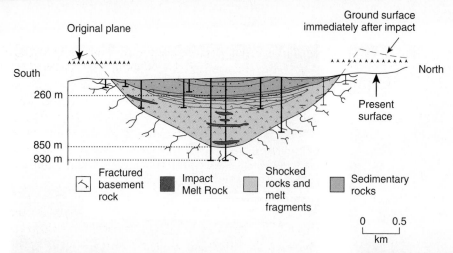

Original plane

Ground surface
immediately after impact

South

North

260 m

850 m
930 m

Present
surface

⬛ Fractured
basement
rock

⬛ Impact
Melt Rock

⬛ Shocked
rocks and
melt
fragments

⬛ Sedimentary
rocks

0   0.5
km

Figure 16.35
Geological cross-section through the
Brent impact crater, Ontario.
Modified from R.A.F. Grieve, *Impact Structures in Canada*, 2006.

Figure 16.36
Panoramic aerial photograph of the Haughton impact crater,
Devon Island, Nunavut.
Source: Canadian Space Agency; photographer, Martin Lipman.

Figure 16.38
The autonomous Arthur Clarke Mars greenhouse designed and
operated by the Canadian Space Agency.
Source: Canadian Space Agency; photographer, Martin Lipman.

Figure 16.37
This 8 m tall block of rock was tossed in the air during the
Haughton impact.
Photo by Martin Lipman.

in diameter and to have struck Earth at a velocity of 25
km/s. No meteorites have been recovered. The surrounding rock, however, is enriched in iridium and contains
impactites, a glass produced by partial fusion of the rock
by the heat generated from the impact.

Pingualuit is "a lake fallen from the sky" in the words
of Dr. Michel Bouchard, leader of several science expedi-
tions to the site. The crater encloses a lake of 3.4 km in
diameter within a well-preserved rim rising some 160 m

Figure 16.39
The Pingualuit crater rises majestically above the flat tundra of northern Quebec.
Photo by Michel Bouchard.

above the water surface. With a depth of 250 m, Pingualuit is one of the deepest freshwater lakes in the world. Only one species of fish, Arctic char, lives in the lake, and there are signs of fish cannibalism. How were fish introduced in the crater? Water levels in the crater changed through time. At one point, Pingualuit Lake overflowed and drained into a neighbouring lake. Fish probably swam upcurrent from that lake into Pingualuit Lake.

The Cretaceous/Tertiary Boundary Event

To learn what happened at the close of Cretaceous time, one should follow the advice spoken by Sherlock Holmes in "The Problem of Thor Bridge": "If you will find the facts, perhaps others may find the explanation." To find the facts of 65-million-year-old events means to examine rock of this age.

The modern search began near Gubbio, Italy, a locality where the Cretaceous/Tertiary boundary, sandwiched between two distinct types of rock, is particularly well exposed. The latest Cretaceous (K) rock is limestone loaded with fossils of unicellular organisms whose individuals had diameters up to 1 mm. The earliest Tertiary (T) limestone above it contains an impoverished and markedly changed fossil assemblage. Between the limestones lies a 1 cm clay layer that marks the Cretaceous/Tertiary (K/T) boundary. Does the K/T boundary clay layer hold facts that might explain the events of its days? The late Luis Alvarez, a Nobel Prize–winning physicist, and his geologist son Walter focused their research efforts on this topic. Their investigation discovered a high percentage of the element iridium in the clay layer, an enrichment about 300 times greater than the normal abundance. Here is a fact begging for an explanation.

Iridium is a siderophile, or iron-loving element. Most of Earth's iridium lies deep in its iron-rich core; it migrated with iron to the core during the time of early heating when Earth separated into layers of different density (Figure 2.12). But the K/T boundary clay layer, which is found in many places around the world, holds an estimated one-half million tonnes of iridium. How did this layer become so enriched in iridium? Luis Alvarez reasoned that since meteorites are enriched in iridium, a 10 km diameter asteroid could have supplied the volume of iridium estimated to be present in the K/T boundary clay.

In a condensed version, here is a popular theory of our times: an asteroid with a 10-km diameter hit Earth; the impact caused a great dying among life worldwide, including the extinction of dinosaurs (excluding birds), and left its incriminating fingerprint as iridium in a global clay layer. The theory is intriguing, easy to grasp, and beguilingly simple to accept. But for a theory to gain widespread approval in the scientific community, it must explain all relevant facts and allow predictions to be made. If these predictions later become supported by facts, then the theory gains wider acceptance. Thus, before the K/T impact theory could gain wide acceptance in the scientific community, many more facts needed to be discovered to verify predictions made by the theory.

EVIDENCE OF THE K/T IMPACT

Once the K/T theory was proposed, it excited scientists worldwide, and the search for facts shifted into high gear. Researchers around the world began examining the K/T boundary clay layer for other evidence of Earth-like versus meteorite-like components. (1) The clay layer was found on the continents, thus ruling out the possibility that the iridium enrichment was due simply to a change in ocean composition. (2) The K/T boundary clay minerals have a different composition from clays in the limestone layers above and below it; they might be explained by a mixture of one part asteroid to 10 parts Earth crust. (3) Quartz grains are present with shocked crystal structures, indicating a short and violent impact. Shocked quartz, with its planar deformation features, has been found only in association with impacts, so its discovery at the K/T boundary is strong evidence of impact. (4) Sand-size spherules of minerals are present, suggesting a melting and resolidification. (5) Ratios of the radioactive element rhenium to its decay product osmium are similar to those in meteorites and are quite different from the ratios in Earth surface rock. (6) Abundant microscopic diamonds, found in some meteorites, occur in the K/T boundary clay layer. (7) Carbon-rich grains with "fluffy" structures indicative of fire are abundant in the K/T boundary clay layer.

SITE OF THE K/T IMPACT

The facts from the K/T boundary clay layer compelled more scientists to agree that a massive impact had occurred, but even more evidence was needed. If an asteroid slammed into Earth some 65 million years ago, then where was the impact site? Could it be found? Or had it been (1) subducted and destroyed? (2) buried beneath a continental glacier? (3) hidden under piles of sediment on land or seafloor? (4) covered by flood basalt? (5) eroded and erased from the face of Earth? (6) crunched into oblivion by a continent collision? Geologists searched for impact scars worldwide, but some were too small, while others were too old or too young.

Then related evidence began to focus the search. On Haiti was found a 65.01 (+ or −0.8) million-year-old sedimentary rock layer containing shocked quartz grains and 1-cm diameter glassy spherules formed from melted rock. In Cuba, a thick, chaotic sedimentary deposit with huge angular blocks was found. In northeastern Mexico, similar particles were found in a thick bed of sediment containing land debris, ripple marks, and other features interpreted as a tsunami deposit; this bed is 65.07 (+ or −0.1) million years old. Similar but thinner deposits were found in the K/T boundary position in the banks of the Brazos River in Texas and in coastal deposits in New Jersey and the Carolinas. The sedimentary features suggested a Caribbean region impact, but where?

The excitement of the search led to the Yucatan Peninsula of Mexico, where the Mexican national petroleum company (PEMEX) had drilled exploratory wells in the region of Merida. At depths of 2 km, the PEMEX well bores had encountered a 90-m thick zone of shattered rock containing shocked quartz grains and glassy blobs of once-melted rock. On the ground surface lie sinkholes aligned in a circular pattern. Geophysical measurements show circular patterns of gravity and magnetic anomalies suggesting a circular disturbance at depth (Figure 16.40). A seismic survey reveals a raised inner ring of 80 km diameter and an outer ring of about 195 km diameter.

These data all help define the Chicxulub structure of 64.98 (+ or −0.06) million years age. The evidence continues to mount that a massive asteroid slammed into the shallow, tropical sea 65 million years ago.

The impact was so great that its effects were not just regional but would have been felt worldwide; they probably played a significant role in the great dying that marked the end of Cretaceous time (see Chapter 15).

Problems for Life from Impacts

What does life have to tolerate when a massive asteroid slams into the land? There are many difficult conditions on both regional and global scales. (1) The impact of the K/T asteroid certainly created an earthquake of monumental magnitude along with numerous gigantic aftershocks. Seismologist Steven M. Day has assumed the magnitude of the K/T earthquake can be estimated by scaling up from the energy released in nuclear explosions. Extrapolating upward from an atomic bomb blast of

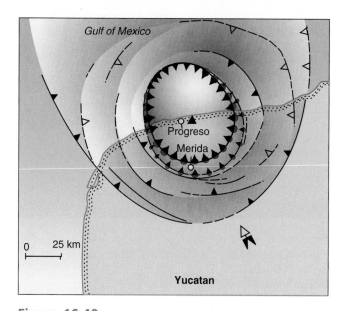

Figure 16.40

(a) A buried impact crater is shown on the tip of the Yucatan Peninsula. Notice how the gravity data appear to open to the northwest, suggesting that the asteroid came from the southeast.

magnitude 4 leads to a K/T impact earthquake of magnitude 11.3 (Figure 4.32). (2) Wildfires would rage regionally, or even globally. A recent study suggests that the K/T impact ejected so much hot debris into the atmosphere that it caused massive wildfires that consumed much of the vegetation in North America, the Indian subcontinent, and the equatorial region of the world. (3) Huge amounts of nitrogen oxides in the atmosphere would fall as acid rain and acidify surface waters. (4) Dust and soot in the atmosphere would block sunlight and turn day into night, thus making photosynthesis difficult and plunging much of the world into dark wintry conditions for weeks to several months. (5) After the atmospheric dust settled, the water vapour and CO_2 remaining in the atmosphere would lead to global warming for years (Figure 16.41).

What additional insults does life have to survive after an oceanic splashdown of a 10 km diameter asteroid? (1) Tsunami up to 300 m tall. (2) A bubble of steam up to 500 km^3 volume that blows into the upper atmosphere carrying Earth rock and asteroid debris. Another problem occurred at Chicxulub where the K/T asteroid landed in shallow, tropical marine water underlain by limestone ($CaCO_3$). The impact must have vaporized enormous quantities of limestone, thus increasing atmospheric CO_2, maybe by an order of magnitude. After the winter-causing asteroidal dust settled, the added CO_2 in the atmosphere could have elevated Earth's climate into global-warming conditions. Average temperatures in the world may have risen 10°C, and life on Earth would have been forced to endure the shift from an "extra cold winter" to an "overly hot and long summer."

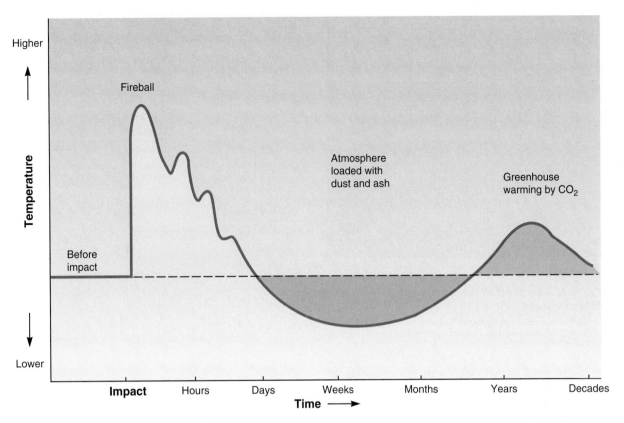

Figure 16.41

Impact of the K/T asteroid had marked effects on Earth's surface temperatures. First, there was a fireball and hot gases that lasted for many hours. Second, temperatures dropped to wintry conditions as airborne dust and soot blocked much incoming sunlight for several months. Third, after the dust settled, CO_2 remained aloft, creating a greenhouse effect that lasted for years.

After David A. Kring, "Impact Events and Their Effect on the Origin, Evolution and Distribution of Life." *GSA Today,* v. 10, no. 8 (2000), p. 4.

Biggest Event of the 20th Century

TUNGUSKA, SIBERIA, 1908

The morning was sunny in central Siberia on 30 June 1908. Then, after 7 a.m., a massive fireball came streaking in from the east. It exploded about 8 km above ground in a monstrous blast heard 1,000 km away. No humans lived immediately under the blast point, but many reindeer did, and they died. A man 60 km away was enveloped in such a mass of heat that he felt his shirt almost catch fire before an air blast threw him 2 m. People and horses 480 km from the explosion site were knocked off their feet. From 650 km away, visible in bright sunlight, a huge column of fire rose 20 km high. The ground shook enough to be registered on seismometers in Russia and Germany. Barometric anomalies were recorded as the air blast travelled twice around the world. In Sweden and Scotland, an extraordinarily strong light appeared in the sky about an hour after sunset; it was possible to read books by this light until after 2 a.m.

Scientists around the world speculated on what had happened, but it was years before an expedition went to the remote area to search for evidence of the event. Near the Tunguska River, the forest in an area greater than 1,000 km² was found to have been knocked down and destroyed; many trunks were charred on one side. Over a broader area exceeding 5,000 km², 80 million trees were down, and many others had tilted trunks, broken branches, and other signs of disturbance (Figure 16.42). But there was no impact crater or even broken ground. The relative lack of facts led unrestrained minds to invent all sorts of wild stories. It was not until 1958 that scientists returned to the site and collected little globules of once-melted metal and silicon-rich rock in the resin of surviving trees.

Several important facts must be explained. There was an intense bluish white streak in the sky, a horrendous explosion, a searing blast of heat, blasts of air that encircled the globe, a brilliant sunset and bright night, yet no impact crater—only little globules of melted material. So what happened? A meteoroid racing through the atmosphere broke up and exploded about 8 km above the ground. It either was a fragment of an icy comet about 50 m in diameter, or it was a large, stony meteorite about 30 m in diameter. The object was travelling about 15 km/s

Figure 16.42
Millions of trees were knocked down and burned by the Tunguska midair explosion.

Photo from the 1927 expedition led by Leonid Kulik.
Source: Fallen Trees Tunguska meteoroid impactttp://commons.wikimedia.org/wiki/Image:Tunguska_event_fallen_trees.jpg

Table 16.2

Ten Closest Asteroid Encounters of the 20th Century

Asteroid Flyby Year and Designation	Miss Distance (Thousands of km)	Diameter (m)
1994 XM1	105	9
1993 KA2	150	6
1994 ES1	164	7
1991 BA	164	7
1995 FF	434	18
1996 JA	449	220
1991 VG	464	6
1989 FC	688	280
1994 WR	718	140
1937 UB	733	900

Table 16.3

The Torino Scale Assessing Comet and Asteroid Impact Hazards

Events with no likely consequences (White zone)

0	No collision hazard, or object is small.

Events meriting careful monitoring (Green zone)

1	Collision is extremely unlikely.

Events of concern (Yellow zone)

2	Collision is very unlikely.
3	Close encounter with > 1% chance of local destruction.
4	Close encounter with >1% chance of regional devastation.

Threatening events (Orange zone)

5	Significant threat of regional devastation.
6	Significant threat of global catastrophe.
7	Extremely significant threat of global catastrophe.

Certain collisions (Red zone)

8	Collision will cause localized destruction (one event each 50 to 1,000 years).
9	Collision will cause regional devastation (one event each 1,000 to 100,000 years).
10	Collision will cause global catastrophe (one event each 100,000 years).

when it disintegrated in a spectacular midair explosion. If it had been a metallic body, it would almost certainly have slammed into the ground. But comets and stony meteorites are weak bodies travelling at outrageous speeds, and the resistance of Earth's atmosphere is so strong that they typically break apart upon entry. At the end of June 1908, the comet Encke was passing by Earth; one of its fragments is the likely culprit for the Tunguska event.

The Tunguska comet explosion rocked a sparsely inhabited area and devastated a forest. Imagine if it had exploded over a large urban centre. How common are these Tunguska-like events? Are such events frequent enough for humans to be concerned about?

Biggest "Near Events" of the 20th Century

On 22 March 1989, the asteroid 1989FC with a diameter of about 500 m crossed Earth's orbit at almost the wrong moment; Earth was at the spot six hours earlier. The asteroid missed us by less than 700,000 km and was not discovered until it had passed Earth! Had a collision occurred on land, the impact would have created a crater about 7 km across. Was this close call a freak occurrence? Apparently not: several thousand such bodies are in Earth-approaching orbits (Table 16.2).

In March 1998, the media widely and excitedly reported that an asteroid labelled 1997XF11 might hit Earth in the year 2028. In the same year, two big-budget Hollywood movies were released, sensationalizing the effects of collision with a comet in *Deep Impact* and with an asteroid in *Armageddon*. In order to communicate calmly the threat of comet and asteroid impacts, Richard Binzel developed the Torino scale (Table 16.3), which assesses the threat on a scale of 0 to 10.

For smaller objects, the number of near misses is surprisingly high. Detailed telescopic examination has shown that up to 50 house-size bodies pass between Earth and Moon each day. Should we worry about the consequences of impacts from speeding bodies of 50 m diameter? Apparently not, because Earth has its own defence system against small bodies—its atmosphere. When comets and stony meteorites travelling at 50,000 km/h hit the atmosphere, the great strains break most of them into smaller pieces that burn up explosively. Most of the flameouts occur 10 to 40 km above Earth's surface, which is too high for significant damage to occur on the ground. However, most iron meteorites are internally strong enough to stay intact as they pass through the atmosphere and they do hit the ground. Luckily, iron meteorites are relatively uncommon.

Frequency of Large Impacts

How often do impacts of large bodies occur? This question is hard to answer looking at our planet because of the continuous recycling of Earth's surface materials by plate tectonics and their destruction by weathering and the agents of erosion. It is easier to answer this question by looking at the long-term record of impacts preserved on the dead surface of the Moon and then extrapolate the results back to Earth (Figure 16.9). The dark volcanic maria on the Moon formed after the few hundred-million-year period of intense asteroidal bombardment over 3.9 billion years ago. The basalt-flooded maria cover 16% (6 million km^2) of the Moon's surface; they formed by about 3,200 million years ago. The maria are scarred by five craters with diameters greater than 50 km and another 24 craters with diameters between 25 to 50 km. This averages to one major impact somewhere on the maria every 110 million years.

Applying these impact rates to Earth generates the following numbers: Earth's surface area is more than 80 times the area of the lunar maria, so it would have had more than 80 times as many impacts, that is, about 2,400 impacts leaving craters greater than 25 km diameter. Land comprises about 30% of Earth's surface, so about 720 of these craters should have formed on land. More than 160 craters have been discovered so far, but most of them are less than 25 km diameter. Most of the missing craters have probably been destroyed or buried.

The odds are extremely small that a large asteroid will hit Earth during your lifetime. However, so many people will be killed when a big space object does hit that it skews the probabilities. Statistically speaking, every individual has a greater chance of being killed by a comet or asteroid than of winning a big jackpot in a lottery! The probabilities of death by meteoroid impact were indirectly assessed in the words of paleontologist George Gaylord Simpson: "Given enough time, anything that is possible is probable." Because the risks from large meteoroid impact are high, they should be of concern to humans. U.S. astronomer David Morrison has described Earth as a target in a cosmic shooting gallery of high-speed asteroids and comets. The situation has been evaluated for defensive actions we humans might take.

A DEFENCE PLAN

The risk presented by space objects with diameters greater than 1 km has been assessed by the United States National Aeronautics and Space Administration (NASA) (Table 16.4). There are over 2,000 near-Earth objects (NEOs), and about 25 to 50% of them will eventually hit Earth. About 90% of the potential impactors are near-Earth asteroids or short-period comets; the other 10% are intermediate- or long-period comets (greater than 20-year return periods). However, the average interval of time between impacts exceeds 100,000 years.

Can we do anything about this threat? Or must we just sit back fatalistically and say, "It will happen if it is meant to be"? The first step in a plan to protect ourselves is to locate the near-Earth objects (NEOs), determine their orbits, and learn which ones present immediate threats. In 1998, the United States Congress authorized $40 million for NASA to find 90% of the near-Earth asteroids (NEAs) greater than 1 km diameter by 2008. The search is being conducted by six international observatories, and their success is impressive and improving (Figure 16.43). By October 2008, they had discovered 5,692 NEOs; 757 are large NEAs and 982 have been classified as potentially hazardous asteroids (PHAs).

Table 16.4

Frequency of Impacts and Annual Probabilities of Death

For globally catastrophic events:	
Average interval between impacts	500,000 years
Assumed fatalities from impact	1/4 of human race
Total annual probability of death	1/2,000,000

For Tunguska-sized events:	
Average interval between impacts	300 years
Average interval for populated areas only	3,000 years
Average interval for urban areas	100,000 years
Total annual probability of death	1/30,000,000

Source: David Morrison (1992).

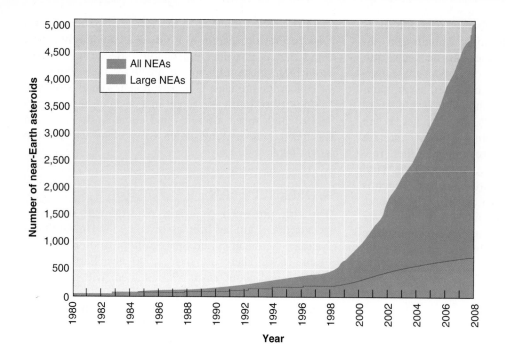

Figure 16.43
Number of near-Earth asteroids (NEAs) by year of discovery. Total NEAs are green; large NEAs (diameter over 1 km) are orange.
Source: Alan Chamberlin, NASA's Near-Earth Object Program Office.

What can be done if we discover a large NEO on a path to impact Earth? We could take an appropriate engineering action. Suggested ways of changing an NEO to alter its collision course include (1) blowing it apart with a nuclear explosion, (2) attaching a rocket engine that could drive it away, (3) using a big mirror to focus sunlight that would vaporize its surface locally, creating a reaction thrust large enough to change its orbit, and (4) sending robots to scoop and toss asteroid rock into space, thus pushing the body in the opposite direction.

A gentler form of protective action has recently been suggested. Simply launch a spacecraft, have it hover near the asteroid, and rely on the resultant gravitational attraction to pull the asteroid in an Earth-avoiding path. An opportunity to practise our defences will come in 2035 and 2036, when the 330 m diameter asteroid 99942 Apophis might hit Earth.

Is a large impact too unlikely an event to take seriously? Arthur C. Clarke said:

> We tend to remember only the extraordinary events, such as the odd coincidences; but we forget that almost every event is an odd coincidence. The asteroid that misses the Earth is on a course every bit as improbable as the one that strikes it.

Are we willing to make a commitment to an Earth defence system? Or is the situation too low a priority for dollars when competing with crime, AIDS, poverty, and other issues?

Summary

- The Sun sends solar wind particles in all directions. When strong gusts of solar wind reach Earth, we experience a magnetic storm.
- Magnetic storms affect several technological systems.
  - The direct hit of charged particles on electronic components can damage circuitry.
  - Radio and GPS signals are lost or become unreliable because of ionospheric disturbances.
  - Spurious induced currents interfere with the normal operations of power transmission lines, telephone lines, and corrosion protection systems.

- Earth revolving around the Sun in the vastness of space can become a target for impact. Space debris colliding with Earth comprises primarily stony or metallic asteroids, or ices from comets.
- The consequences of impact are related to the size of the impactor.
  - Cosmic dust (diameter ≤ 1 mm) burns up due to friction upon entry in the atmosphere or falls on the surface of Earth relatively unchanged.
  - Some impactors with diameters between 1 mm and 100 m reach the surface of the Earth and are recovered as meteorites.
  - Meteoroids larger than 100 m in diameter are slowed little by the atmosphere and may hit the ground at high speeds, explode, and excavate craters.

- The impact of a large asteroid generates tremendous heat and pressure. Rock in the crater and debris thrown out of the crater is broken, melted, and vaporized; minerals develop new atomic structures. As the transient crater is emptied, the crater bottom rebounds upward, and the fractured walls slide inward toward the crater centre, forming a final, enlarged crater.
- It is difficult to recognize impact sites on Earth because plate tectonics and erosion destroy the evidence. Nevertheless, 30 sites have been identified in Canada on the basis of aerial photographs and geological evidence, including the presence of shatter cones and shock minerals.
- Life on Earth is subjected to great stress by a large impact.

Terms to Remember

aphelion   468
astrobleme   465
brecciated   478
Kuiper belt   475
magnetism   461
maria   465

meteor   466
meteoroid   466
Oort cloud   468
perihelion   468
plasma   460
shatter cone   472

shock mineral   465
shooting star   466
solar wind   460
telluric current   461

Questions for Review

1. What causes aurorae?
2. What are telluric currents? How are they generated? How do they interfere with technological networks?
3. Why does the Moon display impact scars so well?
4. Why are impact scars relatively rare on Earth?
5. Distinguish between a meteor, a meteoroid, a meteorite, an asteroid, and a comet.
6. Why are metallic meteorites so commonly collected?
7. Why did the asteroids of the asteroid belt not assemble into a planet?
8. Why does a comet's tail glow brighter as it nears the Sun? Why does a comet's tail point away from the Sun?
9. How much space debris is added to Earth each day? How big must a meteoroid be to pass through the atmosphere with little slowing?
10. Draw a series of cross-sections showing what happens when a 10-km diameter asteroid hits Earth at 32,000 km/h.
11. Make a list of the evidence you could collect to demonstrate that a specific area was the site of an ancient asteroid impact.
12. Describe the sequence of life-threatening events that occur when a 10-km diameter asteroid slams into Earth.
13. Explain the Torino scale of impact hazards.

Questions for Further Thought

1. Who should check space weather forecasts regularly?
2. Extrapolating impact rates from the Moon, about 720 craters with diameters greater than 24 km should have formed on land on Earth; only about 160 have been found so far. Might some of the missing impact sites have been big and caused mass extinctions? How could you proceed scientifically to investigate this possibility?
3. Should the international community spend the money and effort to develop engineering devices that could land on large asteroids and comets and change their courses away from hitting Earth?
4. It is proposed that we send rockets or explosives to divert incoming large asteroids or comets. Might this action just shatter the incoming object into many devastating impactors? Or cause the object to hit Earth on a more direct path?

5. In an Greater Depth box: Energy, Force, Work, Power, and Heat in Chapter 2, it was shown that kinetic energy = 1/2 mv^2 where m is mass and v is velocity. Think through this equation and assess the impact energy of an asteroid and a comet both with diameters of 10 km. Asteroids may have four times as much mass but comets can easily travel twice as fast. Do they bring equivalent amounts of kinetic energy? Upon impact, does it matter that the asteroid is metal and/or rock whereas the comet is mostly ice?
6. What effects have Hollywood movies had on public policy regarding natural disasters?
7. Would it be profitable for an insurance company to offer coverage against accidental death by meteorite impact?

Glossary

A

aa Lava flow with a rough, blocky surface.

acceleration (1) To cause to move faster. (2) The rate of change of motion.

accelerograph An instrument that records the acceleration of the ground during an earthquake.

acoustic fluidization A theorized process where sound waves trapped inside a dry, fallen mass lessen internal friction to enable fluid-like flow.

active volcano Volcano currently erupting or that has erupted in historical times (examples: Etna, Sicily; Tambora, Indonesia).

actualism The concept of using the processes operating on Earth today to interpret the past.

adiabatic process The change in temperature of a mass without adding or subtracting heat. Examples are cooling with expansion and warming upon compression.

aftershock A smaller earthquake following a mainshock on the same section of a fault. Aftershocks can continue for years following a large mainshock.

albedo The reflectivity of a body; for the Earth, how much solar radiation is reflected back to space.

amplitude The maximum displacement or height of a wave crest or depth of a trough.

andesite A volcanic rock named for the Andes Mountains in South America. It is intermediate in composition between basalt and rhyolite, and commonly results from melting of continental rock in basaltic magma.

anoxic Depleted of oxygen.

anticyclone A region of high atmospheric pressure and outflowing air that rotates clockwise in the northern hemisphere.

aphelion The point in the orbit of a body that is farthest from the Sun.

archaea An ancient branch of life whose species can thrive under high pressures and temperatures; these microorganisms derive their energy by breaking the chemical bonds of inorganic molecules.

arrival time The time at which a seismic wave is detected by a seismograph.

asteroid Small, rocky body that orbits the Sun.

asthenosphere The layer of the Earth below the lithosphere in which isostatic adjustments take place. The rocks here deform readily and flow slowly.

astrobleme An ancient impact site on Earth usually recognized by a circular outline and highly disturbed, shocked rocks.

atmosphere The gaseous envelope around the Earth, composed chiefly of nitrogen and oxygen. The average atmospheric pressure at sea level is 101.3 kPa.

avulsion An abrupt change in the course of a stream and adoption of a new channel.

B

backfire A fire deliberately set to consume fuel in front of an advancing wildfire in order to stop it.

basalt A dark, finely crystalline volcanic rock typical of low-viscosity oceanic lavas.

base isolation System protecting buildings from earthquakes by isolating the base of the structure from the shaking ground via rollers, shock absorbers, etc.

base level The level below which a stream cannot erode, usually sea level.

bathymetry The mapping of depths of water in oceans, rivers, and lakes; the underwater equivalent of topography.

BCE Before the common era. Equivalent to BC.

bedrock Solid rock lying beneath loose soil or unconsolidated sediment.

benthic Living on the seafloor.

blitzkrieg hypothesis Tentative explanation for the disappearance of many species of large mammals in the post-glacial period invoking overhunting by humans.

blizzard Strong cold winds filled with snow.

body wave Seismic wave that travels through the body of the Earth. Primary and secondary waves are body waves.

braided stream An overloaded stream so full of sediment that water flow is forced to divide and recombine in a braided pattern.

brecciated Characterized by angular fragments.

brittle Behaviour of material where stress causes abrupt fracture.

C

caldera A large (over 2 km diameter), basin-shaped volcanic depression, roughly circular in map view, that forms by a pistonlike collapse of overlying rock into an underlying, partially evacuated magma chamber.

carbonic acid A common but weak acid (H_2CO_3) formed by carbon dioxide (CO_2) dissolving in water (H_2O).

carrying capacity The maximum population size that can be supported under a given set of environmental conditions.

CE common era. Equivalent to AD.

chaparral A dense, impenetrable thicket of stiff shrubs especially adapted to a dry season about six months long; abundant in the State of California and Baja California. Fire is part of the life cycle of these plants.

chemical weathering The decomposition of rocks under attack of base- or acid-laden waters.

chondrichthyan Fish whose skeletons are made of cartilage rather than bone.

chondrule Small, glassy sphere crystallized in space from semi-molten or molten droplets of rock.

cinder cone Steep volcanic hill made of loose pyroclastic debris.

clay minerals Very small (under 1/256 mm diameter) minerals with sheet- or book-like internal crystal structure. Many varieties absorb water or ions into their layering, causing swelling or shrinking.

climate The average weather conditions at a place over several decades.

cohesion A property of sediments where particles stick together.

combustion Act of burning.

comet Icy body moving through outer space.

composite volcano A volcano constructed of alternating layers of pyroclastic debris and lava flows; also called a stratovolcano.

compression A state of stress that causes a pushing together or contraction.

conduction A process of heat transfer through material by flow of kinetic energy from particle to particle.

continent Lower-density masses of rock, exposed as about 40% of the Earth's surface: 29% as land and 11% as the floor of shallow seas.

continental drift The movement of continents across the face of the Earth, including their splitting apart and recombination into new continents.

convection A process of heat transfer where hot material at depth rises upward due to its lower density while cooler material above sinks because of its higher density.

convergence zone A linear area where plates collide and move closer together. This is a zone of earthquakes, volcanoes, mountain ranges, and deep-ocean trenches.

core The central zone of the Earth about 2,900 km below the surface. The core is made mostly of iron and nickel and exists as a solid inner zone surrounded by a liquid outer shell. The Earth's magnetic field originates within the core.

Coriolis effect The tendency of moving objects on the surface of the Earth to be deflected due to the Earth's rotation; in the northern hemisphere, bodies move toward their right-hand sides, while in the southern hemisphere, they move toward their left-hand sides.

crater An abrupt basin commonly rimmed by ejected material. In volcanoes, craters form by outward explosion, are commonly less than 2 km diameter, and occur at the summit of a volcanic cone. Similar rimmed basins form by impacts with meteorites, asteroids, and comets.

craton A part of the crust that became stable early in Earth's history and has remained largely unchanged since then.

creep The slow, gradual, more or less continuous movement of ice and soil under gravity.

creeping zone Section of a fault where seismic energy is released frequently in small to moderate earthquakes.

cross-section A two-dimensional drawing showing features in the vertical plane as in a canyon wall or road cut.

crust The outermost layer of the lithosphere, composed of relatively low-density materials. The continental crust has lower density than the oceanic crust.

crystallization The growth of minerals in a fluid such as magma.

Curie point The temperature above which a mineral will not be magnetic.

cyanobacterium A group of blue-green photosynthetic microorganisms.

cyclone A region of low atmospheric pressure and converging air that rotates counterclockwise in the northern hemisphere.

D

debris flow Loose sediment plus water that is pulled downslope directly by gravity.

decompression melting The most common process of creating magma. Melting occurs by reducing pressure on hot rock.

derecho Winds that blow straight ahead.

dew point temperature The air temperature where the relative humidity of an air mass reaches 100% and excess water vapour condenses to liquid water.

dielectric constant A measure of a material's ability to store electrical charge.

diffusion A process of heat transfer by intermingling movement of particles flowing from hotter to cooler zones due to thermal agitation.

dike A long artificial mound of earth constructed to hold back water. Dikes differ from levees as they are not necessarily built along river banks.

dip The angle of inclination measured in degrees from the horizontal.

dip-slip fault Faults where most of the movement is either up or down in response to compression or tension.

directivity Phenomenon by which a rupturing fault directs more energy in the direction it is moving.

discharge The volume of water flowing in a stream per unit of time.

divergence zone A linear zone formed where plates pull apart as at a spreading centre.

dormant volcano Volcano that has erupted during the last several thousand years but has been quiet in historical times (example: Mount Baker, Washington State).

drainage basin The land area that contributes water to a river system.

drought A prolonged interval of dryness causing damage to plants and animals.

ductile Behaviour of material where stress causes permanent flow or strain.

duff A mat of organic debris in which fire can smolder for days.

E

earthquake The shaking of the Earth by seismic waves radiating away from a disturbance, most commonly a fault movement.

El Niño A climate pattern that occurs every two to seven years when the trade winds relax and warm ocean water in the equatorial Pacific Ocean flows to the west coast of North America.

elastic Behaviour of material where stress causes deformation that is recoverable; when stress stops, the material returns to its original state.

element Distinct varieties of matter; an atom is the smallest particle of an element.

energy Capacity for performing work.

epicentre The point on the surface of the Earth directly above the fault that moved to generate an earthquake (i.e., the point directly above the hypocentre).

equilibrium A state of balance in a system; a condition in which opposing processes are so balanced that changes cause compensating actions.

erosion The processes that loosen, dissolve, and wear away earth materials. Active agents include gravity, streams, glaciers, winds, and ocean waves.

evolution The change of life forms over time.

extinction The die-off of a species.

extinct volcano Volcano that has not erupted during the last several thousand years and is not expected to erupt again (example: Kilimanjaro, Tanzania).

F

failed rift Site of a spreading centre that did not open wide enough to create an ocean basin.

fall A mass movement where the body moves downward nearly vertically under the influence of gravity.

fault A fracture in rock where the two sides move past each other.

felt area Area of perceptible earthquake ground motion.

fire The rapid combination of oxygen with organic material to produce flame, heat, and light.

firebrand Burning debris such as branches and embers that are lifted above the fire and carried away to possibly start new fires.

fire-danger rating System of computer-generated indices used as indicators of fire hazard.

firestorm A fire of large enough size to disturb the atmosphere with excess heat, thus creating its own winds.

fissure A narrow crack in rock.

flank collapse A catastrophic event where the side of a volcano falls into the sea.

flood Overflowing of a body of water onto normally dry land when discharge exceeds the capacity to contain the flow or when there is obstruction to flow.

flood basalt Tremendous outpourings of basaltic lava that form thick, extensive plateaus.

flood plain The nearly flat lowlands that border a stream and act as the stream bed during floods.

flood stage Level of water beyond which conditions become hazardous along the banks of a flooding river.

flow A mass movement where the moving body of material behaves like a fluid.

footwall The underlying side of a fault.

force Mass times acceleration.

foreshock A smaller earthquake that precedes a mainshock on the same section of a fault.

fracture A general term for any breaks in rock.

fracture zone Major lines of weakness in oceanic crust; former transform faults.

freezing rain Supercooled rain that turns to ice when it touches objects such as trees and powerlines.

frequency Number of events in a given time interval. For waves, it is the number of cycles that pass in a second; frequency = 1/period.

friction The resistance to motion of two bodies in contact.

front A boundary separating air masses of different temperature or moisture content.

fuel Any substance that produces heat by combustion.

fuel-driven fire Fire burning on calm-weather days that advances slowly through the fuel, giving firefighters opportunities to stop the fire.

fuel model Computer algorithm predicting the rate of spread of a fire based on vegetation characteristics.

G

gene The fundamental unit in inheritance; it carries the characteristics of parents to their offspring.

genome The common pool of genetic material shared by members of a species.

geological disaster A natural disaster caused by the dynamic processes shaping the Earth's surface; for example, mass movements and volcanic eruptions.

glacier A large mass of ice that flows downslope or outward due to the internal stresses caused by its own weight.

global climate model (GCM) A three- and four-dimensional computer model of Earth's atmosphere that simulates global climates produced by varying temperature, rainfall, atmospheric pressure, winds, and ocean currents.

global warming potential (GWP) The ability of a greenhouse gas to trap heat in the atmosphere as compared to CO_2.

Gondwanaland A southern supercontinent that included South America, Africa, Antarctica, Australia, New Zealand, and India from about 180 to 75 million years ago.

graded stream An equilibrium stream with evenly sloping bottom adjusted to efficiently handle water flow (discharge) and sediment (load) transport.

gradient The slope of a stream channel bottom; change in elevation divided by distance.

gravity The attraction between bodies of matter.

great natural disaster A natural disaster so overwhelming that outside assistance is needed to handle the response and recovery for the region.

greenhouse effect The buildup of heat beneath substances such as glass, water vapour, and carbon dioxide that allow incoming, short-wavelength solar radiation to pass through but block the return of long-wavelength reradiation.

groundwater The volume of water that has soaked underground to fill fractures and other pores; it flows slowly down the slope of the subsurface water body.

H

Hadley cell A thermally driven atmospheric circulation pattern where hot air rises at the equator, divides and flows toward both poles, and then descends to the surface at about 30°N and S latitude.

hail Precipitation of hard, semispherical pellets of ice.

half-life The length of time needed for half of a radioactive sample to lose its radioactivity via decay.

hangingwall The overlying side of a fault.

haze Fine dust, smoke, water, and salt particles that reduce the clarity of the atmosphere.

heat The capacity to raise the temperature of a mass, expressed in joules.

heat capacity The amount of heat required to raise the temperature of 1 g of a substance by 1°C. Synonym: specific heat.

hertz Unit of frequency. One hertz (Hz) equals one cycle per second.

homeotherm Warm-blooded animal whose internal temperature is independent of the environmental temperature (example: *Homo sapiens*).

hot spot A place on Earth where a plume of magma has risen upward from deep in the mantle and through a plate to reach the surface.

humidity A measure of the amount of water vapour in an air mass.

hurricane A large, tropical cyclonic storm with wind speeds of 119 km/h or more; called a typhoon in the western Pacific Ocean and a cyclone in the Indian Ocean.

hydrograph A plot of discharge with respect to time.

hydrologic cycle The solar-powered cycle where water is evaporated from the oceans, dropped on the land as rain and snow, and pulled by gravity back to the oceans as glaciers, streams, and groundwater.

hypocentre The initial portion of a fault that moved to generate an earthquake. Hypocentres are below the ground surface; epicentres are projected above them on the surface.

I

igneous rock Rock formed by the solidification of magma.

ignition temperature Minimum temperature to which a material must be heated for combustion to start.

inertia The property of matter by which it will remain at rest unless acted on by an external force.

infiltration The slow passage of rainwater through the soil.

intertropical convergence zone (ITCZ) The zone where collision occurs between the trade winds of the northern and southern hemispheres.

intraplate earthquake Earthquake occurring within a tectonic plate, far away from plate boundaries.

intrusion (1) Process by which magma forces into fissures of pre-existing rocks and crystallizes below the surface of the Earth. (2) Bodies formed by the process of intrusion.

inversion layer An atmospheric layer in which the upper portion is warmer or less humid than the lower.

ion An electrically charged atom or group of atoms.

island arc A curved linear belt of volcanoes above an oceanic-oceanic subduction zone (example: Japan).

isoseismal map A map that uses contour lines to represent areas of equal Mercalli intensity.

isostasy The condition of flotational equilibrium wherein the Earth's crust floats upward or downward as loads are removed or added.

isotope Any of two or more forms of the same element. The number of protons is fixed for any element, but the number of neutrons in the nucleus can vary, thus producing isotopes.

J

jet stream Fast-moving belts of air in the upper troposphere that flow toward the east.

jokulhlaup Glacial outburst flood.

K

kinetic energy Energy due to motion. See *potential energy*.

Kuiper belt A flattened disk of comets with orbital periods less than 200 years travelling in an orbital plane similar to the planets of the Solar System but extending out 50 astronomical units.

L

La Nada A climate pattern that occurs when seawater temperatures in the tropical eastern Pacific Ocean are neither excessively warm nor cool but instead are neutral.

La Niña A climate pattern that occurs when cooler than normal seawater exists in the tropical eastern Pacific Ocean.

ladder fuel Vegetation of varying heights in an area that allow fire to move easily from the ground to the tree tops.

lahar A volcanic mudflow composed of unconsolidated volcanic debris and water.

lapse rate The rate at which Earth's atmosphere cools with increasing elevation. The average rate is about 6°C/km.

latent heat The energy absorbed or released during a change of state.

latent heat of condensation The heat released when vapour condenses to liquid. For water, the heat release is about 2,260,000 J/kg.

latent heat of fusion Water releases about 334,000 J/kg when it freezes. In reverse, ice absorbs about 334,000 J/kg when it melts.

latent heat of vaporization Water absorbs about 2,260,000 J/kg when it

evaporates. This stored heat is released during condensation.

lateral spread A translational slide in which a subsurface layer liquefies, causing the overlying material to move down gentle slopes.

Laurasia A northern supercontinent that included most of North America, Greenland, Europe, and Asia (excluding India) from about 180 to 75 million years ago.

lava dome A mountain or hill made from highly viscous lava, which has plugged the central conduit of volcanoes.

lava Magma that flows on the Earth's surface.

left-lateral fault A strike-slip fault where most of the displacement is toward the left hand of a person straddling the fault.

levee A natural or human-built embankment along the sides of a stream channel.

lifting condensation level The altitude in the atmosphere where rising air cools to saturation (100% humidity) and condensation begins.

lightning A flashing of light as atmospheric electricity flows between clouds or between cloud and ground.

limestone A sedimentary rock composed mostly of calcium carbonate ($CaCO_3$), usually precipitated from warm saline water. Limestones on continents may later be dissolved by acidic groundwater to form caves.

liquefaction The temporary transformation of water-saturated, loose sediment into a fluid, typically caused by strong earthquake shaking.

lithosphere The outer rigid shell of the Earth that lies above the asthenosphere and below the atmosphere and hydrosphere.

Little Ice Age A colder interval between about 1400 to 1900 CE with renewed glaciation in the northern hemisphere.

load The amount of material moved and carried by a stream.

locked zone Section of a fault that has not released seismic energy for a long time.

M

magma Molten rock material. It solidifies on the Earth's surface as volcanic rock and at depth as plutonic rock.

magnetic field A region where magnetic forces affect any magnetized bodies or electric currents. Earth is surrounded by a magnetic field.

magnetic pole Either of two regions—the north and south poles—where the lines of force of the magnetic field are perpendicular to the Earth's surface. Magnetic poles do not coincide with geographic poles but are in their vicinity.

magnetism A group of physical phenomena associated with moving electricity.

magnitude An assessment of the amount of energy released during an event. Magnitude scales exist for earthquakes, volcanic eruptions, hurricanes, and tornadoes. In seismology, different magnitudes are calculated for the same earthquake when different types of seismic waves are used.

mainshock The largest earthquake in a sequence.

mantle The largest zone of the Earth comprising 83% by volume and 67% by mass.

map A two-dimensional drawing showing features in the horizontal plane as on the ground.

maria Dark, low-lying areas of the Moon filled with dark volcanic rocks.

mass movement The large-scale transfer of material downslope under the pull of gravity.

Maunder Minimum A cooler interval between 1645 to 1715 CE when astronomers noted a minimum number of sunspots on the Sun's surface.

meander The curves, bends, loops, and turns in the course of an underloaded stream that shifts bank erosion from side to side in its channel.

Medieval Maximum A relatively warm interval in the northern hemisphere between about 1000 to 1300 CE.

megathrust earthquake A very large earthquake that occurs when stress accumulates at the contact between a subducting plate and an overriding plate.

mesosphere The mantle from the base of the asthenosphere to the top of the core.

meteor The light phenomena that occur when a meteoroid enters Earth's atmosphere and vaporizes; commonly called a shooting star.

meteorite A stony or iron-rich body from space that passed through the atmosphere and landed on the surface of the Earth.

meteoroid A general term for space objects made of metal, rock, dust, or ice.

methane A gaseous hydrocarbon (CH_4).

methane hydrate An icelike deposit in deep-sea sediments of methane combined with near-freezing water.

microburst Sudden strong downrushes of wind and water from a thundercloud.

Milankovitch theory Glacial advances and retreats on Earth are controlled by variations in the amount of solar radiation received at high latitudes during summer due to changes in Earth's orbit around the Sun and in the tilt angle and direction of Earth's axis of rotation.

mineral A naturally formed, solid inorganic material with characteristic chemical composition and physical properties that reflect an internally ordered atomic structure.

mitigation Actions taken to minimize the risk associated with a natural hazard.

monsoon Winds that reverse direction seasonally. In summer, warm air rises above hot land, drawing in rain-bearing winds from over the ocean. In winter the flow reverses.

N

natural disaster Extreme event triggered by destructive forces occurring in nature that causes significant disruption to society.

natural hazard A source of danger to life, property, and the environment, from atmospheric and geological phenomena.

niche A site in the environment where an organism or species can successfully exist.

normal fault A dip-slip fault where the upper fault block has moved downward in response to tension.

North Atlantic Oscillation (NAO) A shifting of atmospheric pressures over the North Atlantic Ocean occurring on a multi-year timescale.

nuclear fission Splitting the nucleus of an atom with resultant release of energy.

nuclear fusion Combining of smaller atoms to make larger atoms with resultant release of energy.

nuée ardente A turbulent "glowing cloud" of hot, fast-moving volcanic ash, dust, and gas; also called a pyroclastic flow.

O

obsidian Dark volcanic glass.

Oort cloud A vast and diffuse envelope of comets surrounding the Solar System.

outburst flood A sudden release of large quantities of water.

oxidation Combination with oxygen. In fire, oxygen combines with organic matter; in rust, oxygen combines with iron.

ozone A gaseous molecule composed of three atoms of oxygen.

P

pahoehoe Lava flow with a smooth, ropy surface.

paleontologist Scientist who studies the fossils of animals, plants, and other life forms.

Pangaea A supercontinent that existed during Late Paleozoic time when all the continents were unified into a single landmass.

Panthalassa A massive, single ocean that occupied 60% of Earth's surface in Late Paleozoic time.

perihelion The point in the orbit of a body that is closest to the Sun.

period The length of time for a complete cycle of waves to pass; period = 1/frequency.

permafrost Soil or rock that remains frozen throughout the year.

photosynthesis The process where plants produce organic compounds from water and carbon dioxide using the energy of the Sun.

piping Formation of conduits due to erosion by water moving underground.

plasma State of matter, distinct from solids, liquids, and gases, in which charged particles wander freely among the nuclei of atoms.

plastic The behaviour of a material that flows as a fluid (liquid) over time, but is strong (solid) at a moment in time.

plate A piece of lithosphere that moves atop the asthenosphere. There are a dozen large plates and many smaller ones.

plate tectonics The description of the movements of plates and the effects caused by plate formation, collision, subduction, and slide past.

Plinian eruption Type of volcanic eruption where an immense column of pyroclastic debris and gases is blown vertically to great heights.

plume An arm of magma rising upward from deep in the mantle.

plutonic rock Rock formed by the solidification of magma deep below the surface.

population viability level Number of individuals below which a population will become extinct within a given number of years.

pore-water pressure Pressure buildup in groundwater that offsets part of the weight of overlying rock masses.

porosity The percentage of void space in a rock or sediment.

post-tropical transition Gradual transformation of a hurricane into a post-tropical storm, occurring typically between 30°N and 40°N latitude.

potential energy The energy a body possesses because of its position; for example, a large rock sitting high on a steep slope. See *kinetic energy*.

power The rate of work, expressed in watts.

predation Killing and eating other organisms.

preparedness Actions taken in advance to ensure people are ready when disaster strikes.

primary (P) wave First seismic wave to reach a seismometer. Movement is by alternating push–pull pulses that travel through solids, liquids, and gas.

principle of faunal succession Fossil organisms succeed one another in a definite and recognizable order.

processes of construction Land-building processes of volcanism, seafloor formation, and mountain building fuelled by Earth's internal energy.

processes of destruction Land-destroying processes such as erosion and landsliding fuelled by Earth's external energy sources of Sun and gravity.

pumice Volcanic glass so full of holes that it commonly floats on water.

pyroclastic Pertaining to magma and volcanic rock blasted up into the air.

pyroclastic flow A high-temperature, fast-moving cloud of fine volcanic debris, steam, and other gases; also called a nuée ardente.

pyroclastic surge A variety of pyroclastic flow with higher steam content and less pyroclastic material. Surges are lower density, more dilute, higher velocity, and may flow outward in a radial pattern.

pyrolysis Chemical decomposition by the action of heat.

R

radiation A process of heat transfer where energy is emitted as rays.

radioactive elements Unstable elements containing excess subatomic particles that are emitted to achieve smaller, more stable atoms.

recovery Actions taken in the long-term to restore the pre-disaster conditions of a community.

reef An organism-built structure or current-deposited mound of $CaCO_3$ material (limestone).

resonance The act of resounding or ringing. A vibrating body moves with maximum amplitude when the frequency of an imposed external forcing function is the same as the natural frequency of the body.

response Actions taken in the short-term to provide assistance after an emergency has occurred.

resurgent caldera A large topographic depression formed by piston like collapse of overlying rock into a magma chamber with a later central uplift of the caldera floor.

resurgent dome The uplifted floor and mass of magma in the centre of a large volcanic caldera.

retrofitting Reinforceing or strengthening an existing building or other structure.

retrogressive sliding Sliding in which the rupture extends in the direction opposite to the movement of the displaced material.

return period Amount of time between events of a given size.

reverse fault A dip-slip fault where the upper fault block has moved upward in response to compression.

rhyolite A volcanic rock typical of continents. Typically forms from high-viscosity magma.

ridge Long and narrow volcanic mountain ranges.

rift The valley created at a pull-apart zone.

right-lateral fault A strike-slip fault where most of the displacement is toward the right hand of a person straddling the fault.

risk The possibility of being harmed or damaged, often expressed as the product of vulnerability and hazard.

rock A solid aggregate of minerals.

rogue wave An unusually tall wave created when several waves briefly and locally combine their energies.

rotational slide A downward-and-outward movement of a mass on top of a concave-upward failure surface.

runoff The portion of precipitation that travels across land and ultimately reaches streams.

S

scoria cone A small cone or horseshoe shaped hill made of pyroclastic debris from Hawaiian- or Strombolian-type eruptions. They commonly occur in groups.

seafloor spreading Movement of two oceanic plates away from each other, resulting in magma welling up and solidifying to create new ocean floor.

secondary (S) wave Second seismic wave to reach a seismometer. Movement occurs by shearing particles at right angles to the direction of propagation. S waves move through solids only.

sediment Fragments of material of either inorganic or organic origin. Sizes are gravel (over 2 mm diameter), sand (2 to 0.0625 mm diameter), silt (0.0625 to 0.0039 mm diameter), and clay (less than 0.0039 mm diameter). A mixture of silt and clay forms mud.

seiche An oscillating wave on a lake or landlocked sea that varies in period from a few minutes to several hours. Pronounced *saysh*.

seism Earthquake.

seismic wave A general term for all vibrations generated by earthquakes.

seismic zonation Geographical delineation of areas having similar damage potential from future earthquakes.

seismic-gap method Earthquakes are expected next along those fault segments that have not moved for the longest time.

seismicity Frequency and spatial distribution of earthquakes.

seismogram The record made by a seismograph.

seismograph An instrument that records vibrations of the Earth.

seismology The study of earthquakes and the Earth's interior, based on the analysis of seismic data.

seismometer An instrument that detects Earth motions.

sensitive clay Clay that can suddenly loose strength and liquefy when disturbed.

shakemap Map of Mercalli intensity derived automatically from data recorded by a network of seismographs and computed in near real-time.

shatter cone Distinctively grooved and fractured conical fragments of rock.

shear stress A state of stress that causes internal planes within a body to move parallel to each other.

shield volcano A very wide volcano built of low-viscosity lavas.

shoaling Process whereby waves coming into shallow waters are slowed by seafloor friction and become closer together and higher in amplitude.

shock mineral Rare mineral formed in rock subjected to the passage of a powerful impact shock wave.

shooting star The light phenomena that occur when a meteoroid enters Earth's atmosphere and vaporizes; also called a meteor.

sinkhole A circular depression on the surface created where acidic water has dissolved limestone.

sinuosity The length of a stream channel divided by the straight-line distance between its ends.

slash Debris such as logs, branches, needles left on the ground by logging or high winds.

slate Mud changed to hard rock by the high temperatures and pressures of metamorphism.

slide A mass movement where the body of material moves on top of a failure surface.

slip The actual displacement along a fault surface of formerly continuous points.

sluff A small avalanche usually made up of loose snow.

slump A landslide above a curved failure surface.

slurry A highly mobile, low-viscosity mixture of water and fine sediment.

snowpack Column of snow and ice on the ground, including both the new snow and the previous snow and ice that has not melted.

soil The surface layers of sediment, organic matter, and mineral particles.

solar radiation Energy emitted from the Sun mostly in the infrared, visible light, and ultraviolet wavelengths.

solar wind The outflow of charged particles from the Sun.

species Organisms similar enough in life functions to breed freely together.

specific heat The amount of heat required to increase the temperature of 1 g of a substance by 1°C. Synonym: heat capacity.

spreading centre The site where plates pull apart and magma flows upward to fill the gap and then solidifies as new ocean floor.

storm Violent weather event featuring strong winds and heavy precipitation (rain, snow, or hail).

strain A change in form or size of a body due to external forces.

strata Sedimentary or volcanic rock layers with distinct physical or paleontological characteristics. Singular form is *stratum*.

stratosphere The stable atmospheric layer above the troposphere.

stratovolcano A volcano constructed of alternating layers of pyroclastic debris and lava flows; also called a composite volcano.

stress Force per area; forces include shear, tension, and compression.

strike The compass bearing of the trend of a rock layer as viewed in the horizontal plane.

strike-slip fault Faults where most of the movement is horizontal in response to shear stress.

sturzstrom Long-runout movements of huge masses at great speeds.

subduction The process of one lithospheric plate descending beneath another one.

sublimation Changing from solid to gas without passing through a liquid phase.

subside A mass movement where the material sinks slowly or catastrophically.

supernova The cataclysmic explosion of a star that releases tremendous quantities of energy.

surface tension The attractive force between molecules at the surface of a liquid.

surface wave Seismic wave that travels along the Earth's surface only. Love and Rayleigh waves are surface waves.

surge A large mound of seawater that builds up within the eye of a hurricane and then spills onto the land.

swell One of a series of regular, long-period, somewhat flat-crested waves that travel outward from their origin.

T

talus slope Large pile of boulders that accumulates at the foot of a cliff.

tectonic cycle New lithosphere forms at oceanic volcanic ridges, the lithospheric plates spread apart to open ocean basins, and then the oceanic plates are reabsorbed into the mantle at subduction zones.

tectonics The deformation and movement within the Earth's outer layers.

teleconnection Causal link between weather phenomena in two widely separated locations.

telluric current Electrical current propagating in the Earth or through the sea.

tension A state of stress that tends to pull the body apart.

therapsid Four-legged terrestrial reptiles of the Permian and Triassic periods.

thermohaline flow The flow of deep-ocean waters made denser by coldness (thermo) and saltiness (haline).

thunder The sound given off by rapidly expanding gases along the path of a lightning discharge.

thunderstorm A tall, buoyant cloud of moist air that generates lightning and thunder, usually accompanied by rain, gusty winds, and sometimes hail.

tipping point The point at which long-term small changes suddenly produce large effects.

topography The mapping of the shape of the surface of the Earth; the land equivalent of bathymetry.

topple A mass movement where the body pivots forward from its base as if it were top-heavy.

tornado Spinning funnels of wind whose rotating wind speeds can exceed 500 km/h.

transform fault A strike-slip fault that connects the ends of two offset segments of plate edges such as spreading centres or subduction zones.

translational slide A mass that slides downward and outward on top of an inclined planar surface.

trench The elongate and narrow troughs where ocean water can be more than twice as deep as usual. Trenches mark the downgoing edges of subducting plates.

triple junction A place where three plate edges meet.

tropical cyclone Any weather system formed over tropical waters that rotates counterclockwise in the northern hemisphere.

tropical depression A tropical cyclone with wind speeds between 37 and 63 km/h.

tropical disturbance A low-pressure system in the tropics with thunderstorms and weak surface wind circulation. Winds do not exceed 36 km/h.

tropical storm A tropical cyclone with wind speeds between 64 and 118 km/h.

tropical wave Surface low-pressure system over northwest Africa that moves westward within the trade winds. Above warm Atlantic Ocean water, it may grow into a tropical storm or a hurricane.

tropopause The top of the troposphere.

troposphere The lowest layer of the atmosphere, 18 km thick at the equator to 8 km thick at the poles.

tsunami Long-period sea waves caused by oceanic disturbances, such as fault movements, volcanic eruptions, meteorite impacts, and landslides.

tuya Volcano that erupts initially beneath a glacier, melts through the ice, and develops a flat lava cap.

typhoon A large, tropical cyclonic storm with wind speeds of 119 km/h or more; called hurricane in the Western Hemisphere.

U

ultra-plinian Type of volcanic eruption characterized by exceptionally large outpourings of pyroclastic material in high eruption columns and voluminous ash-flow sheets that cover wide areas.

uniformitarianism The concept that the same laws and processes operating on and within the Earth throughout geological time are the same laws and processes operating today.

V

viscous The more viscous a substance, the less readily it flows.

volatile Substances that readily become gases when pressure is decreased, or temperature increased.

volcanic belt Group of volcanoes located in a specific area.

volcanic rock Rock formed by solidification of magma at the Earth's surface.

volcano An opening of the Earth's surface where magma has poured or blown forth, typically creating hills or mountains.

vulnerability Exposure to being harmed or damaged.

W

water table The upper surface of the groundwater body. It is nearer the surface during rainy intervals and deeper below the surface during droughts.

wavelength The distance between two successive wave crests, or troughs.

weather The state of the air at a place with respect to hot or cold, wet or dry, calm or storm.

weather-related disaster A natural disaster caused by meteorological elements, for example, strong winds and heavy rain.

wildfire Unplanned fire occurring in a forested area or thick brush.

wind-driven fire Wind-driven fire fronts that move quickly. The wind carries firebrands forward, starting spot fires up to 0.6 km ahead. Firefighters scramble to put out spot fires and can do little against the flame front.

work Distance times force.

Index

A

absorption, 233–235
Acasta gneiss, 31, 64
acceleration, 110
accelerographs, 121
acoustic fluidization, 251
active volcano, 174
actualism, 46
adiabatic process, 272
adsorption, 233–235
Africa, 223–225
aftershocks, 80
airplanes, 218, 322–323
Alaska, 99, 101
    Aleutian Islands tsunami and, 158
    Aleutian low, 280
    Lituya Bay tsunami, 162–163
    Mount Katmai volcano and, 192
albedo, 38, 269
Alvarez, Luis, 481
Alvarez, Walter, 481
Amati, Nicolas, 294
amplitude, 93
andesite, 175–176
Annaheim meteorite, 31
anoxic conditions, 447
Antarctica, 287–288
anticyclones, 278
aphelion, 468
Appalachian mountain chain, 64
Arabian plate, 74–76
archaea, 439–440
Aristotle, 410
Arkansas River, 384
Armageddon (film), 484
arrival time, 92
asphalt, 456
asteroids, 27, 28, 43–44
    Dactyl, 466
    defense plan for, 485–486
    extinctions and, 447–448, 452
    Ida, 466
    Solar System and, 466–468
asthenosphere, 34, 177
astroblemes, 465
Atlantic Ocean, 60–61
    Canary Islands and, 162
    hurricanes and, 359–362
    North Atlantic Oscillation (NAO) and, 362
Atlantis, 196–197
atmosphere, 24, 31
    See also weather
    air masses and, 275
    Aleutian low and, 280
    Bermuda high and, 280
    Coriolis effect and, 275, 277
    early Earth, 282–283
    energy transfer in, 39–41
    extinctions and, 446–447
    Ferrel cells and, 275–276, 279–280
    fronts and, 275–276
    general circulation of, 272–280
    Hadley cells and, 273–280
    high latitudes and, 275–276
    Icelandic low and, 280
    intertropical convergence zone (ITCZ) and, 274–276, 364–365

jet streams and, 275–278
    low latitudes and, 273
    middle latitudes and, 275–276
    Pacific high and, 280
    polar fronts and, 275–276
    pressure troughs/ridges and, 278–279
    rotating air bodies and, 278–279
    Siberian high and, 280
    stratosphere and, 272
    Subtropical High Pressure Zone and, 274
    troposphere and, 272–273
Australia, 429–430, 456–457
Automated Natural Hazard Alert Service
    (ANHAS), 122
avalanches. *See* mass movements

B

Babylonia, 393
backfires, 409
Bacon, Francis, 52
Baillarge, M. C., 242
Bangladesh, 367
Bangladesh cyclone, 7
Barot, Hidendre, 50
basalt, 175–176, 185–188, 449, 452
base isolation, 112
base level, 384
bathymetry, 51, 54–55
BCE, 38
Beck, Michael, 454
benthic species, 447
Berinstain, Alain, 478
Bermuda high, 280
Bible, 38, 393
Big Blowup, 424
Billings, L. G., 155, 156
Binzel, Richard, 484
blitzkrieg hypothesis, 453
blizzards, 318–319
Blong, Russell, 216
body waves, 94
Bouchard, Michel, 480
braced frames, 111
braided streams, 385–386
brecciated, 475–477
Brent Crater, 477
bridges, 113
British Airways Flight 9, 218
brittleness, 31
Brock, R. W., 229
Browning, Iben, 122
buildings
    base isolation and, 112
    braced frames and, 111
    deaths during earthquakes and, 75, 102, 105
    fire and, 424
    floods and, 388–389
    foundation materials and, 102, 105
    houses and, 113–114
    hurricanes and, 362–363, 371
    land-use planning and, 371
    retrofitting and, 111, 113
    roofs and, 371
    shear walls and, 111
    wind-borne debris and, 371
buoyancy, 34

buoys, 164
Burin peninsula, 146–148

C

calderas, 340
    Crater Lake, Oregon, 193–194
    different settings of, 193–194
    eruptive sequence of, 198
    giant continental, 197–198
    Krakatau, Indonesia, 194–195
    resurgent, 193, 198
    Santorini, 196–197
    shield volcanoes and, 193
    stratovolcanoes and, 193–194
    Yellowstone National Park, 198
California
    Diablo winds and, 423
    La Brea Tar Pits and, 456
    La Conchita debris flows and, 247, 248
    Oakland-Berkeley Hills fire, 422–423
    Point Fermin slide and, 243–244
    San Diego wildfires and, 428–429
    San Fernando Valley earthquake and, 105–106
    San Francisco earthquakes and, 99
    wildfires of, 422–423, 428–429
California Institute of Technology, 97
calories, 29
Cambrian explosion, 440
Cambrian Time, 442
Cameroon, 223–225
Canada, 118, 119–125
    British Columbia tsunami and, 158–159
    Cascade Range and, 205–214
    drought, 312
    Great Depression, 312
    ice storms and, 319–320
    mitigation of earthquakes, 118–125
    Newfoundland earthquake, 146–148
    Ontario derecho and, 331
    quick-clay slope failures and, 233
    seismic risk, 118–125
    seismic risk map, 121
    ten largest in Canada, 120
    tornadoes and, 335–338
    Turtle Mountain, Alberta flow and, 251–252
    volcanic hazards, 214
Canadian Forest Fire Danger Rating System, 416
Canadian National Seismograph Network
    (CNSN), 121
Cap-aix-Diamants cliff, 4
Cape Verde-type hurricanes, 362–364
carbon dioxide, 299–300
carbonic acid, 255
Caribbean Sea, 364–365
carrying capacity, 16
Caruso, Enrico, 87
Cascadia, 118–120
Cascadia earthquake, 118, 125–127, 130
caves, 255
cement, 235
centrigade temperature scale, 28
Chang Heng, 92
channelization, 398
chaparral, 422–423
Charlevoix Crater, 474
Charlevoix earthquake, 104–105, 117, 118, 134–136